Engineering
Economy

THE MACMILLAN COMPANY
NEW YORK • CHICAGO
DALLAS • ATLANTA • SAN FRANCISCO
LONDON • MANILA

IN CANADA
BRETT-MACMILLAN LTD.
GALT, ONTARIO

Third Edition

of

WOODS
and
DE GARMO

Introduction to
Engineering
Economy

Engineering

Economy

E. PAUL DE GARMO

Registered Professional Engineer
Professor of Industrial Engineering
University of California, Berkeley

THE MACMILLAN COMPANY
New York

Fourth Printing 1964

Library of Congress catalog card number: 60-5033
The Macmillan Company, New York
Brett-Macmillan Ltd., Galt, Ontario
Printed in the United States of America
Previous editions entitled *Introduction to Engineering Economy,* Copyright by The Macmillan Company 1942 and 1953

Preface to Third Edition

Not many years ago there was considerable argument as to whether engineers should be concerned with the economic aspects of engineering projects. Today there is no argument about this. Money is recognized as an engineering material and professional engineers expect to be held accountable for its use. Virtually all registration examinations contain questions and problems dealing with engineering economy. Most accredited engineering curricula require courses in this subject.

As the making of economy studies has become more common it has naturally been expected that they should also be more accurate. New procedures have been developed, and more factors are dealt with in a sophisticated manner. Yet there remains the necessity that economy studies be made by a sound consideration of all the fundamentals involved. With a variety of techniques, formulas, and study patterns in common use, it is essential that the engineer have a thorough understanding of engineering economy fundamentals, so that he can understand the full implications, advantages, and disadvantages of each. He can then make proper use of the procedure which is best suited to the conditions at hand. Likewise, he will be able to understand the full significance of any economy study he may encounter, regardless of the procedure used, and be prepared to interpret the data and results correctly and arrive at sound recommendations and decisions.

This text has as its goal the teaching of fundamentals. All commonly used economy study methods are discussed. There is no single procedure that is best for all purposes. Each is analyzed in terms of the fundamental factors involved. It is hoped that the student thus will be able to understand and use with facility whatever procedure best fits a particular case.

Considerable attempt is made to point out the important role which nonmonetary factors often play in economic decisions. As long as our economy continues to exist for the primary purpose of benefiting people, and decisions are made by humans, such factors will be important and may outweigh numerical data. This fact sometimes appears to be disturbing to young engineers.

While the primary purpose is to teach economy study principles and procedures, considerable effort is given to imparting some understanding of the background which gives depth and meaning to many of the methods that are used. Such an understanding is essential for proper interpretation of economy study results and the making of sound decisions through their use.

Since this book has again been written primarily for college students, it is written so as to stimulate their interest and to help them over the rough spots which more than twenty years of teaching this subject have revealed to the author. It is expected that, as with the previous editions, practicing engineers and others will also find considerable use for it. However, the author asks their pardon for putting them in second place, for a number of subjects would have been presented differently if the book were intended primarily for them.

Although this edition has been almost completely rewritten, and thus contains nothing in the way of direct contribution by the late Baldwin M. Woods, who was coauthor of the previous editions which bore as their title *Introduction to Engineering Economy,* it would be untrue to say that his influence is not present in this edition. The many pleasant hours we spent together working on the previous editions resulted in a contribution by him which will always continue.

I wish to express my very great thanks to my secretary, Mrs. Sarah Brewer, for the superb work she did in typing the manuscript. Thanks also are due to many of my colleagues, engineers in industry, and former students who have been kind enough to offer suggestions as the result of using the previous editions. I trust that users of this edition will find it equally helpful.

E. Paul DeGarmo

Berkeley, California

Contents

Depreciation defined. Market, use, fair, book, salvage, and scrap value. Value for rate-base purposes. Purposes of depreciation. Actual depreciation revealed by time. Physical and functional depreciation. Economic life. Relation of Bureau of Internal Revenue. Requirements of a depreciation method. Straight-line formula. Matheson formula. Sum-of-the-years'-digits method. Sinking fund method. Service output method. Gillette formula. Present worth method. What depreciation method to use. Equivalence of straight-line depreciation with interest on remaining investment and sinking fund depreciation with interest on initial investment. Use of capital recovery factors. Use of capital recovery factors to determine interest rates. Straight-line depreciation plus average interest. Relation of SYD depreciation to income tax savings. Depletion. Common depreciation practices. Valuation. Historical cost valuation. Reproduction cost less depreciation. Prudent investment theory. Supreme Court decisions. Franchise, going, organization, and good-will values. Physical life from mortality data. Individual-unit and annual-rate methods. Mortality data applied to electric lamps.

Importance of capital in engineering projects. Ownership and borrowed capital. Individual ownership. Partnerships. Corporations. Common and preferred stock. Bonds. Classification of bonds. Bond retirement. Callable and noncallable bonds. Amortization schedules. Bond value. Investment rate. Nomogram for bond yields. Depreciation funds as a source of capital. Financing through retained profits. Equipment trust certificates. Sale and lease-back of assets. Average cost of capital. Effects of financing upon economy. Considering source of capital in economy studies.

Purpose of accounting. Fundamental accounting terms. Balance sheets. Income and expense statements. Source of financial statement data. Depreciation accounting. Cost accounting objectives. Types of cost accounting. Elements of cost. Direct and indirect materials and labor. Elements of overhead costs. Methods of distributing overhead costs. Results of different methods of allocation. Interest as an element of cost. Control through standard costs. Effect of production rate on standard costs. Use of standard costs in economy studies.

costs and depreciable assets. Pertinency of results purchased by sunk costs.

Importance of replacement decisions. Reasons for replacements. A typical replacement example. Factors which must be considered in replacement studies. Recognition of past "errors" and sunk costs. Remaining life of old property. Write-off period for replacements. Study period for replacement studies. Methods of handling un-amortized values. Theoretical patterns of costs in replacement studies. Replacement due to inadequacy. Replacement without retirement. Replacement due to obsolescence. Replacement due to excessive operation and maintenance costs. Replacement due to decreasing efficiency. Replacement due to a combination of causes. Replacement where salvage value is zero or unknown. Replacement where salvage value is greater than book value. Considerations of favorable trade-in or disposal price, future growth, excess capacity, and future price changes. Budgetary and personnel considerations. Determining value by replacement theory.

Break-even point theory. Mathematical solutions. Graphical solutions. Break-even point for jigs and fixtures. Limitations in the use of formulas. Break-even charts for business enterprises. Effects of changes in fixed and variable costs. Representation of economic characteristics of businesses. Minimum cost point. Graphical representation of Kelvin's law. Economic lot size. Economic purchase order quantities. Purchase order size for variable price schedules.

Importance of fixed costs and fixed charges. Effect of capacity on first cost. Capacity factor. Effect of utilization on economy of alternatives. Load factor. Diversity factor. Effects of capacity utilization in public utilities. Block-demand rate schedules. Power factor. Capacity and load effects in nonutility industries. Capacity utilization in connection with risk reduction. Investment to reduce fire and flood damage risk.

Problems attendant to increasing future demands. Determining future demands. Adapting basic economy study patterns to future-demand studies. Perpetual future demand. Interpreting future-demand studies. Perpetual demand with limited life. Indefinite or

limited demand with limited asset life. Recognition of additional
life of deferred investments through salvage value. Providing for
future demand with "inferior" assets. Recognition of additional life
as an intangible factor. Determining the break-even deferment
period. Miscellaneous factors.

purpose projects. Authorization of federal projects. Reasons for economy studies of public works. Difficulties inherent in economy studies of public works. Patterns for economy studies of public works. Interest rate in public works studies. Benefits-to-costs ratios. Study of alternative public works. Cost allocations for highway studies. Collection of highway costs through gasoline and ton-mile taxes.

CHAPTER 1

The Nature
and Purpose
of Engineering
Economy Studies

One of the outstanding characteristics of the work of an engineer is that it results in products or services that must be produced *within cost limitations* so that they may be utilized economically by mankind. Cost limitations are an important factor distinguishing the work of the engineer from that of the pure scientist. When the young engineer leaves the classroom and enters upon his professional career in industry, one of the most immediate, and sometimes difficult, adjustments he must make is the recognition that money is an essential material in almost every design that he creates. Thus the engineer can not hope to achieve a high level of professional success unless he deals with money as effectively as he does with the other materials he uses in his designs and projects.

The importance of money as an engineering material may be illustrated by the fact that in order to furnish the plant, equipment, and tools which are necessary to provide a job for one worker in industry in the United States, someone must accumulate and invest, on the average, over $10,000. The capital investment per worker, of course, varies considerably from industry to industry. Some oil companies, for example, have an investment of $70,000 per worker. Public utilities require from $30,000 to $60,000 per worker. While in a few industries the investment per worker is less than $1,000, the average is increasing rapidly. The inevitable and desirable increase in the use of automation will cause very great increases in investment per worker. For example, the investment in a new automated foundry of a large automobile manufacturer is in excess of $70,000 per worker. In fact, it is probable that the rate of increase in the use of automation will not be determined by technological developments as much as by cost factors and the availability of capital.

This requirement of a large investment of capital per worker is one of the outstanding characteristics of the economy of this country. The fact that a large amount has been invested in plant and equipment is one of the principal reasons for the high productivity per worker which brings about our high standard of living.

ENGINEERS ARE MANAGERS

While in earlier years the engineer exercised little responsibility for the utilization of capital, the modern engineer has great interest in the use of capital in industry and government. He, more than most others, is involved in designing, building, or using plants, machines, or structures which cost large sums of money. Industry and governmental agencies expect the engineer to report on the economic aspects as well as the physical aspects of his proposals. In many instances, because of the complex technological nature of engineering projects, it is difficult for the nonengineer to make a proper economic analysis. It is thus important, and often essential, that engineers be capable of determining financial as well as physical feasibility. A recent survey of top executives of large corporations in the United States disclosed that more of them had been trained in engineering than in any other academic field. This is strong evidence as to the importance of engineers acquiring financial "know how" and of their ability to do so.

While in many cases the final decisions regarding engineering projects will be made by those in top management, above the engineer who may make an economy study of the project, very often such decisions will be based upon the facts supplied by the engineer. Thus in many instances the engineer is in a position similar to that of a consultant in that he reports facts and recommendations. Others then make decisions based upon the recommendations. The engineer spends much time and effort in learning the properties and behavior of steel, concrete, and various alloys so that he may use them intelligently and be able to predict accurately the performance of the machine he is designing. Since money is important and necessary, it is essential that the engineer be acquainted with its properties and the laws governing its use. The modern engineer does not shy away from such factors as creep and fatigue, which were formerly disposed of in an "ignorance" factor. It is just as reasonable that in modern engineering money be accounted for in an honest and informed manner.

FINANCIAL EFFICIENCY

In most technical courses studied by the engineer or engineering student he is concerned with obtaining the most effective utilization of materials and/or energy. The degree of effectiveness of the utilization is measured by the familiar equation

$$\text{efficiency} = \frac{\text{output}}{\text{input}}. \tag{1.1}$$

When dealing with energy relationships and ordinary materials, the engineer knows that the efficiency can never exceed 100 per cent. However, when dollars are considered as the material, a different situation exists. This may be expressed as

$$\text{financial efficiency} = \frac{\text{dollars income}}{\text{dollars spent}}. \tag{1.2}$$

It may readily be seen that unless the financial efficiency can and does exceed 100 per cent, a project is not desirable from a purely financial viewpoint.

Engineers will immediately recognize that Equation (1.1) is commonly used in two ways. The first, and less common, use involves the *total* output and input over the life of a project. The second, and more frequent, use involves *instantaneous* values of output and input. The use of electrical meters to determine the input and output of an electric motor is an example of this. This latter type of efficiency is more useful, since one does not wish to wait until a piece of equipment has worn out at the end of its life before being able to determine what its efficiency has been. In the same manner, a shorter period of time is used in obtaining a more usable measure of financial efficiency. In this procedure the rate of return upon the invested capital is determined, expressed in per cent, as

$$\text{rate of return} = \frac{\text{annual net profit}}{\text{capital invested}} \tag{1.3}$$

This is the most commonly used measure of financial efficiency. Obviously there will be a difference in the computed rate of return, depending upon whether the annual net profit is that before or after income taxes have been paid. Thus it is wise to specify whether a computed rate of return is before or after taxes.

NONMONETARY VALUES

Few decisions, either personal or business, are made solely on the basis of financial considerations. Further, the financial efficiency of a project may to a considerable extent be affected by nonmonetary values. If a man goes to a store to buy a new suit of clothes and finds that one in plain black can be obtained for ten dollars less than one of comparable quality in attractive colors, he probably will not make the decision solely on the basis of price. The financial efficiency of the manufacturer of the garments will, without question, be affected by the desires of the customers for color. Thus, satisfactory decisions and recommendations regarding the feasibility of engineering projects must take into account all factors, monetary and nonmonetary, which will affect the undertaking.

Some of the most common nonmonetary factors that must be considered are economic laws, general business conditions, social and human values, personal or corporate objectives, consumer likes and dislikes, and governmental regulations. All business operates within an economic system that functions in accordance with certain general rules. To attempt to operate an engineering project in violation of basic economic laws is to court disaster. Whether a product or service is socially desirable, acceptable, or needed can easily determine the success or failure of a venture. Similarly, whether a product or service meets the existing likes and dislikes of the public, which may change with time, may be all important in the success or failure of an enterprise.

Governmental laws and regulations may affect business ventures in several ways. Obviously, if a business is counter to existing laws it may be forced to cease operations almost immediately. Less obvious but perhaps more frequent effects are those instances in which governmental regulations may restrict the operations of a business, or in which governmentally financed and operated activities may provide competition. Taxation affects every enterprise and thus may be an important factor in decisions regarding investment.

ENGINEERING ECONOMY DEFINED

From the discussion on the previous pages it is apparent that the initiation and operation of engineering projects require the utilization of capital, and that the efficiency of the utilization of that capital is dependent upon a number of factors—some technical, some monetary, and some nonmonetary. Engineering economy studies are for the purpose of determining whether, or in what manner, an engineering project should be undertaken or modified with the objective of obtaining the best utilization of available capital, taking into account all pertinent factors, technical, monetary, and nonmonetary. Thus the general objective of economy studies is to permit the maximization of financial efficiency. However, a broad and long-range point of view is taken, with the knowledge that the ultimate realization of this objective is dependent upon many factors.

DECISIONS ARE BETWEEN ALTERNATIVES

Practically all engineering problems can be solved in more than one way. For example, a steam turbine, a gas turbine, or a Diesel engine may be used to turn a generator. The electrical energy produced is the same and equally useful regardless of the type of prime mover used. However, for the three methods the cost of producing the electrical energy may be quite different. In other instances the results as well as the costs of various alternatives may be different. For such cases both costs and results must be evaluated in choosing between alternatives. In some instances the choice is between doing and not doing. However, this also is a choice between alternatives, since if the capital is not used for a proposed venture, it will be utilized in some other manner, even if only left in the bank.

Most economy study problems involve matters of technology as well as finance and economics. The engineer's technical knowledge makes him particularly well suited for analyzing such problems, provided he also has the necessary understanding of the financial aspects. Seldom does the non-engineer have a sufficient understanding of the technical phases of such problems to enable him to do a satisfactory job of making economy studies. Such studies involve the determination of both technical and financial superiority.

In most engineering economy studies it is necessary to give due consideration to practical realities. A reinforced concrete tool shed would undoubtedly outlast one of light, wooden construction; it would also afford greater protection to the tools. However, to erect such a concrete shed on the site of a house construction job requiring only four months to complete would obviously be wrong. In this case the wooden shed would be a better solution, although it does not possess the fine technical qualities of the concrete shed.

Much engineering work boils down to making a choice among several possible solutions. Necessity for making decisions is not restricted, of course, to the practice of engineering. Every person must make many choices during his life. In fact, a day does not pass without bringing with it the necessity of choosing among various courses of action. The importance of the decision and the various factors influencing the choice will change with age and viewpoint. Whether the blonde or the brunette will be the more economical date on Friday night is a problem of alternatives which is of considerable importance to the engineering student in college. When he is involved in selecting complex designs or equipment in later professional life, he will find that his decisions of college days were rather simple and not always in the interest of maximum economy.

In business practice financial efficiency must be the paramount factor. On a particular job the engineer may be faced with the necessity of digging some ditches. He may employ laborers to do the work by the pick-and-shovel method or he may rent a ditch-digging machine to accomplish the task. His natural desire to do things in a big way will probably tell him to use the machine. His decision is of considerable importance, whereas in his college days any choice he might have made would have had little permanent effect. Now the success of his business demands that he determine which of the two methods will accomplish the task more cheaply. After investigating, he might find that the ground in which the ditch must be dug is full of steam and water pipes, so a ditch-digging machine would be of little value. What appeared to be the slow and inefficient method would turn out to be the correct solution to his problem. The error would be just as serious if conditions indicated that the machine method would be cheaper, and it were not used.

The tremendous scope of modern engineering projects makes it essential that all the factors involved in the economy of an undertaking not only be considered but handled in an accurate, approved manner, in order that the results will be satisfactory from all the viewpoints touched by the project. The selection of the final method should never be a matter of guess or be left to the will of the gods. Hunches and intuition are not reliable enough. Some will raise their voices to protest that much of the information must be based upon estimates, and therefore the final answer can be found by guesswork. Obviously, estimates made after careful study and based on all the information that is available are considerably better than haphazard guesses. It is true that a carefully prepared estimate may also be a guess. However, it is an *enlightened* guess. All the available factors are considered and used. Data that are available only in part are determined as exactly as possible in the light of the experience of the engineer. Such an estimate is much more exact and useful than a wild guess by some uninformed person. In fact, the accuracy of an estimate is usually limited only by the amount of time and money one wishes to spend in preparing the report.

BUSINESS OPERATES FOR PROFIT

Under the capitalistic system in operation in the United States, and in virtually all of the free world, it is essential that an enterprise be profitable. While one may question whether or not capitalism is the best economic system, there is no doubt that mankind has made greater progress and gains under this system than under any other. Further, there can be no argument about the fact that as long as business is conducted under this system profits must be earned to assure that needed capital is available.

Profit may be defined as the excess of income over expenses. Thus

$$\text{profit} = \text{income} - \text{expenses}. \qquad (1.4)$$

Such a generalized equation is not sufficiently specific to indicate the various factors that must be considered in determining profit. Both profit and expense are complex.

Two classes of profit are of interest in economy studies. The first is profit *before* income taxes, while the other is profit *after* income taxes.[1]

Expenses may conveniently be divided into several classes as follows:

$O + M$ = out-of-pocket expenses for operation and maintenance

D = depreciation, always prepaid through purchase of property, buildings, or equipment

i = interest paid for the use of borrowed funds

T = income taxes (not an ordinary expense, since they depend upon profits remaining after other expenses are paid)

Using this notation, Equation (1.4) can be rewritten in more specific form as follows:

$$E_a = G - (O + M + D + I) - T \qquad (1.5)$$

where E_a = net profits (or earnings) after taxes

and G = gross income or receipts

Since interest paid for the use of borrowed capital is included as an expense, the profits shown in Equation (1.5) are those belonging to the owners of the equity capital. Engineering economy studies deal with all of the factors in Equation (1.5) in order to determine what course of action should be followed to assure optimum efficiency in the use of capital.

[1] In the case of a person, personal income taxes; for a corporation, corporation income taxes.

HUMAN FACTORS ARE OF INCREASING IMPORTANCE

There is another factor which may have a tremendous effect upon the economy of an engineering undertaking. This is the relationship of the human individual to the project. It appears that industry is becoming increasingly conscious of the interdependence of humanity and itself and realizes that business without human beings would be impossible. It is only too true that the effect of the human element cannot be written down in an equation or set of rules, nor can it be accurately predicted at all times, yet it may be so great as to outweigh all other factors. Much of the knowledge about this factor can be learned only through long, and sometimes bitter, experience. However, as long as it is present, the engineer can ill afford to close his eyes to it.

At times the reaction of the public to an engineering innovation may be almost immediate. At other times there is a slow, cumulative effect over a period of years. Either case may be beneficial or disastrous. The present situation in automotive design is an excellent example of the effect of immediate public reaction. Engineers are well aware of the advantages of placing the engine of an automobile in the rear of the car and of the need for improved streamlining. Yet no manufacturer dares to attempt to make his product as good as he is able to in these two respects. The public reaction to the Chrysler Airflow models, introduced in 1934, is well remembered. These cars embodied many excellent engineering advances which were little known to the average person and which were incorporated into nearly all cars in later years. The advance that was probably least perfect from an engineering viewpoint was the change in body appearance. It was a poor example of true streamlining, yet Chrysler engineers at that time felt the public was not ready for the radical change that would accompany good streamlining. Therefore they made only a moderate change. It was soon apparent that the motoring public was not ready to accept even this moderate deviation from conventional body design, and the models were abandoned after a few years.

This experience undoubtedly was one factor that caused this corporation to follow an ultraconservative styling policy for many years so that by 1955–1956 its sales had decreased to a precariously low volume. In 1956 the corporation again made relatively radical styling changes in its 1957 line of cars; this time the public accepted the designs and the company's percentage of the automotive market increased substantially.

In some instances the human factor acts only after accumulating momentum during a long period of time. This was well illustrated in the attitude of people toward public utility companies. Neglect of the human factor for a long period of time by some of these companies brought the whole industry into ill repute. As a result, all were condemned by many people who knew nothing of the facts concerning a particular company against which they held a grudge. Such an attitude had a very definite effect upon the economy of these utilities. Some of the companies, despite radical changes in their operating policies, are still unable to overcome public opposition.

The recent turmoil and conflict between labor and management is another example of trouble that may arise through long-time neglect of the human factor. No one will deny that this strife affects the economy of the entire nation. One might well paraphrase the old saying, "You can't fool all the people all the time," as "It is foolish to disregard any of the people any of the time." If the engineer is to take a leading role in the future conduct of industry, he must not neglect the human factor in his application of engineering economy. It is true that the human element may be ignored for a short time without any noticeable reaction. However, since it is so apparent that continued neglect will bring disaster, it is risky to conclude that this factor may be neglected at all without some reaction.

REQUIREMENTS OF AN ECONOMY STUDY OF AN ENGINEERING PROJECT

In order to justify the expenditure of time and money, an economy study should satisfy the following requirements:

1. It should be based upon consideration of all available factors.
2. When some factors *must* be estimated, these estimates should be made intelligently, in the light of experience and sound judgment.
3. The study should show a measure of financial efficiency, such as the the annual rate of return upon the required investment.
4. Insofar as they apply correctly, the study should make use of the same factors that the accountant will use in determining the financial efficiency of the investment after it is made.
5. The study should contain a recommended course of action, together with the reasons for the recommendation.

Studies made in this manner will assure that those who must make investment decisions related to engineering projects will have the necessary facts for optimum utilization of capital funds.

PROBLEMS

1-1 Define "Engineering Economy."

1-2 What is one reason why oil companies can be less concerned over paying high wage rates than manufacturing companies?

1-3 How does financial efficiency differ from mechanical efficiency?

1-4 What is the most commonly used measure of financial efficiency?

1-5 Give two examples of engineering projects in which nonmonetary values are of considerable importance.

1-6 What are two ways in which governmental regulations may affect the economy of a project?

1-7 Why is profit necessary in a capitalistic system?

1-8 Give four requirements for an engineering economy study.

CHAPTER 2

Some
Economic
Relationships

All business enterprise is governed by certain economic laws which are the result of the interaction between people and wealth. Therefore economics and basic economic laws are important factors in many economy studies. Just as the highway-speed laws that are enforced would be an important factor in setting up a bus schedule between cities, so must basic laws of economics be taken into account in determining the feasibility of investment.

Economics has been defined in many ways. One definition is that it is a social science which deals with people and their money. Another definition states that it is the study of wealth, its value, creation, and distribution.

ECONOMICS IS NOT AN EXACT SCIENCE

Engineers and engineering students frequently have some difficulty with economics. This usually is due to their failure to realize that economics is not an exact science. Using physical laws, such as Newton's or Ohm's laws, exact results can be obtained. It is this type of phenomena with which the engineer is accustomed to dealing. Since economics involves the reactions of *people,* it is apparent that economic laws must be based upon the behavior or reactions of *groups* of people, and that the reactions of groups of people can be described only in *general* terms. Thus economic laws might be described as *generalized* laws, or generalizations.

Since generalizations are not specific, one must realize that while economic laws are valid statements as to the most likely interaction between people, as a group, and wealth, it does not follow that *every* person will react in the manner described by the law. It is seldom difficult to find some

11

individuals who do not act in the usual group pattern. Further, it is to be expected that certain groups may react quite differently from others. For example, if one hundred loaves of bread were dropped near a crowd of one thousand well-fed Americans, the results would be quite different from those if the same number of half-starved people for a southeastern Asian country were involved. However, even though economic laws are generalizations, they have a profound effect on business activities, since business operates for the purpose of satisfying people's wants for goods and services.

Everyone should be concerned with the basic principles of economics. For the successful engineer, however, a knowledge of certain economic principles is a "must." Engineers, as a group, probably do more than any other to alter the economic status of people. Through their inventions and manufacturing techniques they bring about tremendous changes in our civilization. In their work they utilize capital in various forms. Their enterprises, therefore, are subject to the forces of economics just as are those of the banker. Many economy study decisions must be based on a consideration of *intangible factors* which can not be reduced to monetary values. Frequently these intangibles are the effects of economic laws which may influence a project.

In the world of finance and trade the laws of economics are encountered so frequently that they become the basis of everyday practice. Some of the principles are not of immediate concern to the engineer. However, a few are encountered so frequently in connection with engineering projects that special consideration is warranted.

CONSUMER AND PRODUCER GOODS AND SERVICES

The goods and services that are produced and utilized may be divided conveniently into two classes. *Consumer goods* and services are those products or services that are directly used by people to satisfy their wants. Food, clothing, homes, cars, television sets, haircuts, opera, and medical services are examples. The producers and vendors of consumer goods and services must be aware of and are subject to the whims and caprices of the people to whom their products are sold. At the same time, the demand for such goods and services is directly related to people and in many cases, as will be discussed later, may be determined with considerable certainty.

Producer goods and services are used to produce consumer goods and services. Machine tools, factory buildings, busses, and farm machinery are examples. These, while in the long run they serve to satisfy human wants, are means to that end. The amount of producer goods needed is determined, indirectly, by the amount of consumer goods or services that are demanded by people. Once the consumer needs are known, the amount of producer goods required can be determined rather easily.

NECESSITIES AND LUXURIES

Consumer goods and services may be divided into *necessities* and *luxuries*. Obviously these terms are relative. Necessities are those products or services that are required to support human life and activities, that will be purchased in somewhat the same quantity even though the price varies considerably. Luxuries, on the other hand, are desired by humans and will be purchased if money is available *after* the required necessities have been obtained.

It is apparent that what will be considered a luxury by one person or group of persons might be thought of as a necessity by others who have more money. A certain amount, and even certain types, of food would be considered a necessity by practically all people. However, a modest automobile would be considered a luxury by almost all people in Asia, whereas it is a necessity for thousands of Americans who would be unable to get to their places of work without one.

The concept of necessary and luxury goods is important in business, and in engineering economy, since producers and vendors of the two types are affected differently by changing economic conditions and by competition. This is due to the fact that the demands for the two types vary in different manners as economic conditions change. Thus, capital invested in a consumer-goods industry will be affected differently by changing economic conditions than if it were invested in a producer-goods industry. Figure 2–1

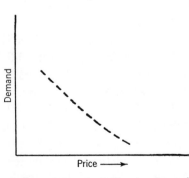

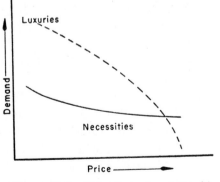

Figure 2–1. General price-demand relationship.

Figure 2–2. Price-demand relationship for luxuries and necessities.

shows the general relationship between price and the demand for goods. Since people will stop buying luxury goods if the price goes up before they decrease their consumption of necessities, a more complete relationship between price and demand is as illustrated in Figure 2–2. The curves in this figure illustrate an everyday experience—that when prices rise we all reduce our buying of luxury goods more drastically than our purchasing of necessities.

The extent to which price changes may influence demand may vary in several ways. If the mathematical product of volume and price is constant, the *elasticity* of demand is said to be *unitary*. This merely means that the *total* amount which will be spent for the product will be the same regardless of the selling price. Thus, a drop in price would produce a corresponding increase in sales. The demand for products is called *elastic* when a decrease in the selling price results in a greater than proportionate increase in sales. For example, a drop of one per cent in selling price might produce a much greater increase in sales. On the other hand, when a decrease in selling price produces a less than proportionate increase in sales the demand is said to be *inelastic*. In such a case it might require a three per cent drop in selling price to bring about a one per cent increase in sales.

It becomes apparent that luxury items have a much greater elasticity of demand than do necessary goods. Sales of luxury items will be more affected by price changes than will the sales of necessities. On the other hand, a change in demand will have a much greater effect on the price of necessities than in the case of luxuries.

COMPETITION

Since economic laws are general statements regarding the interaction of people and wealth, they will be affected by the economic environment in which the people and the wealth exist. Most general economic principles are stated for situations in which *perfect competition* exists.

Perfect competition occurs in a situation in which any given product is supplied by a number of vendors and there is no restriction against additional vendors entering the market. Under such conditions, there is assurance of complete freedom on the part of both buyer and seller. Actually, of course, perfect competition may never exist because of a multitude of factors which may impose some degree of limitation upon the actions of buyers or sellers, or both. However, with conditions of perfect competition assumed, it is easier to formulate general economic laws. When deviations from perfect competition are known to exist, their probable effects upon the laws can be taken into account.

The existing competitive situation is an important factor in most economy studies. It will have a very real effect upon decisions that are made. Unless information is available to the contrary, it should be assumed that competition does or will exist, and the resulting effects should be taken into account.

MONOPOLY

Monopoly is at the opposite pole from perfect competition. A perfect monopoly exists when a unique product or service is available from only a single vendor and that vendor can prevent the entry of all others into the market. Under such conditions the buyer is at the complete mercy of the vendor as to the availability and price of the product. Actually there seldom is a perfect monopoly. This is due to the fact that few products are so unique that substitutes can not be used satisfactorily, or to the fact that governmental regulations prohibit monopolies if they are unduly restrictive.

A monopoly may be of great benefit to a producer in that he may be able to control the supply and the price to provide the maximum profit. While this might result in high prices for the product, higher *total* profits may be obtained from lower prices and wider distribution. Under some conditions, a monopoly may avoid costly duplication of facilities and thus make possible lower prices for products and services. This situation is recognized by governing bodies in granting public utilities exclusive rights to render service in a given territory. Such a practice, for example, avoids having two electric power companies duplicate power-distribution lines and equipment in the same city. When vendors are granted such a monopolistic position, the governmental body also regulates the rates that the utility can charge for its services in order to assure that the customers are not overcharged. Thus governmental regulation takes the place of competition in determining prices.

A semimonopoly may be permitted for a limited time through the issuance of patents or copyrights which help to maintain the uniqueness of a product by preventing identical products from being marketed.

OLIGOPOLY

An *oligopoly* exists when there are so few suppliers of a product or service that action by one will almost inevitably result in similar action by the others. Thus, if one of the only three gasoline stations in an isolated town raises the price of its product by one cent per gallon, the other two would undoubtedly do the same, since they could do so and still retain their previous competitive positions.

It is apparent that many conditions between those of perfect competition, perfect monopoly, and oligopoly can and do exist. Thus it is to be expected that *actual* relationships between supply, price, and demand will be somewhat different from those derived for the ideal conditions. Also, it would be extremely difficult to state or depict such relationships for all of the possible conditions. Therefore, it is most practicable to derive these relationships for the case of perfect competition; the changes that would result from nonperfect conditions are usually quite apparent.

THE LAW OF SUPPLY AND DEMAND

As was discussed previously, and illustrated in Figure 2–1, under competitive conditions there is a relationship between the price customers must pay for a product and the amount that they will buy. There is also a similar relationship between the price at which a product can be sold and the amount that will be made available. If the price they can get for their products is high, more producers will be willing to work harder, or perhaps risk more capital, in order to reap the greater reward. If the price they can obtain for their products declines, they will not produce as much because of the smaller reward which they can obtain for their labor and risk. Some will stop producing and turn their efforts to other endeavors. This relationship between price and the volume of product produced can be portrayed by the curve shown in Figure 2–3.

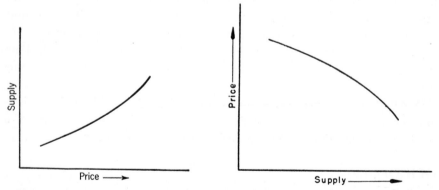

Figure 2–3. General price-supply relationship.

Figure 2–4. Price-supply relationship with supply as abscissa.

Economists frequently draw price-supply curves as shown in Figure 2–4, with supply considered to be the independent variable and shown as the abscissa. Thus the price is the result of the supply offered on the market.

Since, as shown in Figures 2–1 and 2–3, both the demand for and the supply of a given product are functions of price, both curves may be portrayed on a single chart, as shown in Figure 2–5. When this is done it may be seen that N units of supply will be offered on the market at price P which will just meet the demand that exists for the product at this price. Or, in other words, under conditions of perfect competition the price at which a

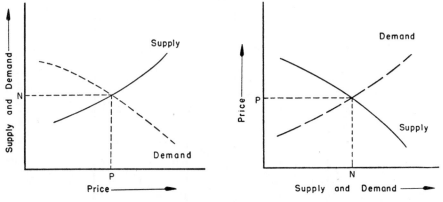

Figure 2–5. Price-supply-demand relationship, showing price, P, corresponding to N units.

Figure 2–6. Price-supply-demand relationship with price as the ordinate.

given product will be supplied and purchased is such that the amount supplied will equal the amount demanded. This is known as the *law of supply and demand*. In simple terms, it states that price is determined by supply and demand. Plotted in the usual manner of the economist, with supply and demand as independent variables, the price-supply-demand relationship is as shown in Figure 2–6.

The importance of the law of supply and demand in relationship to economy studies lies in the fact that proposed investments frequently involve increasing the supply of a product, or influencing the demand for it. The effect of such changes upon the price at which the product can be sold may be an important factor to be considered.

THE LAW OF DIMINISHING RETURNS

The law of diminishing returns is another basic economic principle that frequently is a factor in economy studies. All engineers have encountered this principle, but often they have not realized the fact. For example, Figure 2–7 shows an input-output curve for an electric motor. It is typical of many similar curves with which every engineer has dealt. Yet seldom would the engineer attempt to explain the characteristic shape of this curve as being due to the law of diminishing returns. However, this actually is true.

The *law of diminishing returns* may be stated as follows: When the use of one of the factors of production is limited, either in increasing cost or by absolute quantity, a point will be reached beyond which an increase in the variable factors will result in a less than proportionate increase in output.

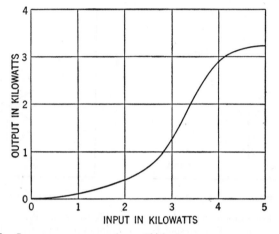

Figure 2–7.   Input-output curve for a 3½-horsepower constant-speed motor.

An examination of this statement reveals that it applies to two particular conditions:

1. One factor can not be increased.
2. All of the factors of production can be increased, but only with increasing difficulty.

The first studies of the law were probably made in the field of agriculture. Here the first condition is exemplified. Suppose a farmer has one hundred acres of land on which he raises corn. If he is an average farmer and does not employ other labor, he will probably get a yield of not over thirty-five bushels from each acre. The size of his crop is determined by a number of factors. These are (*a*) sunshine, (*b*) fertilizer, (*c*) cultivation, (*d*) the amount of land, (*e*) the labor available at the correct time, and (*f*) rain. All of these factors may be varied except the amount of land; only one hundred acres are available for cultivation. (Of course, some of the factors may not vary at the farmer's will, but at least they are not rigidly fixed.) The successful growing of corn depends largely upon having the ground in the proper condition at a particular time. The time at which the seed must be planted and the amount of time available for preparation of the soil are determined largely by the weather. Working by himself, the amount of ground which the farmer can prepare and the quality of the preparation are limited. If he employs a hired hand, more ground will be better prepared, and the yield might be increased from 35 to 40 bushels per acre. If he employs a second man to help in the preparation of the ground and in planting the seed, he might obtain a further increase of two bushels per acre. It is likely, however, that the addition of a third man would result in little, if any, increase in the crop yield. After sufficient labor is employed to prepare all of the land in a reasonably adequate manner and plant the seed, there will be very little gain from the employment of additional labor. The amount of land is definitely fixed, and the law of diminishing returns applies to the results obtained from increasing the amount of labor utilized.

An examination of the other factors necessary for the corn crop reveals that increasing them will effect an increase in the yield of the land, up to a certain point. Beyond this point the return is less than proportional, and the yield may actually decrease. No rain will result in no crop. A reasonable amount of rain will cause a large increase in the total amount of corn. However, increasing the amount of rain greatly will actually lessen the yield from the 100 acres. The same result will be obtained from increases in the amount of sunshine, fertilizer, and cultivation.

Thus, in agriculture the effect of diminishing returns may readily be seen. Its effect is much the same as that obtained by the rider who whips his horse. A small amount gives a great increase in speed, but too much whipping results in a great decrease in speed—at least in a forward direction. In nonagricultural pursuits the point of diminishing returns is usually not reached as quickly.

Referring to the motor test, the results of which are depicted in Figure 2–7, Table 2–1 shows test data and computed results. This particular motor was of $3\frac{1}{2}$-horsepower capacity and wound to give a constant speed of 1,290 r.p.m. The computed results are contained in the last two columns. The column headed "Proportional output" is computed to show what the output would have been had it continued to increase at the rate shown on the previous reading. Thus

$$\frac{c_B}{b_B} = \frac{d_C}{b_C}.$$

By comparing the actual output with the proportional output, one can determine whether an increase in input results in less than proportionate, proportionate, or greater than proportionate increase in output.

TABLE 2-1   Load Test Data for 3½-Horsepower Constant-Speed Motor Showing Proportional and Actual Output per Unit of Input

(a)	(b) Input, kw.	(c) Actual output, kw.	(d) Proportional output, kw.	(e) Output per unit of input
A	0.5	0.00		0.000
B	1.0	0.10		0.100
C	1.5	0.25	0.15	0.167
D	2.0	0.41	0.33	0.205
E	2.5	0.70	0.51	0.280
F	3.0	1.20	0.84	0.400
G	3.5	2.20	1.40	0.628
H	4.0	2.92	2.52	0.730
I	4.5	3.15	3.28	0.700
J	5.0	3.20	3.50	0.640

Two factors of production were present in this experiment—the motor and the input of electric energy. The motor was a fixed factor, but the input could be varied at will. Each increase in input might have given any one of five possible results in output

1. No increase,
2. Less than proportional increase,
3. Proportional increase,
4. Greater than proportional increase, or
5. Decrease.

Three of these conditions are shown in the table, and a fourth was present but did not appear as such. The first reading shows that, although the input was increased from zero to 0.5 kw., no increase in output occurred. From B to H, inclusive, each successive increase in input resulted in a greater than proportional increase in output. At some point between H and I the increase in output was evidently proportional to the increase in input. Starting with I, the increase in output was less than proportional to the increase in input. Danger of "burning out" the motor prevented any additional increase in input where the internal losses might have resulted in an actual decrease in output.

This experiment, of course, shows only a special case of diminishing returns. It does illustrate a condition that is very common—output that continues to increase, but with decreasing efficiency. The table shows that maximum efficiency was 73 per cent [1] when the output was 2.92 kw. A

---

[1] This unusually low efficiency for an electric motor is due to this motor being a special constant-speed type.

maximum output of 3.2 kw. was obtained but the efficiency was only 64 per cent. When such an occurrence is tied up with dollars and cents, it may readily be seen why continued increase in output may result in a smaller rate of return on the investment and possibly in actual loss.

Another example of diminishing returns is found in the performance of the ordinary automobile engine. Here the input is a mixture of gasoline and air. It is common experience to find that if the ratio of gasoline to air is made too low by adjustment of the carburetor, the engine will develop very little power. As the ratio is increased, the performance of the motor improves and greater power is developed. If the ratio of gasoline to air is further increased, a point of maximum output is obtained. Increasing the ratio beyond this point results in poorer performance and an actual decrease in the output of the engine so that it does not run smoothly. The fuel mixture is said to be too rich.

When improvements are to be made upon urban property, the principle of diminishing returns becomes very important. Here, again, the available land is the fixed factor. The amount of money which may be spent in erecting buildings upon a given piece of land is practically unlimited. The return that can be realized from the money invested will be dependent on both the land and the investment. The person investing money in such improvements is interested in obtaining a maximum rate of return. Increasing the amount invested when the returns not only do not increase proportionately, but actually decrease, eventually leads to no profit. Such a condition is, however, entirely possible.

Suppose the cost of erecting a four-story building on a given city lot is $500,000. To build a six-story building, instead of one having four stories, would probably cost an additional $300,000. These two additional stories will cost $150,000 each, while the originally considered four stories cost only $125,000 each. The difference is due to the fact that the additional two stories must be considered as being built under the original four stories and therefore must be of sufficient strength to support the additional weight. (This assumes that each story of the building is the same from the standpoint of ornamentation and physical characteristics.) In addition, elevators and service stacks must be provided up through the lower four floors to provide access and service to the fifth and sixth stories. These not only cost money but also take away some valuable space from the first four stories.

If two more stories were added, making an eight-story building, those two additional stories would probably cost approximately $175,000 each, or $350,000. Again, this is due to the necessity of building these additional stories so that they will support the previous six and to the fact that the building materials and workmen must be raised a greater distance above the ground. The necessity for additional elevators and service stacks will again decrease the usable space on the lower floors. The results of increasing this building from four to eight stories in height are shown in Table 2–2.

TABLE 2–2   Cost of Buildings of Various Heights

Stories	Cost of addition	Total cost
4	$500,000	$ 500,000
6	300,000	800,000
8	350,000	1,150,000

It may readily be seen that increasing the usable space less than 100 per cent increased the cost of the building 130 per cent. The increased income derived from the additional stories would be much less than 100 per cent, since the rental rate of the upper levels of nearly all buildings is considerably less than that of the lower floors. Diminishing returns present a very real problem in this type of project. Results of an actual study of this type are shown on page 268. The conclusions show that the architect who dreamed of designing a building so tall that only the top floor could be used, because all the floors below would be taken up with service stacks and elevators, may not have been entirely insane.

Businesses may be affected by the law of diminishing returns in a number of ways. Initial amounts of capital may be available at relatively low costs, for the starting of a business, through the savings of the owner. As the business expands, it may be necessary to borrow additional capital at a higher cost, thus imposing an increasing cost factor. Or, during the initial stages of a small business the owner may do a considerable portion of the total work. As the business grows, he may have to employ labor which may not always be as efficiently used, particularly at certain stages of growth. The market in a particular area may be limited, and if wider markets are entered, the cost of obtaining added customers may be greater than in the past. Thus the fixed or limited factors may take a variety of forms. As a consequence, it is wise to look for possible fixed or limited factors when making economy studies.

It must be remembered that the law of diminishing returns is stated for "equilibrium" conditions. In many instances the engineer deals with such conditions where the machines, plants, or facilities can not be changed. On the other hand, in many cases increases in production are obtained by changing equipment or conditions in such a manner that the possible effects of the law of diminishing returns are offset by the increased efficiency of the new method. In effect, an entirely new set of conditions has been brought into existence. In such cases the engineer must recognize that the effect of the law of diminishing returns will be modified. However, it cannot be ignored.

MINIMUM-COST POINTS

Capital usually is invested in engineering projects for the purpose of producing a profit. Once such projects are established, they ordinarily can be operated at various levels of output, from zero up to full capacity. The level at which an industrial plant, for example, is operated may have considerable effect upon its profitability. Likewise, the mechanical efficiency may also be considerably affected. The previous example of the electric motor illustrated the effect of diminishing returns upon mechanical efficiency. The effect upon financial efficiency can also be demonstrated.

To study the effect of diminishing returns upon unit cost where two factors of production are involved and one is fixed, examine Table 2–3.

TABLE 2–3   Monetary Cost of Units of Output of a 3½-Horsepower Constant-Speed Motor

	Input, kw.	Output, kw.	Input per unit of output		Monetary unit cost		Total unit cost, cents
			Variable factor	Fixed [a] factor	Fixed factor, @ 8 cents	Variable factor, @ 2 cents	
A	0.5	0.00					
B	1.0	0.10	10.00	10.00	80.00	20.00	100.00
C	1.5	0.25	6.00	4.00	32.00	12.00	44.00
D	2.0	0.41	4.88	2.44	19.52	9.76	29.28
E	2.5	0.70	3.57	1.43	11.44	7.14	18.58
F	3.0	1.20	2.50	0.83	6.64	5.00	11.64
G	3.5	2.20	1.59	0.45	3.60	3.18	6.78
H	4.0	2.92	1.37	0.34	2.72	2.74	5.46
I	4.5	3.15	1.43	0.32	2.56	2.86	5.42
J	5.0	3.20	1.56	0.31	2.48	3.12	5.60

[a] Number of motors to give 1.0 kw. output.

The first two columns of figures are the same as in Table 2–1 and concern the same test of a constant-speed electric motor. The fixed factor in this case is the motor. The third column shows the number of units of the variable factor which would be required in order to obtain one unit (1.0 kw.) of output. Thus, in line B, since 1.0 kw. of input produced an output of only 0.1 kw., to obtain 1.0 kw. of output 10 kw. input would be required.

In the fourth column similar data are tabulated for the fixed factor, the motor. Thus in line *C,* since one motor produced only 0.25 kw. of output, four motors would be required to produce 1.0 kw. of output if all were operated under the assumed conditions of load and efficiency.

In order to determine the monetary cost of obtaining one unit of output, it is necessary to know the monetary value of the required units of input. In this case the variable input factor, electric energy, was assumed to cost 2 cents per kw.-hr. The cost of the fixed factor—the motor—was more difficult to determine. This cost is made up of the depreciation of the motor, rent on the building where it is housed, taxes, insurance, and other overhead costs. In this case it was assumed that the total of these costs was 8 cents per hour for one motor.

In this table it will be noted that the lowest total cost occurs at *I* where the output is 3.15 kw. In Table 2–1 the maximum mechanical efficiency occurred at *H* where the output was only 2.92 kw. The maximum output, however, is at *J* and is 3.20 kw. This is a situation which is frequently difficult for engineers to accept. If maximum financial efficiency (lowest unit cost) is desired, the motor should not be operated at either the point of maximum mechanical efficiency or maximum output. If a machine is to operate continuously at a fixed load, it would be desirable to have the three points of maximum output coincide. On the other hand, if the machine were to operate at three-quarters load 90 per cent of the time, it would be desirable to have the points of maximum mechanical and financial efficiency near 75 per cent of capacity.

The example just cited is a rather simple case of diminishing returns, since only two input factors were involved. As will be discussed in Chapter 12, many economy studies involve fixed and variable factors and the concepts of minimum costs or maximum returns. In fact, such studies frequently are considered to be a distinct class of economy studies. When one makes such studies, it is helpful to remember their relationship to the basic concept of diminishing returns.

INCREMENT AND MARGINAL COSTS AND REVENUE

When an income factor is added to the volume-cost relationship, another economic principle is encountered. This is the effect of marginal revenue and marginal costs on maximum profits. One normally is interested in obtaining the maximum profit from an enterprise. The total income received is the product of the number of units sold and the price received for each unit. However, it has been shown that the number of units of a product that can be sold is a function of the price, and that the cost of production is likewise affected by the volume produced. The cost-volume relationship is due to the fact that certain expenses are fixed regardless of volume changes over a considerable range, while other expenses vary with changes in output, sometimes increasing and sometimes decreasing in terms of expense per unit produced. The resulting effect is illustrated in Table 2–4.

In Table 2–4 it will be noted that if the selling price is decreased by certain amounts, more units can be sold. The resulting revenue obtained from the sale of the units is shown in Column (c). The sale of each additional number of units produces a certain added amount or *increment* of revenue. This added revenue, which is the result of selling one additional unit, is called *increment revenue*. Because the additional units can be sold only by lowering the price, the increment revenue decreases with each increase in sales. It should be noted that by selling three units instead of two, for example, although the average selling price is $57, the increment revenue from the third unit is only $41. The increment revenue for each sales volume is shown in Column (d) of Table 2–4.

In Table 2–4 it is assumed that the fixed costs of production are $75 as shown in Column (e). The variable costs are assumed to vary as shown in Column (f). Adding the fixed and variable costs gives total costs as shown in Column (g). It may be seen that the total *added* cost of producing an additional unit is not the same for different levels of output. Thus the increased cost of producing the fourth unit is $25 while the added cost for producing the fifth unit is only $20. This added cost which is caused by the production of an additional unit is called the *increment cost*.

It will be noted that at one volume, five units, the increment cost is equal to the increment revenue. The economist commonly refers to the increment cost and increment revenue at this point as the *marginal cost* and *marginal revenue*. Thus, in this concept the marginal unit of production is that unit from the sale of which the marginal revenue derived will just cover the marginal cost.[2]

The actual profit obtained from the production and sale of the different numbers of units is shown in Column (j). It will be noted that maximum profit is obtained from the sale of either four or five units. Beyond five units, the volume where marginal cost and marginal revenue are equal, the profit decreases. This illustrates another basic and important economic concept— for maximum profits volume should not exceed the point where marginal

---

[2] The economist frequently uses the terms "marginal cost" and "marginal revenue" in place of "increment cost" and "increment revenue." However, there now is a tendency to apply the term "marginal" only to that case where increment revenue and cost are equal.

TABLE 2-4 Cost-Revenue Relationships for Different Outputs of an Assumed Product

(a) Quantity	(b) Price	(c) Revenue	(d) Increment revenue	(e) Fixed costs	(f) Variable costs	(g) Total costs	(h) Increment cost	(i) Average unit cost	(j) Profit
2	$65	$130		$75	$ 62	$137		$68.50	−$ 7
3	57	171	$41	75	90	165	$28	55.00	+ 6
4	50	200	29	75	115	190	25	47.50	+ 10
5	44	220	20	75	135	210	20	42.00	+ 10
6	39	234	14	75	160	235	25	39.17	− 1
7	35	245	11	75	190	265	30	37.86	− 20

cost is equal to marginal revenue. This is an important economic principle which is of considerable interest in making economy studies. It is intimately related to one whole class of economy studies—namely, those involving *fixed* and *increment costs*—which will be discussed in a later chapter.

It is important to remember that where the producer has a monopoly on the market, he may adjust his selling price to obtain the maximum return. Just what this price must be is difficult to determine and must be found by experiment or by a very careful market analysis. But ordinarily a complete monopoly does not exist, and competition will affect the selling price of the product. Even under competitive conditions, however, the producer will have considerable freedom in adjusting his price and production to obtain a more favorable return.

INCREASING- AND DECREASING-COST INDUSTRIES

All the examples of diminishing returns thus far considered lead to a single conclusion: a change in the output of a business may increase, decrease, or not affect unit costs. The effect of diminishing returns on the farmer who raised corn was noted when only a small increase in output was attempted. The automobile engine and the electric motor showed an increasing rate of output per unit of input when the output was first increased beyond zero. A decrease in the rate of output per unit of input did not come until a large increase in output was attempted. It is thus apparent that certain types of enterprises are affected more than others.

If various industries are examined, it will be found that certain types have characteristic tendencies in respect to the increase or decrease of unit costs with changing rates of production. These tendencies are closely tied up with the particular industry's use of durable goods. These durable instruments of production represent fixed, or approximately fixed, factors of production. Compared with a steel mill, a tailor makes very little use of durable goods. If the tailor operates at low capacity, he has only a small amount of capital tied up in unused goods. The large steel mill, operating at 20 per cent of capacity, has a tremendous sum invested in unproductive equipment. Doubling output would cause a great decrease in the unit costs of the steel mill but would lower the tailor's unit costs little, if at all.

Another influence on the tendency of costs to increase or decrease is the dependence of the particular industry upon natural factors. A coal mine has only one source from which to obtain its product. As more coal is produced, the supply will probably become scarce and difficult to obtain. The farmer or stock raiser is again very subject to the influence of natural factors. The producer of Mickey Mouse pictures, however, is very little affected by such conditions.

A third condition that will influence the effect of diminishing returns upon an industry is the extent to which it may be able to utilize mass production. Mass production methods are usually accompanied by important savings which will overbalance or at least lessen the effect of diminishing returns. Manufacturing industries are notably different from agriculture in this respect.

It is thus apparent that industries may be operating in such a condition that increased production will give increased costs, constant costs, or decreased costs. It is characteristic for certain types of business to show one of these three tendencies under ordinary operating conditions. For this reason agricultural industries are often referred to as increasing-cost industries while manufacturing enterprises are known as decreasing- or normal-cost industries. It must be remembered that this is a broad classification which applies only to normal industries operating at normal capacity. Under other conditions, and even at times under ordinary conditions, industries may be in other classes. The classification does, however, indicate a tendency worth remembering. Whether an industry is of increasing- or decreasing-cost type frequently is a significant factor to consider in analyzing the results of an economy study to determine whether investment should be made.

KELVIN'S LAW

In 1881 Lord Kelvin originated an economic law of particular interest to the engineer. In determining the size of electric conductor which would be most economical to conduct a given current, the following rule was established:

The most economical area of conductor is that for which the annual cost of energy lost equals investment charges for the copper used.

In this particular case, each increase in the size of the conductor causes a decrease in the loss of electric energy owing to the resistance of the conductor. On the other hand, each increase in the size of the conductor involves additional cost for copper, depreciation, interest, and tax charges and often for extra poles and equipment. An example of this exact problem is shown in Chapter 14.

Kelvin made a number of important assumptions in deriving his law. The effect of increased wire size upon the cost of supports and insulation was not considered. It was assumed that all investment costs vary directly with the area of the wire cross section and that energy-loss costs vary inversely. Since electrical conductor, for example, usually costs a different amount per pound for different diameters, Kelvin's law in its simple form is not of much practical value. However, it forms the basis of more refined methods of analysis that may be applied to any type of conductor problem, such as water, gas, or petroleum pipelines, where the cost for increased conductor size is balanced against decreased pumping cost.

PROBLEMS

2–1   Why can't the engineer ignore basic economic laws?

2–2   Why can't economic laws be as specific as physical laws?

2–3   What is meant by an "intangible factor"?

2–4   How do producers' goods differ from consumers' goods?

2–5   Explain why the terms "luxuries" and "necessities" are relative terms.

2–6   What is meant by the "elasticity" of demand?

2–7   Explain the basic idea of the law of supply and demand.

2–8   Assume that all of the common salt in the United States is produced by three companies. What would be the effects of a fourth large company entering this field of production?

2–9   What is meant by the term "perfect competition"?

2–10   How does an oligopoly differ from a monopoly?

2–11   What are the conditions which make an enterprise subject to the law of diminishing returns?

2–12   Explain how a service-station owner in an isolated town would be affected by the law of diminishing returns as he attempted to expand his business.

2–13   What is meant by "marginal cost"?

2–14   Why may it be poor policy for a producer having a monopoly to charge a very high price for his product?

2–15   What is meant by a "decreasing-cost" industry?

2–16   Explain how Kelvin's law would apply to an oil pipeline.

2–17   At the same time two new producers, each capable of supplying the same percentage of the total existing market, started to produce—one making pianos and the other bread. In which product would there be a greater relative change in the selling price, assuming ideal competitive conditions?

CHAPTER 3

Selections
in Present
Economy

FACTORS DETERMINING PRESENT ECONOMY

In the majority of economy studies time is a factor, and its effects upon capital and property must be considered in order to arrive at a correct result. There are, however, many important situations in which time and its effects need not be considered. In general, problems in present economy fall into one or more of the following categories:

1. Problems in which no investment in property is involved.
2. Problems involving no property which has a life of more than one year.
3. Problems in which the time involved in the various alternative solutions is the same, so that the one having the lowest immediate cost will also have the lowest ultimate cost, provided the periodic costs of maintenance and/or operation are the same, or are in proportion to the first costs, or are zero.
4. Problems in which the alternatives have identical effects upon depreciable equipment.
5. Problems in which the time effect is included in an hourly (or daily, monthly, etc.) use rate for equipment.

In any case, the ultimate criterion must be that the neglect of time will not affect the decision.

Present economy problems usually have another common characteristic. The obtaining and compiling of the data are the major difficulties in making such studies, while rather little analysis of the mathematical results is required in order to arrive at a correct selection between alternatives.

In broad terms, present economy studies usually involve selection between alternative materials, alternative methods, or alternative designs. In some instances studies of all three of these factors must be made before a product can be produced with maximum economy. As an example, consider the production of the case of a new electric desk clock. The case could be made of wood, steel, aluminum, or plastic. Each of these materials would make a satisfactory case that would have an adequate life. Yet each material would cost a different amount.

If plastic were selected as the material from which the clock case were to be produced, a decision would have to be made as to the molding method to be used. Either compression or injection molding could be used. These two methods would very probably not have identical costs, yet the resulting products would be equally satisfactory from a functional viewpoint.

Numerous variations in the design of the clock case might affect the cost of production. For example, the case might be made either in one piece or in two pieces. Several methods of attaching the clock unit to the case might be considered in designing the case. Any of the designs might be satisfactory from a functional viewpoint, not be affected by time, and yet have considerable effect upon economy.

Decisions of this type are continually being made by engineers and others. In some instances the factors are so simple and evident that the economy study is merely a brief mental weighing of the factors. In other cases many cost factors must be assembled and evaluated in order to arrive at the correct answer.

THE NECESSITY FOR EQUIVALENT RESULTS

One important factor which must be kept in mind in present economy studies is that the results of the various alternatives must be substantially equivalent. For example, if one were considering the alternatives of digging a ditch by pick and shovel or by a ditch-digging machine and found that the narrowest ditch which could be dug by the machine was one foot wider than was wanted, the results could hardly be said to be equivalent. Thus one must be certain that each alternative being considered will produce results which are satisfactory. This concept of equivalence does not mean that the results must always be identical. If it did not matter that the ditch were somewhat wider than a certain minimum, then the extra width produced by the machine would be neither an advantage nor a disadvantage. Frequently materials or methods must be compared which are not in all ways identical yet may be used so as to produce equivalent results. For example, a mild-steel bolt with a cross-sectional area of 1.0 square inch has an ultimate strength in tension of approximately 60,000 pounds. A nickel-steel alloy bolt of the same size would have a strength of 90,000 pounds. If strength were a factor in the design, it would not be correct to compare the cost of mild-steel and nickel-steel bolts of the same size. Yet a fair selection could be made between a mild-steel bolt with a cross-sectional area of 1.0 square inch and a nickel-steel bolt having a cross section of only 0.667 square inch, since both have identical strengths.

Thus, in setting up the data for selection in present economy one must be certain that the immediate results are equivalent. In most of these problems there is little difficulty in making the correct choice after the facts have been properly assembled. However, the task of obtaining the necessary information and arranging it so a correct comparison may be made often requires a great amount of work and considerable knowledge and experience.

SELECTION AMONG MATERIALS

One of the most frequent types of present economy studies is that in which selection must be made among materials. As more new and specialized materials become available, such problems become more numerous. Such studies are frequently complicated by the fact that materials usually differ from each other in more than one property. For example, consider the choice between using ordinary low-carbon steel and a low alloy-high yield strength steel in an application where yield strength is the design criterion upon which the selection must be based. The properties of the two materials are as follows:

	Low carbon steel	Low alloy-high yield strength steel
Yield strength	32,000 psi.	52,000 psi.
Ultimate strength	64,000 psi.	75,000 psi.
Cost per pound	$0.08	$0.10

These materials may be compared on the basis of the cost to obtain a pound of yield strength in the following manner:

Low carbon steel
$0.08/32,000 = $0.0000025

Low alloy-high yield strength steel
$0.10/52,000 = $0.00000192

Thus for this application the low alloy-high yield strength steel would be cheaper.

In making selections between two or more materials one must make certain that the proper criterion is used. For example, if one were selecting between steel and aluminum for a given product, both rigidity and strength might be of importance. It would therefore be necessary to consider both the strength and the modulus of elasticity of each material in order to arrive at a proper decision. Since materials usually differ with respect to more than one property, one must be certain that true equivalence is achieved.

MATERIAL SELECTION INVOLVING PROCESSING

In many cases selection of materials can not be based upon physical or mechanical properties or material cost alone without considering other costs that may be affected. One of the most frequent complicating factors is the cost of processing. Different materials often require different processing procedures, with accompanying changes in processing costs. As an example, consider the part shown in Figure 3–1. This part was produced in considerable quantities. The strength required was relatively small, but the piece could not have any of its dimensions changed. It was produced on a small, high-speed turret lathe. In the past, 1112 screw machine steel, costing $0.10 per pound, had been used. A study was made to determine if the part might be produced more cheaply by using brass screw stock, which cost $0.70 per pound but could be machined at a much higher rate. A time study of the production process using the two materials showed the following:

	Time in seconds	
Operations	1112	Brass
Feed stock to stop and lock chuck	5.0	5.0
Index turret	2.0	2.0
Turn ¼-in. diameter and center drill	17.5	5.0
Index turret	2.0	2.0
Drill #30 hole	16.5	7.0
Index turret	2.0	2.0
Cut ¼-in. thread	5.0	3.0
Index turret	2.0	2.0
Cut off piece	3.5	2.0
Reverse cross turret	2.0	2.0
Total	57.5	32.0
10% allowance	5.5	3.0
Standard time	63.0	35.0
Pieces per hour	57.1	102.9

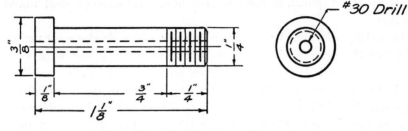

Figure 3-1.   Small screw-machine product.

The labor cost for making this part was at the rate of $2.00 per hour. Over-
head was figured at the rate of $1.50 per hour. The weight of material
required was 0.0353 pound of 1112 steel or 0.0384 pound of brass screw
stock. Using these figures, the cost per piece with each type of stock was:

	1112	*Brass*
Overhead	$0.0262	$0.0146
Labor	0.0350	0.0195
Material	0.0035	0.0269
Cost per piece	$0.0647	$0.0610
Saving per piece by using brass		$0.0037

Since many thousands were to be made, the saving of $3.70 per thousand
was an appreciable amount. In this example any effect of time is accounted
for by the overhead charge, so that a solution may be obtained without considering time as a direct factor.

As labor wage rates and overhead costs increase, processing costs become
very important in selecting materials. This situation and economy studies
have resulted in the development of new materials, such as free-machining
stainless steel, which permit low over-all cost to be obtained. In making a
selection between different materials, one must be careful that they are
exactly equivalent in results. The low-carbon and nickel-steel bolts previously mentioned are examples of this. If two materials are not exactly
equivalent in results, they can not be compared on as simple a basis. If one
material has superior qualities but, because of size or design limitations,
advantage can not be taken of those qualities, its superiority becomes of no
value and may have to be ignored in the solution of the problem at hand.
If the superior material should be found to be more economical, even
though it would not be used to the limit of its possibilities, it should be used.
Such a material merely carries a handicap in cost comparisons with other
materials. The important point to remember is that each material being

considered must satisfy the minimum requirements. Qualities above those required may have no value.

MATERIAL SELECTION INVOLVING SHIPPING COSTS

Many economy studies of material selection require a consideration of shipping costs. The case of the part shown in Figure 3–1 was one of this type. Most of the output was shipped by air express at an average cost of $0.79 per pound. This fact led to a study of the use of an aluminum alloy that would have to be heat treated. Bar stock of the aluminum alloy could be purchased for $0.85 per pound, and the finished parts could be heat treated at an outside plant for $0.018 each. A check indicated that the aluminum alloy could be machined at the same speeds as the brass stock.

Because the specific gravities of the brass and aluminum alloy were 8.7 and 2.75 respectively, the raw and finished weights of the part made from the two materials were:

	Brass	*Al. alloy*
Raw material	0.0384 lb.	0.0122 lb.
Finished part	0.0150 lb.	0.00474 lb.

The comparative costs of the part from the two materials were as follows:

	Brass	*Al. alloy*
Overhead	$0.0146	$0.0146
Labor	0.0195	0.0195
Material	0.0260	0.0104
Heat treatment	——	0.0180
Shipping	0.0119	0.0038
Total cost per piece	$0.0720	$0.0663

These figures show that for parts that did not have to be shipped brass was the more economical material. However, for those parts that had to be shipped by air express the aluminum alloy was more economical.

EFFECT OF SCRAP ON MATERIAL SELECTION

A very important factor that must be considered in material selection is the yield of finished product that can be obtained from a given weight of raw material. Different materials frequently do not come in the same sheet sizes or bar lengths. As a result, there may be a considerable difference in the amount of scrap. If a low cost material is involved, a fairly high percentage of scrap may not be of real economic importance. On the other hand, if a high cost material is used, the loss incurred by a very modest percentage of scrap may be considerable.

Numerous examples of difficulty due to this factor were experienced by companies which changed to aluminum from steel for making some of their products following World War II. Because of the low cost of steel prior to the war, they had not given much attention to the loss due to scrap, and the percentage of scrap was very high in many cases. When the change to aluminum was made, the companies suddenly found that they were losing a lot of money because of the much higher value of the aluminum scrap that was being thrown away.

SELECTION OF METHODS OR PROCESSES

A very large number of present economy studies involve selection between two or more methods or processes that accomplish the same basic purpose. The number of such possible situations is almost unlimited. As manufacturing technology is continuously advancing, it must be expected that more and more new methods and processes will be devised. The engineer must be prepared to make an economic analysis of each available method and to select the proper one. His work then becomes economically, as well as mechanically, efficient.

A simple example of selection among alternative methods is the analysis of the stresses in the members of a roof truss. Either mathematical or graphical solution would yield sufficiently accurate results. Yet it would be found that if the mathematical solution required four hours, the same answers could be obtained by graphical means in about two hours. If a designer were being paid to determine the stresses at the rate of $3 per hour, the two methods would have to be compared as follows:

Mathematical solution, four hours at $3	$12
Graphical solution, two hours at $3	6
Saving through the use of the graphical method	$ 6

With the two methods yielding identical results, it would be rather foolish to use the more expensive method.

Most cases of methods selection are somewhat more complex than this simple example. Several typical examples will be discussed.

SELECTION OF FABRICATION METHODS

Figure 3–2 shows two equivalent sheave housings which were produced by different methods—casting and welding. The cast housing was produced by the use of a rough casting, which required considerable machining

Figure 3–2. Cast-iron and welded sheave housings. (From *Procedure Handbook of Arc Welding Design and Practice*. Courtesy Lincoln Electric Co.)

to obtain the holes and mounting surfaces. The welded housing was made from steel plate and bar stock. All the parts were cut by the use of a shear and torch. The main body was formed by cutting a single plate to shape and bending it in the form of a "U." All holes except one were cut with a torch. The costs of the two methods were found to be as follows:

	Casting	Welding
Rough casting	$2.50	
Steel		$1.20
Cutting and forming		0.92
Cost of welding		0.42
Machining	1.12	0.31
Total cost	$3.62	$2.85

Saving $3.62 − $2.85 = $0.77

It is seen that in this case a saving of 21 per cent is possible by using welding instead of casting. For other products the opposite might be true, and casting would be more economical.

ECONOMY OF LOCATION

Many problems of location, particularly those of alternate locations for manufacturing plants, warehouses, retail stores, etc., involve time because of differences in construction costs, taxes, insurance rates, and operating costs. Such examples will be considered in later chapters. However some location problems are not affected by time. The following is a typical example.

In connection with surfacing a new highway, the contractor has a choice of two sites on which to set up his asphalt-treating equipment. He will pay a subcontractor $0.20 per cubic yard per mile for hauling the mixed material from the mixing plant to the job site. Factors relating to the two sites are as follows:

	Site A	Site B
Average hauling distance	3 miles	2 miles
Monthly rental	$ 100.00	$ 500.00
Cost to set up and remove equipment	$1,500.00	$2,500.00

If site B is selected, there will be an added charge of $12.00 per day for a flagman.

The job involves 50,000 cubic yards of mixed material. It is estimated that four months (seventeen weeks of five working days per week) will be required for the job.

The two sites may be compared in the following manner:

	Site A		Site B	
Rental	$4 \times \$100.00 =$	$ 400.00	$4 \times \$500.00 =$	$ 2,000.00
Setup cost	=	1,500.00	=	2,500.00
Flagman			$5 \times 17 \times \$12.00 =$	1,020.00
Hauling	$50,000 \times \$0.20 \times 3 =$	30,000.00	$50,000 \times \$0.20 \times 2 =$	20,000.00
Totals	=	$31,900.00		$25,520.00

It is thus apparent that site B will be more economical.

MAKE-READY AND PUT-AWAY TIMES

In many operations a considerable proportion of the total time consumed is due to the *make-ready* and *put-away* activities prior to and following the actual productive portion of the cycle. These make-ready and put-away operations usually require a fixed amount of time regardless of the volume of work run. For example, in a certain office a considerable amount of Mimeographing was done. Since certain stencils were rerun at various intervals, when such stencils were removed from the machine they were cleaned and placed in a suitable file until again needed. The time required for obtaining a stencil from the file, placing it on the Mimeograph, placing the machine in operation, removing the stencil from the machine, cleaning it, and placing back in the file was eleven minutes. Once the Mimeograph was started, the work was turned out at the rate of one copy each 0.6 second. Thus the time required for any number of copies was as shown in Figure 3–3.

It is apparent that the total time required is the sum of a fixed amount (11 minutes) plus a variable amount equal to 0.01 N, where N is the number of copies. It is also evident that the cost per copy produced will be affected by the number of copies that are run each time the duplicator is set up. If the operator of the machine receives $1.80 per hour, the cost per copy, as a function of the number of copies in a single run, would vary as follows:

Copies per run	Time required	Cost per copy
10	11.1 minutes	$0.03360
50	11.5 minutes	0.00690
100	12.0 minutes	0.00360
200	13.0 minutes	0.00195
300	14.0 minutes	0.00140
500	16.0 minutes	0.00096
1,000	21.0 minutes	0.00063

These results are shown in graphical form in Figure 3–4.

It becomes apparent from an examination of Figure 3–4 that neither this curve nor the tabular data given above provide an answer as to how many copies should be run in a single setup of the duplicator. However, they do supply information upon which a decision may be based. It is apparent that one should endeavor not to run less than about 200 copies at each setup. One may also determine, for example, that the cost of producing 1,000 copies in five runs of 200 each would be $1.95, as compared with $0.63 if the same number of copies were produced in a single run. Thus an economy study of this type can supply useful information upon which a decision may be based.

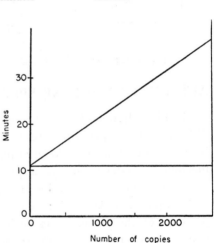

Figure 3–3. Total time required to set up and mimeograph copies of material.

This type of analysis assumes that the amount of money tied up in unused product between runs is negligible and that the productive value of the machine during the time required for setup may be neglected. In many cases these factors can not be neglected. Under such conditions, time must be taken into account, and such problems will be considered later in the discussion of economic lot size.

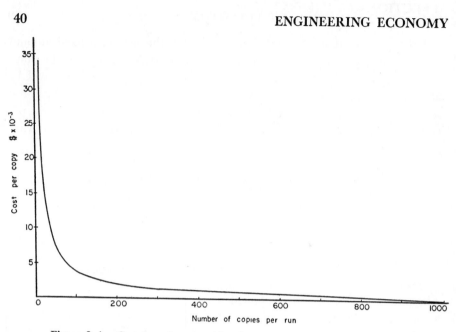

Figure 3-4.   Cost for mimeographing runs of various numbers of copies.

ALTERNATE MACHINE SPEEDS

Machines frequently can be operated at different speeds, resulting in different rates of product output. However, this usually results in different frequencies of "machine-down" time to permit servicing or maintaining the machine or resharpening or adjusting its tooling. Such situations lead to economy studies to determine the optimum or preferred operating speed.

A simple example of this type occurred in the planing of number. Lumber put through the planer increased in value $0.02 per board foot. When the planer was operated at a cutting speed of 5,000 feet per minute, the blades had to be sharpened after two hours of operation, and lumber could be planed at the rate of 1,000 board feet per hour. When the machine was operated at 6,000 feet per minute, the blades had to be sharpened after one and one-half hours of operation, and the rate of planing was 1,200 board feet per hour. Each time the blades were changed the machine had to be shut down for fifteen minutes. The blades, unsharpened, cost $5.00 per set and could be sharpened ten times before having to be discarded. Sharpening cost $1.00 per set. The crew that operated the planer changed and reset the blades. At what speed should the planer be operated?

Since the labor cost for the crew would be the same for either speed of operation, and since there was no discernible difference in wear upon the planer, these factors did not have to be included in the study.

In problems of this type, the operating time plus the delay time due to the necessity for tool changes constitute a cycle of time which determines the output from the machine. The time required for the complete cycle determines the number of cycles that can be completed in a period of available time—for example, one day—and a certain portion of each complete cycle is productive. The actual productive time will be the product of the productive time per cycle and the number of cycles per day.

At 5,000 feet per minute
Cycle time = 2 hrs. + 0.25 hr. = 2.25 hrs.
Cycles per day = 8 ÷ 2.25 = 3.555
Value added by planing = 1,000 × 3.555 × 2 × $0.02 = 142.20
Cost of resharpening blades = 3.555 × $1.00 = $3.56

Cost of blades = $3.555 \times \dfrac{\$5.00}{10}$ = 1.78

Total cost   5.34
Net increase in value per day $136.86

At 6,000 feet per minute
Cycle time = 1.5 hrs. + 0.25 hr. = 1.75 hrs.
Cycles per day = 8 ÷ 1.75 = 4.57
Value added by planing = 4.57 × 1.5 × 1,200 × $0.02 = 164.50
Cost of resharpening blades = 4.57 × $1.00 = $4.57

Cost of blades = $4.57 \times \dfrac{\$5.00}{10}$ = 2.29

Total cost   6.86
Net increase in value per day $157.64

Thus it was more economic to operate at the higher speed, in spite of the more frequent sharpening of blades that was required.

This type of study is of great importance in connection with metal-cutting machine tool operations. Changes of cutting speeds can have a great effect upon tool life. In addition, since the cost of machine tools and wage rates have increased, it is more important that productivity be maintained at as high a level as possible. Under these conditions, it has frequently been found that increased cutting speeds give greater over-all economy, even though the cutting tool life is considerably less than was accepted practice in former years. This is particularly true if rapid means can be devised for changing tools when required.

MACHINE-DOWN TIME DUE TO MULTIPLE INPUT MATERIALS

A fairly common situation that requires a present economy study is that in which a machine is fed with several input materials which require that the machine be shut down each time any one of them must be replenished.

Under such a condition, as the number of input materials increases, the frequency of the required shutdowns also increases. As a result, the machine may be shut down for servicing more time than it is operating unless some special procedures are devised.

As an example of this type, consider the assembly machine illustrated schematically in Figure 3–5. This was a machine used to assemble four

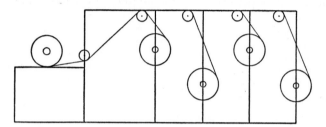

Figure 3–5.   Schematic diagram of a machine to assemble a four-ply product.

single plies of plastic-treated paper into a four-ply product. Each roll of the treated paper contained approximately 5,000 linear feet, but the actual length varied from 4,850 to 5,150 feet. The assembly machine ran at a speed of 500 feet per minute. Whenever any of the input rolls was depleted, the machine had to be stopped, a new roll put in place, and the leading end of the paper attached to the end of the paper from the depleted roll. The changing of the rolls and the splicing required three minutes and was done by the machine operator, who was paid $2.19 per hour. While the machine was stopped, two other members of the machine crew, who were each paid $1.65 per hour, were idle. The overhead costs for this machine were $0.70 per hour.

Since during the running of a 5,000-foot roll the machine would, on the average, be shut down three times for changing rolls, the operating cycle for running 1,000 feet of the four-ply product was

$$\text{Cycle time per 1,000 feet} = \left[\frac{5,000}{500} + 3 + 3 \times 3 \right] \tfrac{1}{5} = 4.4 \text{ minutes.}$$

The cost of running 1,000 feet of finished product was

$$\frac{4.4}{60} \times \$6.19 = \$0.454.$$

A study was made to determine whether it would be more economical to change all four rolls of paper whenever the first one became depleted and throw away any materials remaining on the other three rolls. As the first step, the actual lengths of a number of rolls were measured. This provided the distribution curve shown in Figure 3–6. From these distribution data, it was found statistically that the average length of assembled four-ply stock that could be obtained from four rolls of raw material would be 4,935 feet, and that a total of 268 feet of raw material would have to be scrapped from each group of four rolls.

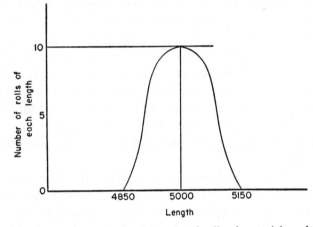

Figure 3–6. Distribution curve of roll-lengths of rolls of material used in assembling a four-ply product.

It was found that all of the crew, working together, could change all four rolls of paper in five minutes. The value of the raw material was $0.001 per foot. Under these conditions, the cost of assembling 1,000 feet of finished product would be as follows:

$$\text{Cycle time per 1,000 feet} = \left[\frac{4,935}{500} + 5 \right] \frac{1}{4.935} \qquad = 3.02 \text{ minutes}$$

$$\text{Labor and machine cost per 1,000 feet} = \frac{3.02}{60} \times \$6.19 \quad = \$0.312$$

$$\text{Scrapped material} = \frac{268 \times \$0.001}{4.935} \qquad\qquad = \ 0.055$$

$$\text{Total} \qquad\qquad\qquad\qquad\qquad\qquad = \overline{\$0.367}$$

It was therefore more economical to follow this procedure.

An analysis of this type of problem will reveal that as the number of input elements increases the percentage of machine-down time increases considerably if each input roll must be used completely. On the other hand, if all rolls are changed when the first one is depleted, the average yield obtained from a set of input rolls tends to decrease as the number of input factors increases, and there is a greater than proportionate increase in the roll-end material that must be thrown away, depending upon the distribution of roll lengths. Therefore, a very careful statistical analysis of each case must be made in order to arrive at a proper method of operating.

ECONOMY OF TOOL MAINTENANCE
IN TRANSFER-TYPE MACHINES

The problem of most economical cutting speeds and tool maintenance becomes extremely complex and important in the large transfer-type machine tools that are used in modern mass production. Such machines may involve as many as eighty individual, but interconnected, self-contained power-head units, and two to four hundred cutting tools. If each tool were operated at optimum cutting speed, only by chance would more than one become dull and require changing at the same time. With such a large number of cutting tools involved, if the entire machine were shut down whenever an individual tool became dull or worn, the machine would be idle most of the time.

In order to obtain a high percentage of productive time, each machining operation must be distributed among a proper number of cutting tools in order to obtain approximately the same length of life from a group of tools. An elaborate recording mechanism, such as that shown in Figure 3–7, is used to record the wear on each group of tools and shut down the machine when it is time for the tools to be changed.

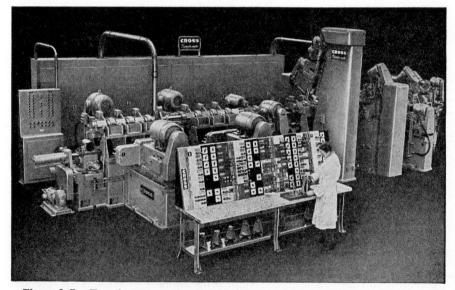

Figure 3–7. Transfer-type production unit, showing the control panel which stops the machine when tools need sharpening. (Courtesy The Cross Company.)

ECONOMY OF CREW SIZE

The proper number of workmen to be used in a crew can usually be determined by present economy studies. An example of this type occurred in a factory where a certain overhaul job was done with considerable frequency. It was customary to use a three-man crew. However, when such a crew was used it was found that, because of limitations in work space, two of the men were idle 33 per cent of the time; one of these men was also idle an additional 50 per cent of the time. All three men worked simultaneously only 17 per cent of the time, and it was found that there actually was no portion of the job on which more than one man was required at a given time. Each workman was paid $2.17 per hour. Each job required the use of a kit of tools and equipment that was worth $2.00 per hour and would be required regardless of crew size. If the three-man crew required four hours to do the job, what size crew would be most economical?

Figure 3–8 shows the working and idle time of each crew member. It is apparent that the total work content of the job is

$$4(1.00 + 0.67 + 0.17) = 7.36 \text{ hours.}$$

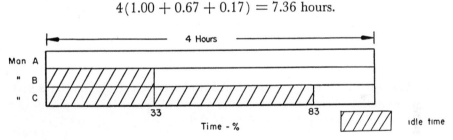

Figure 3–8. Working and idle times of the members of a three-man repair crew.

Since any portion of the work can be done by a single man, the crew could consist of any desired size. If there were only one man in the crew, he would have no delay. If two men were used, only one of them could work during 0.33×4 hours or 1.32 hours. This would leave 6.04 man-hours which would require 3.02 hours of elapsed time. Thus the total time required for a two-man crew would be 4.34 hours. For one-, two-, and three-man crews the cost of doing the job would then be as follows:

No. of men	Hours required	Labor cost	Tool cost	Total
1	7.36	$15.97	$14.72	$30.69
2	4.34	18.84	8.68	27.52
3	4.0	26.04	8.00	34.04

It is thus apparent that a two-man crew is most economical.

PROCESSING MATERIALS HAVING LIMITED AND UNLIMITED SUPPLY

Some present economy studies involve alternative methods of processing raw materials that sometimes are limited in quantity. When this restriction is present, certain precautions must be observed that need not be considered when the supply is unlimited.

As an example of this type, consider two methods that are available for processing a certain ore to recover the contained metal. The ore, as it comes from a certain mine, contains 22 per cent of the metal. Two methods of treatment for the ore are available. Each uses the same equipment, but they involve the use of different chemicals and grinding to different degrees of fineness. To process a ton of ore by method A costs $14.35 and recovers 84 per cent of the contained metal. Processing by method B costs $16.70 per ton of ore, and 91 per cent of the metal is recovered. If the recovered metal can be sold for $0.06 per pound, which method of processing should be used?

There is only a certain amount of ore in the mine; thus the supply of raw material obviously is limited. However, the fact that a different total amount of metal will be recovered and sold when the two different processes are used must be taken into account in the economy study. Such problems can be handled in either of two ways.

Probably the most foolproof method is to base the calculations on a unit of raw material—in this case a ton of ore. This procedure automatically puts each alternative on the proper basis.

Method A
 Profit per ton of ore $= 2,000 \times 0.22 \times 0.84 \times \$0.06 - \$14.35 = \$7.82$
Method B
 Profit per ton of ore $= 2,000 \times 0.22 \times 0.91 \times \$0.06 - \$16.70 = \$7.32$

Thus, although method B would result in more metal being recovered and sold, the profit obtained would not be as great as if method A were used.

A second method of working this type of problem is to determine either the cost of producing a unit of output—a pound of metal in this case—by each method of processing, or to determine the profit obtained from the sale of one pound. However, one must then take into account the fact that, because of the different recoveries from the same amount of ore, the two methods will not produce the same total number of pounds of the product.

When the supply of the raw material is not limited, the procedure of

determining which method of processing will give the lowest cost for producing a unit of output is a satisfactory, and usually somewhat simpler,
procedure. Since there is no limitation on the amount that can be produced,
one need only be concerned with obtaining each unit of product at the
least cost.

PROFICIENCY OF LABOR

Workers of different proficencies frequently produce different amounts of
output in a given time. Through the use of various types of incentives, either
monetary or nonmonetary, workers of all types may be induced to develop
and exhibit different degrees of proficiency, resulting in various levels of
output. Present economy studies are useful in establishing and maintaining
the proper incentives.

As an example of this type, consider the case of a product that was made
by hand in a small factory. The workers were paid $0.20 per acceptable
piece produced. It was found that if a worker produced eighty pieces per
day, 5 per cent would be rejected. If ninety pieces were produced per day,
10 per cent would be rejected, and at a rate of one hundred pieces per day,
20 per cent would be rejected. The cost for materials was $0.50 per piece,
and the materials in any rejected products had to be thrown away. There
was a fixed overhead expense of $10.00 per day per worker, regardless of
considerable change in output. Three questions arose concerning the situation: (a) at which of the three outputs did the workers make the highest
wages; (b) at which output did the factory achieve the lowest unit cost; and
(c) was some adjustment in the wage payment situation desirable?

The wages obtained by the workers for the three output rates were:

Pieces produced per day	80	90	100
Rejects	4	9	20
Acceptable pieces per day (N)	76	81	80
Earnings ($N \times \$0.20$)	$15.20	$16.20	$16.00

It was thus evident that it was to the workers' advantage to produce at the
rate of 90 pieces per day.

From the viewpoint of unit cost, the situation was

Rate per day	80	90	100
Material cost	$40.00	$45.00	$ 50.00
Labor cost	15.20	16.20	16.00
Overhead	10.00	10.00	10.00
Total	$65.20	$71.20	$ 76.00
Cost per acceptable piece	$ 0.858	$ 0.879	$ 0.950

The calculations showed that the lowest unit cost would be obtained at an output rate of 80 pieces per day. It was thus evident that the degree of proficiency which was likely to result from the incentive wage system would not be best from the viewpoint of the company. A change in the wage structure was therefore desirable.

SELECTION OF DESIGN

Most machines and structures can be designed in more than one way to accomplish the same function. Whether an automobile has air-cushion or torsion-bar suspension may make virtually no difference in its life or operating characteristics. However, the cost of manufacturing may be quite different. Whether a welded bridge is designed and built of ordinary low-carbon structural steel or of heat-treated and tempered alloy steel will have no effect upon its life and serviceability, but the cost of construction is almost certain to be different. Therefore, when alternative designs which will produce equivalent results are possible, present economy studies are necessary to determine which design will be most economical.

This type of economy study is of particular importance in the civil engineering and architectural fields, where the cost of the product (structure) may be great and alternative designs are apt to show considerable differences in cost. In most cases, a series of economy studies of increasing detail and accuracy are made in order to arrive at the final design decision. Obviously an accurate economy study of two designs can not be made until the designs are virtually complete. Yet in many instances one wishes to eliminate further consideration of one or more alternative design possibilities without the expense of carrying the design into advanced stages. Therefore, the first economy study in the series is usually quite rough and is based upon very approximate design and cost data, in order to determine whether certain designs are far out of line and to enable the selection of two or three for more detailed consideration. For this purpose, generalized cost curves (which will be discussed later) and cost data are adequate and are used. As the selected designs are completed in more detail, more accurate economy studies are made, upon which final design decisions may be based.

ECONOMIC DESIGN OF A BEAM

Since there are almost unlimited possibilities of design selection, one simple and two more complex problems will be discussed as typical. Consider the problem of selecting a wooden beam to support a uniformly distributed load of 2,200 pounds over a span of 12 feet. The beam is to be of select structural grade Douglas fir and the deflection limited to 1/300 of the span. From suitable handbooks it is found that there are three common sizes of beams which will support the load under these conditions. These sizes and their safe loads are

Nominal size	Safe load
4 by 8 inches	2,270 pounds
3 by 10 inches	2,630 pounds
2 by 12 inches	2,390 pounds

Thus from the standpoint of ability to support the desired load, each of these sizes is satisfactory. Each is also found to be satisfactory for other requirements, such as lateral buckling.

When one attempts to determine the cost of using each of these beams, he finds that the three sizes do not cost the same per unit volume. The 4-by-8-inch and 3-by-10-inch sizes list at $140.00 per thousand board feet while the 2-by-12-inch size costs only $104.00 per thousand board feet. This difference is due to the facts that some sizes are more readily obtained in the cutting of the tree into lumber and that certain sizes are more widely used and as a result are produced in greater volume.

Another factor that affects the cost of the various sizes of beams is the actual volume of material in them. The 4-by-8-inch beam contains 32 board feet. The 3-by-10 has 30 board feet, while the 2-by-12-inch size contains only 24 board feet. The final cost figures for the three sizes appear as follows:

Nominal size	Cost per M board feet	Board feet	Cost per beam
4 by 8 inches	$140.00	32	$4.48
3 by 10 inches	140.00	30	4.20
2 by 12 inches	104.00	24	2.50

From this table it can be seen that there is a decided advantage in using the 2-by-12-inch beam.

ECONOMIC SPAN LENGTH FOR BRIDGES

In the case of the wooden beam each successive size contained a smaller volume of material and was more economical to use. Also the cost per unit volume of material decreased as the depth of the beam increased. Thus both factors which affected the cost decreased. In many cases where design selection is involved, this is not true. Usually some of the cost factors in-

crease while others decrease. The problem then becomes one of selecting that
design which gives the lowest total cost.

An excellent example of this type of problem is seen in Figure 3–9, which
shows a set of cost curves taken from J. A. L. Waddell's classical work,
Economics of Bridgework. These curves show the cost per foot of structure
for low-level combined bridges on sand foundations 200 feet deep. In this

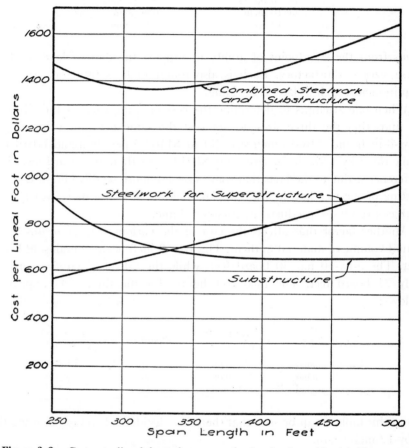

Figure 3–9. Costs per lineal foot of structure for low-level combined bridges on sand
foundations 200 feet deep. (Reprinted by permission from *Economics of Bridgework*
by J. A. L. Waddell, published by John Wiley & Sons, Inc.)

case the cost of the substructure decreases slightly. The cost of the steelwork
of the bridge increases rapidly as the span length is increased, owing to the
necessity for heavier construction. With these conditions, one would expect
that one particular length of span would be more economical than all
others. The curves show that this condition exists at approximately 325

feet. Thus, if a bridge of this type, 1,200 feet in length, were to be built, one might use a design of either 300- or 400-foot spans and have all spans of the same length. However, the curves of Figure 3–9 show that the cost of the two designs would be as follows:

Length of spans	Number of spans	Cost per foot	Total cost
300 feet	4	$1,380	$1,656,000
400 feet	3	$1,440	$1,728,000

The saving of $72,000 through the use of 300-foot span lengths is well worth the time required to make the necessary computations and comparison.

The cost curves shown in Figure 3–9 represent the type of data that frequently are used in making the preliminary economy studies of design that were discussed previously. In using such data, one must be sure to ascertain the conditions for which the data were determined and to make allowances for deviations in current conditions and costs. In most cases such generalized cost curves and data are suitable only for preliminary, approximate economy studies and should not be used for the final studies.

ECONOMIC BUTTRESS SPACING
FOR MULTIPLE-ARCH DAMS

Another example of a complex design economy problem is the spacing of buttresses in a dam. Figure 3–10 shows a generalized curve, in terms of a cost index, for the relationship between buttress spacing and cost for an Ambursen flat-slab dam 20 feet high. The sections of such a multiple arch

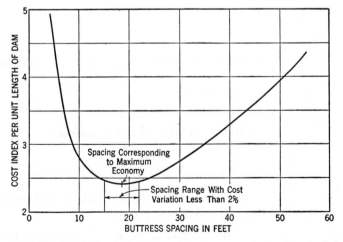

Figure 3–10. Typical relation between buttress spacing and cost of dam.

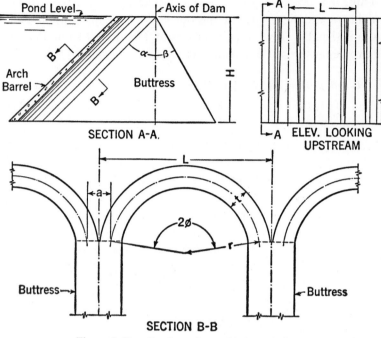

Figure 3–11.   Sections of a multiple-arch dam.

dam are shown in Figure 3–11. F. C. Rogers [1] has derived an equation which allows one to compute the most economical spacing for such structures. This equation is

$$L^2 = a^2 + \frac{4K_f \sin \phi (HB - aA)}{K_c A z}$$

where

L = buttress spacing in feet

a = horizontal dimension between mean arch radii at upstream face of buttress

K_f = cost of forms per square foot

ϕ = one-half of central arch angle, in degrees

H = height of dam, in feet (pond level to foundation)

$B = \tan \alpha + \tan \beta$ (see Figure 3–11)

$A = \dfrac{\pi \phi}{90 \sin \phi \cos \alpha}$ (see Figure 3–11)

K_c = cost of concrete and included steel, per cubic foot of concrete

z = arch design constant = t/r (see Figure 3–11).

[1] F. C. Rogers: "Economical Buttress Spacing for Reinforced Concrete Dams," *Civil Engineering,* August, 1938.

The obvious advantage of a cost formula of this type over the curves shown in Figure 3–9 is that by inserting current values for the cost of the forms and the costs of concrete and reinforcing steel, the economic spacing of the buttresses can be determined for current conditions.

THE RELATION OF DESIGN TO SALES

Design may affect the economy of projects in numerous ways. One common relationship is that of design to sales. Often acceptance of a product by the consumers is greatly influenced by the appearance of the product itself or by its packaging. One company, for example, greatly increased its sales of a high-quality gun oil by marketing it in a new, transparent plastic container with the product name and instructions for its use printed on the inside so that they could be read through the clear oil. Before this change in packaging, when the oil was sold in metal cans, sales were very small. Such examples are numerous and show the necessity for considering alternative designs to determine their effect upon economy.

A similar way in which design may affect sales is through the ease or difficulty of servicing or maintaining a product, which is often the result of design features.

THE RELATION OF DESIGN AND QUALITY
TO PRODUCTION COST

Alternative designs frequently must be considered from the viewpoint of economy of manufacture. Some designs contain features which are inherently more costly to produce than others. The effect of dimensional tolerances on the cost to produce is an example. Figure 3–12 illustrates the relative cost of obtaining different dimensional accuracies.

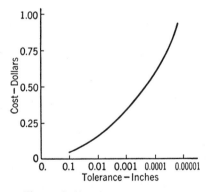

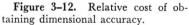

Figure 3–12. Relative cost of obtaining dimensional accuracy.

Another aspect of dimensional accuracy is the fact that the specification of a certain degree of accuracy usually determines the machines and processes that must be utilized to produce a part or product. Ordinarily the freedom to select alternative machines or processes is greatly decreased as the required accuracy is increased. This may impose other difficulties than increased cost.

The cost of quality is a similar situation. Inspection and control procedures which are necessary to insure high quality are costly. In most instances it is found to be more economical to allow a small number of defects to pass the inspection barriers and to pay the necessary costs for replacements and repairs on these defective products than to pay the expense which would be required to eliminate all defects.

ALTERNATIVES WITH DIFFERENT LIVES MAY BE PROBLEMS IN PRESENT ECONOMY

In most cases where the various alternatives being considered have different lives, they can not be handled as problems in present economy. The comparison, for example, of a wooden building and a concrete building is usually not a problem in present economy, since one has a much longer life and a lower maintenance cost than the other. However, if the life required of a building were very short, so that a wooden structure would have an adequate life and there would be no necessity for maintenance over the short period of years, it would be entirely correct to make the study on the basis of present economy. By recognizing that life in excess of that which is needed has no value, it frequently is possible to simplify economy studies by reducing the problem to one of present economy.

CHANGING CONDITIONS REQUIRE RESTUDY

One word of caution should be added concerning the results obtained through selections in present economy. The correct solution today may not be correct tomorrow if the conditions upon which the data were based have changed. An excellent example of this is found in the effect on the gold-mining industry of the increase in price of gold from $20.67 to $35.00 per ounce in 1934. Prior to that date it was not profitable to use certain processes which were necessary to recover the gold from low-grade ores. As a result, large piles of "tailings," which were considered worthless, were accumulated at many mines. After the price of gold was increased, it was found that a considerable portion of the low-grade ores and tailings could be put through more expensive recovery processes so the gold could be recovered and a substantial profit earned.

Thus, because one has made a correct analysis of a problem today and selected the proper method, material, or design, he should not be unmindful of new methods, materials, and processes which are being developed and which may have a vital effect upon the economy of his operation. It is indeed rare that anything is done so efficiently that time will not reveal even better methods.

LIMITATIONS OF PRESENT ECONOMY STUDIES

While selections involving present economy have many applications, as indicated in the various examples which have been mentioned, the larger proportion of selection problems are outside the scope of present economy because time is a factor. In many cases the dividing line between present economy and long-term economy is not distinct. A slight change in conditions or viewpoint may shift the problem from one classification to the other. As a result, each set of conditions must be carefully handled to assure that all the controlling factors are considered. Since the engineer is vitally concerned with all types of economic selection, it is necessary for him to understand how investments—in the form of structures and equipment or their equivalent, money—are affected by time. The two factors which are most important as the result of the passage of time are interest and depreciation. For this reason, the next few chapters are devoted to those subjects, so that all of the necessary tools may be available for use in solving all types of problems in economic selection.

PROBLEMS

3–1 John Jones, Inc., has a contract to pave a five-mile stretch of highway. He has a choice of two sites on which to set up his asphalt-mixing equipment. From these sites the mix will be hauled to the job by a trucking firm to which he will have to pay $0.06 per cubic yard per mile of haul. Factors relating to the two sites are as follows:

	A	B
Average hauling distance	5 miles	2 miles
Monthly rental	$ 100.00	$ 500.00
Cost to set up and remove equipment	$1,500.00	$3,500.00

If site B is selected, there will be an added charge of $15.00 per day for a flagman.

The job involves 60,000 cubic yards of mixed material. It is estimated that the job will require six months (26 weeks), working five days per week.

Which site should be selected?

3–2 A low-level combined bridge which will have a total length of 2,400 feet is to be constructed on sand foundations 200 feet deep. It is necessary to have one span in the bridge not less than 400 feet long. Two designs are being considered: (*a*) six equal spans of 400 feet; (*b*) a center span of 450 feet and three equal spans of 325 feet on each side of the center span. Using the curves shown in Figure 3–9 (page 50), determine which of the proposed designs is the more economical.

3–3   On a small automatic-transfer machine three speeds are available, giving the following outputs per hour and times between tool regrinding when cutting a certain rather hard material.

> Speed *A:* 400 pieces per hour; time between tool grinds, 12 hours
> Speed *B:* 480 pieces per hour; time between tool grinds, 10 hours
> Speed *C:* 540 pieces per hour; time between tool grinds, 7 hours

A set of tools costs $80.00 and can be ground thirty times. Cost of each regrinding is $10.00. The time required to change tools is 1½ hours. The machine operator is paid $2.20 per hour, including tool-change time. The tool setter receives $4.00 per hour. Overhead is charged for the machine at the rate of $3.75 per hour, including tool-change time. At which speed should the machine be operated?

3–4   A man who has invented a new type of garden tool wishes to interest some manufacturer in purchasing his patent. He desires to send some type of illustration of the tool to one hundred manufacturers. Two possible methods of doing this are being considered.

(*a*)   A draftsman could prepare pictorial drawings of the tool on vellum, and, from these, one hundred black-and-white prints could be made; the draftsman will charge $60.00 for the drawing, and the prints will cost $0.30 each for the first fifty and $0.25 for each additional print.

(*b*)   The inventor has a number of small photographs of the tool being used under a variety of conditions, which could be mounted and photographed as one large photograph; making the negative of the large photograph would cost $5.00 and the prints $0.90 each.

Which method would be more economical?

3–5   In Problem 3–4, what other factors beside cost should be considered in making a decision as to the better method to use?

3–6   In manufacturing an automobile accessory, it is necessary to produce two ⅜-inch holes in each product. If these holes are drilled with the aid of a jig, each hole will require one-half minute to complete. The drill jig would cost $20.00 to construct, and the drill-press operator is paid $1.75 per hour. Overhead costs on the drill press are $1.00 per hour.

If the holes are made on a punch press both holes can be made simultaneously in ten seconds, including handling time. The required die would cost $80.00 and it would require one-half hour to set up the die on the press and the same amount of time to tear it down when the job is completed. Overhead charges for the punch press are $2.50 per hour. The press operator receives $1.65 per hour, and the set-up man is paid $3.50 per hour.

If 5,000 parts are to be produced, overhead costs are charged on the basis of productive time only, and the jig or die could be used only on this one job, which method should be used?

3–7 Stainless steel having a yield strength of 33,000 pounds per square inch can be purchased for $0.90 per pound. An aluminum alloy having a yield strength of 20,000 pounds per square inch is available for $0.55 per pound. For a particular job either material is equally suitable if design is based upon the yield strength. The specific gravities of stainless steel and the aluminum alloy are 7.77 and 2.79 respectively. Which material will be the more economical?

3–8 Type *A* concrete has 30 per cent greater heat insulating value than type *B*. A specification calls for a 4-inch thickness of type *A* or its equivalent. If type *B* costs $9.00 per cubic yard and type *A* costs $11.50, which will be the more economical?

3–9 In order to provide additional playground area at an elementary school, it is necessary to buy additional land and do some grading and filling.

On one side of the school, the required land can be purchased for $6,000.00. To make this land usable, 2,500 yards of dirt would have to be moved from one portion of the area and used to fill in another portion. It is estimated that this work could be done for $1.00 per yard.

On the other side of the school, a somewhat larger tract of low land is available for only $1,000.00. To use this land would require removing some trees at an estimated cost of $500.00 and bringing in 5,000 cubic yards of fill at a cost of $1.50 per yard. It is also estimated that an additional $1,000.00 would have to be spent within a year to resurface the playground because of probable irregular earth settlement due to the large amount of fill in certain portions.

Which piece of land would you recommend?

3–10 If filter *A* is used in a Diesel switching locomotive, with premium quality lubricating oil costing $1.20 per gallon, the filter and the oil will have to be changed after 1,000 hours of operation, and one gallon of new oil added after each 100 hours. This type of filter costs $25.00. Forty gallons of oil fill the motor.

Equally satisfactory service can be obtained by using filter *B*, which costs $35.00, and a lower grade of oil, which costs $1.00 per gallon. In this case the filter would be changed each 1,000 hours, the oil completely changed after each 500 hours, and one gallon of oil added after each 250 hours of use.

Which combination should be used?

3–11   The ore of the Golden Lady gold mine contains 0.8 ounces of gold per ton. One method of processing the ore costs $9.80 per ton and recovers 94.5 per cent of the gold. If the ore is processed by a second method, which involves no substantial change in the equipment or in the time required, the cost is $7.10 per ton, and 81.5 per cent of the gold is recovered.

    a. If gold is worth $35.00 per ounce, which method should be used?

    b. Would a decrease in the price of gold to $25.00 per ounce affect the answer?

3–12   Sea water contains 2.1 pounds of magnesium per ton. One method of processing, *A*, will recover 85 per cent of the metal and costs $0.73 per ton of water processed. A second process, *B*, recovers 70 per cent of the metal and costs $0.55 per ton. The two processes are substantially equivalent for the investment and time requirements. If the extracted magnesium can be sold for $0.50 per pound, which method of extraction should be used?

3–13   A repair operation which is repeated a considerable number of times each year in connection with servicing a large number of machines in a plant is being done by a three-man repair crew. The task requires three hours when done by this crew, each member of which is paid $2.20 per hour.

    Because of space limitations one man is idle 50 per cent of the time. During 25 per cent of the time two of the men work together at one portion of the task which can be done more readily by two men, but which could be done by one man with the expenditure of 25 per cent more man-hours. All other parts of the job are independent and can be done by one man.

    There is an overhead charge of $3.00 per hour for tools which are used, and the same kit of tools would be required regardless of the number of men in the crew.

    What number of men should be used in the repair crew for greatest economy?

CHAPTER 4

Interest
and Annuity
Relationships

ORIGIN AND DEFINITION OF INTEREST

Whenever time is a factor in an economy study, interest must be taken into account. Like taxes, interest has existed from the time of man's earliest recorded history. Records reveal its existence in Babylon in 2000 B.C. In the earliest instances interest was paid for the use of grain or other commodities which were borrowed; it was also paid in the form of grain or other goods. Many of the existing interest practices stem from the early customs in the borrowing and repayment of grain and other crops.

History also reveals that the idea of interest became so well established that a firm of international bankers existed in 575 B.C., with home offices in Babylon. Its income was derived from the high interest rates it charged for the use of its money for financing international trade. Interest is not only one of our oldest institutions, but its uses have suffered little change through the years.

In spite of its age and history, and its constant presence in business transactions, interest is often misunderstood, and sometimes ignored, in engineering and industrial calculations. The term "interest" is often applied to items which in reality are not interest but *profit*. Such use of the term is not at all disastrous, if understood, and it is doubtful that the misuse will ever be entirely eliminated. Whenever two factors of a problem under consideration are money (or its equivalent) and time, interest automatically also becomes a factor.

Interest may be defined as the money paid for the use of borrowed capital or the income produced by money which has been loaned. It may be illus-

59

trated in yet another way. Suppose John Jones comes to Henry Smith and wants to borrow $100, saying he will pay it back one year from now. Henry has $100 in his pocket, with which he had planned to purchase a few luxuries which he does not now possess, but which he could do without. The thought of these quickly passes through his mind. He decides that it would not be too bad to go without these luxuries if John Jones would promise to pay him something extra for his doing without these personal pleasures for a year. He thinks that $5 would be a fair price for this year of sacrifice on his part.

He quickly remembers that, although he has known John for some time and believes he is entirely honest, human nature has its weaknesses, and there is some possibility that John might run off and not repay what he has borrowed. Also he remembers how many innocent people are killed by automobiles each year and realizes that this might happen to his friend, so that he would not get back his money. He feels that he should also be paid something for these risks he will be taking by loaning him money and thinks he is entitled to an additional $5 because of this. He tells John Jones he will be glad to let him use the $100 for one year if John will promise to give him back $110 at the end of the year. John agrees to do this, and the deal is made. The extra $10 which Henry receives at the end of the year are said to be the *interest* which he earns from his $100 investment.

THE REASONS FOR INTEREST

In order to understand its place in economy studies, it is helpful to know some of the reasons for interest. From the example that was just discussed, it is apparent that the interest represents payment for the use of the borrowed money. However, it represents payment to the lender for several things.

First, it pays him for foregoing the use of his money during the time the borrower has it. Second, it is payment for the risk he took in permitting another person to use his money. Third, the fact that he can get interest by loaning money acts as an incentive for him to accumulate capital to lend. Thus interest usually represents payment for several factors. This is ordinarily the case in business transactions.

In the transaction between John Jones and Henry Smith, John Jones promised to repay Henry Smith the amount he borrowed and in addition agreed to pay a specified rate of interest. Thus, the amount of principal to be repaid, and the rate of interest, were guaranteed by the borrower. These are fundamental conditions where interest is involved. Repayment of the principal is guaranteed by the borrower, and the rate of pay for the use of the borrowed funds is specified. Thus there is a clear distinction between *interest* and *profit,* since profit accrues from the investment of capital in business ventures where there is no guarantee of return of the capital and no assurance as to what, if any, the rate of return will be.

THE PRODUCTIVITY OF CAPITAL

Many people often wonder how a person can afford to borrow money to undertake business operations when not only the capital but interest must be repaid. The fact that capital is productive explains this; that is, equipment which is purchased with the borrowed capital enables the borrower to produce more income than he could without it. He can thus repay the borrowed money plus interest and still have a greater profit than he otherwise would have been able to earn. The following example illustrates this fact.

Mr. Gardner earns his living by mowing and otherwise taking care of lawns. Using an ordinary lawn mower and trimming shears, he takes care of twenty lawns at a fee of $20 per month. His annual earnings are

$$20 \times \$20 \times 12 = \$4,800.$$

He buys a gasoline-powered lawn mower and some electric trimming shears. These cost a total of $135. In order to finance the purchase of this equipment, he has to pay $10 in interest. However, with the aid of the new equipment he can now take care of twenty-five lawns. His annual income is now

$$25 \times \$20 \times 12 = \$6,000.$$

His expenses are as follows:

Lawn mower and shears	$135
Interest	10
Gasoline	40
	$185

His net annual earnings are as follows:

Income	$6,000
Expenses	185
Net earnings	$5,815

These calculations assume that the new lawn mower and shears will last only one year. The resulting increase in productivity due to the utilization of $135 of capital is obvious.

The productivity of capital explains why there is a constant interchange of money in business activity. In order to increase our productivity and thereby our standard of living, there has to be a constant flow of capital into business enterprise. Interest and profit are therefore essential factors in making it possible to have an adequate supply of capital available so that the economy of this country can expand and provide jobs. Unless interest and profit rates are adequate, the necessary capital will not be available.

INTEREST AND PROFIT AS INCOME AND EXPENSE

Considerable confusion is caused by the fact that the terms "interest" and "profit" are used by different people to denote entirely different things. The difficulty probably arises from two sources. One is the fact that interest earned can be a profit, and profit, as well as interest, may constitute an expense of doing business, although legal requirements usually prevent it from being treated as such. The second source of the confusion derives from the old classical economists' definition of "interest" as the money returned to the owners for the use of their capital. Thus, whatever was received because capital was employed was considered to be interest.

In the example of borrower John Jones and lender Henry Smith, the interest paid was expense for Mr. Jones. However, this same interest was a profit received by Mr. Smith through the use of his capital. Thus there is no question but that true interest—that paid for the use of *borrowed* capital—is an expense paid by the borrower. It is so considered legally and is deductible as an expense, just as is material expense, in computing profits and income taxes thereon.

Profit—that resulting from the use of *owned* capital—must be treated differently. As has been pointed out, profit is essential; without it the capital required for the operation of a business would not be forthcoming. Obviously, if capital could be obtained without the necessity of paying the owners any profits, the products or services of a business could be made and sold more cheaply. The same would be true if raw materials could be obtained for a lower price or for nothing. Thus, from this viewpoint it is sound to say that profits sufficient to assure the required flow of capital are a cost of production. However, since the profits are paid by the owners of a business to themselves, they can not be considered to be an expense in the same sense as is interest. Thus profits can not be included legally as an operating or financial expense, and they can not be deducted as an expense in determining income taxes. Obviously, if profits were permitted to be deducted as an expense, the subtraction of total expense from income would always produce zero, and thus no income tax.

It is thus easy to understand why "profit" and "interest" are often used interchangeably. In many cases no confusion results; in others the result is far from good. Since the vast majority of business uses the terms in the manner explained above, it appears desirable to confine their usage to the more precise definitions and thus avoid misunderstanding wherever possible. If this is not done, one must be certain that he knows exactly what is meant when the term "interest" is used in the broad manner that is sometimes employed.

Modern economists are turning away from the classical definition of interest. They now tend to drop the broad usage of the term and substitute such terms as "gain" or "return on capital." In the chapters which follow, "interest" will be used only when speaking of borrowed capital. Gain from the use of owned capital will be called "return" or "profit." In this manner it is hoped that greater clarity and understanding will result.

WHEN MUST INTEREST BE CONSIDERED?

There are very few, if any, economy studies where interest is not a factor that has to be considered. Since economy studies are made in terms of money, interest automatically enters the picture.

If the capital necessary to finance an enterprise must be borrowed, the cost of obtaining this capital is an expense of the venture. If the person or corporation owns sufficient capital to finance the proposed project, there is no borrowed money involved, and, in the true meaning of the term, there is no interest expense. However, in this case one must decide if the expected rate of return (profit) is sufficient to justify the investment. In order to do this, it is usually necessary to compare the expected profit with the rate of interest which could be obtained from lending the same capital at a specified rate. Thus, interest is a factor that must be considered, although not as an expense in the strict sense.

It is, and will probably remain, a common practice to include profit on owned capital as though it were an item of expense. While from a strict interpretation of the definition of interest such inclusion is not correct, it is justified by the fact that in order to invest capital in an enterprise one must forego lending this money at guaranteed interest rates, and thus one of the expenses of investment is the return that has been sacrified. What is actually meant is that the person does not wish to invest capital where risk is involved unless he will receive a rate of return in excess of what he could obtain from a conservative investment at guaranteed interest rates. When profit upon owned capital is included in such a manner, the results may be confusing

unless one understands exactly what is meant and realizes that correct interpretation of the results is necessary. As long as the usage is understood and
correctly interpreted, there is no serious objection to it. In fact, inclusion of
such "interest" (profit) in this manner gives a very convenient and useful
method of comparing the cost of alternative investments. Such methods will
be discussed in later chapters. However, if return on invested capital is to be
included as if it were an expense, it is desirable that it be shown under a
true name, such as "profit," "required profit," or "minimum required
profit."

There are, obviously, some cases where interest may be neglected in certain portions of economy studies without affecting the accuracy appreciably.
If the time involved is only one or two years and the interest rate is not
more than 2 or 3%, the error introduced by omitting these factors would
not be serious. In nearly all cases it would be less than the error due to other
factors that are included. However, good judgment must be exercised in
deciding whether interest can be neglected in any particular situation.
Except in the most obvious cases, the safer course is to consider all the
factors that might affect the results, and interest is one of these.

WHAT INTEREST RATES SHOULD BE USED?

Much has been written about what interest rate should be used in economy studies. If one is speaking about interest in accordance with the strict
definition, the answer is simple. One should use the rate that has been, or
would be, paid for the use of the borrowed money. In comparisons of
expected profits with the rate of interest that could be obtained from
investment of capital funds in some other manner, one should again use the
rate that could be obtained from such investment.

Comparison is often made between predicted rate of profit and another
possible profit, such as would be obtained from leaving capital in its existing
place in a business instead of using it for expansion or the purchase of new
equipment. In such instances, the basis for comparison is the average rate
of profit of all the capital invested in the business. This would usually be
different from, and greater than, ordinary interest rates.

If one speaks of "return on the investment" as "interest," the question
of what rate to use becomes complex, since the real question is, "What
return is sufficient to justify the investment of capital?" Similarly if one is
concerned with the "cost of capital," the problem is complex. Since both of
these questions involve factors that have not yet been discussed, they will be
dealt with in later chapters.

SIMPLE INTEREST

In the example of John Jones and Henry Smith, cited previously, the capital involved was $100. This amount, for the use of which interest is paid, is known as the *principal*. The *rate of interest* is the amount of interest earned by a *unit of principal* in a *unit of time*. In common practice the unit of time is taken as one year, unless otherwise specified. Thus in our example one hundred units of principal earned ten units of interest in one unit of time, or the rate of interest was $10/100 = 0.1$, or 10% per annum. This is the customary way of expressing interest rates—per cent per annum.

In the simplest type of time-money transaction, a given principal is invested for a stated period of time at a designated rate of interest. The debt is to be repaid at the end of the period of time, which may or may not be the same length of time as that upon which the interest rate is based. The interest, however, is directly proportional to the time which the loan runs.

If one wishes to know how much interest will be earned during the time of such a transaction, it may be found in the following manner. Let P represent the principal, i the interest rate, and n the number of units of time or the interest periods. The interest I is found by the formula

$$I = Pni, \tag{4.1}$$

since the interest earned is directly proportional to the principal involved, the interest rate, and the number of interest periods for which the principal is loaned. Thus if $100 is loaned for three years at an interest rate of 5% per annum, the interest earned will be

$$I = \$100 \times 0.05 \times 3 = \$15.$$

If one wishes to know the entire *amount, S,* due (principal plus interest),

$$S = P + I = P + Pni = P(1 + ni). \tag{4.2}$$

Interest computed in this manner is known as *simple interest.*

ORDINARY AND EXACT SIMPLE INTEREST

Ordinarily the unit of time for the interest period is considered to be one year, and the resulting interest rate is the rate per year. When it is necessary to calculate the interest due for a fraction of one year, it is often the practice to assume that a year is made up of twelve months of thirty days each, or 360 days. The exact number of days involved is used. Thus 50 days are considered to be 50/360 of one year. Interest computed on this basis is called *ordinary simple interest.*

If, however, the interest is computed on the basis of a 365-day year, the result is called *exact simple interest*. Table I of the Appendix, *The Number of Each Day of the Year,* makes it easy to determine the number of days between any two dates.

COMPOUND INTEREST

In the case of simple interest, the interest does not become due until the end of the loan period and is directly proportional to the time involved. Now consider a loan that is made for a length of time equal to several interest periods. Provision is made that the *earned interest is due at the end of each interest period*. However, the borrower is allowed to keep the earned interest but must thereafter pay interest upon these amounts, just as he does upon the principal. Thus, interest that has been earned, but is not paid, is assumed to be converted into principal. This procedure takes place at the end of each interest period. The borrower at the end of the first interest period has the use of the original principal P plus the interest I earned during this period, all of which belongs to the lender. Thus the total amount of money due the lender at the end of the first period, and used by the borrower during the second interest period, is

$$P + Pi = P(1 + i).$$

Similarly, since the lender is entitled to interest upon all the money due him, the interest earned during the second interest period is

$$(P + Pi)i = Pi + Pi^2.$$

The amount due the lender at the end of the second interest period, and available to the borrower at the beginning of the third period, is

$$P + Pi + (Pi + Pi^2) = P(1 + i)^2.$$

Thus, because of interest, one unit of principal at the beginning of an interest period will amount to $1 + i$ units at the end of the period. The results may be shown as follows:

Period	Principal at beginning of period	Interest earned during period	Amount at end of period
1	P	Pi	$P + Pi = P(1 + i)$
2	$P(1 + i)$	$P(1 + i)i$	$P + Pi + P(1 + i)i = P(1 + i)^2$
3	$P(1 + i)^2$	$P(1 + i)^2 i$	$P + Pi + P(1 + i)i + P(1 + i)^2 i = P(1 + i)^3$
n	$P(1 + i)^{n-1}$	$P(1 + i)^{n-1} i$	$P(1 + i)^{n-1} + P(1 + i)^{n-1} i = P(1 + i)^n$

Thus the formula for the amount due at the end of n interest period is

$$S = P(1 + i)^n. \qquad (4.3)$$

In this process, where earned interest is added to the principal and interest is thereafter paid on the total amount, the interest is said to be *compounded* or *converted* each interest period. In the most general case, where the interest period is one year, the interest is said to be compounded annually.

The factor $(1 + i)^n$ is commonly designated by the symbol s^n and is called the *compound amount factor*. In the second column of Tables II to XXII inclusive of the Appendix, values of $(1 + i)^n$ are tabulated for various values of i, so that problems involving this factor may readily be solved.

It is customary practice to use exact simple interest for computing interest for less than one conversion period, and compound interest for all transactions involving more than one conversion period. Where fractional periods above one are involved, compound interest is used for the whole number of conversion periods and exact simple interest for the additional fraction of a period.

If \$100.00 principal is loaned for a period of three years with interest at 5% compounded annually, the total sum due at the end of the three years may be found by Equation (4.3) as follows:

$$P = \$100.00$$
$$i = 5\% \text{ compounded annually}$$
$$n = 3$$

From Appendix Table XVIII, $(1 + i)^n$ for these values $= 1.157625$, and

$$S = \$100.00 \times 1.157625 = \$115.76.$$

Very often the interest period, or time between successive conversions, is something less than one year. It has also become customary to quote interest rates upon an annual basis and designate the conversion period. If the interest rate is 3% per interest period and the interest period is six months, it is customary to speak of this rate as "6% compounded semiannually." Interest rates quoted in this manner are known as *nominal interest rates*. The actual annual rate of return upon the principal is not 6% but something greater. For instance, consider \$100.00 to be invested at a nominal rate of 6% compounded semiannually. The interest earned during the year would be as follows:

First 6 months

$$I = \$100.00 \times 0.03 = \$3.00$$

Total principal at beginning of the second period
$$P + Pi = \$100.00 + \$3.00 = \$103.00$$

Interest earned second 6 months
$$\$103.00 \times 0.03 = \$3.09$$

Total interest earned during year
$$\$3.00 + \$3.09 = \$6.09$$

Actual annual interest rate
$$\frac{6.09}{100} \times 100 = 6.09\%$$

This actual rate of return upon the principal during one year is known as the *effective interest rate. It should be noted that effective interest rates always are on an annual basis.*

If nominal interest rates are quoted and the length of time involved is given in years, any problem can easily be solved by the general formula, $S = P(1 + i)^n$, by converting the nominal rate into rate per interest period and determining the number of actual interest periods. Thus, if \$100 is invested for ten years at 6% compounded quarterly, there are four conversions per year, and the interest rate per interest period is $6/4 = 1.5\%$. The total number of interest periods is $10 \times 4 = 40$. Using these values in Equation (4.3),

$$S = \$100.00(1 + 0.015)^{40}$$
$$= \$181.40.$$

In this manner problems involving nominal interest rates can very easily be solved. It is only necessary to remember that in Equation (4.3) n is the *actual number of interest periods* and i the *rate per interest period.*

The use of this method and Equation (4.3) gives a simple means of determining the effective rate corresponding to any given nominal rate of interest. For example, in the case just cited the nominal rate is 6% compounded quarterly. What is the effective rate?

Rate per interest period $= 6/4 = 1.5\%$
Number of periods per year $= 4$
Amount of 1 unit per year $= S = P(1 + i)^n$

From Table XI in the Appendix, for $n = 4$

$$(1 + i)^n = 1.06136,$$
and

$$S = 1 \times 1.06136 = 1.06136.$$
Interest earned in 1 year $= S - 1 = 0.06136$

Since effective rate has been defined as the interest earned by *one* unit of principal in one year, 0.06136, or 6.136%, represents the effective rate corresponding to a nominal rate of 6% compounded quarterly. Therefore

$$\text{Effective rate} = S - 1 \qquad (4.4)$$

when S is the amount of 1 for one year at the nominal rate.

Effective interest rates provide a means of comparing nominal interest rates. For example, it is difficult to tell which is greater, 3% compounded monthly, or 3½% compounded semiannually, when they are expressed as nominal rates. These nominal rates may be converted to effective rates as follows:

3% compounded monthly

$$n = 12$$
$$i = 3/12 = ¼\% \text{ per period}$$

From Table II (Appendix)

$$S = 1.0304$$
$$\text{Effective rate} = S - 1 = 3.04\%$$

3½% compounded semiannually

$$n = 2$$
$$i = 3½/2 = 1.75\% \text{ per period}$$

From Table XII (Appendix)

$$S = 1.0353$$
$$\text{Effective rate} = S - 1 = 3.53\%$$

Thus 3½%, compounded semiannually, is found to be the higher rate of interest.

PRESENT VALUE

One frequently wishes to determine the value at the present time of a sum of money which will be available at some time in the future. Because time is a part of the problem, interest must be considered. For example, suppose someone purchased a $25.00 United States government savings bond and gave it to you. The bond would state that ten years after the date of purchase the government would pay the holder of the bond $25.00. How much would the bond be worth to you at the time you received it? Obviously it would be worth just what was paid for it, namely $18.75. Thus $18.75 could be said to be the present value of the $25.00 which was to be received ten years hence, *with interest* at approximately 3% per annum. The $18.75 and the $25.00 are related by time and interest factors. From

Equation (4.3), $S = P(1 + i)^n$, it was shown that P units of principal invested at rate i will amount to S units at the end of n periods. Thus at rate i, P is the *present value* of S.

If in Equation (4.3) $S = 1$, and v is defined as the present value of 1 due one interest period hence,

$$1 = v(1 + i),$$

and

$$v = \frac{1}{1 + i}. \tag{4.5}$$

Since

$$P = S \times \frac{1}{(1 + i)^n}$$
$$P = Sv^n. \tag{4.6}$$

The third column of Tables II to XXII inclusive of the Appendix, headed *Present Value of 1*, gives values of v^n so problems involving present value may be readily solved. Table XXIII gives values of v^n for higher rates of interest. The factor v^n is commonly called the *present value factor*.

The present value of $100.00 due five years hence with interest at 6% per annum would be calculated as follows:

$$S = \$100.00$$
$$n = 5$$
$$i = 6\%.$$

From Table XIX (Appendix)

$$v^n = 0.747258$$
$$P = \$100.00 \times 0.747258 = \$74.73.$$

For a nominal rate of 6% compounded semiannually, the solution would be as follows:

$$n = 5 \times 2 = 10$$
$$i = 6/2 = 3\%$$
$$v^n = 0.744094$$
$$P = \$100.00 \times 0.744094 = \$74.41$$

DISCOUNT

Two types of transactions in which discount is involved are sometimes encountered. In the first, the holder of negotiable paper, such as a note or a sales contract, which is not due and payable until some future date desires to exchange the paper for immediate cash. In order to do this, he will accept a sum of cash smaller in amount than the face value of the paper. The difference between the present value (the amount received for the paper in cash) and the worth of the paper at some time in the future (the face value of the paper or principal) is known as the *discount* for the period involved.

The second type of transaction occurs in many bank loans. As an example, a man may wish to borrow $100.00 from a bank for one year at an interest rate of 6%. The bank computes the interest, $6.00 and *deducts* this amount from the $100.00, giving the borrower only $94.00. The borrower signs a note promising to repay $100.00 at the end of a year. The $6.00 which was deducted represents interest paid in advance. It also represents the difference between the present value of the note received by the borrower—$94.00—and the value of the note at the end of one year—$100.00. It is therefore the discount for the period involved. The *rate of discount* is defined as the discount on one unit of principal for one unit of time. If the rate of discount is designated by d, it is equal to the difference between 1 and its present value, v.

$$d = 1 - v = 1 - \frac{1}{1+i} = iv \qquad (4.7)$$

and

$$i = \frac{d}{v} = \frac{d}{1-d} \qquad (4.8)$$

For the example cited, the discount was $6.00. The rate of discount was

$$d = \$6.00/\$100.00 = 0.06 = 6\%.$$

The interest rate, based upon the principal actually received by the borrower, was

$$i = \$6.00/\$94.00 = 0.0638 = 6.38\%.$$

Since the present value factor, v, involves the interest rate, i, Equation (4.8) must be solved in the form $i = d/(1-d)$. For example, if a sixty-day note having a face value of $100.00 is discounted $1.00, the rate of discount for the sixty-day period is

$$d = 1 - 0.99 = 0.01$$

$$i = \frac{d}{1-d} = \frac{0.01}{1-0.01} = \frac{0.01}{0.99}$$
$$= 0.01010.$$

For the effective rate, from Equation (4.4),

$$n = 6$$
$$i = 0.01010$$
$$S - 1 = (1 + 0.01010)^6 - 1$$
$$= 1.0622 - 1 = 0.0622$$
$$= 6.22\%.$$

ANNUITIES

Many business transactions, as well as the majority of economy studies, involve the occurrence of a series of equal periodic payments or changes in value. Such transactions arise

(a) when a debt is paid by making a series of equal periodic payments,
(b) when a series of equal periodic payments is made in order to accumulate a desired amount,
(c) when one receives a series of equal periodic payments in lieu of a single lump sum which is due,
(d) when one wishes to account for the decrease in value of property which is going to occur in the future, or
(e) when one wishes to determine a series of equal, periodic payments which would be equivalent to a group of unequal payments made at unequal intervals of time.

All of these transactions involve annuities, although some frequently are called by other names. In actual practice the solution of such problems is obtained quickly by means of *annuity tables*. However, much as with the use of logarithms, one must understand what annuity relationship is involved and set up the problem properly before the annuity tables may be used intelligently.

An *annuity* is a series of equal payments occurring at equal periods of time. In the business usage of annuities, compound interest is paid on all accumulated sums. The term was derived from the fact that at one time the usual period for such payments (as well as for most other financial transactions) was one year. It should be remembered, however, that the period of time between successive payments may be of any length desired, provided all the periods are equal. Obviously, any rate of interest which may be involved must be the rate per period, and the interest is compounded at the time of each payment.

Case (a) cited above is commonly encountered in "installment buying," "deferred payments," or so-called buying from income. This method is used to a great extent in the purchase of automobiles, homes, and many other familiar items. In this case the buyer is in debt to the seller for a definite amount and is to discharge this indebtedness by making a specified number of equal periodic payments. This method of payment at once makes the transaction a form of an annuity. The seller is entitled to interest on any amount due. As will be pointed out later, many transactions of this type do not follow the ordinary annuity concept of charging interest upon only the accumulated amount due.

Case (b) arises when one wishes to have a definite amount available at some future date. He wishes to accumulate this amount by setting aside smaller uniform amounts at equal intervals which, with the interest they will earn during such time as they are set aside, will add up to the desired amount at the time of the last deposit. This type of transaction, while clearly a form of an annuity, is more commonly known as a *sinking fund*. Its use is common in connection with the retirement of bonds and in providing for depreciation reserves. The latter use is encountered in connection with the decrease in value of property mentioned as Case (d) above. Both of these cases will be considered later.

The case mentioned as (c) is perhaps most often encountered in life insurance and old-age retirement plans. These are often known as *income annuities* or *retirement annuities*. In this case, instead of accepting a lump sum which belongs and is due to him, the person elects to receive a series of equal periodic payments. He also receives interest upon the balance of the amount due to him, so that a portion of each periodic payment is interest and the remainder is part of the principal.

Now consider the general form of an annuity. In an *ordinary annuity, the payments are considered as occurring at the end of each period*. Figure 4–1 shows the "picture" of an ordinary annuity having payments of 1 made for n periods. The entire annuity diagram in this figure has been enclosed in a dashed-line frame. Three of the essential elements of an ordinary annuity are portrayed in this illustration. These are

1. All payments are equal in amount.
2. Payments occur at equal time intervals.
3. The first payment occurs at the *end of the first* period, or the annuity begins one period *prior* to the occurrence of the first payment.

The annuity pictured in Figure 4–1 may be considered either at position A, the time the annuity begins, or at position B, the time the last payment has occurred. In either case, it is necessary to take into account the other two essential elements of ordinary annuities. These are

4. Compound interest is paid on all accumulated amounts.
5. The interest is compounded each payment period.

With all of the five elements in mind, the value, or worth, of the ordinary annuity having payments of 1 can be determined at position A. At the end of each period, up to and including period n, a payment of 1 is to be made.

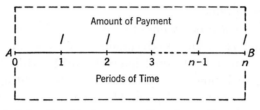

Figure 4–1.   Graphical representation of an ordinary annuity.

At time 0 a payment of 1 to be made one period later has a present value of v^1 (v^n being dependent upon the interest rate per period, i). Similarly, the payment of 1 to be made two periods from time 0 has a present value of v^2. The present value, $a_{\overline{n}|}$, at time 0 of all the future payments is

$$a_{\overline{n}|} = v^1 + v^2 + v^3 \cdots v^{n-1} + v^n.$$

This is a geometrical series, having a common ratio of v, whose sum is [1]

$$a_{\overline{n}|} = \frac{v - v^{n+1}}{1 - v} = \frac{1 - v^n}{1/v - 1}.$$

Since $1/v - 1 = i$ [Equation (4.5)],

$$a_{\overline{n}|} = \frac{1 - v^n}{i}. \tag{4.9}$$

Thus an equation for the present value of a series of future equal periodic payments of 1 is obtained. If the payments are R instead of 1, the present value, A, of such an annuity is

$$A = Ra_{\overline{n}|}. \tag{4.10}$$

The fourth column of Tables II to XXII (Appendix) inclusive, headed *Present Value of an Annuity of 1*, gives values of $a_{\overline{n}|}$ for various rates of interest and may be used in the solution of problems involving the present value of annuities. For convenience the factor $a_{\overline{n}|}$ is commonly called the *series present value factor.*

[1] Obtained by multiplying both sides of the previous equation by $1 - v$ and simplifying.

Now consider the annuity pictured in Figure 4–1 at position B, when the last payment of 1 has just occurred. The first payment of 1 was made $n - 1$ periods previously and, because of interest, it now amounts to $1(1 + i)^{n-1}$. Likewise, the payment made at the end of the second period has been accumulating for $n - 2$ periods and at time n is worth $1(1 + i)^{n-2}$. The amount of the other payments can be determined in the same manner. The amount, $s_{\overline{n}|}$, of this annuity of n payments of 1 each is

$$s_{\overline{n}|} = (1 + i)^{n-1} + (1 + i)^{n-2} + (1 + i)^{n-3} \cdots$$
$$+ (1 + i)^{n-(n-1)} + (1 + i)^{n-n}$$

Again this is a geometrical series, the common ratio being $(1 + i)^{-1}$, and [2]

$$s_{\overline{n}|} = \frac{(1 + i)^{n-1} - (1 + i)^{-1}}{1 - (1 + i)^{-1}}.$$

Simplifying by multiplying numerator and denominator by $(1 + i)$,

$$s_{\overline{n}|} = \frac{(1 + i)^n - 1}{i}. \tag{4.11}$$

This gives an expression for the *amount of an annuity of 1*. The amount, S, of an annuity have payments of R will then be

$$S = Rs_{\overline{n}|}. \tag{4.12}$$

Values of $s_{\overline{n}|}$ for various rates of interest are given in the fifth column of Appendix Tables II to XXII inclusive, headed *Amount of an Annuity of 1*. This factor commonly is called the *series compound amount factor* or, more simply, the *series amount factor*.

Equation (4.11) may also be obtained in another way. $s_{\overline{n}|}$ is the amount of a series of payments, the present value of which is $a_{\overline{n}|}$. In other words, $a_{\overline{n}|}$ will amount to $s_{\overline{n}|}$ in n periods. Therefore,

$$s_{\overline{n}|} = a_{\overline{n}|}(1 + i)^n$$
$$= \frac{1 - v^n}{i} \times (1 + i)^n = \frac{(1 + i)^n - 1}{i(1 + i)^n} \times (1 + i)^n$$
$$= \frac{(1 + i)^n - 1}{i}.$$

The value $1/s_{\overline{n}|}$ is called the *sinking fund factor* and is used frequently in connection with sinking funds and in economy studies for computing depreciation by the sinking fund method. Values of $1/s_{\overline{n}|}$ for various rates of interest up to 25% are given in Table XXIV of the Appendix.

[2] To obtain, multiply both sides of the previous equation by $1 - (1 + i)^{-1}$.

It is convenient to have another set of tables for working certain types of annuity problems. What series of annuity payments can be purchased by a single payment of 1? This is known as the *annuity whose present value is 1*. The value may be found by solving Equation (4.10) for R when $A = 1$.

$$R = \frac{1}{a_{\overline{n}|}} \tag{4.13}$$

Thought of in another way, the factor $1/a_{\overline{n}|}$ represents the magnitude of each of a series of n periodic payments that will return to an investor his investment of one unit of principal, together with interest at the rate of $i\%$ per period upon all portions of the original principal which remain invested. In general terms of an investment of P,

$$R = P \times 1/a_{\overline{n}|}. \tag{4.14}$$

Thus by multiplying an amount of principal, P, by the factor $1/a_{\overline{n}|}$ one can determine what series of n year-end (or periodic) payments will return the principal (capital) P, together with interest on the unrecovered portion of the capital. For this reason the factor $1/a_{\overline{n}|}$ is commonly called the *capital recovery factor* and frequently is used in economy studies.

Since $s_{\overline{n}|} = \dfrac{(1+i)^n - 1}{i}$ and $a_{\overline{n}|} = \dfrac{1 - v^n}{i}$, it can readily be shown that

$1/a_{\overline{n}|} = 1/s_{\overline{n}|} + i$. Thus the capital recovery factor is equal to the sinking fund factor plus the interest rate. The sixth column of Tables II to XXII inclusive gives values of $1/a_{\overline{n}|}$ for various interest rates up to 10%, and Table XXV gives values of this single factor for interest rates up to 25%.

DESIGNATION OF INTEREST FACTORS

In using the compound amount factor, present value factor, series present value factor, series compound amount factor, sinking fund factor, or capital recovery factor, it is convenient to have a simple method of indicating the interest rate involved. This may be done by using a small numeral in parentheses as a subscript following the symbol. Thus

$$s^n_{(6)}$$
$$v^n_{(6)}$$
$$a_{\overline{n}|(6)}$$
$$s_{\overline{n}|(6)}$$
$$\frac{1}{s_{\overline{n}|(6)}}$$
$$\frac{1}{a_{\overline{n}|(6)}}$$

indicate that interest at the rate of 6 per cent per period is included in each factor. This method of designation will be used throughout this text.

EXAMPLES USING ORDINARY ANNUITIES

With the formulas which have been derived, solution of problems arising from the various types of annuities will now be considered. In all annuity problems it must be remembered that the interest rate is the rate per period between successive payments. Thus, if nominal rates of interest are given, they must be converted into the corresponding rate per period.

APPLICATIONS AND SOLUTIONS

EXAMPLE 1. What is the present value of a 10-year annuity paying $100.00 at the end of each year? Interest at 4% per annum. From Equation (4.10),

$$A = Ra_{\overline{n}|}$$

From Table XVII (Appendix),

$$a_{\overline{10}|(4)} = 8.1108958$$
$$A = \$100.00 \times 8.1108958 = \$811.09.$$

EXAMPLE 2. What would be the present value of a 10-year annuity paying $50.00 every six months with interest at 4% nominal? In this case,

$$n = 2 \times 10 = 20$$
$$i = 4/2 = 2\% \text{ per period.}$$

From Table XIII (Appendix),

$$a_{\overline{20}|(2)} = 16.3514333$$
$$A = \$50 \times 16.3514333 = \$817.57.$$

EXAMPLE 3. If a man buys an automobile and is to pay for it by making twenty monthly payments of $40.00 each, with interest on the unpaid balance at 6% nominal, what is the purchase price?

This is Case (a) cited on page 72. The cost of the car is the present value of the series of equal periodic payments which is to be made.

$$A = Ra_{\overline{n}|}$$
$$R = \$40.00$$
$$n = 20$$
$$i = 6/12 = 0.5\% \text{ per period of one month.}$$

From Table V (Appendix),

$$a_{\overline{20}|\,(\frac{1}{2})} = 18.9874192$$
$$A = \$40.00 \times 18.9874192 = \$759.50.$$

EXAMPLE 4.   A man purchases a car for $1,000.00 and pays $400.00 in cash. He wishes to pay the balance in twelve monthly payments. What must each payment be if interest on the unpaid balance is charged at the nominal rate of 6%?

The balance to be paid = $1,000.00 − $400.00 = $600.00. This is the present value of the series of twelve payments which he must make. Therefore,

$$\$600.00 = Ra_{\overline{12}|\,(i)}$$
$$R = \$600.00 \times \frac{1}{a_{\overline{12}|\,(i)}}$$
$$i = 6/12 = 0.5\% \text{ per month.}$$

From Table V (Appendix),

$$\frac{1}{a_{\overline{12}|\,(\frac{1}{2})}} = 0.0860664$$
$$R = \$600.00 \times 0.0860664 = \$51.64.$$

EXAMPLE 5.   After the man in Example 3 has made ten payments, what single cash payment would be required to pay the remainder of the obligation?

If ten payments have been made, ten additional monthly payments of $40.00 each would be required to settle the debt. Thus there remains a ten-payment annuity of $40.00 per month. The single cash payment must be equivalent in value to this ten-payment annuity—in other words, the present value of an annuity of ten monthly payments of $40.00 each with interest at 6% nominal. Since

$$A = \$40.00 a_{\overline{10}|\,(\frac{1}{2})}$$
$$a_{\overline{10}|\,(\frac{1}{2})} = 9.7304119$$
$$A = \$40.00 \times 9.7304119 = \$389.22,$$

$389.22 is the single cash payment which would pay the remaining debt.

EXAMPLE 6.   A company wishes to accumulate $10,000.00 by making equal annual deposits over a period of five years. If the money will earn interest at the rate of 4% per annum, what must the annual payment be? This is Case (b) discussed on page 72. From Equation (4.12),

$$R = S/s_{\overline{n}|}$$
$$n = 5$$
$$i = 4\%.$$

From Table XVII (Appendix),

$$s_{\overline{5}|(4)} = 5.4163226$$
$$R = \$10,000.00/5.4163226 = \$1,846.27.$$

EXAMPLE 7. After three payments of the above sinking fund have been made, what is the amount accumulated in the sinking fund?

If the amount to be accumulated in n periods is K, the annual payment is $K/s_{\overline{n}|}$. This becomes the annual payment R of Equation (4.12), and

$$S = K \frac{s_{\overline{3}|(4)}}{s_{\overline{n}|(4)}}$$

$$= \$10,000.00 \times \frac{3.1216000}{5.4163226} = \$5,763.32.$$

From this the equation for the amount in a sinking fund after a payments have been made is

$$S = K \frac{s_{\overline{a}|}}{s_{\overline{n}|}}. \tag{4.15}$$

EXAMPLE 8. To provide for his son's college education, a man wishes to deposit a sum of money in a bank and have the bank send the boy checks of $300.00 four times each year for four years. The bank will pay 4% nominal interest on all money on deposit. How much must the father deposit if the first check is to be sent three months later? This is Case (c) discussed on page 72.

The plan provides for a sixteen-payment annuity with equal payments of $300.00. The amount deposited is the present worth of such an annuity:

$$A = R a_{\overline{n}|}$$
$$n = 16$$
$$i = 4/4 = 1\% \text{ per period of three months.}$$

From Table IX (Appendix),

$$a_{\overline{16}|(1)} = 14.7178738$$
$$A = \$300.00 \times 14.7178738 = \$4,415.36.$$

INSTALLMENT FINANCING

When a series of deferred equal periodic payments are substituted for a single cash payment, as in the case where merchandise such as an automobile is purchased, a modification of the ordinary annuity frequently is used. An "interest" charge is made upon the total amount owed at the beginning of the series of payments instead of only upon the unpaid balance. Such a charge is, of course, not in accord with the true nature and definition of interest. To see what the situation actually is in such cases, consider the following example:

EXAMPLE 9.   A national finance company advertises a "6% plan" for financing the purchase of automobiles. To the amount remaining to be paid through installment payments 6% is added. This total is divided by the number of months over which the payments are to be made, and the result is the amount of the monthly payments. For example, a man purchases a $2,000.00 automobile under this plan and makes an initial cash payment of $500.00. He wishes to pay the balance in twelve monthly payments. What will be the amount of each payment, and what rate of interest does he actually pay?

Purchase price	= $2,000.00
Initial payment	= 500.00
Balance due	= $1,500.00
6% finance charge = .06 × $1,500.00 =	90.00
Total to be paid	= $1,590.00
Monthly payments = $1,590.00/12	= $ 132.50

Since there are to be twelve payments of $132.50 each, made at the end of each month, these constitute an annuity *at some unknown rate of interest computed only upon the unpaid balance.* Therefore,

$$A = Ra_{\overline{n}|}$$
$$A = \$1,500.00$$
$$R = \$132.50$$
$$a_{\overline{12}|\,(i)} = \$1,500.00/\$132.50 = 11.3208.$$

By interpolation between Tables VIII and IX of the Appendix, $a_{\overline{12}|} = 11.3208$ corresponds to the value for approximately 0.91% interest rate. Thus the actual interest rate *per period of one month* involved in this finance plan is 0.91%, which is a nominal rate of 10.92%, compounded monthly.

EQUIVALENT EQUAL ANNUAL AMOUNT

A very common use of interest and annuity relationships in economy studies is in determining a theoretical series of equal payments made at the ends of equal intervals of time which will have the same present value as an actual set of unequal payments that have been, or will be, made at unequal periods of time. Such a situation occurs, for example, when various amounts will be expended at various times for the maintenance of a property. One would like to know what equal expense, paid each year, would be required for this maintenance.

EXAMPLE 10. Assume that the actual maintenance expenses on a property will be as follows:

End of the first year	$ 500.00
End of the third year	1,000.00
End of the sixth year	4,000.00
End of the tenth year	7,000.00
Total	$12,500.00

The equivalent equal annual expense can be determined by finding the annual annuity of ten payments that has a present value the same as the present value of the actual series of payments. Thus if money is worth 8%, the present value of the actual payments is as follows:

$$\$\ 500.00 \times v^{1}_{(8)} = \$\ 500.00 \times 0.92592593 = \$\ 462.96$$
$$\$1,000.00 \times v^{3}_{(8)} = \$1,000.00 \times 0.79383224 = \quad 793.83$$
$$\$4,000.00 \times v^{6}_{(8)} = \$4,000.00 \times 0.63016963 = \quad 2,520.68$$
$$\$7,000.00 \times v^{10}_{(8)} = \$7,000.00 \times 0.46319349 = \quad 3,242.35$$
$$\text{Present value} = \$7,019.82$$

Using Equation (4.10),

$$A = Ra_{\overline{n}|}$$
$$\$7,019.82 = Ra_{\overline{10}|\,(8)}$$
$$R = \$7,019.82/6.71008140$$
$$R = \$1,046.16$$

Thus an annual year-end expense of $1,046.16 would be financially equivalent to the actual predicted expenses.

In general terms, an equivalent equal annual amount may be found by dividing the present value of the actual amounts by the series present value factor, $a_{\overline{n}|}$, n corresponding to the number of years (or periods) until the last actual payment is made.

DEFERRED ANNUITIES

In the case of ordinary annuities, the first payment is made at the end of the first period. If the first payment does not begin until some later date, the annuity is known as a deferred annuity. If the annuity is deferred m periods it is designated by the symbols $m|a_{\overline{n}|}$, indicating the present value of an n period annuity of 1 with payments deferred m periods. Figure 4-2 portrays such a deferred annuity. It will be noted in this figure that the entire framed ordinary annuity, as shown in Figure 4-1, has been removed from "Time Present" by m periods. *It must be remembered that in an annuity deferred m periods the first payment is made at the end of the* $(m + 1)$ *period.* In an ordinary annuity the first payment is made at the end of the first period. Deferring the annuity defers the entire procedure and will therefore defer the first payment until the end of the $(m + 1)$ period.

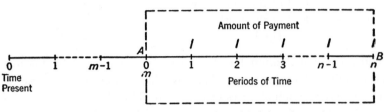

Figure 4–2. Graphical representation of a deferred annuity.

The present value of an annuity of 1 at the time 0 (one period before the first payment is made) is $a_{\overline{n}|}$. The value of $a_{\overline{n}|}$ at time $0 - m$ (m periods previous to time 0) will be $v^m a_{\overline{n}|}$. Therefore,

$$m|a_{\overline{n}|} = v^m a_{\overline{n}|}. \tag{4.16}$$

EXAMPLE 11.   How much would the father in Example 8 (page 79) have had to deposit at the time the son was born if the first payment to the son was to be made at age $20\frac{1}{4}$ years? Assume interest at 4% compounded quarterly.

$$Ra_{\overline{n}|} = \$4,415.36 \text{ (from Example 8)}$$
$$m = 20 \times 4 = 80$$
$$i = 4/4 = 1\% \text{ per period}$$

From Table IX (Appendix),

$$v^{80}_{(1)} = 0.4511179$$
$$m|A = 0.4511179 \times \$4,415.36 = \$1,992.12.$$

ANNUITIES DUE

Another special form of annuity is one where the payments are made at the beginning of each period instead of at the end. This is called an *annuity due*. The present value of such an annuity, having payments of 1, is represented by $\mathbf{a}_{\overline{n}|}$ and the amount by $\mathbf{s}_{\overline{n}|}$.

If we have an annuity of this type and neglect the first payment of 1, the remaining payments make an ordinary annuity of 1 running $n - 1$ periods. Therefore

$$\mathbf{a}_{\overline{n}|} = 1 + a_{\overline{n-1}|}. \tag{4.17}$$

The amount, $s_{\overline{n}|}$, of an annuity due, having payments of 1, may be obtained by considering it an ordinary annuity having $n + 1$ periods with the final payment omitted. Then

$$s_{\overline{n}|} = s_{\overline{n+1}|} - 1. \tag{4.18}$$

PARTIAL-PAYMENT ANNUITIES

In some transactions payments occur more frequently than the interest conversion periods. For example, suppose a man deposits $10.00 per month in a bank at the end of each month for ten years and that the bank pays interest at the rate of 3% per annum, but converts the earned interest into principal only at the end of each year. Obviously these conditions do not meet the requirements for an ordinary annuity. Instead, the monthly payments constitute partial payments of an ordinary annuity.

The amount of a partial payment annuity can be determined in the following manner. Let the annuity be 1 per year paid in p equal payments of $1/p$ each. There is some nominal rate of interest, $j_{(p)}$, which converted p times per year will be equivalent to the effective rate i. If there are payments continuing over n years the accumulated amount $s_{\overline{n}|}^{(p)}$, will be

$$s_{\overline{n}|}^{(p)} = \frac{1}{p} \times s_{\overline{np}|}, \text{ at the rate } j_{(p)}/p. \tag{4.19}$$

Writing $s_{\overline{np}|}$ in terms of the interest rate,

$$s_{\overline{n}|}^{(p)} = \frac{1}{p} \times \frac{\left(1 + \frac{j_{(p)}}{p}\right)^{np} - 1}{\frac{j_{(p)}}{p}} = \frac{\left(1 + \frac{j_{(p)}}{p}\right)^{np} - 1}{j_{(p)}}. \tag{4.20}$$

Since by definition the nominal rate $j_{(p)}/p$ converted p times will be equal to the annual rate i,

$$\left(1 + \frac{j_{(p)}}{p}\right)^{p} = (1 + i), \tag{4.21}$$

and

$$\left(1 + \frac{j_{(p)}}{p}\right)^{np} = (1 + i)^{n}. \tag{4.22}$$

Therefore, from Equation (4.20),

$$s_{\overline{n}|}^{(p)} = \frac{(1 + i)^{n} - 1}{j_{(p)}}. \tag{4.23}$$

Multiplying both numerator and denominator by i,

$$s_{\overline{n}|}^{(p)} = \frac{(1+i)^n - 1}{i} \times \frac{i}{j_{(p)}}. \tag{4.24}$$

Thus,

$$s_{\overline{n}|}^{(p)} = s_{\overline{n}|} \times \frac{i}{j_{(p)}}. \tag{4.25}$$

For a given rate of interest, i, values of $i/j_{(p)}$ can be computed and tabulated as a function of the number of partial payments, p, per regular annuity period. These values, known as the "amount at end of year of p deposits each of $1/p$ made at the end of each pth part of a year," and designated by the symbol $s_{\overline{1}|}^{(p)}$, are given for several interest rates in Table XXVI of the Appendix.

PERPETUITIES AND CAPITALIZED COST

One other type of annuity of interest to the engineer, known as a *perpetuity*, is a series in which the payments continue indefinitely. The present value of a perpetuity may be determined by reasoning that to yield a perpetual income of 1 per period, $1/i$ units of principal must be invested. This can be seen from Equation (4.9), which is

$$a_{\overline{n}|} = \frac{1 - v^n}{i},$$

by letting n approach infinity. Since v is always less than 1, v^n approaches 0 and the expression becomes $1/i$.

The present value of a perpetuity having payments of R is equal to R/i and is often spoken of as the *capitalized value* of R.

In providing for the perpetual care of some structure, or the maintenance of endowed foundations, a special type of perpetuity is often encountered. A certain amount S may be needed every k periods to provide for replacement or maintenance. The owner, or founder, wishes to provide a fund of sufficient size so that the earnings from it will provide for this periodic demand.

To be available perpetually, S must be accumulated in k periods from the interest I which is earned by some amount of principal X, invested at rate i. Thus the periodic deposit toward this accumulation will be Xi. And

$$S = Xis_{\overline{k}|}$$

$$X = \frac{S}{i} \times \frac{1}{s_{\overline{k}|}}. \tag{4.26}$$

If the first cost of the structure, or project, is added to X, the sum is known as the *capitalized cost*. Thus the capitalized cost of an article is the amount of sufficient size to purchase the article and also provide for its perpetual maintenance.

By substituting for $s_{\overline{n}|}$ and $a_{\overline{n}|}$ their equivalent values in terms of i, it can easily be shown that

$$\frac{1}{s_{\overline{n}|}} = \frac{1}{a_{\overline{n}|}} - i. \tag{4.27}$$

This gives a convenient method of determining the factor $1/s_{\overline{n}|}$ for solution of problems involving this term.

From Equation (4.26) we can obtain a convenient equation for the capitalized cost of an article which must be entirely replaced periodically at a cost equal to the first cost. Thus the *first cost and the amount required for periodic replacement are both equal to S*. The capitalized cost is

$$S + \frac{S}{i} \times \frac{1}{s_{\overline{k}|}} = S + \frac{S}{i}\left(\frac{1}{a_{\overline{k}|}} - i\right)$$

$$= \frac{Sia_{\overline{k}|} + S - Sia_{\overline{k}|}}{ia_{\overline{k}|}}$$

$$= \frac{S}{i} \times \frac{1}{a_{\overline{k}|}}. \tag{4.28}$$

EXAMPLE 12. Machine A costs \$100.00 and has a life of five years. Machine B costs \$150.00 and will last eight years. Assume an interest rate of 5% per annum. Both machines can be replaced at the end of their useful lives at a cost equal to that of their original purchase price. Determine which machine is cheaper by comparing their capitalized costs.

For machine A

$$\text{Capitalized cost} = \frac{\$100.00}{0.05} \times 0.2309748$$
$$= \$461.95.$$

For machine B

$$\text{Capitalized cost} = \frac{\$150.00}{0.05} \times 0.1547218$$
$$= \$464.17.$$

Machine A is found to be cheaper, since its capitalized cost is \$2.22 less than that of machine B.

PROBLEMS

4-1   Find the number of days between September 24, 1959, and April 12, 1960.

4-2   What is the interest due on a $500 note for 2 years and 4 months if it bears 5% ordinary simple interest?

4-3   What is the exact simple interest on a $500 note from May 2 to December 12, 1959, if interest is at the rate of 8%?

4-4   If a $1,200 loan earns $30 interest in six months, what is the ordinary simple interest rate?

4-5   How long will it take $1 to double if invested at the rate of 5%, compounded semiannually?

4-6   What interest rate, compounded quarterly, will have to be earned in order for $1,000 to amount to $2,208 in ten years?

4-7   Find the effective interest rate of 12% compounded monthly.

4-8   On January 1, 1849, a gold miner deposited $1.00 in a California bank with the agreement that on January 1, 1950, the principal plus interest should be given to an eastern college. The bank paid 4% simple interest on the deposit up to January 1, 1900. From January 1, 1900, to January 1, 1935, interest was paid at the rate of 4%, compounded annually. On January 1, 1935, the interest rate was changed to 3%, compounded semiannually. What was the amount the college received on January 1, 1950?

4-9   When his son was born a man deposited a sum of money in a savings bank at 3% interest, compounded semiannually. On his twentieth birthday the son received the $1,000 that had accumulated. How much did the father deposit?

4-10 Find the present value of $600 due in ten years if interest is at the rate of 6%, compounded semiannually.

4-11 A large corporation has made two offers to the owner of a small company for the purchase of his business. Offer A is $150,000 in cash. Offer B is $10,000 in cash, $50,000 at the end of one year, and $100,000 at the end of three years. If money is worth 6%, and income tax considerations are neglected, which is the better offer from the viewpoint of the owner of the small company?

4-12 A man borrows $2,000 for four years, agreeing to pay 5% interest, compounded annually. He later requests and receives permission to repay the obligation by making three equal payments at the end of one, two, and three years, instead of the single payment at the end of four years. If the same rate of interest is involved, how much should each payment be?

4-13 A man signed a note at a bank agreeing to repay $500 at the end of six months. The bank discounted the note and gave him $480 in cash.

    a. What was the rate of discount?

    b. What interest rate did he pay?

4-14 A negotiable paper bearing interest at 3% and having a face value of $400 was discounted for six months at a bank so that the bank received an effective rate of 10% on its money. How much did the original holder of the paper receive for it?

4-15 What monthly annuity of fifty payments, receivable at the end of each month, can be purchased for a single cash payment of $1,000, with interest at 8% nominal?

4-16 How much will have to be deposited at the end of each year for twenty years in order to amount to $12,000 if interest is earned at the rate of 5%?

4-17 What amount will be required to purchase on a man's fortieth birthday an annuity to consist of thirty equal semiannual payments of $1,000 each, the first to be received on his sixtieth birthday, if interest at 4%, compounded semiannually, is received on all deposited amounts?

4-18 An inventor sold his patent to a corporation and was given his choice of three offers: (*a*) $50,000 in cash; (*b*) an annual royalty of 8% on sales during the remaining ten years of the patent life, annual sales being estimated to be $75,000 per year; (*c*) a twenty-year annuity of $4,000 payments to be made at the end of each year. If money is worth 4% to the inventor, which offer should he accept? (Neglect tax effects.)

4-19 A man purchased a car, making a 25% down payment and agreeing to make thirty monthly payments to settle the balance. Interest on the unpaid balance was to be charged at the rate of 1% per month. At the time he made his fifteenth monthly payment he obtained permission to make an additional payment of $806 to settle the remaining balance. If interest in the final settlement was at the same rate as in the initial transaction, what was the purchase price of the car?

4-20 A company purchased a fleet of trucks for $78,000. Payment was made by an immediate cash payment of $5,000 and twelve month-end payments of $6,486 each. Another dealer offered to finance the same purchase at an interest rate of ¾% per month on the unpaid balance. Which offer should the company have accepted?

4-21 A young engineer wishes to make provision for a college education for his son who has just passed his second birthday. He would like to provide $2,000 each year on the son's eighteenth, nineteenth, twentieth, and twenty-first birthdays, but finds that for each of the next five years he can put aside only $300 per year, starting on the son's third birthday. If he does this, how much would he have to deposit at the end of each of the following ten years to provide the required funds? Assume that each of the ten payments is the same amount and that 4% interest, compounded annually, can be obtained on the funds.

4–22   Taking advantage of income tax laws, a public utility is refinancing its employee retirement system as follows:

(a) A sum, X, is to be set aside and permitted to earn profit at the rate of 5% through participation in the earnings of the company.

(b) At the end of each year for ten years a sum, Y, will be taken out of fund X and placed in fund Z, where it will earn 3%, compounded annually.

(c) At the end of ten years Z will amount to a sum the *present* value of which is $28,200,000. X will at that time be exhausted.

How much must be put into fund X?

4–23   When an engineer joins the staff of a manufacturing company at 25 years of age he becomes a member of the retirement system. He contributes $250 of his earnings each year toward a retirement fund and the company matches these contributions. The combined funds are invested at the end of each year to earn a yield of 4%, compounded annually. When he reaches 65 years of age, what annual annuity, running for twenty years, can be purchased with the accumulated funds? Assume that the 4% interest rate holds throughout and that he is to receive the first payment on his 65th birthday.

4–24   Under a government-sponsored housing plan, one may purchase a new home by making a down payment equal to 5% of the first $16,000 of the value of the house and lot and 10% of the value above $16,000, and pay the balance in monthly installments over a 25-year period, with interest upon the unpaid balance at a nominal rate of 4¾%. In addition, the owner must pay one-twelfth of the annual taxes and insurance each month. Taxes and insurance are estimated to be $15 per year for each $1,000 of the value of house and lot. Determine the down payment and the monthly payment required to purchase, under this plan, a house and lot costing $22,000.

4–25   Determine the capitalized cost of a structure which costs $40,000 and requires $3,000 per year for annual upkeep, interest at 4%.

4–26   What amount will be required to endow a research laboratory which requires $80,000 for original construction, $40,000 per year for operating expenses, and $10,000 every four years for new equipment, with interest at 4% per annum?

4–27   A mining property which cost $30,723 produced an annual year-end return of $5,000 for ten years, after which it was worthless. What uniform rate of profit did the owner receive?

4–28   The annual year-end costs for operating a piece of equipment for five years were $1,100, $1,410, $1,650, $1,720, and $1,840. Using an 8% interest rate, determine the equivalent equal annual costs.

4–29   A loan company advertises that one may borrow $100.00 and repay in twenty monthly payments of $5.82 each. What rate of interest is the loan company receiving on its money?

4–30   A sum of money is accumulated by depositing $2,000 annually, in monthly installments, for ten years. Interest is paid at the annual rate of 4%. What amount will be accumulated at the end of the ten-year period?

4–31   Find the amount of year-end deposits and month-end deposits required to accumulate $10,000 in five years if interest is at the annual rate of 3%.

CHAPTER 5

Depreciation
and Valuation

One of the most common and bothersome facts encountered in the business world is that physical properties usually decrease in value as they age.[1] When a machine or structure is used in production of goods or services, some of the decrease in value is due to physical wear which makes the property less able to render the service for which it was designed. Some effects of age and use are commonly and easily recognized, such as noise, slowing down, or increase in maintenance costs. However, there are other causes of decrease in value which accompany the aging process and which are not so easily recognized. New types of equipment which will bring about lower production costs may cause value to decline. Style changes and consumers' whims may likewise cause a decrease in value. All of these decreases in value are called *depreciation*.

That the realization of the fact that physical properties suffer a decrease in value with time is not a new one may be seen by an examination of the following statement from the writings of Vitruvius,[2] probably written before 27 A.D.

Therefore when arbitrators [3] are taken for party-walls, they do not value them at the price at which they were made, but when from the accounts they find the tenders for them, they deduct as price of the passing of each year the 80th part, and so—in that from the remaining sum repayment is made for these walls—they pronounce the opinion that the walls cannot last more than

---

[1] Notable exceptions are rare antiques, liquors, and some musical instruments.
[2] *Vitruvius on Architecture,* translated by Frank Granger, Vol. 1, p. 117.
[3] For building laws.

90

80 years. There is no deduction [4] made from the value of brick walls provided that they remain plumb; but they are always valued at as much as they were built for.

DEFINITIONS OF VALUE

Since depreciation is defined as decrease in "value," it is necessary to give some consideration to the meaning of that term. Unfortunately, one discovers that there are several meanings attached to it. Probably the best definition of value, in a commercial sense, is that it is the present worth of all the future profits that are to be received through ownership of a particular property. This undoubtedly excellent definition is, however, difficult to apply in actual practice, since one can seldom determine profits far in advance. Thus several other measures of value are commonly used, some of which are approximations of the above definition.

The most commonly encountered measure of value is *market value*. This is what will be paid by a willing buyer to a willing seller for a property [5] where each has equal advantage and is under no compulsion to buy or sell. The buyer is willing to pay the market price because he believes it approximates the present value of what he will receive through ownership *with some rate of interest or profit included*. In most matters relating to depreciation, it is market value that is used. For new properties the cost on the open market is used as the original value.

Next to market value, probably the most important kind of value is *use value*. This is what the property is worth to the owner as an operating unit. A property may be worth more to the person who possesses it and has it in operation than it would be to someone else who, if he purchased it, might have to spend additional funds to move it and get it into operation. Use value is, of course, very closely akin to the original definition of value which was stated previously. Again, it is difficult to determine for the same reasons.

A third type of value is known as *fair value*. This usually is determined by a disinterested party in order to establish a price that is fair to both seller and buyer.

Book value is the worth of a property as shown on the accounting records of a company. It is ordinarily taken to mean the original cost of the property less the amounts which have been charged as depreciation expense. It thus represents the amount of capital which remains invested in the property and

---

[4] This could only come in when the improved methods of brick building were established under the Empire.

[5] The term property is used in this chapter in a general sense. It thus includes buildings, machines, goods, etc.

must be recovered in the future through the depreciation accounting process. It should be remembered, however, that since companies may use various depreciation accounting methods, which produce different results, book value may have little or no relationship to the actual or market value of the property involved.

Salvage, or *resale, value* is the price that can be obtained from the sale of the property second-hand. Salvage value implies that the property has further utility. It is affected by several factors. The reason of the present owner for selling may influence the salvage value. If the owner is selling because there is very little commercial need for the property, this will affect the resale value; change of ownership will probably not increase the commercial utility of the article. Salvage value will also be affected by the present cost of reproducing the property; price levels may either increase or decrease the resale value. A third factor which may affect salvage value is the location of the property. This is particularly true in the case of structures which must be moved in order to be of further use. The physical condition of property will also have a great influence upon the resale price that can be obtained. A structure which has been well maintained and is in good condition will obviously be of greater value than one which has been neglected and would require considerable repair before it could be used.

Scrap value is ordinarily considered to be the amount that the property would bring if sold for junk. The utility of the article is assumed to be zero. Since for most materials, except the precious metals, the scrap price usually fluctuates considerably over a period of time, the fact that there is an existing scrap value does not assure that there will be in the future. Therefore it is questionable practice to assume that a property will have more than a minimum scrap value at a future date. Unless it is certain that a stated scrap value will always exist, in most economy studies the future scrap value should be assumed to be zero.

It may be seen that the various definitions of value vary considerably. While a person normally possesses property so that he may receive benefits from it, some of the benefits frequently are not in the form of money. This fact further complicates the setting of value in monetary terms in order to place an ordinary commercial value upon property.

VALUE FOR RATE SETTING

One exception, where value defined as a measure of future profits can not be used, is in the determination of value for setting utility rates. These rates are usually set by a governmental agency so they will yield a fair profit upon the value of the property. The value assigned to the property for purposes of establishing rates is called the *rate base value*. If this value were measured by the present value of the future profits, a vicious circle would be established. The higher the rates that were set, the greater would be the profits. In turn, the greater the profits, the higher the rates would have to be in order to yield a reasonable return upon the value of the property. For rate setting some other method of determining value must be utilized. This problem will be discussed at length later in this chapter.

PURPOSES OF DEPRECIATION

Since property decreases in value, it is desirable to consider the effect that this depreciation has on engineering projects. Primarily, it is necessary to consider depreciation for two reasons:

1. To provide for the recovery of capital which has been invested in physical property.
2. To enable the expense of depreciation to be charged to the cost of producing products that are turned out by the property.

To understand these purposes, consider the case of a man who invested $3,000.00 in a machine for making a special type of concrete building tile. He found that with his own labor in operating the machine he could produce 500 tiles per day. Working 300 days per year he could make 150,000 tiles. He was able to sell the tiles for $40.00 per thousand. The necessary materials and power cost $20.00 per thousand tiles.

At the end of the first year he had sold 150,000 tiles and computed his total profit, at the rate of $20.00 per thousand, to be $3,000.00 This continued for two years, at which time the machine was worn out and would not operate longer. To continue in business he would have to purchase a new machine.

During the three-year period, believing he was actually making a profit of $3,000.00 per year, he had spent the entire amount for his annual living expenses. He suddenly found that he no longer had his original $3,000.00 of capital, his machine was worn out, and he had no money with which to purchase a new one.

Analysis of the situation reveals that no provision had been made for recovering the capital invested in the tile machine. The machine, which was valued at $3,000.00 when purchased, had decreased in value until it was worthless. Through this depreciation, $3,000.00 of capital had been used in making the tiles.

The obvious error was the failure to recognize that depreciation would take place and make adequate provision to recover the capital which had been invested in the tile machine. Depreciation was just as much an expense of producing the tiles as was the cost of the material and labor. However, depreciation differs from these other expenses in that it always is paid in advance. *Thus it is essential that depreciation be considered so that the capital which is used to prepay this expense may be recovered.* Failure to do this will always result ultimately in the depletion of capital.

Since capital must be maintained, it is necessary that the recovery be made by charging the depreciation which has taken place to the cost of producing whatever has been produced. Thus, in the case of the tile machine production of 450,000 tiles "consumed" the machine. One might say that each thousand tiles produced decreased the value of the machine $3,000.00/450 = $6.67. Therefore $6.67 should be charged as the cost of depreciation for making each thousand tiles. Adding this cost of depreciation to $20.00, the cost of materials and power, gives the true cost of producing a thousand tiles. With the true cost known, the actual profit can then be determined. At the same time, with depreciation charged as an expense, a means for recovery of capital is provided.

Thus depreciation accounting has a twofold purpose. First, it provides for the maintenance of capital. Secondly, it enables the proper amounts to be charged as the expense of depreciation in determining production costs, and ultimately in determining profits. It is this second purpose that is of primary importance to the engineer in making economy studies.

ACTUAL DEPRECIATION IS REVEALED BY TIME

Depreciation, unlike most other costs of production, is always paid in advance. It is an expense, but is not an annual disbursement of money. Yet the actual depreciation cost can not be determined until the machine or property has been utilized to the extent desired and disposed of through resale or being scrapped. Only at this time may its final value be known, and only then the actual decrease in value over the time involved can be determined.

Nevertheless, it is clear that in economy studies there is a need to know in advance what the depreciation expense will be. Since depreciation is one of the costs of production, just as are material expense and labor expense, it must be included. It is apparent, then, that the depreciation expense in economy studies must be in the form of an estimate, as are the other expenses.

It must be recognized that, being estimated, the amount included as depreciation expense will probably not be completely accurate—some error is likely to exist. This should not be too disturbing since the same is true with the other estimated expense items. However, there is one significant difference. Whereas such expense items as labor and material have not been prepaid and can be controlled as conditions vary, such is not the case with depreciation. The decrease in the value of equipment is inexorable. Thus, if future conditions change and the demand for a product decreases, there may be a decline in the amount of material used, and probably a decrease in the profits. However, the depreciation expense, having been prepaid, may continue as before, and the result may be a loss of capital through failure to recover what has been prepaid.

TYPES OF DEPRECIATION

Decreases in value with the passage of time may be classified as

1. Normal depreciation:
   a. Physical.
   b. Functional.
2. Depreciation due to changes in price level.
3. Depletion.

Physical depreciation is nearly always due to the passage of time. Functional depreciation may be the result of age, but the greater portion is usually due to other factors. Since depletion has some unique characteristics, it will be considered separately.

Physical depreciation is due to the lessening of the physical ability of a property to produce results. Its common causes are wear and deterioration. These cause operation and maintenance costs to increase and output to decrease. As a result, the profits decrease. Physical depreciation is mainly a function of time and use. It will be affected greatly by the maintenance policy of the owner. Some people contend that it is possible to maintain a property so that it remains "good as new." This subject is open to discussion, but it is doubtful if anything that is subject to depreciation can ever be as good as new, regardless of maintenance. A property might be improved so that it is more valuable than when it was new, but it is then not the same as it was originally. Improvement has been confused with maintenance.

Functional depreciation is more difficult to determine than physical depreciation. It is the decrease in value which is due to the lessening in the demand for the function which the property was designed to render. This lessening may be brought about in many ways. Styles change, population centers shift, more efficient machines are produced, or markets are saturated. Increased demand may mean that an existing machine is no longer able to produce the required volume. Thus, *inadequacy* is a cause of functional depreciation. The engineer does much to bring about these changed conditions which cause functional depreciation. The result of such changes is to lessen the need for the output of a particular machine or property. This directly affects the profits to be derived from its use, and thus its value.

While physical depreciation may be reasonably anticipated and estimated, functional depreciation is much more elusive. It is caused by events which have not yet occurred. Who can foretell what is to happen? Yet functional depreciation is very real and its importance is increasing. Modern industry is characterized by rapid improvement and change. Indeed, in many businesses the greater portion of the total depreciation cost is due to functional factors. While it is difficult to determine, it can not be ignored.

Reference was made previously to the idea that property might be maintained "good as new." This idea once was held to a considerable extent regarding railroad rights of way. It is probably true that a well-maintained right of way may be in as good physical condition when it is ten years old as it was when new. But what about the functional depreciation? The competition of trucks and busses had a very great effect upon the functional depreciation of railroad rights of way. It appears that neglect of the functional depreciation factor during years of large profits may have contributed substantially to the financial difficulties which many railroads experienced during the years 1929 to 1940.

Depreciation due to changes in price levels is almost impossible to predict and is seldom accounted for in economy studies. Yet this type of depreciation is very real and troublesome. If price levels rise during the life of a property, even if all of the capital invested at the time of original purchase has been recovered through proper depreciation procedure, this recovered capital will not be sufficient to provide an identical replacement. While there has been a recovery of the invested capital, the capital has decreased in value. Thus it is the capital, and not the property, that has depreciated. This is a primary reason why such depreciation is not considered in economy studies. Another reason is that such a practice is not permitted in determining profits for income tax purposes.

Obviously there have been times when price levels have decreased and *appreciation,* the opposite of depreciation, results. However, the long-term historical trend has been one of continued inflation.

Since depreciation is measured by loss in value, and value is determined by future profits, those factors which affect the future profits must also affect depreciation. Any attempt to determine depreciation should consider such factors as the life of the property, future expenses for maintenance, operation and taxes, and future technological changes which may cause obsolescence. This complex situation can not be solved exactly. Future conditions can not be determined exactly. However, it is necessary that depreciation be determined as closely as is reasonably possible. Not only must provision be made for replacement of equipment as it wears, but the correct depreciation charge must be made before the true net profit can be found. In addition, depreciation must be considered in establishing value for rate setting.

ECONOMIC LIFE

Since obsolescence is a prime factor in depreciation, it is apparent that the physical life of a property is often not the life which must be considered in establishing depreciation rates. What is often called the *economic life* is more applicable. By this is meant the length of time during which the property will probably be operated upon an economical basis. The entire amount of depreciation should be written off during this economic life. In this manner, equipment which is unsatisfactory from the viewpoint of economy may be replaced without causing a capital loss, even though it may be in fair physical condition.

Quite a few data are available regarding the probable life of various types of structures and equipment. These have been prepared by various engineers, industrial authorities, and the United States Bureau of Internal Revenue. It should be remembered, however, that such data are based, for the most part, on averages and past performance. There is no guarantee that the future will bring the same results. However, they do give much useful information.

DEPRECIATION AND THE BUREAU
OF INTERNAL REVENUE

When Congress enacted the income tax laws, the Bureau of Internal Revenue was charged with the duty of collecting the proper amount of tax from the individuals and corporations involved. Since the Bureau recognized that depreciation is a legitimate expense which should be deducted from income in order to determine the profit upon which income tax must be based, various rules and suggestions by the Bureau have had considerable effect upon depreciation practice and also upon certain other matters which are affected by depreciation practices. Obviously, the life over which the total depreciation may be spread has a very marked effect upon the annual depreciation expense which is deducted from income in order to determine income taxes. The Bureau of Internal Revenue issued Bulletin "F," revised in 1931 and 1942, entitled *Income Tax Depreciation and Obsolescence—Estimated Useful Lives and Depreciation Rates*. The first page of this bulletin contains the following statement:

This bulletin supersedes Bulletin "F" (revised January 1931) and "Depreciation Studies" (published January 1931). It contains information and statistical data relating to the determination of deductions for depreciation and obsolescence, from which taxpayers and their counsel may obtain the best available indication of Bureau practice and the trend and tendency of official opinion in the administration of pertinent provisions of the Internal Revenue Code and corresponding or similar provisions of prior Revenue Acts. It does not have the force and effect of a Treasury Decision and does not commit the Department to any interpretation of the law which has not been formally approved and promulgated by the Secretary of the Treasury.

Taxpayers and officers of the Bureau are cautioned against reaching conclusions in any case solely on information contained herein and should base their judgment on the application of all pertinent provisions of the law, regulations, and other Treasury Decisions to all the facts in any particular case. The estimated useful lives and rates of depreciation indicated in this bulletin are based upon averages and not prescribed for use in any particular case. They are set forth solely as a guide or starting point from which correct rates may be determined in the light of the experience of the property under consideration and all other pertinent evidence.

In this bulletin are given average useful life data for many types of property. It is apparent from the previous quotation that the Bureau *denies* any intent to compel taxpayers to use the suggested lives given in the bulletin. It is also apparent, however, that the taxpayer must be able to support, to the Bureau's satisfaction, any life that is used in computing depreciation deductions. Many persons maintain that as long as the taxpayer uses the life given in Bulletin "F" for computing depreciation, no questions will be raised by the Bureau, but that the use of shorter lives will be questioned and in most cases not permitted without long and expensive litigation. These persons claim that under this procedure the life data "suggested" by the Bureau of Internal Revenue in fact determine the depreciation policy for the country. There seems to be considerable evidence that this view is to a great extent true. Under these conditions, the validity of the suggested lives in Bulletin "F" are of great importance. Some of these data are shown in Table 5–1.

TABLE 5–1 Selected Average Useful Life Data from U.S. Bureau
of Internal Revenue Bulletin "F"

	Years		Years
Cement kilns	30	Sensitive drills	17
Cereal hullers	15	Radial drills	25
Soap machinery	20	Lathes: Automatic	25
Sulphuric acid converters	14	Engine	25
Oxygen holders	25	Milling machines, horizontal	20
Clay products mills	15	Saws, metalworking	25
Coffee grinders	15	Motion picture cameras	10
Coffee roasters	16	Motion picture projectors	10
Construction equipment:		Boilers, power	10–22
Bulldozers	4–8	Generators, alternators, motors and	
Compressors, gasoline	6	dynamos	14–28
Concrete mixers, gasoline	3–5	Transformers	25
Fresno scrapers	2	Rubber mills	25
Dairy pasteurizers	15	Rubber calenders	25
Bottle washers	16	Buildings:	
Annealing furnaces	22	Apartments	50
Ingot molds	6	Dwellings	60
Merchant bar mills	25	Hotels	50
Sand slingers	10	Machine Shops	60
Electric welding equipment	20	Office	67
Laundry dryers	15	Stores	67
Die casting machines	15	Warehouses	75

An obvious disadvantage of the values listed in Bulletin "F" is that they must be based upon past experience, and conditions change. For example, to one acquainted with modern production practice an average life of 25 years for either an automatic or engine lathe is unsound. There is considerable evidence that the existence of life tables such as those given in Bulletin "F," and the implied endorsement of them by the Bureau of Internal Revenue, has had undue influence in causing companies to keep equipment in operation after it was obsolete and should have been replaced. As a result of considerable study and agitation, the tax laws were modified in 1956 to permit the taxpayer more freedom in adopting write-off periods that are in accord with his business conditions, and to allow use of the *sum-of-the-years'-digits* and the *declining-balance methods* of computing depreciation. Both of these provide for writing off a larger percentage of the initial cost of property during the first few years of life.

Under the present provisions of the income tax laws there is considerable, and probably adequate, flexibility with regard to depreciation allowances. There are still some who advocate that business should be permitted to base depreciation on replacement cost rather than first cost, thus accounting for changes in price levels. This seems of very doubtful merit, and it is rather probable that these same persons would be completely against their own proposals if price levels should suddenly drop. Regardless of whether or not the policies of the Bureau of Internal Revenue are correct, there is no doubt that they must be taken into account in setting up any depreciation procedure. The problems with which the Bureau must deal are not simple. It seems probable that too much rigidity in administering depreciation allowances has existed in the past. Fortunately, there appears to be some change toward more flexible policies.

REQUIREMENTS OF A DEPRECIATION METHOD

The Department of Internal Revenue has the following to say in its instructions for the filing of corporate income tax returns:

The amount deductible on account of depreciation . . . is an amount reasonably measuring the portion of the investment in depreciable property used in the trade or business by reason of exhaustion, wear and tear, including a reasonable allowance for obsolescence, which is properly chargeable for the year. . . . The capital sum to be recovered should be charged off ratably over the useful life of the property. Whatever plan or method of apportionment is adopted must be reasonable and must have due regard to operating conditions during the taxable year and should be described in the return.

Standing against these instructions are the decisions of the United States Supreme Court, which has held that there can be no set method of determining depreciation and value. This court has consistently held that each case must be decided in the light of testimony of competent experts.

From the standpoint of accounting and management planning, there are certain requirements which it is desirable that a depreciation method fulfill. These are:

1. It should be simple.
2. The annual depreciation expense should be constant.
3. It should recover or maintain capital.
4. The results should be factual—that is, book value should be in agreement with actual value.
5. The method should be accepted by the Bureau of Internal Revenue.

Many methods have been devised in attempts to satisfy these requirements. It is doubtful if any are completely satisfactory. The most common are discussed in the following paragraphs.

THE STRAIGHT-LINE FORMULA

This method of computing depreciation assumes that the loss in value is directly proportional to the age of the structure. This straight-line relationship gives rise to the name of the method. Thus with this formula if

L = useful life of the structure in years
C = the original cost
d = the annual cost of depreciation
C_A = the value at the end of A years
C_L = the value at the end of the life of the structure, the scrap value (including gain or loss due to removal)
D_A = depreciation up to age A years,

then

$$d = \frac{C - C_L}{L} \tag{5.1}$$

$$D_A = \frac{A(C - C_L)}{L} \tag{5.2}$$

$$C_A = C - \frac{A(C - C_L)}{L}. \tag{5.3}$$

EXAMPLE. Determine the yearly cost of depreciation, salvage value at the end of the sixth year, and total depreciation up to the end of the sixth year on a structure which cost $120 new and has an estimated scrap value of $20 at the end of ten years.

$$d = \frac{\$120 - \$20}{10} = \$10 \text{ per year}$$

$$D_6 = \frac{6(\$120 - \$20)}{10} = \$60$$

$$C_6 = \$120 - \frac{6(\$120 - \$20)}{10} = \$60$$

This method of computing depreciation is more widely used than any other. It is simple and gives a uniform annual charge. In addition, it has the approval of the Internal Revenue Department. It does not take into account interest, operation and maintenance costs, or profits. Its proponents hold that these factors tend to balance each other and that since operation and maintenance, as well as the useful life, must be estimated, there is little reason for attempting to use a more complex formula.

THE MATHESON FORMULA

This method is also known as the *diminishing-balance method,* the *declining-balance method,* or the *constant-percentage method.* It assumes that the annual cost of depreciation is a fixed percentage of the salvage value at the beginning of the year. The ratio of the depreciation in any one year to the salvage value at the beginning of that year is constant throughout the life of the structure and is designated by k. Thus,

Depreciation during the first year

$$d_1 = Ck \tag{5.4}$$

Depreciation during the Ath year

$$d_A = (C_{A-1})k \tag{5.5}$$

Salvage value at age L years

$$C_L = C(1 - k)^L \tag{5.6}$$

Salvage value at age A years

$$C_A = C(1 - k)^A = C\left(\frac{C_L}{C}\right)^{\frac{A}{L}} \tag{5.7}$$

Rate of depreciation

$$k = 1 - \sqrt[A]{\frac{C_A}{C}} = 1 - \sqrt[L]{\frac{C_L}{C}} \tag{5.8}$$

The Matheson formula, like the straight-line method, is simple to apply. However, it has two serious defects. The annual cost of depreciation is different each year. More serious is the fact that with this formula a structure can never depreciate to zero value.

The Bureau of Internal Revenue now specifically permits the use of the declining-balance method, provided the depreciation charge in any year does not exceed twice that which would result from the use of the straight-line procedure.

A comparison of the results of using the Matheson formula with those resulting from the use of the straight-line and other procedures is shown in Figure 5–1.

EXAMPLE.   Determine the rate of depreciation and salvage value at the end of the sixth year for a structure that cost $120.00 when new and has an estimated life of ten years. Scrap value at the end of its life is $20.00.

$$k = 1 - \sqrt[10]{\frac{\$20.00}{\$120.00}} = 0.1641$$
$$C_6 = \$120.00(1 - 0.1641)^6 = \$40.94$$

It will be noted that this method of determining salvage value gives a figure approximately $20.00 less than that found by the straight-line method. The heaviest depreciation costs occur during the first years of a structure's life. Proponents of this formula assert that the results more nearly parallel the actual second-hand sales value than do those obtained by other methods.

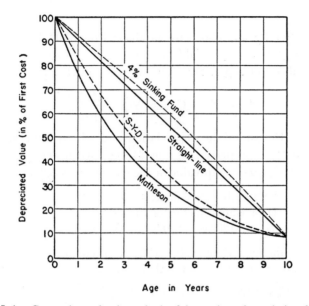

Age in Years

Figure 5–1.   Comparison of values obtained by various depreciation formulas.

This is undoubtedly true in the case of such things as automobiles, where new models and style changes are large factors in establishing the salvage value. However, it is not true of most industrial structures and equipment. The important thing is to obtain a measure of the future profits which can be expected.

SUM-OF-THE-YEARS'-DIGITS METHOD

To obtain the depreciation charge in any year of life by the *sum-of-the-years'-digits* method (commonly designated by SYD), the digits corresponding to the number of each year of life are listed in reverse order. The sum of the digits is then determined. The depreciation factor for any year is the reverse digit for that year divided by the sum of the digits. For example, for a property having a life of five years,

Year	Number of the year in reverse order (digits)	Depreciation
1	5	5/15
2	4	4/15
3	3	3/15
4	2	2/15
5	1	1/15
Sum of the digits	15	

The depreciation for any year is the product of the SYD depreciation factor for that year and the depreciable value, $C - C_L$. The general expression for the annual cost of depreciation for any year, A, when the total life is L, is

$$d_A = (C - C_L) \times \frac{2(L - A + 1)}{L(L + 1)}.$$ (5.9)

EXAMPLE.   Determine the depreciation and salvage value at the end of the sixth year for a property that cost $120.00 when new and has an estimated life of ten years. Scrap value at the end of life is $20.00.

> Sum of the years' digits = 55
> Depreciation factor for the sixth year = 5/55
> $d_6 = (\$120.00 - \$20.00)5/55 = \$9.09$

Since 45/55 of the depreciable value will have been written off by the end of the sixth year, the value at the end of that year will be

$$C_6 = \$120.00 - (\$120.00 - \$20.00)45/55 = \$38.19.$$

In Figure 5–1 it will be noted that the SYD method provides for very rapid depreciation during the early years of life. Further, it is evident that the method enables properties to be depreciated to zero value and is easier to use than the Matheson formula. The method is now approved by the Bureau of Internal Revenue, and since it has certain immediate income tax advantages, it is now being used rather widely for accounting purposes.

THE SINKING FUND FORMULA

This formula assumes that a sinking fund is established in which funds will accumulate for replacement purposes. The total depreciation which has taken place up to any given time is assumed to be equal to the accumulated value of the sinking fund at that time. In this manner the invested capital is preserved.

With this formula, if the estimated life, scrap value, and interest rate on the sinking fund are known, a uniform yearly deposit can be computed. This deposit is the annual cost of depreciation. Thus,

$$d = (C - C_L) \frac{1}{s_{\overline{L}|}} \qquad\qquad (5.10)$$

$$D_A = (C - C_L) \frac{s_{\overline{A}|}}{s_{\overline{L}|}} \qquad\qquad (5.11)$$

$$C_A = C - (C - C_L) \frac{s_{\overline{A}|}}{s_{\overline{L}|}}. \qquad\qquad (5.12)$$

EXAMPLE. Using the sinking fund formula, determine the annual cost of depreciation and the salvage value at the end of the sixth year for a structure which cost $120.00 when new and which has an estimated life of ten years and scrap value of $20.00. Interest on all deposits at the rate of 3% per annum.

$$d = (\$120.00 - \$20.00) \frac{1}{11.4638793} = \$8.72$$

$$C_6 = \$120.00 - (\$120.00 - \$20.00) \frac{6.46840988}{11.4638793} = \$63.60$$

Although the sinking fund method is not used extensively for accounting purposes, it has many valuable features. It is relatively simple, the annual cost for depreciation is uniform, and interest is taken into account. The greatest drawback to its use lies in the fact that few businesses ever maintain an actual depreciation sinking fund. The interest rate which could be obtained upon such deposits would be small—probably not over 3%. An active business is constantly in need of working capital, and this capital will earn much more than 3%. It is therefore a reasonable rule that all funds should be kept invested in the business and not remain idle. As a result, a fictitious depreciation fund is used. The actual amounts which have been charged to depreciation are left in the business in the form of assets and an account referred to as "Reserve for Depreciation" is used to record these funds. (This is fully explained in Chapter 7.)

Using the sinking fund method in the customary accounting procedure, where a "depreciation reserve" is utilized, the business is actually borrowing and using its own depreciation funds. Therefore, there is no place from which interest on these funds can be obtained except the business itself. Thus, if the sinking fund method is used for accounting purposes, the business must, in effect, pay itself interest for the use of its own money. To accomplish this, the cost of depreciation, equal to the sinking fund deposit, must be charged as an operating expense, and then interest (profit) on the accumulated sinking funds must be charged as an expense and added to the depreciation reserve account. Unless this procedure is used, the correct amount will not be accumulated in the depreciation "reserve" during the write-off period. Such a practice accurately accounts for all depreciation costs but requires some explanation to the income tax authorities.

Since in actual practice the depreciation funds are reinvested in the business, this meets the requirements of the theory of the sinking fund method of depreciation. It will be shown later that for this reason the sinking fund theory is the only one that gives correct results when used in economy studies. Therefore, it forms the basis for estimating depreciation expense in making economy studies.

SERVICE-OUTPUT METHOD

Some companies attempt to compute the depreciation of equipment on the basis of its output. When equipment is purchased, an estimate is made of the amount of service it will render during its economic life. Depreciation for any period is then charged on the basis of the service that has been rendered during that period. This method has the advantages of making the unit cost of depreciation constant and giving low depreciation expense during periods of low production. That it is difficult to apply may be understood by realizing that not only the economic life, but also the total amount of service which the equipment will render during this period, must be estimated.

For some types of equipment the service-output method is recognized by the Bureau of Internal Revenue. For example, a depreciation rate of one cent per mile is considered reasonable for taxicabs.

The so-called *machine-hour method* of depreciation is a modification of this procedure.

THE GILLETTE FORMULA

Numerous formulas have been derived to give the salvage value of a property at any age. Most of these special formulas have been designed to meet unusual conditions, particularly cases where structures are built larger than is necessary for existing needs in order to provide for future requirements. In the early years of life such properties may operate at a loss, but they become profitable in later years. Such properties may easily be worth more when they are a few years old, and the unprofitable years have passed, than they are at age zero. Some of the more specialized depreciation and valuation formulas have attempted to take such factors into account. Each is based upon some hypothesis stating the factors which the originator of the formula thought should be considered in determining value. None of these is widely used, and many are of doubtful value. Two, however, do have some merit.

The first was originated by H. P. Gillette. This formula is based upon the principle that the owner of a structure is entitled to such a resale price as will enable the buyer to produce each unit at as low a cost as the average unit cost of production during the entire life of the structure.[6] This assumes annual service cost to be on the basis of

$$
\text{Annual service cost} = w = \begin{cases} \text{Depreciation} \left[(C - C_L) \dfrac{1}{s_{\overline{L}|}} \right] \\ + \\ \text{Fixed charges [Cost } (C) \times \text{ rate } (r)] \\ + \\ \text{Operation cost } [O] \\ + \\ \text{Maintenance cost } [M]. \end{cases}
$$

From the above, the unit cost over the L years of life, where U units are produced annually, would be

$$
w_L = \frac{1}{U} \left[\frac{(C - C_L)}{s_{\overline{L}|}} + Cr + O + M \right]. \tag{5.13}
$$

For the buyer at structure's age A, producing U'' units annually and with fixed charges at the rate r'', operation costs O'', and maintenance M'',

$$
w_{L-A} = \frac{1}{U''} \left[\frac{(C_A - C_L)}{s_{\overline{L-A}|}} + C_A r'' + O'' + M'' \right]. \tag{5.14}
$$

By the principle of the Gillette formula, $w_L = w_{L-A}$. Thus,

$$
\begin{aligned}
\frac{1}{U} & \left[\frac{(C - C_L)}{s_{\overline{L}|}} + Cr + O + M \right] = \\
& \frac{1}{U''} \left[\frac{(C_A - C_L)}{s_{\overline{L-A}|}} + C_A r'' + O'' + M'' \right].
\end{aligned} \tag{5.15}
$$

Solving for C_A, the salvage value at age A years is

$$
C_A = \frac{\dfrac{U''}{U} \left[\dfrac{(C - C_L)}{s_{\overline{L}|}} + Cr + O + M \right] s_{\overline{L-A}|} + C_L - (O'' + M'') s_{\overline{L-A}|}}{1 + r'' s_{\overline{L-A}|}}. \tag{5.16}
$$

This formula makes a correct interpretation of unit costs. However, there is room for argument as to whether the buyer is entitled to the same unit

[6] H. P. Gillette, *Handbook of Cost Data*.

costs as would be obtained throughout the entire life of the structure. The additional difficulty in applying this formula is that many items can be obtained only through estimate. It is doubtful that the future charges can be estimated with enough accuracy to justify such a complicated formula. The same difficulty exists in the case of future output.

PRESENT-WORTH DEPRECIATION FORMULA

This formula is essentially the same as that given by Marston and Agg in their excellent book on *Engineering Valuation*.[7] Several changes have been made in order to give a somewhat simpler formula. It is based upon the principle that value is the present worth of all the future profits to be expected from the structure. Thus

$$C_A = \left(\begin{array}{c}\text{present worth of future}\\ \text{operations' returns}\end{array}\right) + \left(\begin{array}{c}\text{present worth of}\\ \text{scrap value}\end{array}\right) \qquad (5.17)$$

$$C_A = g'' s_{\overline{L-A}|} v^{L-A} + C_L v^{L-A} \qquad (5.18)$$

$$C_A = g'' a_{\overline{L-A}|} + C_L v^{L-A} \qquad (5.19)$$

where g'' = equivalent equal annual profit plus annual depreciation cost for the $L - A$ years,

= an equivalent equal annual sum, having the same present value as the present value of [all future gross profits] − [all charges except depreciation] for the $L - A$ years.

Equation (5.19) may be used where it is possible to determine the factor g'' with some degree of certainty. This necessitates knowing pretty well what future income and expenses will be. These can seldom be known with any degree of exactness. About the best that can be done is to make an estimate of how future returns and expenses will compare with the past, basing this estimate upon expert opinion and careful study of all the factors involved. This estimate is expressed in the form of a ratio, being

$$R = g''/g$$

where g corresponds to g'', but for the entire L years of life. At age zero

$$C = g a_{\overline{L}|} + C_L v^L, \qquad (5.20)$$

and

$$g = \frac{C - C_L v^L}{a_{\overline{L}|}}; \qquad (5.21)$$

also

$$g'' = Rg = R \frac{(C - C_L v^L)}{a_{\overline{L}|}}. \qquad (5.22)$$

[7] A. Marston and T. R. Agg, *Engineering Valuation*.

Substituting this value of g'' in Equation (5.19)

$$C_A = R(C - C_L v^L) \frac{a_{\overline{L-A}|}}{a_{\overline{L}|}} + C_L v^{L-A}. \qquad (5.23)$$

Equation (5.23) may be used to obtain the value of C_A when R is estimated.

In using Equation (5.23), it must be remembered that C is not necessarily the first cost of the structure. If i is the *actual* rate of profit upon the initial investment, then C is the actual first cost. As a rule, however, one desires to determine what price, C_A, should be paid for a structure in order for it to earn a certain rate of return which corresponds to the i used in the calculations. In this case, in order to use Equation (5.23), one must first determine the value of C corresponding to the desired rate of return i. This is done by solving for C in Equation (5.23). This computed value of C is then used in the solution of Equation (5.20).

While the present-worth equation is theoretically correct, one can easily see that it is somewhat difficult to apply. It also involves a number of factors that are usually not known with any degree of certainty. The vital factor R must be based upon estimate. As a consequence, it is doubtful that the results obtained by the use of this formula are ordinarily superior to those which may be had through the use of the simple straight-line method. Thus it appears that the more complex depreciation formulas have little actual value except in a few situations. It is not difficult to understand the widespread use of the straight-line method.

WHAT DEPRECIATION METHOD SHOULD BE USED?

With a number of methods of computing depreciation available, one needs to know which to use. Three of the simpler methods will suffice for nearly all cases. But these three are not interchangeable and are by no means sufficient unless used with discretion.

It should be emphasized that no depreciation formula should be used unless modifications are made in the established rates whenever the facts show that the theoretical salvage values are at variance with actual values. Book values of all properties should be examined periodically and adjusted when necessary so as to prevent their being greater than actual value. As the Supreme Court has stated, there can be no substitute for expert opinion which is guided by all the facts. Failure to apply good judgment to depreciation methods can result in only one end—loss of capital. It should be remembered that the prime purpose of considering depreciation is to preserve capital. When adopted methods of depreciation are failing to accomplish this purpose, they should be changed.

When it is necessary to alter depreciation rates or write off capital losses which have occurred because the rates have been in error, the Bureau of Internal Revenue requires a complete explanation of the adjustments. However, if they are founded on fact, such claims of loss usually will be allowed.

In deciding which depreciation method to use, it is well to recall the two primary purposes of depreciation accounting. One is to provide for the recovery of capital over the life of the property. The second is to enable the *cost* of depreciation over a unit of time, or per unit of production, to be determined so that it may be included as an expense of production. The first of these purposes is primarily the concern of the accountant. The second purpose is a matter of prime concern to the engineer in making economy studies and is, of course, of interest to the cost accountant. In making economy studies depreciation must be estimated in such a manner that the predicted profit will be accurately determined.

It may be demonstrated that either the sinking fund, straight-line, or sum-of-the-years'-digits methods will satisfy the first purpose of depreciation, providing properly for the recovery of capital. However, in making estimates of future costs and profits *before taxes,* as is done in economy studies, only the sinking fund method will produce correct results. This may be shown by a simple example.

Consider a case where $100.00 is invested in a project that will last ten years and will be worthless at the end of that time. The annual net profit before depreciation charges are deducted (gross profit less all expenses except depreciation) will be $14.24. The average rate of earning of all capital invested in the business is 7%. It is desired to determine the prospective rate of return and compare this with the actual results, first by the sinking fund method, and second, by straight-line depreciation.

With the conditions as stated, the annual depreciation charge by the sinking fund method would be

$$d = \$100.00/s_{\overline{n}|},$$

where $n = 10$ years and i, the rate of interest, would be 7%, since the depreciation funds could be invested in the business and earn the same return as other capital. Thus

$$d = \$100.00/13.8 = \$7.24.$$

The indicated rate of return on the investment would therefore be

$$\text{Rate of return} = \frac{\$14.24 - \$7.24}{\$100.00} \times 100 = 7\%.$$

The actual resulting profits by use of the sinking fund method are shown in Table 5–2. Column (2) shows the annual profit before the depreciation

TABLE 5–2   Effect of Using the Sinking Fund Method of Computing Depreciation

(1)	(2)	(3)	(4)	(5)	(6)	(7)	(8)
Year	Profit before deduction for depreciation	Depreciation charge	Operating profit (2) − (3)	Depreciation funds at beginning of year	Profit earned by and paid to depreciation fund	Total profits (4)	Worth at end of 10 years (7) × $(1 + i)^n$
1	$14.24	$7.24	$7.00	—	—	$ 7.00	$12.87
2	14.24	7.24	7.00	$ 7.24	$0.51	7.00	12.03
3	14.24	7.24	7.00	14.99	1.05	7.00	11.24
4	14.24	7.24	7.00	23.28	1.63	7.00	10.51
5	14.24	7.24	7.00	32.15	2.25	7.00	9.82
6	14.24	7.24	7.00	41.64	2.91	7.00	9.18
7	14.24	7.24	7.00	51.79	3.63	7.00	8.58
8	14.24	7.24	7.00	62.66	4.39	7.00	8.01
9	14.24	7.24	7.00	74.29	5.20	7.00	7.49
10	14.24	7.24	7.00	86.73	6.07	7.00	7.00
						$70.00	$96.73

charge is deducted. The uniform annual depreciation charge of $7.24 is shown in Column (3). Column (4) shows the annual operating profit obtained from the investment to be $7.00.

Since funds invested in the company earn an average return of 7% per annum, the amounts deposited in the sinking fund are invested in the business and therefore earn a profit at the rate of 7%. The amount in the sinking fund at the beginning of each year will earn profit during that year. The profit earned by the sinking fund must be paid into the sinking fund, since it belongs to the fund and helps toward the accumulation of the amount needed for replacement at the end of the life of the investment. This profit corresponds to the interest earned by an ordinary sinking fund. Only by this process is the capital maintained.

Column (5) shows the amount in the depreciation fund at the beginning of each year. This, for the beginning of any year, is equal to the amount available at the beginning of the previous year, plus the deposit made at the end of that year, plus the interest earned during that year. Column (6) indicates the interest earned by the invested amounts in the sinking fund.

These earnings are paid into the sinking fund. Column (7) shows the total profit available to the owners of the business, being the same as Column (4). At the end of ten years these profits have amounted to $70.00, or a uniform annual return of 7% on the $100.00 capital which has been invested. It is thus noted that the actual return agrees with the estimated value.

Now consider the same example, this time using the straight-line depreciation method. The annual charge for depreciation would be

$$d = \$100.00/10 = \$10.00.$$

The estimated profit would be

$$\text{Rate of return} = \frac{\$14.24 - \$10.00}{\$100.00} \times 100 = 4.24\%.$$

Next examine Table 5–3 which shows the actual amounts which would

TABLE 5-3   Effect of Using the Straight-Line Method of Computing Depreciation

(1) Year	(2) Profit before deduction for depreciation	(3) Depreciation charge	(4) Operating profit (2) − (3)	(5) Depreciation funds at beginning of year	(6) Profit from depreciation fund paid to owners	(7) Total profit (4) + (6)	(8) Worth at end of 10 years (7) × $(1 + i)^n$
1	$14.24	$10	$4.24	—	—	$ 4.24	$ 7.80
2	14.24	10	4.24	$10.00	$0.70	4.94	8.49
3	14.24	10	4.24	20.00	1.40	5.64	9.06
4	14.24	10	4.24	30.00	2.10	6.34	9.51
5	14.24	10	4.24	40.00	2.80	7.04	9.87
6	14.24	10	4.24	50.00	3.50	7.74	10.15
7	14.24	10	4.24	60.00	4.20	8.44	10.34
8	14.24	10	4.24	70.00	4.90	9.14	10.46
9	14.24	10	4.24	80.00	5.60	9.84	10.53
10	14.24	10	4.24	90.00	6.30	10.54 $73.90	10.54 $96.75

be involved after the investment had been made. Column (2) gives the annual profit before deduction of depreciation charges. The annual depreciation charge is shown in Column (3). Column (4) shows the operating profit which remains after depreciation is deducted.

In the ordinary use of straight-line depreciation in a business, the amounts charged for depreciation are not put aside into a fund, but are left in the company in the form of working capital or other assets.[8] A reserve account is established to indicate the claim of this depreciation reserve upon some of the assets. With the depreciation funds left in the business in this manner, they act like any other capital funds and earn annual returns at the same rate. When a "Reserve for Depreciation" of this type is used in connection with straight-line depreciation methods, the earnings of the funds which have been charged for depreciation are available and paid to the owners as a portion of the profits of the business. Thus Column (6) indicates the profits which are earned by the depreciation funds. Column (7) then shows the total profits which the owners receive from the business, being the summation of Columns (4) and (6). During the ten-year period, these would amount to $73.90.

A comparison of the totals of the "Total Profit" columns in the two tables indicates that there is some apparent discrepancy between the two methods of depreciation. This is clarified by examining Column (8) in each table. In this column the profits of the various years have been reduced to a common time—the end of the tenth year—by multiplying by the compound amount factor, $(1 + i)^n$. The totals of these two columns are seen to be identical within the accuracy of slide-rule computations. One may thus conclude that either the straight-line or sinking fund depreciation method is satisfactory for the accounting purpose of providing for capital recovery. The only possibility of difference occurs when the total accumulated profits must be determined at some intermediate point between the beginning and end of the life of the investment. This difference at any time is so small that it may be neglected. Since the straight-line method is the simpler, it is apparent why it is used so frequently for accounting purposes.

When one compares the predicted rates of return obtained by the two methods, he concludes that they are far from equivalent. The totals of Column (8) in each table were the same. Therefore, the average earnings in Table 5–3, where straight-line depreciation was used, must have been the same as in Table 5–2. This indicates that the predicted rate of return based upon straight-line depreciation was wrong. The straight-line method fails to account for the earnings of the accumulated depreciation funds. Therefore, it always gives a predicted rate of return that is lower than the actual rate will be. Thus one may conclude that for accounting purposes either the straight-line or sinking fund method may be used without appreciable error. *For engineering estimates, however, the sinking fund method should be used in order to obtain a true answer.*

Since with the sum-of-the-years'-digits method the depreciation charge

[8] See Chapter 7 for a more complete explanation of this procedure.

each year is different, it is obvious that this method can not be used directly in estimating a uniform rate of profit that will be derived from an investment. Some understanding of what results from the use of this depreciation method may be gained from an examination of Table 5–4. This table

TABLE 5–4   Effect of Using the Sum-of-the-Years'-Digits Method of Computing Depreciation

(1)	(2)	(3)	(4)	(5)	(6)	(7)	(8)
Year	Profit before deduction for depreciation	Depreciation charge	Operating profit (2) − (3)	Depr. funds at beginning of year	Profit from depr. fund paid to owners	Total profits to owners (4) + (6)	Worth at end of 10 years (7) × (1 + i)ⁿ
1	$14.24	$ 18.20	−$ 3.96	—	—	−$ 3.96	−$ 7.28
2	14.24	16.40	− 2.16	$18.20	$1.27	− 0.89	− 1.53
3	14.24	14.60	− 0.36	34.60	2.42	+ 2.06	+ 3.31
4	14.24	12.70	+ 1.54	49.20	3.44	4.98	7.47
5	14.24	10.90	3.34	61.90	4.33	7.67	10.76
6	14.24	9.10	5.14	72.80	5.10	10.24	13.42
7	14.24	7.30	6.94	81.90	5.73	12.67	15.52
8	14.24	5.50	8.74	89.20	6.24	14.98	17.15
9	14.24	3.60	10.64	94.70	6.63	17.27	18.48
10	14.24	1.70	12.54	98.30	6.88	19.42	19.42
		$100.00				$84.44	$96.72

gives the results from applying SYD depreciation to the same $100.00 investment discussed previously.

Column (3) of this table shows the depreciation charge of each year as computed by the SYD method. The operating profit is shown in Column (4). It will be noted that in each of the first three years there is a computed loss, due to the high depreciation charges during these years. Column (5) shows the amount in the depreciation reserve, and reinvested in the business, at the beginning of each year. The profits resulting from the use of the depreciation funds, and paid to the owners, are shown in Column (6). Column (7) shows the total profits received by the owners.

Examination of the totals for Columns (3), (7), and (8) reveals several interesting facts. First, the total of Column (3) shows that the use of the SYD method, of course, recovers the correct amount of capital. Second, the total of Column (7) makes it appear that much higher profits result from the use of this method than are obtained by using either the sinking fund or straight-line methods. The fact that the total of Column (8) is the same as that in Tables 5–2 and 5–3 proves that there is no real difference in the total profits obtained (before taxes) through the use of each of the three methods. The considerable difference indicated in the total profits paid to the owners, as shown in Column (7), is due to the fact that, using SYD depreciation, profits are withheld from the owners during the early years and reinvested in the business. As a result, a larger amount of capital is active in the business and is earning profits during the later years. This fact, that the owners are in effect forced to forego profits and reinvest them in the business during the early years when the SYD depreciation method is used, seems not to be understood by many people.

EQUIVALENCE OF STRAIGHT-LINE DEPRECIATION WITH SIMPLE INTEREST ON REMAINING INVESTMENT AND SINKING FUND DEPRECIATION WITH SIMPLE INTEREST ON INITIAL INVESTMENT

In connection with concepts which will be discussed later, it is essential to have a clear understanding of the fact that the use of straight-line depreciation with simple interest (profit) paid on the remaining investment of capital is exactly equivalent to the use of sinking fund depreciation with simple interest (profit) paid on the original investment. If one considers an individual investment without realizing that it is only one out of many involved in a business, as the cost of depreciation is recovered out of income it is returned to the investor, and thus the amount of capital invested is decreased. Therefore the profit each year must be related to the remaining investment of capital in order to compute an actual rate of return. Obviously, if the profit is constant but the amount invested decreases each year, the rate of profit will change each year. Because of this fact, a uniform equivalent rate of profit on the actual remaining investment can not be computed by using the profit and investment figures for any one year. Yet such a uniform equivalent value is needed in making an investment decision.

It can readily be shown that the use of straight-line depreciation with simple interest (profit) paid on the remaining invested capital is exactly equivalent to the use of sinking fund depreciation with simple interest (profit) paid on the original investment. Tables 5–5 and 5–6 demonstrate this fact by showing that the present worths of the amounts received by the investor are the same. Therefore, for economy study purposes, sinking fund depreciation with interest (profit) on the original investment may be

TABLE 5-5 Present Worth of Profits and Returned Capital Resulting from the Use
of Straight-Line Depreciation and 7% Simple Interest (Profit)
on the Remaining Investment

Year	Investment during year	Depreciation paid at end of year to owner	Profit paid at end of year	Total paid to owner	Present worth factor, v^n	Present worth of payments
1	$1,000	$ 200	$ 70	$ 270	.9346	$ 252
2	800	200	56	256	.8734	224
3	600	200	42	242	.8163	197
4	400	200	28	228	.7629	174
5	200	200	14	214	.7130	153
		$1,000	$210	$1,210		$1,000

used in order to obtain a uniform rate of profit with full knowledge that the
long-range results are exactly equivalent to the use of straight-line depreciation and profit on the remaining investment.

By using the same procedure that was utilized in developing Table 5-5, it
also can be shown that use of the sum-of-the-years'-digits method and simple
interest on the remaining investment is equivalent to the use of sinking fund
depreciation and interest on the original investment. Thus, in economy
studies sinking fund depreciation may be used with a uniform rate of return
on the initial investment which will be exactly equivalent to the uniform rate
of return on the diminishing investment plus straight-line or S-Y-D depreciation.

TABLE 5-6 Present Worth of Profits and Returned Capital Resulting from the Use
of Sinking Fund Depreciation and 7% Simple Interest (Profit)
on the Original Investment

Year	Investment during year (Interest base)	Depreciation paid at end of year to owner	Profit paid at end of year	Total paid to owner	Present worth factor, v^n	Present worth of payments
1	$1,000	$174	$ 70	$ 244	.9346	$ 228
2	1,000	174	70	244	.8734	213
3	1,000	174	70	244	.8163	199
4	1,000	174	70	244	.7629	186
5	1,000	174	70	244	.7130	174
		$870	$350	$1,220		$1,000

USE OF CAPITAL RECOVERY FACTORS IN DEPRECIATION

One common method of handling depreciation in economy studies is the
use of the capital recovery factor, $1/a_{\overline{n}|}$. The significance of its use and its

relationship to the sinking fund method of depreciation is frequently misunderstood. These may be shown in the following manner.

Referring to Equation (1.4), profit = income − expenses, this may be expressed as

$$\text{profit} = \text{income} - (\text{out-of-pocket costs}) - (\text{depreciation}).$$

This latter relationship can be written as an equation of the form

$$E = [G - (O + M + I)] - D \qquad (5.24)$$

Let the quantity $[G - (O + M + I)] = E_{bd} =$ earnings before depreciation. Then,

$$\frac{E}{C} = \frac{E_{bd} - D}{C} = i = \text{rate of return on invested capital}, \qquad (5.25)$$

and

$$\frac{E}{C} = \frac{E_{bd} - C \times 1/s_{\overline{L}|}}{C} = i, \qquad (5.26)$$

$$E_{bd} - C \times 1/s_{\overline{L}|} = C \times i, \qquad (5.27)$$

$$E_{bd} = [C \times 1/s_{\overline{L}|}] + [C \times i]. \qquad (5.28)$$

Since

$$C \times 1/s_{\overline{L}|} = \text{depreciation cost},$$

and

$$C \times i = \text{profit on invested capital},$$
$$E_{bd} = \text{depreciation cost} + \text{profit on invested capital}. \qquad (5.29)$$

Equation (5.29) may be written in the form

$$E_{bd} = C(1/s_{\overline{L}|} + i). \qquad (5.30)$$

Then, since

$$1/s_{\overline{L}|} + i = 1/a_{\overline{L}|} = \text{Capital Recovery Factor (CRF)},$$
$$E_{bd} = C \times \text{CRF}. \qquad (5.31)$$

It follows from Equations (5.29) and (5.31) that multiplying the capital by the capital recovery factor provides for depreciation plus profit on the invested capital. Thus its use is exactly equivalent to using sinking fund depreciation and including a minimum required profit as an item of cost. As will be discussed later, both methods can be, and are, used in economy studies. Each has certain advantages and disadvantages. In either case, it is necessary to understand what is involved so that one may know the significance of the results.

In using capital recovery factors, one must make special provision if the property being depreciated has salvage or scrap value. This may be done by multiplying only the depreciable value $(C - C_L)$ by the capital recovery factor and then including an additional amount equal to the salvage or scrap value times the profit or interest rate. The entry would then be

$$(C - C_L) \times \mathrm{CRF} + C_L \times i$$

where i is the desired profit rate on the invested capital and is the same as the interest rate involved in the capital recovery factor.

It can readily be shown that the depreciation charge (capital recovery) plus the profit or interest on the remaining investment is exactly equivalent, over the life of the property, for the sinking fund, straight-line, and the SYD methods. Thus if income tax effects are neglected, a capital recovery factor can be used for economy study purposes in cases where it is known that the SYD method of depreciation will be used for accounting purposes.

USING THE CAPITAL RECOVERY FACTOR TO DETERMINE INTEREST RATES

Since the capital recovery factors provide for both the recovery of capital (depreciation) and interest (or profit) on the invested capital, they frequently furnish a convenient method for determining the interest (profit) rate that is received from an investment. For example, suppose that an investment of $10,000 produces an income of $1,490 per year for ten years with no further income or return of capital after that time. What rate of return was received from the investment?

Both profit and capital was included in the annual income payments. Therefore, $1,490/$10,000 = CRF for ten years at some rate of interest. Since $1,490/$10,000 = 0.1490, by consulting Table XXI of the Appendix, it is found that this corresponds to an interest rate of 8%.

STRAIGHT-LINE DEPRECIATION PLUS AVERAGE INTEREST

In order to avoid the use of interest and annuity tables, some engineers use an approximate method involving straight-line depreciation instead of a capital recovery factor. This method uses straight-line depreciation plus average interest on the invested capital. The average interest is obtained by computing the interest on the capital invested during the first year and the last year and using the average of these two values.

The interest for the first year would be Ci. For the last year the remaining investment would be $\dfrac{(C - C_L)}{L} + C_L$ and the interest $\left[\dfrac{(C - C_L)}{L} + C_L\right] i$. Combining these two amounts and dividing by 2 gives for the average interest:

$$\text{Average interest} = \left(\frac{C - C_L}{L} + C_L + C\right)\frac{i}{2}$$

$$= (C - C_L)\left(\frac{L + 1}{L}\right)\frac{i}{2} + C_L i \qquad (5.32)$$

If the salvage value is zero, the expression for average interest becomes

$$C\left(\frac{L + 1}{L}\right)\frac{i}{2} \qquad (5.33)$$

Since this method gives only approximate results and requires quite a bit of calculating, there is little justification for its use in place of the sinking fund method or a capital recovery factor except where interest tables are not available.

RELATIONSHIP OF DEPRECIATION COSTS TO FIRST COST

In certain economy studies it is essential to recognize that the first cost of a depreciable property is equal to the present worth of all of the future depreciation costs plus profit on the investment. This can be shown in the following way:

$$\text{Annual depreciation} = C \times 1/s_{\overline{n}|}$$
$$\text{Annual profit} \qquad\quad = C \times i$$

Present worth of all future annual depreciation plus all future profits

$$= C(1/s_{\overline{n}|} + i)\, a_{\overline{n}|}$$

Since $(1/s_{\overline{n}|} + i)\, a_{\overline{n}|}$ is equal to 1, the above expression reduces to C, the first cost of the depreciable property.

INCOME TAX SAVINGS THROUGH SYD DEPRECIATION

Whereas the use of the SYD depreciation method produces results that are equivalent to those obtained by straight-line or sinking fund depreciation when income taxes are not considered, the SYD method has some immediate advantages when taxes must be considered. This is due to the fact that the greater amount of money withheld as a depreciation charge by using the

SYD method is not subject to income tax, whereas if the stockholders were to reinvest an equivalent amount of profits, they would first have to pay income taxes on these profits. A detailed discussion of this matter is contained in Chapter 18.

DEPLETION

When natural resources are being consumed in producing products or services, the term "depletion" is used to indicate the decrease in value that has occurred. The term is commonly used in connection with mining properties, oil and gas wells, timber lands, etc. In any given parcel of mineral property, for example, there is a definite quantity of ore, oil, or gas available. As some of the mineral is mined and sold, the reserve decreases and the value of the property normally diminishes.

There appears to be a great amount of misunderstanding in the minds of many mining men, engineers and others as to the relationship between depletion and depreciation. In the case of mineral resources it is clear that a portion of the property is disposed of with each sale. However, when a machine in a factory is used to produce goods for sale, although a physical portion of the machine is not disposed of with each sale, a portion of its economic production ability is a part of each product and thus is disposed of with each sale. The mineral resource has value only because the mineral may be sold. Similarly, the machine has value primarily because what it can produce can be sold. In each case the value of the property decreases through its use in production. Thus both depletion and depreciation represent decreases in value through the using up of the value of the property utilized in production.

However, there is a difference in the manner in which the amounts recovered through depletion and depreciation must be handled. In the case of depreciation, the property involved usually may be replaced with similar property when it has become fully depreciated. In the case of depletion of mineral or other natural resources, such replacement usually is not possible. Once the gold has been removed from a mine, or the oil from an oil well, it can not be replaced. Thus, in a manufacturing or other business where depreciation occurs, the principal of maintenance of capital is practiced, and the amounts charged for depreciation expense are reinvested in new equipment so as to continue the business in operation indefinitely. On the other hand, in the case of a mining or other mineral industry, the amounts charged as depletion can not be used to replace the sold natural resource, and the company, in effect, may sell itself out of business, bit by bit, as it carries out its normal operations. Such companies frequently pay out to the owners each year the amounts recovered as depletion. Thus the annual payment to the owners is made up of two parts—first, the profit which has been earned and, second, a portion of the owner's capital which is being returned, marked as depletion. In such cases, if the natural resource were eventually completely consumed, the company would be out of business, and the stockholder would hold stock which was theoretically worthless but would have received back all of his invested capital.

In the actual operation of many natural resource businesses, the depletion funds may be used to acquire new properties, such as new mines and oil-producing properties, and thus give continuity to the enterprise.

While the theoretical depletion for a year would be

$$\frac{\text{Cost of property}}{\text{Number of units in the property}} \times \text{Units sold during year,}$$

in actual practice the depletion is based upon a percentage of the year's income as permitted by the Bureau of Internal Revenue. Depletion allowances on oil, gas, and mineral properties may be computed as a percentage of the gross income, provided that the amount charged for depletion does not exceed 50 per cent of the taxable income before deducting the depletion allowance. Typical percentage depletion allowances are

Oil and gas wells	$27\frac{1}{2}\%$
Antimony, bismuth, cadmium, cobalt, lead, manganese, nickel, tin, tungsten, vanadium, zinc, sulfur, uranium, asbestos, bauxite, graphite, mica	23%
Other metal mines not in the 23% group	15%
Coal, lignite, sodium chloride	10%
Brick and tile clay, peat, pumice, sand	5%

It is apparent that the total amount that can be charged for depletion over the life of a property under this procedure may be far more than the original cost.

High depletion allowances have often been justified as being necessary to encourage the discovery and development of mineral resources. In many instances considerable political pressure has been evident in their establishment.

COMMON DEPRECIATION PRACTICES

Because of the complexity of the depreciation problem, many companies have adopted certain rules and practices for use in their businesses. Many tend to use write-off periods which are considerably shorter than the actual expected life when making economy studies. Recent studies have shown a definite trend toward the use of shorter write-off periods by most companies. Almost all companies use a write-off period of ten years or less, and about 75 per cent use five years or less. Many companies set such short write-off periods in order to prevent the investment of money in any equipment which would not pay for itself in a very short period, thus avoiding any possibility of loss. However, such arbitrary periods are usually intended as, and should be used as, rule-of-thumb guides. Where the circumstances obviously warrant a longer and more realistic write-off period, such a period should be used. Sometimes what are intended to be rough guides actually become unwritten law within a given company. Of course, such a procedure will prevent any money from being lost due to rapid obsolescence. At the same time, it may prevent investment in many worth-while undertakings. One can be too safe as well as too venturesome. It is somewhat like building a 100 per cent safe airplane. It could be built, but it probably would never get off the ground. The depreciation period used in an economy study should undoubtedly be on the conservative side—but only reasonably and realistically so.

In most cases, no depreciation is included on land. As a rule, land is more apt to increase than decrease in value. However, there are a few cases where depreciation on land should be considered.

One must always make certain that the scrap or resale value of a property is taken into account in computing depreciation, *if there will be such value.* In many cases the probable scrap value is very difficult to determine, or there is considerable likelihood that there may be no scrap value. Unless there are very definite indications of scrap value, the usual practice in making economy studies is to assume that the scrap value is zero.

VALUATION

The engineer is frequently called upon to decide the value of engineering properties. An adequate discussion of the methods used to arrive at the correct value of any property would require at least a good-sized volume; it is obviously beyond the scope of this book. However, a few of the principles involved will be considered, since they are so intimately connected with the subject of depreciation.

The reasons for determining the value of property vary. Similarly, a valuation that is correct for one need may not be correct for another. The need for determining the value of property often occurs when a private buyer is purchasing the property from a private owner. Again, the value of property may need to be known to serve as a tax base. When a municipality wishes to purchase a privately owned utility plant, the value must be decided upon. In establishing utility rates, the regulating bodies must arrive at a fair value of the property which is used to render the service. If a company examines the book value of its property at periodic intervals in order to determine whether the established depreciation rates are adequate, it must have some method of estimating the correct value of the property.

It would often be desirable to determine the present worth of the future profits which will accrue from ownership and use this figure as the value of the property. Such a determination, however, usually presents many difficulties. The future is usually most uncertain. In addition, some rate of interest must be used in the calculations, and the choice of this interest rate will affect the final value.

In actual practice, the valuation process often attempts to determine how much would have to be spent to acquire a plant or property which, under similar conditions, would render the same future service as the property under consideration. In other words, value is often taken as the amount that would have to be spent to acquire a plant which would in the future render an equal amount of service at no greater unit cost. In order to do this, a common method is to determine what it would cost to reproduce the property under existing conditions, prices, and methods and then theoretically to depreciate this "new" property to the point where it would have only the same ability to render future service as does the old property. When using this procedure, it must be remembered that it is future *service* that is to be provided; the theoretical new property must not merely be depreciated by the same number of years of service that the existing property has experienced.

Some of the methods which are used to determine the value of property will now be considered.

HISTORICAL COST LESS DEPRECIATION

The first method which might be used is sometimes called *historical cost less depreciation*. In arriving at value by this method, one considers the actual expenses which have been incurred in obtaining the property being valued. This historical cost is then reduced by the amount of depreciation that appears to have occurred. This depreciation must be considered in terms of the ability of the present property to render service. The depreciated historical cost is then taken as the true value.

It is apparent that the historical-cost method neglects many factors. For example, no consideration is given to advances in technological methods which have occurred since the property was acquired. It is obvious that if an equivalent plant could be built, using modern methods and equipment, which would render the future service at much less unit cost, the existing plant could never be worth more than the more modern plant, regardless of how much might have been expended in acquiring the old plant.

The historical-cost method also gives no consideration to changes in price levels which have taken place since the time of original construction. Drastic changes in price have sometimes made it possible to build a new plant at much less cost than was required for the old plant. It is apparent that such a factor should not be neglected in determining value.

Another serious objection to the historical-cost method is that no consideration is given to the fact that the owners may have made unwise decisions and investments in the old property. Such a situation implies that unwise expenditure in acquiring the property adds to its second-hand value. This condition, of course, is absurd.

REPRODUCTION-COST-NEW LESS DEPRECIATION

In order to overcome the weaknesses of the historical cost method, the fictitious equivalent plant or property is usually assumed to be obtained by building it by the most modern methods, according to most efficient design. This theoretical plant is then depreciated until it would be capable of rendering only the same amount of future service as the existing plant. This method is often called *reproduction-cost-new less depreciation*. In this manner, technological progress and changes in price level are given consideration.

The results of this method are of obvious advantage to the seller of industrial property when price levels have risen; consequently, it gained considerable favor during the period of 1900–1930. The method, however, does not consider whether the existing property is of correct size for actual future demand or whether it is the result of unwise investment policy. The question also remains of whether or not the owners should be given full advantage of increases in price levels which may have occurred.

PRUDENT INVESTMENT

Numerous persons believe that all the owners should be entitled to receive for any industrial property is the total that was "prudently" invested in the property less the depreciation which has taken place. It is apparent that prospective profits do not enter into value determinations when this theory is applied. The Constitution and the Supreme Court of the United States have protected property *value* rather than actual *investment*. However, some regulating bodies appear to be swinging toward the prudent investment principle when establishing value for rate bases. The general argument behind such a trend is that the public should not pay more for a service than a fair return upon what has been prudently invested to provide this service. Where an enterprise is dependent upon the favor of the public for its existence and profits, the prudent-investment theory has considerable merit. It will not be surprising if this theory gains wider favor among regulating bodies, and even the courts.[10]

It is apparent that, regardless of which theory of valuation is applied, a great amount of judgment must be exercised in determining what depreciation has taken place, or just what the ability of the property to render service may be. It is thus easy to understand why the Supreme Court has held that all the factors and the testimony of competent experts must be considered.

SUPREME COURT DECISIONS

Since valuation figures are often involved in legal litigation, it is well to examine briefly some of the decisions of the Supreme Court regarding these matters.

Smyth vs. Ames, 1898, 18 Sup. Ct. Rep. 418. In this early case involving valuation, the Supreme Court established a number of principles which have stood as the basis for many later decisions. These were

[1] What a company is entitled to ask is a fair return upon the value of that which it employs for the public convenience.

[2] The public is entitled to demand . . . that no more be exacted from it . . . than the services rendered . . . are reasonably worth.

[3] In order to ascertain the fair value (all factors) are . . . matters for consideration, and are to be given such weight as may be just and right in each case.

These principles have been referred to in many cases where the court has decided what value should be assigned to property which is involved in rate cases.

City of Knoxville vs. Knoxville Water Co., 1909, 29 Sup. Ct. Rep. 148. In this case the court held that accrued depreciation must be subtracted in

[10] It is interesting to note that most advocates of the prudent-investment principle do not discuss the application of this theory to a situation where, despite the most prudent investment, property values have declined. Thus the owner is apparently expected to stand any decline in value which may have occurred, despite his greatest care and honesty, but is not allowed to profit by increases in value.

determining value and that the owners have a right to fair prices which will allow a fair net return after the cost of depreciation has been deducted.

Minnesota Rate Cases, 1913, 230 U. S. 352. The court denied the use of fixed formulas for determining value in the following statement:

The ascertainment of . . . value is not controlled by artificial rules. It is not a matter of formulas, but there must be a reasonable judgment having its basis in a proper consideration of all relevant facts.

McCardle et al. vs. Indianapolis Water Co., 1926, 47 Sup. Ct. Rep. 144.

It is well established that values of utility's properties fluctuate, and that the owners must bear the decline and are entitled to the increase. . . . But this does not mean that the original cost or the present cost or some figure arbitrarily chosen between these two is to be taken as the measure. The weight to be given to such cost figures and other items or classes of business is to be determined by the facts of the case involved.

Los Angeles Gas and Electric Corp. vs. Railroad Commission of California et al., 1933, 53 Sup. Ct. Rep. 637.

This court has further declared that, in order to determine present value, the cost of reproducing the property is a relevant fact which should have appropriate consideration.

All of these decisions may be summed up in two conclusions:
1. There is no fixed method of determining depreciation and value.
2. In determining value all factors must be considered. Among these are
   a. First cost.
   b. Condition of the structure.
   c. Actual depreciation.
   d. Increase or decrease of price levels.

INTANGIBLE VALUES

In determining the value of industrial property or equipment, four intangible items are often encountered. The first of these is *good will*. This item arises out of the public or trade favor which an enterprise may have earned through the service it has rendered. This may be of very real value to the business. In the sale of a structure, good will is a legitimate item and is of value to the buyer. In establishing value for rate setting, however, little if any consideration is given to this item. In this case, good will must have come through the business done with the consumers. The courts do not allow good will to be included, since this would require the consumers to pay the utility a profit upon something which they have bestowed upon the business.

The second intangible item is value of *franchises*. This is also granted to the utility by the consumers. Therefore it can not be considered in rate cases. Where value is being determined for sale purposes, franchises have a real value to the buyer and may be considered.

The fact that an enterprise which is actually doing business is worth more than a similar one which possesses the same physical assets, but is not operating, is recognized in *going value*. Money must be spent to get the business into an operating condition. The courts recognize this fact and allow this item to be included in all valuation work. As a rule, from 8 to 15 per cent of the value of the assets is allowed for going value.

The fourth intangible is *organization cost*. Some money must be spent in organizing almost any business and arranging for its financing and building. These are legitimate expenses and are recognized as such by the courts.

PHYSICAL LIFE FROM MORTALITY DATA

Throughout this chapter it has been pointed out that probably the most difficult problem in connection with depreciation is the determination of the life which an asset may be expected to have. It obviously would be desirable to have a better method for determining probable life than estimating or guessing. For some types of properties, under certain conditions, well-established statistical techniques can be used. It must be pointed out, however, that these techniques can be applied in a very limited number of cases. Where functional depreciation and technological progress are important parts of the total depreciation, such procedures are of little help.

Just as human beings are born, live, grow old, and die, physical properties are produced, put into service, render service, and are removed from use. The same procedures that are used to determine the probable mortality, average life, and life expectancy for human beings may also be used for determining and estimating the life that may be expected from physical property, *provided certain conditions exist*. These basic conditions are

1. A sufficient number of basically identical units must be involved so that averages may be used.
2. The service conditions must be the same for future units as for those for which the mortality data were obtained.
3. The study period must be long enough to assure valid data.

TABLE 5–7   Life Tables for White Males in the United States: 1939–1941

Age	Number Surviving	Age	Number Surviving	Age	Number Surviving	Age	Number Surviving	Age	Number Surviving
0	100,000	20	92,293	40	86,880	60	67,787	80	19,860
1	95,188	21	92,098	41	86,434	61	66,060	81	17,383
2	94,724	22	91,893	42	85,855	62	64,274	82	15,042
3	94,474	23	91,697	43	85,440	63	62,351	83	12,855
4	94,295	24	91,461	44	84,885	64	60,370	84	10,841
5	94,150	25	91,241	45	84,285	65	58,305	85	9,013
6	94,020	26	91,019	46	83,639	66	56,157	86	7,382
7	93,904	27	90,796	47	82,943	67	53,925	87	5,950
8	93,796	28	90,568	48	82,193	68	51,610	88	4,717
9	93,697	29	90,334	49	81,387	69	49,214	89	3,675
10	93,601	30	90,092	50	80,521	70	46,739	90	2,812
11	93,508	31	89,841	51	79,591	71	44,190	91	2,112
12	93,413	32	89,579	52	78,594	72	41,572	92	1,556
13	93,314	33	89,305	53	77,525	73	38,894	93	1,124
14	93,208	34	89,017	54	76,380	74	36,166	94	796
15	93,089	35	88,713	55	75,156	75	33,404	95	552
16	92,956	36	88,391	56	73,851	76	30,627	96	375
17	92,809	37	88,049	57	72,461	77	27,858	97	249
18	92,649	38	87,685	58	70,988	78	25,123	98	162
19	92,477	39	87,296	59	69,430	79	22,448	99	103
								100	65

Studies of mortality data for human beings have been conducted for many years and form the basis for all life insurance. Table 5–7 shows the mortality statistics for 100,000 white males during the years 1939–1941. From these data the curves shown in Figure 5–2 were drawn. The survivor curve is a direct plot of the data given in Table 5–7. From this curve the average life for the group was obtained by dividing the area under the curve by the original ordinate. Thus the average life for the group of 100,000 white males is 62.81 years. The probable life curve was obtained by treating that portion of the survivor curve to the right of any *attained* age in the same manner (dividing the area to the right by the number who had attained the age), in order to determine the *additional* years which the group, *on the average,* could be expected to live and then adding this

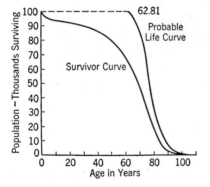

Figure 5–2.   Survivor and probable life curves for white males.

number to the attained age. Thus the probable life curve shows to what age those who had attained any certain age might, on the average, expect to live.

It is evident that if this type of data and curves can be obtained for physical property, the desired average life can be determined. Such data are available for certain properties. Table 5–8, for example, gives mortality data

TABLE 5–8   Mortality of Electric Lamps: Probable Life Curve

Life in hours	Lamps in service	Expectancy	Probable life
1,999.5	0	0	1,999.5
1,899.5	755	50.0	1,949.5
1,799.5	1,897	89.8	1,889.3
1,699.5	4,237	112.5	1,812.0
1,599.5	7,559	141.1	1,740.6
1,499.5	11,334	177.2	1,676.7
1,399.5	15,637	214.9	1,614.4
1,299.5	20,620	250.5	1,550.0
1,199.5	26,131	287.4	1,486.9
1,099.5	31,969	325.8	1,425.3
999.5	37,857	367.5	1,367.0
899.5	43,745	411.2	1,310.7
799.5	49,483	457.7	1,257.2
699.5	54,994	506.8	1,206.3
599.5	59,977	560.6	1,160.1
499.5	64,280	619.7	1,119.2
399.5	68,055	682.5	1,082.0
299.5	71,377	748.5	1,048.0
199.5	73,717	823.1	1,022.6
99.5	74,859	909.8	1,009.3
−0.5	75,614	1,000.2	999.7

for electric lamps, and Figure 5–3 shows the survivor and probable life curves for these lamps. Note that the average life of the entire group is shown (approximately 1,000 hours) and the expectancy (500 hours) of lamps having attained an age of 700 hours, giving a probable life for these lamps of 1,200 hours.

MORTALITY CURVES BY THE INDIVIDUAL-UNIT METHOD

The simplest method for compiling life experience data of a given type of physical property is to record the age in years of each individual unit of property of that class as it goes out of service. This is known as the *individual-unit method* of mortality table compilation. When a large number of such individual lives have thus been recorded, the data can be summarized and presented as shown in Table 5–7.

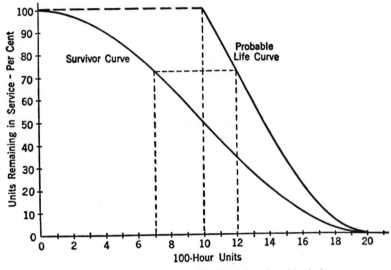

Figure 5–3. Survivor and probable life curves for electric lamps.

While this method is simple, it requires that a substantial number of identical units be placed in service at the same time, and the results can not be obtained until all of the units have been removed from service. This frequently would require a considerable number of years. With railway ties telephone poles, electric cable, and similar physical units, this method would call for continuing the experiment until—in all probability—the need for the results had passed. Further, design practices change, and the data finally obtained would picture equipment no longer representative. On this account, it is customary to gather data on material of all ages at one time for a period of appropriate length, often several years. The annual rates of replacement are used to derive the desired mortality tables and curves. Thus the *annual-rate method* is obtained.

MORTALITY CURVES BY THE ANNUAL-RATE METHOD

To obtain mortality curves by the annual-rate method, it is necessary to have in service a considerable number of substantially identical units of all possible ages—zero up to the oldest on record. A study period is then selected, usually three to five years.[6] During each year of the study period a record is kept of all removals from service. These are tabulated according to their age at the time of removal. Thus, for each year it can be determined what per cent of the total number of units in service were removed at age 1,

[6] A single year sometimes is used, but a longer period is desirable in order to assure that representative results are obtained.

2, 3, . . . *n*. At the end of the study period the values are averaged so as to give the mortality data for an average year. These data show what percentage of all units attain and are removed at each possible age, and thus give the information necessary for plotting survivor curves. The desired mortality information is obtained in a relatively short period and can be applied to those units remaining in service or to new ones to be placed in service, *so long as the service conditions do not change*.

LIMITATIONS IN THE USE OF MORTALITY DATA

In the preceding discussion it has been pointed out that mortality data are obtained for specific units in service under certain specific conditions. It is apparent that they can be applied with validity only to the same type of units which will be subjected to the same service conditions. This places very severe limitations upon the use of such data for determining life for depreciation purposes. There are relatively few physical properties which, because of technological advances or changed service requirements, are not considerably changed with the passage of time. For example, a 1960-model automobile is vastly different from a 1950-model of the same make. Therefore it can not be expected that mortality data for 1950-automobiles can be applied to 1960-cars for the same service conditions. Likewise, service conditions frequently change. If a new engine lathe made in 1935 were subjected to typical 1955 operating conditions, its life would be much different from that predicted by mortality data obtained under 1935 conditions. Therefore, it is apparent why relatively few statistically valid mortality data are available. Furthermore, considerable caution should be exercised in using available data, to make certain the units and conditions are the same as those for which the data were obtained.

It should be pointed out that a considerable amount of the mortality data published in handbooks and other sources is not based on actual statistical studies, but only on someone's estimate or personal experience.

While mortality data can not be used for most types of property, they are very useful for a number of items such as wooden telephone and power-line poles, railroad ties, telephone cable, and electric lamps. Where such data are available and apply, they certainly should be used.

LIFE CHARACTERISTICS AND RENEWAL RATE
FOR FILAMENT ELECTRIC LAMPS

Mortality curves sometimes serve not only to indicate the life which can be expected from equipment, but also to help in determining when it

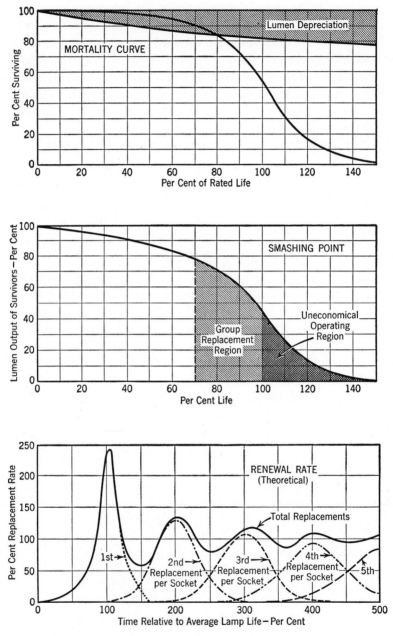

Figure 5–4. Mortality data for electric lamps, for replacement use.

132

should be replaced in order to avoid failure and to achieve economy. Figure 5–4 shows such curves supplied by an electric lamp manufacturer.[7] The company states in introducing the curves that they are based upon hundreds of thousands of lamps which are life-tested annually. The *Mortality Curve* shows separately depreciation caused by the evaporation of the filament throughout the life of the lamp, which decreases its power input, and concurrently the output of light, measured in lumens. On the same figure is shown the mortality curve for the lamps themselves to the point of burn-out. In most uses of lamps the vital consideration is the amount of light provided by the lamp. Hence, a combination of these two curves provides the next curve, entitled *Smashing Point,* showing the mortality of lumens delivered by the lamps throughout their lives. The area under the curve represents total lumen-hours provided; the per cent life is translated into hours. Whereas the lives for different lamps can be designed from a small fraction of one hour up to 3,000 hours or more, typical values are 750 hours, 1,000 hours, 1,500 hours, or 2,000 hours.

With the data provided in these two figures, it is possible to undertake determination of the most economical method of replacement. It will be noted, for example, that at 70 per cent of rated life, 90 per cent of the lamps are still in service. The output of light has dropped, however, to somewhat less than 80 per cent. It may be desirable at this point to start replacement by groups. On the other hand, it may be that the intention of the manufacturer is to present a curve which shows at 100 per cent of life the economical point for replacing the entire group of lamps. The third figure shows what would happen in the renewal rate if each lamp were replaced at burn-out. It will be noted that the variation in life of the lamps calls for few replacements at the beginning, and at 100 per cent of lamp life, a peak which is approximately 250 per cent of an average replacement rate to be reached in time. With successive replacements, the curve approaches more and more closely the 100 per cent line for replacement. The manufacturer suggests in the "smashing point" curve that at 100 per cent of the rated life the remaining lamps should be discarded, since their further operation is uneconomical. While the curve for renewal is a theoretical one, practice does not show very large variations from it, especially after several renewals have taken place. If the light is to exceed a predetermined minimum, it is clear that this is the point for replacement.

---

[7] From G. E. Lamp Bulletin LD 1, October, 1950, issued by the General Electric Company, Engineering Division, Lamp Department, Cleveland, Ohio.

CONCLUSION

The primary purpose of depreciation is to provide for recovery of capital that has been invested in physical property. It is a cost of production wherever production causes property to decline in value. Indirectly, it affords a method of providing capital for replacement of depreciated equipment.

Since most businesses are not directly affected by Supreme Court decisions as to their methods of determining depreciation, a simple formula, which gives results that are as accurate as the estimated values used, is desirable. The straight-line formula meets this need insofar as accounting is concerned and is favored by the income tax authorities. The usefulness and need of more complicated methods is questionable, except in making estimates of future profits. For this type of work, it is desirable that the sinking fund method be used in order to give satisfactory results.

The functional element is so great in modern industrial depreciation that it would seem advisable to devote considerable attention to making certain that depreciation methods provide adequately for this factor. Adequate yet reasonable depreciation charges are of more importance than refined methods based upon debatable hypotheses. Regardless of what method is used, it is important that the results be examined periodically, so that the computed values will not be at variance with obvious facts. When the theoretical values are found to be different from actual values, the theoretical figures should be adjusted. Failure to do this can result only in trouble.

The process of valuation is usually an attempt either to make an estimate of the present value of the future profits which will be obtained through ownership of a property or to determine what would have to be spent to obtain a property capable of rendering, at least as efficiently, the same future service as the property being valued. While the former is probably the correct process from a theoretical viewpoint, the latter procedure is encountered in most valuation work.

While all factors should be considered in arriving at a correct value, the weight to be given to each can not be arbitrarily established. What is just and proper in one case may be unjust and improper in another. All must be decided in the light of the circumstances and in accordance with good judgment.

PROBLEMS

5–1 Which types of value are most commonly encountered in connection with depreciation

5–2 Why is market value not necessarily a good measure of the present worth of the profits that are expected to be received through ownership?

5–3 Explain the difference between salvage value and scrap value.

5–4 Explain how the engineer may affect physical and functional depreciation.

5–5 Explain why the concept of value, as the present worth of future profits, can not be used to determine rate base value.

5–6 Explain why the use of straight-line depreciation, unmodified, in an economy study, does not produce accurate results.

5–7 What are the two basic purposes of depreciation?

5–8 Two companies purchased identical pieces of equipment costing $1,000 and estimated to have no salvage or scrap value. Company A used the Matheson depreciation method, with $k = 0.25$. Company B used the sum-of-the-years'-digits method with an estimated life of five years. Compute the depreciation cost for each company for the third year and determine which company had the higher book value at the end of the third year.

5–9 An asset cost $50,000 and is being depreciated by the sum-of-the-years'-digits method, using an estimated life of ten years. How much more will be in the "Reserve for Depreciation" account at the end of five years than if the straight-line procedure had been used?

5–10 The Grover company requires that all assets costing less than $50,000 be written off in five years or less in economy studies. Using a 10% interest rate and the sinking fund method, what would be the minimum annual depreciation charge for a $30,000 item which has an estimated life of eight years?

5–11 An asset, purchased for $10,000, had a trade-in value of $8,000 at the end of the first year, $6,400 at the end of the second year, $5,120 at the end of the third year, $4,096 at the end of the fourth year, and $3,277 at the end of the fifth year. Using a 10% interest rate, determine:

a. the depreciation during each of the years.

b. the interest upon the unrecovered investment each year.

c. the annual cost of depreciation plus interest on the unrecovered investment, using the capital recovery factor, for the five-year period. Compare the last result with the uniform annual year-end amount, which is equivalent to depreciation plus interest.

5–12 A company purchased a machine for $3,000 and sold it at the end of five years for $800. For a profit of 10%, what was the equivalent annual capital recovery plus profit on the investment?

5–13   A mine cost $800,000 to purchase and develop. It is expected that all of the ore will be removed at a uniform rate over a ten-year period. If a return of 10% on the invested capital is desired, what must be the annual charge for depletion plus profit?

5–14   A building was built larger than necessary for immediate needs, at a first cost of $750,000. It was expected to last fifty years at which time it would have a scrap value of $35,000. The income for the first twenty years was estimated to be $150,000 per year, and the operation and maintenance expense $120,000 per year. During the last thirty years, the income is expected to be $225,000 per year and the operation and maintenance $170,000 per year. Using an 8% interest rate, determine the salvage value at the end of twenty years; use the present-worth formula.

5–15   Mr. Jones purchased an automobile for $3,100, kept it for four years, and then sold it for $600. During this time he drove the car 60,000 miles. Assuming his capital to be worth 4%, determine the annual cost for depreciation and interest. What was the cost per mile for these two items?

5–16   For tax purposes, one state values automobiles at the following percentages of the first cost at the end of each year:

Year	Per cent
1	85
2	70
3	55
4	40
5	30
6	25
7	15
8	10
9 or more	5

Determine the value of k which would give the same value at the end of nine years by using the Matheson formula as obtained by the above table. Determine the maximum difference that would result between the values determined by the table and the Matheson formula.

5–17   Ten years ago a company purchased a building for $40,000, and it has been writing off depreciation on a straight-line basis using an estimated life of forty years. It now needs to move to a similar building in a different location and finds that the new building will cost $60,000 and the old one can be sold for $20,000. How much new capital will be required to purchase the new building, assuming that the money which has been set aside as depreciation expense is available?

5–18   a. In a period of declining price levels, which method of valuation would a public utility be more likely to prefer, the historical-cost method or the prudent-investment method?

   b. Would the same be true in times of increasing price levels?

5–19   The mortality statistics on certain telephone cable are as follows:

Years in use	Per cent displaced each year	Years in use	Per cent displaced each year
1	0.4	16	7.1
2	0.8	17	6.5
3	1.5	18	5.4
4	1.9	19	5.0
5	2.1	20	4.1
6	2.9	21	3.4
7	3.4	22	2.6
8	4.0	23	2.4
9	4.5	24	1.9
10	5.1	25	1.4
11	5.3	26	1.1
12	5.9	27	0.5
13	6.5		
14	7.0		
15	7.3		

Assume a given installation consists of 100 miles of 50-pair cable costing $1,200 per 1,000 feet in place.

a. Assume 12 per cent of the installation to be fifteen years old. Find its expectancy and present value, using both the sinking fund and straight-line methods. (Use 3% interest, compounded quarterly.)

b. If life for all cable is taken arbitrarily at eighteen years, what is the present value of the 12 per cent which is fifteen years old? Use both the sinking fund and straight-line methods.

CHAPTER 6

Financing
Engineering
Enterprises

Since capital is an important factor in nearly all engineering projects, the methods of obtaining it and the accompanying costs must be considered in most economy studies. Engineers have sometimes taken the position that the problem of obtaining the requisite capital should be left to the bankers and financiers. Unfortunately the problem can not be dealt with quite so easily. When considering ordinary materials, the details of obtaining them may be left to the purchasing agent, but the engineer must take into account their cost and the limitations that their properties impose on his designs. In the same way, not all capital costs the same, and the various sources and means of obtaining it impose certain requirements and restrictions on its use. A perfectly sound and proper project may be impossible to carry out because funds are not obtainable. Many well-engineered projects have failed because of improper or costly financing. It is therefore desirable for the engineer to have some understanding of the possible ways in which business enterprises may be financed, so that the advantages and disadvantages may be taken into account in economy studies.

In our capitalistic economy, the capital for most enterprises is obtained from private individuals. Some operations are financed by obtaining the capital from governmental agencies: federal, state, or local. This is becoming increasingly common in the case of very large engineering projects.[1] In a later chapter governmentally financed projects will be considered. In this chapter various methods of private financing will be discussed.

[1] It should be noted that in the Communist or so-called noncapitalistic countries capital has not been eliminated. The ownership of all capital has been assumed by the state.

138

OWNERSHIP AND BORROWED CAPITAL

Capital funds may be classified broadly into two types. *Ownership funds* are those furnished by the owners of an enterprise. They are frequently called *equity funds* or *equity capital*. These funds are supplied primarily by individuals out of savings, by corporations out of capital recovered through depreciation or profits retained and invested in the business, or by governmental agencies through taxation. This type of capital is ventured in the hope of making a profit in the case of private enterprise, or of providing for a required service in the case of a governmental activity. There is no guarantee that a profit will be obtained, or even that the capital will be recovered. Likewise, there are no limitations placed upon the use of the funds except the wishes of the owners.

While equity capital has many obvious advantages, there usually is a practical limit to the amount that can be obtained for a particular venture. In addition, there are at times certain advantages to be gained from the use of *borrowed capital*. When funds are borrowed, the borrower usually gives some type of security in order to assure that the money will be repaid. In some cases, however, there is no security except the good reputation of the borrower. In addition, he agrees to pay a specified rate of interest and to repay the funds at a definite time.

Obviously, when borrowed funds are used, the borrower must make certain that he can pay the interest whenever due and be prepared to repay the funds when the specified time arrives. These requirements place some limitations on the uses to which such funds can be put.

INDIVIDUAL OWNERSHIP

The simplest form of business organization for providing and utilizing capital is individual ownership. As a simple example, the bootblack on the corner requires only a few dollars to establish himself in business. What he needs he usually will obtain by saving. When he has saved a sufficient amount, he can establish himself in business. He alone has provided the capital, and he is the sole owner of the enterprise. Whatever benefits accrue, financial or otherwise, belong to him. Any financial reverses which may occur he must assume. Thus this individual ownership form of financing is simple and direct.

Most small businesses are financed in this manner through the savings of the owner. Funds for expansion ordinarily are accumulated from the earnings of the business. It is a fairly satisfactory method for small enterprises and has worked as well for a few very large concerns. There are, however, some drawbacks to its usefulness. First, the amount of equity capital which can be accumulated is limited. Secondly, the life of the enterprise is determined by the life of the owner. In case of his death, all the financial obligations of the business become due and the business usually has to be reorganized. Moreover, because of the uncertainty as to the life of the enterprise, it is very difficult to obtain any money for long-term expansion through loans from ordinary lending agencies. For these reasons the individual ownership form of financing is seldom used for other than very small businesses.

THE PARTNERSHIP

One obvious solution to the limited amount of capital which ordinarily can be raised through individual ownership is for two or more persons to become partners and pool their resources so that the required capital will be obtained. This method was used to a great extent in this country during the nineteenth century.

The partnership has a number of advantages. It is bound by few legal requirements as to its accounts, procedures, tax forms, and other items of operation. Dissolution of the partnership may take place at any time by mere agreement of the partners with practically no consideration of outside persons. It provides an easy method whereby two persons of differing talents may enter into business, each carrying those burdens which he can best handle; this is often the case where one partner is a technician and the other a salesman.

The partnership, however, has four serious disadvantages. First, the amount of capital that can be accumulated is definitely limited. Second, the life of the partnership is determined by the life of the individual partners. When *any* partner dies, the partnership automatically ends. Third, there may be serious disagreement among the individual partners. Fourth, each member of the partnership is liable for all the debts of the partnership. This particular disadvantage is one of the most serious.

THE CORPORATION

The corporation is a form of organization that was originated to avoid as many as possible of the disadvantages of the individual and partnership forms of ownership. A corporation is a fictitious being, recognized by law, which can engage in almost any type of business transaction in which a real person could occupy himself. It operates under a charter which is granted by a state, most states requiring three or more persons to sign the charter application and be interested stockholders. It enjoys certain privileges, important among which is perpetual life without regard to any change in the person of its owners, the stockholders. In payment for these privileges and the enjoyment of legal entity, the corporation is subject to certain restrictions. It is limited in its field of action by the provisions of its charter, which define the activities in which it may engage. In order to enter new fields of enterprise, it must apply for a revision of its charter or obtain a new one. Special taxes are also assessed against it.

The capital of a corporation is acquired through the sale of stock. The purchasers of the stock are part-owners of the corporation and its assets. In this manner the ownership may be spread throughout the entire world, and as a result enormous sums of capital can be accumulated. The ultimate example of this type of organization is the American Telephone and Telegraph Company, which has common stock with a par value of over $6,200,-000,000 owned by over 1,492,000 stockholders. No single stockholder owns as much as one per cent of the total stock. With few exceptions, the stockholders of a corporation, while they are the owners and entitled to share in the profits, are not liable for the debts of the corporation. They are thus never compelled to suffer any loss beyond the value of their stock. As the life of a corporation is continuous, long-term investments can be made and the future faced with some degree of certainty.

The widespread ownership that is possible in corporations usually results in the responsibility for operation being delegated by the owners to a group of hired managers. Frequently the management may own very little or no stock in the corporation. At the same time, the stockholders may exercise little or no influence in the running of the corporation and may be interested only in the annual dividends that they receive. As a result, the management sometimes tends to make decisions on the basis of what is best for them rather than what is best for the stockholders.

Certificates are issued as evidence of stock-ownership. Actual proof of ownership is shown only on the record books of the corporation. In most states stock certificates are not negotiable in the strict legal sense, although they may be treated as such in commercial practice.

The value of stock is expressed in several ways. Frequently a value is stated on the stock certificates. This is called the *par value* and ordinarily is approximately what the stock first sold for when marketed. Actually such stated par value may have little relationship to the real value of the stock, which must be measured by what can be obtained from ownership of it. As a result, many stocks have no stated par value and are known as *no-par-value* stocks. *Market value* is the price a willing buyer will pay a willing seller for the stock. It may be less or more than the par value, depending on the earnings of the business, the value of the property owned by it, and general market and business conditions. It is, of course, a reflection of what the investing public believes will be received through ownership of the stock. *Book value* is determined by subtracting the corporation's debts from its assets to obtain its net worth and then dividing this net worth by the number of shares of stock outstanding. This assumes that the stock is all of one type. There are a number of types of stock, but two of these are of major importance. These two are common and preferred stocks

COMMON STOCK

Common stock represents ordinary ownership without special guarantees of return. Its ownership usually grants to the stockholder the rights to

1. Vote at stockholders' meetings.
2. Elect directors and delegate to them power to conduct the affairs of the business.
3. Sell or dissolve the corporation.
4. Make and amend the bylaws of the corporation.
5. Subject to state approval, amend, or change the charter or capital structure.
6. Participate in the profits.
7. Have reasonable access to corporate records.

Common stock represents ownership of a portion of the corporation's assets, and the stockholder has a claim on a certain percentage of the net worth of the corporation at all times. While the corporation is a going concern, he receives a portion of the profits which may have resulted from operations. In case of failure of the business, he is entitled to share in what remains of the corporation's assets after all legitimate debts have been paid. An increase in the outstanding common stock results in increasing working capital for the corporation but does not set up fixed obligations that must be met from earnings, since no return is guaranteed to the common stockholders. The ownership is usually spread over more persons by such an increase, but the new owners must look to net earnings for their reward.

A rather recent development is the sale of nonvoting common stock. This stock usually carries all the rights of ordinary common stock except the privilege of voting at stockholders' meetings. This type of stock is ordinarily issued when a new company is being organized. The organizers of the company, usually a small group, wish to obtain additional capital without relinquishing any control over the affairs of the company. Such stock is obviously not of as great value as ordinary common stock. The holders have been guaranteed neither return nor power to exercise any control over the affairs of the company in which they have invested their funds.

Nonvoting preferred stock is sometimes issued for a similar purpose. In this case, however, the stockholders have a definite rate of return promised to them.

A few old and respectable companies have sold nonvoting stock to obtain additional capital. In these cases the dividend-paying policies of the companies were well established. The investors had great confidence in the officers of the companies and were willing to invest their savings without having any voice in the management.

Since the value of common stock must be a measure of the earnings that will be received through ownership of the stock, it is dependent upon several factors. However, these can probably all be summed up under two headings—dividends and market price. The market price will be affected by dividends as well as by general business conditions, future prospects of the corporation, the general money market, and the investing public's fancy. In addition, it may be drastically altered by speculation, which may bring about a market price that is in no way a true measure of the actual worth of the stock. Likewise, the mere payment of a large dividend is not proof that the stock has great value. Corporations have the unfortunate habit of suddenly failing to make their dividend payments, doing this too often on those stocks which have paid abnormally large returns. If the corporation does a consistently profitable business and is well managed, the holder of common stock will likely realize a handsome return on his investment. If this is not the case, he may not only fail to get any profit but may also lose part or all of his capital. Since common stocks represent ownership of real property, their value is affected by changes in the general price level. Thus, during times of inflation their value rises.

Because of the possible fluctuations in value, common stocks are considered to be somewhat speculative—the degree being dependent upon the particular stock and the past record of the corporation.

PREFERRED STOCK

Preferred stock also represents ownership, but the owner has certain additional privileges and restrictions not assigned to the holder of common stock. Preferred stockholders are guaranteed a definite dividend on their stock, usually a percentage of its par value, before the holders of the common stock may receive any return. In case of dissolution of the corporation, the assets must be used to satisfy the claims of the preferred stockholders before those of the holders of the common stock. Preferred stockholders usually have voting rights, but not always. Occasionally they are granted certain special privileges, such as the election of special representatives on the board of directors, if their preferred dividends are not paid for a specified period.

Because the dividend rate is fixed, preferred stock is a more conservative investment than common stock. For the same reason, the market value of such stock is less likely to fluctuate. In some corporations the preferred stockholders are permitted to share in the profits beyond their guaranteed returns if the dividends on the common stock exceed a prescribed amount. This, however, is not the usual case.

BONDS

There comes a time in the life of most corporations when there is a need for more working capital. This need might be met by selling more stock. However, this would spread the ownership over more people and thus thin the equity of the original owners. To obtain additional capital and at the same time keep the ownership intact, it is desirable to borrow money from some source at a fixed rate of interest, pledging some of the corporation's assets as security. Such action, of course, puts the corporation in debt. However, if through the use of capital costing only 4 to 6% a profit of 10 to 15% can be made, it would undoubtedly be a wise business transaction to borrow the needed capital. Before embarking on such a course, however, one should always remember that once the debt is incurred fixed costs in the form of interest must be paid, regardless of whether or not the venture is successful. In addition, the debt must someday be repaid.

If the additional capital is needed for only a short time, it will usually be obtained through signing a note at a bank or other lending agency. The note is merely a promise to repay the amount borrowed, with interest, at a fixed future date. The bank may require something of tangible value as security for the loan. Such loans usually do not run for more than two years and are known as short-term notes.

If capital must be secured through short-term notes, the corporation is faced with the necessity of refinancing these loans every two years or more often. Obviously, this prevents long-range planning of operations, since there is always some uncertainty as to whether or not the needed capital will be available when required. The refinancing may also involve extra expense.

For these reasons, corporations resort to bond issues for obtaining long-term additions to working capital without thinning ownership.

A bond is essentially a long-term note, giving as security a trust deed upon certain of the corporation's assets. In return for the money loaned, the corporation promises to repay the loan and interest upon it at a specified rate. In addition, the corporation gives a deed to certain of its assets which becomes effective if it defaults in the payment of interest or principal as promised. Through these provisions the bondholder has a more stable and secure investment than does the holder of common or preferred stock. Since the bond merely represents corporate indebtedness, the bondholder has no voice in the affairs of the business as long as his interest is paid, and of course he is not entitled to any share of the profits.

Bonds are usually issued in units of from $100 to $1,000 each, in order to facilitate obtaining the desired capital from a wide source. As a rule every bond should show the following items:

1. Acknowledgment of the indebtedness for value received.
2. A promise to repay the principal and to pay a stated rate of interest until such repayment, with time, place, and method of payment of each stipulated.
3. A description of the entire bond issue of which the bond is a part.
4. A description of the security behind the bond issue.
5. A statement of the rights of the bondholder in case of default.
6. An endorsement by an authorized authority.

The amount named on the bond is known as the *face* or *par value* of the bond. This is to be repaid the lender at the end of a specified period of time. When the face value has been repaid, the bond is said to have been *retired* or *redeemed*. The interest rate quoted on the bond is called the *bond rate*.

Interest may be paid in either of two manners. The name of the owner of *registered bonds* is recorded on the record books of the corporation, and interest payments are sent to the owner as they become due without any action on his part. *Coupon bonds* have a coupon attached to the bond for each interest payment which will come due during the life of the bond. When an interest payment is due, the holder clips the corresponding coupon from the bond and can convert it into cash, usually at any bank. A registered bond thus requires no action on the part of the holder, but it is not as easily transferred to new ownership as is the coupon bond.

CLASSIFICATION OF BONDS

Bonds may be classified in many ways. Perhaps one of the best, and yet simple methods is to classify them according to the security behind them. In this grouping we have

1. *Mortgage bonds.* This is the most common type of bond. As security for the money borrowed, the corporation gives the lender a mortgage upon certain of its assets in the form of a trust deed. Title to the property never passes to the bondholders unless the corporation defaults on the payments called for in the bond. In case of default, the bondholders, through proper court orders, may obtain possession of the mortgaged property and sell it to obtain the money which was loaned and the accrued interest.

These bonds may be issued as *first mortgage* bonds, in which case the holders have first claim upon the mortgaged property. Second, third, or fourth mortgage bonds may also be issued. The claims of holders of these bonds are not satisfied until after those of the holders of prior mortgage bonds. These latter bonds are, of course, not as good an investment as the first mortgage bonds of the same corporation. They usually pay a slightly higher rate of interest and are often called *junior lien* bonds. Second or third mortgage bonds of certain corporations, however, are better and more conservative investments than the first mortgage bonds of some other corporations. The particular case must govern the rule.

Mortgage bonds may contain clauses that require the corporation to maintain the mortgaged property in a certain condition. Clauses may also prevent further mortgages upon the property. The corporation may be restricted from purchasing or disposing of any property or from issuing any additional bonds of any kind. Such clauses are desirable from the viewpoint of the bondholders but are a damper upon the activities of the corporation. They are included in order to make the bond issue more attractive to the investing public, and possibly to permit a lower interest rate.

2. *Collateral bonds.* In this type of bond the security is some form of recognized commercial collateral such as the stocks or bonds of a well-established subsidiary. Thus the security for these bonds is essentially a second mortgage upon certain assets of the subsidiary. Therefore the buyer must look to the subsidiary for his security unless the bonds contain provisions giving additional claims upon the parent company in case of default. They are usually issued only by a well-established corporation, and the reputation of the parent is of some value.

3. *Debentures.* These are in reality long-term notes, since they have no security behind them except a promise to pay. Until recently they were not

very common and were seldom used as a method of obtaining capital. In the last ten years, however, a number of large issues, some amounting to over $30,000,000, have been sold. These were issued by large corporations whose financial records were so sound and of such long standing that the investing public was willing to purchase such securities. In most cases these corporations had little or no other indebtedness, and the interest rates paid were remarkably low, usually between $3\frac{1}{2}$ and $4\frac{1}{2}\%$.

The advantages of using debentures to obtain capital are quite apparent. Long-term capital is obtained without changing ownership or acquiring mortgage restrictions. However, they seldom can be sold by other than well-established firms having a long and successful financial history.

BOND RETIREMENT

Since stock represents ownership, it is unnecessary for a corporation to make special provision for payments to the stockholders. If profits remain after the operating expenses are paid, these are divided among the stockholders. Bonds, on the other hand, represent debt, and the interest upon them is a cost of doing business. In addition to this periodic cost, the corporation must look forward to the day when the bonds become due and the principal must be repaid to the bondholders. Provision may be made for repaying the principal by two different methods.

If the business has prospered and general market conditions are good when the bonds come due, the corporation may be able to sell a new issue of bonds and use the proceeds to pay off the holders of the old issue. If conditions are right, the new issue may bear a lower rate of interest than the original bonds. If this is the case, the corporation maintains the desired capital at a decreased cost. On the other hand, if business conditions are bad when the time for refinancing arrives, the bond market may not be favorable, and it may be impossible to sell a new bond issue, or possible only at an increased interest rate. This would probably be a serious handicap to the corporation. In addition, the bondholders wish to have assurance that provision is being made so that there will be no doubt concerning the availability of funds with which their bonds will be retired. A serious weakness of this method of retirement is the fact that the corporate indebtedness is not reduced through this "borrowing from Peter to pay Paul." From their continued use of this method of financing it appears that some corporations never expect, or desire, to cease operating on borrowed capital—in other words, to get out of debt.

In most cases, however, the corporation wishes to avoid the uncertainties of the method just described and also to reduce its indebtedness and fixed expenses. Thus some systematic provision ordinarily is made for repaying the bondholders when the maturity date arrives. Such provision, planned in advance, gives assurance to the bondholders and makes the bonds more attractive to the investing public; it may also allow the bonds to be issued at a lower rate of interest.

In many cases the corporation periodically sets aside definite sums which, with the interest they earn, will accumulate to the amount needed to retire the bonds at the time they are due. Since it is convenient to have these periodic deposits equal in amount, the retirement procedure becomes a sinking fund. This is one of the most common uses of a sinking fund. By its use the bondholders know that adequate provision is being made to safeguard their investment. The corporation knows in advance what the annual cost for bond retirement will be.

If a bond issue of $100,000 in ten-year bonds, in $1,000 units, paying 6% interest in semiannual payments, must be retired by the use of a sinking fund which earns 4% compounded semiannually, the annual cost for retirement will be as follows:

From the sinking-fund formula

$$R = S/s_{\overline{n}|}$$
$$S = \$100,000$$
$$i = 4/2 = 2\% \text{ per period}$$
$$n = 2 \times 10 = 20 \text{ periods}$$

From Table XIII (Appendix)

$$s_{\overline{20}|\,(2)} = 24.2973698$$
$$R = \frac{\$100,000}{24.2973698} = \$4,115.67$$

This will be the semiannual cost for retirement. In addition, the semiannual interest on the bonds must be paid. This would be calculated as follows:

$$I = \$100,000 \times \frac{0.06}{2} = \$3,000$$
Total semiannual cost $= \$4,115.67 + \$3,000 = \$7,115.67$
Annual cost $= \$7,115.67 \times 2 = \$14,231.34$

The total cost for interest and retirement of the entire bond issue will be

$$\$7,115.67 \times 20 = \$142,313.40.$$

CALLABLE BONDS

In the problem just considered, none of the bonds were retired until the end of ten years. The money in the sinking fund earned interest at the rate of 4% compounded semiannually. At the same time, the corporation was paying 6% compounded semiannually on the money it had borrowed. It would obviously be advantageous for the company to be able to buy back its outstanding bonds with the money in the sinking fund and obtain an interest saving of 2%. Since bonds usually have a higher rate of interest than can be obtained on sinking fund deposits in a bank or in short-term investments, it is an advantage for the corporation to be able to retire bonds whenever it has money available in the sinking fund. This procedure is usually not desired by the bondholders, since they do not wish to relinquish a good bond which pays a good yield. Thus, what is advantageous for the corporation may not be desired by the bondholder. In order to make bonds which may be retired before maturity more attractive to the investor, provision is often made that a price above par will be paid if they are redeemed before the maturity date.

Bonds that contain clauses permitting repayment before maturity are known as *callable bonds*. One method is to retire a certain number of bonds each interest date, selecting the bonds to be retired by lot. Some bond issues definitely state that those having certain serial numbers will be retired at specified dates.

Now consider what saving would be effected if the bond issue cited on the previous pages had been callable. Since the interest rate on the sinking fund would be the same as the bond rate, the total semiannual cost would be

$$R + I = S\left[\frac{1}{s_{\overline{n}|}} + i\right] = S \times \frac{1}{a_{\overline{n}|}}.$$

To retire the issue in ten years

$$S = \$100,000.00$$
$$i = 6/2 = 3\% \text{ per period}$$
$$n = 10 \times 2 = 20 \text{ periods}$$

From Table XV (Appendix)

$$\frac{1}{a_{\overline{20}|(3)}} = 0.0672157$$

$$R + I = \$100,000.00 \times 0.0672157 = \$6,721.57$$

The interest which must be paid the first period is $3,000. The amount left for bond retirement would be

$$\$6,721.57 - \$3,000.00 = \$3,721.57$$

Since the bonds are in units of $1,000.00, any retirement must be in a multiple of this amount. The multiple of $1,000.00 nearest to $3,721.57 is four. Thus at the end of the first six months the bond interest would be paid, and, in addition, four $1,000.00 bonds would be retired. If a similar procedure is carried out at the end of each interest period, the results will be as shown in Table 6–1. From the $6,721.57 set aside each period, the interest

TABLE 6–1   Amortization Schedule for a $100,000 Bond Issue

Interest period	Principal	Interest at 3% per period	Number of bonds retired	Principal repaid	Total payment for period
1	$100,000	$3,000	4	$ 4,000	$ 7,000
2	96,000	2,880	4	4,000	6,880
3	92,000	2,760	4	4,000	6,760
4	88,000	2,640	4	4,000	6,640
5	84,000	2,520	4	4,000	6,520
6	80,000	2,400	4	4,000	6,400
7	76,000	2,280	4	4,000	6,280
8	72,000	2,160	5	5,000	7,160
9	67,000	2,010	5	5,000	7,010
10	62,000	1,860	5	5,000	6,860
11	57,000	1,710	5	5,000	6,710
12	52,000	1,560	5	5,000	6,560
13	47,000	1,410	5	5,000	6,410
14	42,000	1,260	5	5,000	6,260
15	37,000	1,110	6	6,000	7,110
16	31,000	930	6	6,000	6,930
17	25,000	750	6	6,000	6,750
18	19,000	570	6	6,000	6,570
19	13,000	390	6	6,000	6,390
20	7,000	210	7	7,000	7,210
				$100,000	$134,410

on the outstanding bonds is first paid. With the money remaining, as many bonds as possible are retired—using the number of bonds which have a redemption value nearest to the amount remaining. In some cases this will require slightly more than the normally provided amount and at other times less will be required. The difference will never be greater than one-half the price of the bond. Such a process of bond retirement is known as *amortization*,[2] and a tabulation like that shown in Table 6–1 is called an *amortization schedule*.

From the amortization schedule it is seen that the total cost of interest and bond retirement by this method is $134,410.00. By comparing this with $142,313.40, which was the total cost of the $100,000.00 issue of noncallable

[2] The term *amortization* may be applied to any method of extinguishing a debt, principal and interest, by a series of equal payments at equal intervals.

bonds it can be seen that the different method of retirement resulted in a saving of $7,903.40. This is almost 8% of the face value of the bond issue. The advantage of callable bonds to the corporation is thus quite apparent.

In some bond issues provision is made in the amorization schedule that no bonds will have to be retired during the first few years. This recognizes the fact that bonds usually are sold to finance long-term expansion. Such programs ordinarily involve plants or other facilities which take some time to construct and place in operation and thus will not produce profits immediately. Bond retirement is thus deferred until the facilities have an opportunity to become productive.

In some cases the issuer of noncallable bonds can obtain the advantages of callable bonds by buying back his own bonds on the open market. He, in effect, invests his sinking funds in his own bonds, thus receiving the same interest rate upon the sinking funds as the bond rate. Of course, this relationship would be exactly true only when he is able to purchase his bonds on the open market at par. Frequently he is not able to do this.

BOND VALUE

The real value of a bond, like that of any other business property, is a function of what the holder will receive in the future through his ownership. In monetary terms it is the present value of all the money he will receive in the future due to his possession of the bond. In the case of a bond let

F = face, or par, value
C = redemption or disposal price (often equal to F)
r = the bond rate per interest period
n = the number of periods before redemption
i = the investment rate per period
V_n = value of the bond n periods prior to redemption.

The owner of a bond will receive two types of payments. The first consists of the series of periodic interest payments he will receive until the bond is retired. There will be n such payments, each amounting to Fr. These constitute an annuity of n payments. In addition, when the bond is retired or sold, he will receive a single payment in amount equal to C. Since the present value of the bond is the present value of these two types of payments,

$$V_n = Cv^n + Fra_{\overline{n}|}. \tag{6.1}$$

EXAMPLE.   Find the cost (present value) of a ten-year 6% bond, interest payable semiannually, which is redeemable at par, if bought to yield 5%; par value is $1,000.

$$n = 10 \times 2 = 20 \text{ periods}$$
$$r = 6/2 = 3\% \text{ per period}$$
$$i = 5/2 = 2.5\% \text{ per period}$$
$$C = F = \$1,000$$
$$V_n = Cv^n + Fra_{\overline{n}|}$$

From Appendix Table XIV $(i = 2.5\%)$

$$v^{20} = 0.6102709$$
$$a_{\overline{20}|} = 15.5891623$$
$$V_n = \$1,000 \times 0.6102709 + 0.03 \times \$1,000 \times 15.5891623$$
$$= \$610.27 + \$467.67 = \$1,077.94$$

INVESTMENT RATE

The price which should be paid for any bond in order to obtain an investment rate of i can be determined by means of Equation (6.1). Unfortunately, one usually can not often purchase a bond at exactly the price he might like to pay but instead must pay whatever the market price happens to be. In addition, an owner frequently disposes of a bond prior to the maturity date, receiving the market price, which usually is not the par value. Thus the redemption or disposal price is not equal to F. The actual yield which the bond owner receives on his investment is thus affected by what he pays for the bond at the time of purchase and what he receives for it at the time of sale, as well as by the periodic interest payments he receives during the period of possession. Obviously, one important matter is determining what the actual yield on the investment has been.

If Equation (6.1) is written in terms of i it becomes

$$V_n = \frac{C}{(1+i)^n} + Fr\frac{(1+i)^n - 1}{i(1+i)^n}. \qquad (6.2)$$

In terms of i, this equation is of the degree $n + 1$ and therefore can not be solved for i by direct methods. It can be solved by "cut-and-try" methods or, to a fair degree of accuracy, by interpolation methods. The latter method is ordinarily of sufficient accuracy, and the results are obtained quickly.

Consider a $\$1,000$ bond which is to mature in twelve years, having a bond rate of 4% with interest payable semiannually. If the bond sells for $\$1,025$ and is to be redeemed at par, what is the actual investment rate? By using Equation (6.1), the price corresponding to various investment rates can be found. For a rate of $3\frac{1}{2}\%$ this would be as follows:

$$F = C = \$1,000$$
$$n = 12 \times 2 = 24 \text{ periods}$$
$$r = 4/2 = 2\% \text{ per period}$$
$$i = 3.5/2 = 1.75\% \text{ per period}$$

From Table XII ($i = 1.75\%$)

$$v^{24} = 0.6594380$$
$$a_{\overline{24}|} = 19.4606856$$
$$V_n = \$1,000 \times 0.6594380 + \$1,000 \times 0.02 \times 19.4606856$$
$$= \$659.44 + \$389.21 = \$1,048.65$$

In the same manner the other values shown on Figure 6–1 can be found and plotted. It can be seen that the line drawn through the various plotted points is a curve which is slightly concave upwardly. However, between any two adjacent points, it so closely resembles a straight line that straight-line interpolation between adjacent points will cause very little error.

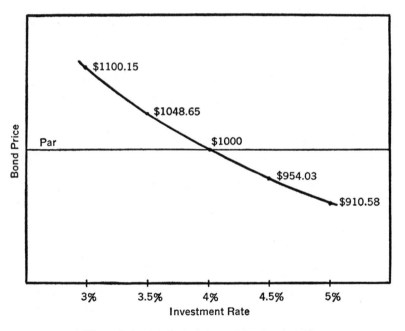

Figure 6–1. Method of determining bond yield.

For the problem being considered, the bond price lies between the prices corresponding to 4% and 3½%. This can be illustrated as follows:

Price	Investment rate (nominal)
$1,000.00	4%
1,025.00	X%
1,048.65	3½%

Therefore, by interpolation,

$$(4 - 3\tfrac{1}{2}) : (4 - X) = (1,048.65 - 1,000) : (1,025 - 1,000),$$

and

$$X = 3.74\%.$$

The results obtained by this method will be slightly greater than the true value. However, if one does not interpolate over a range greater than $\tfrac{1}{2}\%$, the error is so small that for amounts under \$100,000 it may be ignored.

A NOMOGRAM FOR BOND YIELDS

A very ingenious nomogram has been devised by A. S. Levens and P. C. Reyes which enables bond values and yields to be determined by graphical means. This chart is shown in Figure 6–2, with instructions for its use. The chart is available in a larger size, which permits yields to be determined to the nearest tenth of one per cent.

DEPRECIATION FUNDS AS A SOURCE OF CAPITAL

As was explained in Chapter 5, the funds that are set aside out of income as the cost of depreciation are usually retained in a business. These funds are available for reinvestment and must be utilized to the best advantage. They thus are an important internal source of capital for financing new projects.

Since one of the purposes of depreciation accounting is to provide for replacement of a property when required, one might conclude that depreciation funds provide only for such replacement and never for new equipment of a different type. This, however, is only partially true. In a great many instances when a particular property or piece of equipment has become of no further economic value, the function for which it was originally purchased no longer exists. Under such conditions, one does not wish to replace it with a similar piece of equipment. Instead, other needs have developed, and different equipment or property is needed. The accumulated depreciation funds may thus be used to meet the new needs.

In other instances a piece of equipment may continue to be used after its original value has been recovered through normal depreciation procedures. Here again the accumulated funds are available for other use until the original equipment must be replaced. If depreciation procedures are used which provide for the recovery of a large portion of the initial cost during the first few years of life, such as the Matheson or the SYD methods, there usually will be excess funds available before the equipment must be

$V_n = Cv^n + Fr\,A_{\overline{n}|} =$ BOND PRESENT VALUE
C = BOND REDEMPTION OR DISPOSAL PRICE IN DOLLARS
F = BOND FACE OR PAR VALUE = FIXED AT $1000.00
r = BOND RATE PER INTEREST PERIOD IN PERCENT

$v^n = 1/(1+i)^n$, $A_{\overline{n}|} = (1-v^n)/i$
i = BOND INVESTMENT RATE PER PERIOD IN PERCENT
n = NUMBER OF INTEREST PERIODS

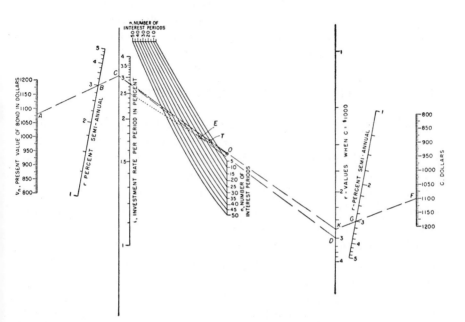

EXAMPLE 1

Find the yield on a 10 yr, 6% bond, interest payable semi-annually, redeemable at $1,000 par value, and having a present value of $1,080.

SOLUTION:

(a) Connect points A and B and locate point C.
(b) Connect points C and D. Line CD intersects curve n = 20 (20 semi-annual periods) at point E.
(c) Connect points O and E and read 2.5% on the i-scale. This value, 2.5%, is the semi-annual rate of return, or the yield is 5% per year.

EXAMPLE 2

The bond in Example 1 was held 5 years and the value of the bond at that time was $1,100. What was the yield?

SOLUTION:

(a) Locate point C as before.
(b) Connect points F and G and locate point K. Line CK intersects the curve n = 10 at point T.
(c) Join O and T and read 2.8% on the i-scale. The annual yield is 2 × 2.8% or 5.6%.

Figure 6–2. Nomogram for determining bond yields.

replaced. This is one of the reasons why companies like to use these methods of accounting for depreciation.

In effect, the depreciation funds provide a revolving investment fund which may be used to the best possible advantage. The funds are thus an important source of capital for financing new ventures within an existing enterprise. They are particularly important since, not being subject to income taxes, they are available in their entirety. Obviously the depreciation funds must be managed so that required capital is available for replacing essential equipment when the time for replacement arrives.

FINANCING THROUGH RETAINED PROFITS

Another important source of internal capital for expansion of existing enterprises is retained profits which are reinvested in the business instead of being paid to the owners. While this method of financing is used by most companies, there are three factors which tend to limit its use.

Probably the greatest deterrent is the fact that the owners (the stockholders in the case of a corporation) usually expect and demand that they receive some profits from their investment. Therefore it usually is necessary for a large portion of the profits to be paid to the owners in the form of dividends. This is essential to assure the availability of equity capital when it is needed. However, it usually is possible, and a good practice, to obtain part of needed capital for expansion by retaining a portion of the profits. Often from 10 to 50 per cent is retained. While such a retention of profits reduces the immediate amount of the dividends per share of stock, it increases the value of the stock and should also result in greater future dividends and/or resale value for the stock.

The second, and also serious, limitation on the use of retained profits is the fact that income taxes must be paid upon them and deducted from them, before they may be used. With taxes taking as much as 30 to 80 per cent of the individual's income and 52 per cent of most corporations', this severely limits the amount available after dividends and taxes have been paid.

A third, and less important deterrent, is the fact that as profits are retained and used, the total annual profits and the profits per share of stock should increase. This gives the impression that a company is able to pay higher wage rates. Such an implication frequently is used by unions in wage negotiations without acknowledging that the larger profits are due to the investment of increased amounts of capital by each shareholder through retained profits. This disadvantage may be quite easily avoided by issuing stock dividends in lieu of the retained profits, thereby maintaining a fairly constant rate of profit per share.

EQUIPMENT TRUST CERTIFICATES

The transportation industry frequently uses equipment trust certificates as a means of financing rolling stock, such as locomotives, freight and passenger cars, trucks and busses. Using this method, a financial organization, such as a bank or a trust company, purchases the equipment and then leases it to the transportation company on a lease-purchase basis. The company pays a monthly or annual "rental" for the exclusive use of the equipment. This "rental" fee includes a purchase payment plus interest on the unpaid balance. The procedure is thus a form of deferred-payment purchasing.

The financial organization may furnish the capital for purchasing the equipment directly or may sell equipment trust certificates to investors to obtain the required funds. Since title of the equipment resides in the financial house, which acts as trustee until the equipment has been fully paid for, and the transportation company must pay the use fee in order to have and operate the essential equipment, there is a reduction in risk, and capital may be obtained at a lower rate than if the transportation company were to attempt to obtain the necessary funds through direct borrowing from investors.

SALE AND LEASE-BACK OF FIXED ASSETS

Another method that sometimes is used by businesses to obtain capital for expansion involves selling certain fixed assets, such as buildings, and then leasing these assets from the new owners. In this way fixed assets are converted into cash, and, at the same time, the assets are retained for use by the business. The advantages of this procedure usually involve income tax considerations. The method will therefore be discussed in Chapter 18.

THE AVERAGE COST OF CAPITAL

Most businesses do not operate entirely on either equity capital or borrowed capital. Instead, in most instances good practice calls for most of the capital to be obtained from equity sources, a smaller portion being borrowed. To obtain the desired amount of equity capital, a sufficient rate of dividends must be maintained to make the investment attractive to investors in view of the risks involved. Because of the absence of security, the rate that must be paid for equity capital is virtually always greater than must be paid to obtain borrowed capital.

When both types of capital are used for the general financing of an enterprise, the real cost of the capital is not that paid for equity capital or for borrowed capital. Instead, it is some intermediate rate, depending upon the proportions of each type of capital used. In computing the actual cost of the capital, one must take into account the fact that the rate that must be paid to the stockholders is an after-tax rate, while no income tax is involved in the cost for obtaining borrowed capital. For example, if a corporation can obtain borrowed capital for 5% but must pay stockholders a 7% dividend and is in a 52% income tax bracket, Table 6–2 shows the true or average

TABLE 6–2   Average Cost of Capital for Various Percentages of Equity
and Borrowed Capital

Per cent of borrowed capital

	0%	10%	20%	30%	40%	50%
(a) Total capital	$10,000	$10,000	$10,000	$10,000	$10,000	$10,000
(b) Borrowed capital	0	1,000	2,000	3,000	4,000	5,000
(c) Interest	0	50	100	150	200	250
(d) Equity capital	10,000	9,000	8,000	7,000	6,000	5,000
(e) Dividends paid	700	630	560	490	420	350
(f) Profits, before taxes, to provide dividends	1,458	1,313	1,167	1,021	867	729
(g) Total cost (c) + (f)	1,458	1,363	1,267	1,171	1,067	979
(h) Average rate	14.58%	13.63%	12.67%	11.71%	10.67%	9.79%

cost of capital for various percentages of borrowed and equity capital. An examination of the cost of the equity capital as compared with the same amount of borrowed capital makes the attractiveness of financing with borrowed capital apparent. Likewise, it is apparent that the average cost of the capital employed may be considerably different from either the borrowed or equity capital cost.

In many economy studies it is clear that only borrowed capital or only owned capital will be employed. In such cases the corresponding cost of capital should be used in the calculations. In many other cases, however, general funds of the business are to be employed, and if a portion of these funds are borrowed and the remainder are obtained from equity sources, an average rate of capital cost should be computed and used.

EFFECTS OF FINANCING METHODS UPON ECONOMY

The methods by which capital is obtained may have considerable effect upon the economy of an enterprise and thus should be considered when economy studies are made. Where owned capital is available, it is possible to make the economy studies without assigning the cost of the capital directly as an expense. It is not necessary to worry about fixed financial charges to be met whether business is good or bad. At the other extreme is the case where capital can not be obtained at any reasonable cost. If capital is required but can not be obtained, the project can not be undertaken. The fact that capital can not be obtained does not necessarily mean that the project itself is not feasible and sound. A proposition that is economically sound for one person may not be so for another who does not possess the necessary capital. Thus small companies and municipalities may find that they can obtain lowest unit cost by performing certain operations by manual labor. A larger company or city might obtain lowest cost by utilizing machinery to do the same task.

For many cases falling between the two extremes mentioned in the previous paragraph, capital is obtained through some form of borrowing. In some, ordinary loans may be used. In others, bonds may be sold. In each instance, all of the costs and obligations must be carefully considered in the economy study. The following case illustrates some of the factors which must be considered.

The Blank Co., a privately owned business, has an opportunity to buy the Small Co., from which it purchases a large amount of its raw materials. The purchase price is to be $50,000. It is estimated that the Blank Co. can realize a saving of $5,000 annually from operating the Small Co. instead of having to purchase its raw materials from it. The anticipated profit of $5,000 is exclusive of any financial expense which might be involved in the transaction but includes provision for writing off the investment over a twenty-year period.

The Blank Co. does not have $50,000 available which it can use to buy the Small Co. However, it can sell a $50,000 bond issue and use the proceeds for this purpose. The bonds will be issued as twenty-year 7% bonds. Should the Blank Co. issue the bonds and buy the Small Co.?

The correct solution of this problem requires a careful consideration of the effect of the method of obtaining the required capital upon the economy of the project. This effect is best revealed by first determining what the results would be if the Blank Co. had sufficient funds available to consummate the deal without borrowing. This result is readily determined. Since there was provision for a twenty-year write-off of the investment, computed by a 7% sinking fund method, included in the determination of the $5,000 saving, this figure is the net saving which should be realized. Thus the return on the required investment of $50,000 would be 10%.

Now determine what additional expenses would be involved if bonds were issued to finance the purchase of the Small Co. In the first place, payment of the bond interest would require $3,500 annually. This would be an actual expense of operating the Small Co. if borrowed funds are used.

A second item is a consideration of the method that will be used to retire the bond issue when it becomes due. The principle of maintenance of capital requires that the Blank Co. have as much capital at the time the investment in the Small Co. is completely written off as it had when it made the investment. As far as its investment in the Small Co. is concerned, this amount of capital is *zero*. It is not using *its* capital to purchase the Small Co. Instead, it is using some other person's capital. Therefore there is no necessity for it to provide for capital maintenance on its own funds through depreciation. It is required only to repay the money which it has borrowed. In other words, it must maintain the other fellow's capital which has been entrusted to it. Thus, the amounts that were included as depreciation expense may be used to retire the bonds. Since the time provided for write-off is the same as the period of the bond issue, and the interest rates are the same, the expense of retiring the bond issue has already been included in the study and adds no additional expense. By a proper consideration of the principle of maintenance of capital, one can avoid the double write-off of investments by providing for both depreciation and retirement of borrowed funds. At the same time, one can be certain that all the legitimate expenses have been included.

If the bond-interest expense is subtracted from the saving of $5,000, the net saving, or profit, is found to be $1,500. This amount can not actually be related to the required investment to determine the percentage return on the capital outlay, since the Blank Co. really has none of its money invested in the proposition. However, in practice it should be related to the amount of borrowed capital involved in order to show the percentage of profit above the actual expense. In this case this figure is

$$\frac{\$1,500}{\$50,000} \times 100 = 3\%.$$

This means that the Blank Co. will receive a return of 3% upon the $50,000 which it has borrowed and for which it is liable. It may use this figure for comparing this project with some other it might undertake with the same borrowed funds.

A more significant fact about the figure of 3% is that if conditions change so that this profit of 3% is wiped out, the company will then lose money on the proposition. Thus, there is only a 3% margin between profit and loss. This figure becomes the one on which the decision as to investment must be based. There are few industrial projects where a prospective margin of 3% between the maximum profit and possible loss would be sufficient to justify the investment of borrowed funds. This is especially true if the pay-out period is more than a year or two. It may thus be seen that the use of borrowed capital may change the entire economy of a project. Whenever borrowed funds are to be used, it should always be remembered that a reversal of conditions may wipe out the expected profit, but the debt will still remain.

It is quite apparent that the use of borrowed capital frequently is advisable and that the advantages must be balanced against the disadvantages and hazards to determine whether such financing procedures should be used. Borrowed capital, in effect, extends the opportunities which are available to owned capital. For example, John Jones has the opportunity to purchase two small grocery stores; each requires the investment of $5,000 and each, on the basis of past experience, will produce a net profit of $2,000 per year. Mr. Jones has only $5,000 of owned capital. He can, however, borrow $5,000 at an interest rate of 6% if he wishes to do so in order to buy the second store.

If Mr. Jones uses only his owned capital, he will earn a profit of $2,000 per year, which is a return of 40% on his invested capital. If he borrows $5,000 and purchases both stores, he will incur an annual expense of $300 per year for interest but will obtain $2,000 added profit bringing the total net profit to $3,700. This would be an annual profit of 74% on *owned* capital. Thus the use of borrowed capital would greatly increase the profit potentiality of Mr. Jones' capital. However, Mr. Jones must be prepared to assume whatever risks are attendant to the indebtedness which he would incur and be ready to repay the borrowed capital at the time agreed upon. This last matter is frequently one which causes difficulty, since borrowed capital often is obtained for a shorter period than the depreciation period of the fixed assets which that capital purchases. In such cases the ordinary amounts set aside as depreciation are not sufficient to repay the borrowed capital, and, if depreciation funds are used for this purpose, one is then faced at a later date with the necessity of replacing worn-out equipment without capital being available for the purpose. Thus it is always advisable to remember that if one is to continue in business, borrowed capital can only be repaid out of profits.

As will be discussed in a later chapter, income tax provisions frequently are important in deciding upon the use of borrowed capital.

Where an undertaking is being financed by public funds, such as a municipal, state, or federal project, the money is ultimately to come from taxation. Municipal governments ordinarily issue bonds to cover each project, such as water district bonds, sewer bonds. State and federal governments, however, usually provide for the necessary capital out of fiscal appropriations. Thus in state and federal projects there is usually no attempt to provide for direct repayment of the borrowed capital out of the earnings of the project, even if it is of the self-liquidating type. Many government projects, of course, are not intended to earn direct monetary returns.

When it is necessary to issue bonds to finance some projects, it is often easier to dispose of a large amount than of a small amount of bonds. Such financing is usually done through investment bankers, who buy the entire bond issue and then sell it in small lots to the investing public at slightly higher prices. The necessary investigation and selling expenses of the investment banker are considerable. For a small amount of bonds these would be prohibitive. Studies have found that the cost of selling an issue of bonds of $50,000 or less may run as high as 22%, as compared with 10 to 16% for much larger issues.

CONSIDERING THE SOURCE OF CAPITAL IN ECONOMY STUDIES

It is often advisable to make an economy study in the usual manner, determining the possible return from the required investment, before considering the source of the required capital and its effects.[3] This is because the true merits of the project will then be known. If the proposition has definite possibilities when sufficient capital is available, one will be justified in making proper efforts to finance it in the correct manner. The effects of the source of the capital are financial matters, which should be considered as such. While they may make the undertaking not desirable, it should be definitely known that these were the limiting factors. At a later date the capital may be available, and the true economy of the project will then be known so it may be acted upon.

If capital has to be procured, all the possible methods should be con-

---

[3] This statement applies to ordinary industrial studies. If the study is for a government project, this fact may be considered at the time the study is made. This is discussed at greater length in a later chapter.

sidered and the advantages and disadvantages weighed carefully. The serious difficulty that may arise in times of depression when fixed obligations on borrowed capital must be met, probably from severely reduced revenues, should always be remembered. The attendant advantages and disadvantages of each method should be understood and used to the best advantage. Only after the effects of the source of capital have been considered can an economy study lead to a correct decision.

PROBLEMS

6-1   What are equity funds?

6-2   Explain why the market value of common stock may be higher than the book value.

6-3   Why is it easier for a corporation to borrow long-term capital than it is for a privately owned company having the same worth?

6-4   Why do people buy common stock rather than bonds as a hedge against inflation?

6-5   Explain what difference there is between the security behind a debenture and that behind a promissory note.

6-6   Following World War II most railroads financed their conversions to Diesel locomotives through the use of equipment trust certificates. Why did they use this method instead of bonds?

6-7   What degree of control does a bondholder ordinarily have over the affairs of the issuing company?

6-8   Why does preferred stock usually pay a higher rate of return than bonds of the same company?

6-9   Two brothers, each having $25,000, are forming a small corporation and need $20,000 of additional capital. Two alternative methods of obtaining the capital are available: (a) to sell $20,000 worth of common stock to a third person; (b) to borrow the required capital on a 10-year note at an interest rate of 7%. Discuss the merits of the two alternatives.

6-10 What are some of the difficulties in financing plant expansion through retained earnings?

6-11 Two companies, A and B, are attempting to obtain additional capital for expansion. Company A has 100,000 shares of common stock outstanding with a par value of $1,000,000. The stock is held by 4,000 stockholders, with no one holding more than 5% of the total. Company B is capitalized at $100,000, represented by stock held in equal amounts by 5 individuals.

  a. Discuss the problems faced by each company if it were to sell $30,000 in additional common stock to one individual.

  b. Assuming each company to be fairly profitable, would there be any advantage in selling bonds to obtain the needed capital? Why?

6-12 What price should be paid for a $1,000 bond, having a twenty-year maturity date and bearing interest at the rate of 5%, payable semi-annually, if the purchaser desires a yield of 4% nominal on his money?

6–13 A $4,000,000 issue of 4% bonds having a ten-year maturity date, with interest payable semiannually, was sold at a price to yield 3½% nominal interest. What was the selling price?

6–14 On July 1, 1959, a state sold a large number of $1,000 school bonds. Interest at the nominal rate of 3½% was to be paid by coupon on January 1 and July 1 of each year. One group of the bonds was sold to yield 3% nominal. The bonds were due for payment on July 1, 1979. What was the selling price?

6–15 One of the bonds in Problem 6–14 was immediately resold for $1,110. What was the "yield to maturity" for the new purchaser?

6–16 A man is considering buying a twenty-year $1,000 callable bond which, according to its serial number, will be retired in ten years at $1,025. The bond will pay interest at the nominal rate of 6%, payable semiannually.

a. What price should he pay for this bond if he desires a nominal yield of 4% on his investment?

b. Suppose the above bond was not callable. For the same yield, how much more (or less) would he have to pay for the bond?

6–17 A $500 bond, purchased at par and bearing interest at the nominal rate of 5%, payable semiannually, was bought back by the issuing corporation after eight years at a premium of $50. What was the yield received by the original purchaser of the bond?

6–18 A company issues $200,000 in bonds in units of $1,000 each. The bond rate is 4%. The bonds have a ten-year maturity date but are callable by lot after five years. The company expects to retire as nearly uniform amounts of bonds as possible each year beginning with the end of the fifth year. Set up an amortization schedule showing the total cost of the bond issue each year.

6–19 Assume that the company in Problem 6–18 desired to set aside a uniform amount of money at the end of each year to pay the total cost of the bond issue. All money on deposit would receive interest at the rate of 2% per annum. Set up an amortization schedule on this basis and compare the total cost of the bond issue. Assume that after five years the company would retire as many bonds as available money permits each year.

6–20 An irrigation district sells $300,000 in 5% twenty-year bonds which are callable after five years, except that not more than 25% of the bonds may be retired in any one year. The district wishes to set aside equal annual amounts throughout the life of the bond issue to retire them, retiring as many as possible at the end of five years. Amounts on deposit will receive interest at the rate of 2½% per annum. What will be the annual amount required to cover the cost of the bond issue?

CHAPTER 7

The Relationship
of Accounting
to Economy Studies

When capital is invested in a business venture, procedures are established so that financial events relating to the investment can be recorded and the financial efficiency determined. At the same time, through the use of proper financial information, controls can be established and utilized to aid in guiding the venture toward the desired financial goals. General accounting and cost accounting are the procedures that provide these necessary services in a business organization.

The accountant is, in a sense, the financial historian of a business. He is somewhat like a data recorder in a scientific experiment. Such a recorder observes the pertinent gages, meters, etc., and records all the essential data during the course of an experiment. From these it is then possible to determine the results of the experiment. Similarly, the accountant records all significant financial events connected with an investment and from these data can determine whether the results have been satisfactory. Thus business depends upon accounting data to determine whether or not an investment of capital has been successful.

Since the purpose of economy studies is to provide the information and recommendations as to whether an investment of capital should be made, and since accounting determines the effectiveness of the investment after it has been made, the fact that there is a close relationship between the two fields is apparent. The accountant has an obvious advantage over the engineer, since he records facts, for the most part, as or after they occur. The engineer, on the other hand, attempts to predict what will happen before it actually occurs. Naturally, the engineer would like to have the accounting records confirm his predictions. It would be too much to expect that all the

events surrounding an investment should always turn out to be just as predicted in the economy study. Time has a way of producing unforeseen
events and circumstances which make the actual results differ from the best
of estimates. However, an engineer can have little hope of having his figures
agree with those of the accountant if he does not consider the same cost
factors as will be used in the final accounting records. Otherwise, agreement
would be mere chance. Thus, while it may appear at first that the engineer
does not need to concern himself with accounting, such is not the case. It is
true that the engineer need not concern himself with much of the detail of
accounting in order to make satisfactory economy studies. However, a
knowledge and understanding of the important fundamentals upon which
accounting practice is based, together with an acquaintance with a few of
those accounting details which are closely related to economy studies, will be
found to be a real help to him.[1]

Many of the detailed figures of accounting practice are not used, and
indeed are not usable, in economy studies. However, some supply information which is needed. Unless the engineer has some understanding of
accounting procedures, he will not know what needed information the accounting records can provide, and, just as important, he may not know
which accounting data can not be used in economy studies. Furthermore,
since the studies of both the engineer and the accountant are used by the
business world, it is most helpful if they use the same terminology and, when
dealing with the same item, use identical and consistent procedures. In this
way understanding, harmony, and efficiency are promoted. When this is
done, the final accounting of an investment will tend to be a reflection of the
results of the economy study which brought it about.

It is therefore not the purpose of this chapter to provide a short course
in accounting. Instead, it will attempt to

1. Explain the fundamental objectives of general and cost accounting.
2. Discuss the information available in the two most common accounting
   statements—the *balance sheet* and the *income-and-expense* statement.
3. Explain the method by which the accountant handles depreciation
   funds.
4. Demonstrate the method by which costs and standard costs are determined.
5. Point out the limitations of the use of cost accounting data in economy
   studies, and the types of cost data that may be available from the cost
   accountant.

---

[1] It is doubtful that there is any other subject of which a thorough mastery would be of
more value than accounting to the engineer who is making economy studies.

THE FUNDAMENTAL TERMS OF ACCOUNTING

Since accounting deals with monetary values which are owned or used by a person or business, the equation

$$\text{Assets} = \text{Equities} \qquad (7.1)$$

is a simple expression of the fundamental relationship of accounting. *Assets* are defined as things of value. This definition is extremely broad—as it must be since it must include everything of commercial worth. *Equity* is the claim of anyone to ownership. If one buys a $1,000 automobile but pays the dealer only $500, leaving a balance of $500 due, both the buyer and the dealer have an equity in the car. Equity, then, may be distributed among numerous persons. The equity of the person who normally possesses the asset is commonly known as *ownership*. The claims of others than the owners upon the assets are designated as *liabilities*. These liabilities would have to be paid by the owners in order for them to have complete title to all of the assets. Because the equities are usually divided in the manner which has just been mentioned, Equation (7.1) is often written in the following form:

$$\text{Assets} = \text{Liabilities} + \text{Ownership} \qquad (7.2)$$

This is often considered to be the fundamental equation of accounting. The item "Ownership" is sometimes referred to as *Proprietorship*.

Liabilities may take many forms but usually are grouped into two classes. If the person who purchased the car mentioned in the preceding paragraph had agreed to pay the dealer the remaining $500 in thirty days, this claim upon the automobile would be said to be a *current liability*. This class of liabilities represents claims against the owners which must be paid in the near future. There is no exact rule as to how immediate the claim must be to be classed as a current liability. In general practice those claims which must be paid during the next accounting period (usually one year) are classed as current liabilities. The exact classification will vary from one business to another.

Liabilities that are not due for payment until a time more than one year distant are usually listed as *fixed liabilities*. These are usually in the form of bonds or long-term notes, for which some refunding provision is being made.

A third type of liability is *prepaid income*. This type of liability arises when a business receives payment for a service before it actually renders the service. In this case the assets of the company have been increased through receipt of money. The person who paid the money is entitled to receive future services and therefore has a claim against the company until these are fully rendered.

Assets may also be divided into several different classes. A business will possess cash and numerous other items which will be converted into cash or salable goods *in the normal process of business* during the next accounting period. Such items of value are classed as *current assets*. These will include cash, accounts receivable during the next period, raw materials, and inventories of finished goods which will be sold.

Those assets which will not be converted into cash, sold, or converted into salable form during the coming accounting period are *fixed assets*. These include the buildings, land, machinery, furniture, and fixtures which are utilized in producing the goods or services that are to be offered for sale. The term "fixed" does not, however, necessarily mean fixed as to position or location. A railroad locomotive is a fixed asset but is not stationary.

A third type of asset corresponds to the third type of liability which was mentioned and is called either *deferred charges* or *prepaid expense*. In this case a charge, or expense, has been paid before any benefit has been received from it. An example is prepaid insurance. It is customary to pay insurance premiums in advance. Thus, when a year's premium is paid at the beginning of the year, the purchaser is entitled to receive protection during the year to follow. Until he has received all of this protection, the unused portion is of value to him and is therefore an asset.

Proprietorship may also exist in several forms. In the case of a single owner it is in the capital account of Mr. X. For a partnership, X and Y will each have capital accounts. In a corporation the shares of common and preferred stock represent ownership. If the business has earned profits, these are shown as *Undeclared Dividends* or as *Surplus* until they are distributed to the owners or transferred to their capital accounts as additions to their investment in the business.

THE BALANCE SHEET

One of the most important factors in any business is the relationship between its assets, liabilities, and ownership. The principal reason for accounting is to make it possible to determine this relationship at any particular time. If Equation (7.2) is rewritten in the following form

$$\text{Assets} - \text{Liabilities} = \text{Ownership} \qquad (7.3)$$

a convenient method is indicated for determining the amount of ownership.

For example, Henry Smith wishes to determine just what his ownership or *net worth* is, and does it in the following manner. On one sheet of paper he makes a list of all his possessions of value, as shown in Figure 7–1. On

POSSESSIONS OF HENRY SMITH

1. Cash	$	78.00
2. Government bond		100.00
3. Automobile		900.00
4. Furniture		600.00
Total		$1,678.00

Figure 7–1.   Assets of Henry Smith.

another sheet he lists all the amounts he owes to other people; this list, shown in Figure 7–2, constitutes his liabilities. He now can perform the operation

WHAT HENRY SMITH OWES

5. Borrowed from John Jones	$	2.00
6. Grocery bill		6.00
7. Balance due on car		250.00
		$258.00

Excess of Possessions over Debts

8. Ownership (net worth) $1,420.00

Figure 7–2.   Liabilities and ownership of Henry Smith.

which was indicated in Equation (7.3) and thus determine his net worth. This he does as follows:

Assets	$1,678.00
Less Liabilities	258.00
Ownership	$1,420.00

The excess of assets over liabilities is the claim Henry Smith has on the assets he possesses, or is his net worth or ownership. He records this amount on the second sheet of paper, as shown in Figure 7–2.

BALANCE SHEET

Henry Smith

March 10, 1958

Assets			*Liabilities*		
Cash	$	78.00	Borrowed from		
Government bond		100.00	John Jones	$ 2.00	
Automobile		900.00	Grocery bill	6.00	
Furniture		600.00	Due on car	250.00	
			Total liabilities		$ 258.00
			Ownership		1,420.00
		$1,678.00			$1,678.00

Figure 7–3.   Balance sheet for Henry Smith.

These two sheets of figures show the relationship between Henry Smith's assets, liabilities, and ownership at one particular time. It is customary to list all of these items on one page, placing the assets on the left-hand side of the page and the liabilities and ownership on the right. In this form it is known as a *balance sheet,* probably deriving this name from the fact that the totals of the items listed on each half of the sheet are the same. This form of balance sheet for Henry Smith is shown in Figure 7–3.

Henry Smith's balance sheet showed the relationship between his assets, liabilities, and ownership at one time, in this case March 10, 1958. If he should spend 50 cents for a movie the relationship would be changed, and a new balance sheet would be required to show the new condition of his finances. This is one of the fundamental facts about a balance sheet—it shows the relationship between the assets, liabilities, and ownership *at one specified time.* Any additional transaction renders the balance sheet obsolete.

Since the balance sheet for Henry Smith included only a few items, the

BALANCE SHEET

Jameson Manufacturing Co.

December 31, 1958

Current Assets			*Current Liabilities*		
Cash	$ 68,352.12		Accounts Payable	$ 15,287.52	
Government Bonds	10,000.00		Notes Payable	1,200.00	
Accounts Receivable	21,550.00		Total		$ 16,487.52
Inventory	37,250.00		*Fixed Liabilities*		
Total		$137,152.12	7% Bonds	$ 15,000.00	15,000.00
Fixed Assets			*Ownership*		
Factory Buildings	$100,000.00		Preferred Stock	$ 25,000.00	
Trucks	3,852.00		Common Stock	150,000.00	
Machinery	87,350.00				
	$191,202.00		Total		$175,000.00
Less Reserve for Depreciation	32,400.00		*Surplus*	$ 90,000.00	90,000.00
Total		$158,802.00			
Prepaid Charges					
Insurance	$ 462.40				
Taxes	71.00				
Total		533.40			
		$296,487.52			$296,487.52

Figure 7–4.   Balance sheet for a moderate-sized business.

statement was very simple. In a large business there are a great number of assets and liabilities, and the balance sheet must be more complicated. A balance sheet of a medium-sized business is shown in Figure 7–4. This balance sheet is in the most common form. Assets and liabilities are divided into several groups to give greater clarity. The totals of each group are given so that comparisons of the different groups may be readily made.

Balance sheets are also commonly arranged in the form shown in Figure 7–5. This "vertical" form is more convenient where large amounts of money and longer descriptive phrases are involved. The *comparative* type of balance sheet, shown in Figure 7–6, is used quite frequently and has certain obvious advantages since it permits comparisons to be made between values for the two or more dates shown.

Since a balance sheet is designed to state information about the financial condition of a business, it is important that the information it contains be accurate and present a true picture. It is just as important that the information be presented in a simple, concise form that may be understood by the persons who are going to make use of the statement. Preparation of a balance sheet in a form that will mislead the user as to the financial condition of the business is little different from the use of false figures in the statement. In recent years there has been a strong trend toward the presentation of balance sheet data in simple, and sometimes pictorial, form. This has resulted primarily from the desire to supply the financial facts of companies to their workers.[2] Most financial statements now are presented in more simplified form than previously was the case. In fact, in a few instances the form has been so modernized and altered that it is a bit difficult to find the information for which one is accustomed to look.

INCOME-AND-EXPENSE STATEMENTS

While a comparative balance sheet shows the relationship between assets, liabilities, and ownership at the beginning and end of a period of time, it tells very little about the causes of the changes that have occurred. Obviously, it is of great importance to know whether a business is operating at a profit or a loss, and to know what the sources of the profit or loss are. This information is shown in summarized form on an income-and-expense statement.

If one analyzes the changes that occur in the balances of balance sheet

[2] One of the early leaders in this movement supplied a simplified annual report to its workers but sent the usual, more complicated type to its stockholders. Some of the workers' reports got into the hands of stockholders, and the company received numerous requests that in the future the stockholders also be supplied with simple reports that they could understand.

Bank of America
NATIONAL TRUST AND SAVINGS ASSOCIATION

CONDENSED STATEMENT OF CONDITION JUNE 30, 1958
(Figures of Overseas Branches are as of June 24, 1958)

RESOURCES

CASH AND DUE FROM BANKS	$ 1,631,183,927.79
UNITED STATES GOVERNMENT SECURITIES AND SECURITIES	
GUARANTEED BY THE GOVERNMENT	2,260,498,347.35
FEDERAL AGENCY SECURITIES	151,107,046.98
STATE, COUNTY, AND MUNICIPAL SECURITIES	754,724,106.65
OTHER SECURITIES	148,401,216.09
STOCK IN FEDERAL RESERVE BANK	13,500,000.00
LOANS GUARANTEED OR INSURED BY THE UNITED STATES GOVERNMENT	
OR ITS AGENCIES	1,315,150,219.95
OTHER LOANS AND DISCOUNTS	4,147,829,437.70
ACCRUED INTEREST AND ACCOUNTS RECEIVABLE	64,252,726.31
BANK PREMISES, FURNITURE, FIXTURES, AND SAFE DEPOSIT VAULTS	123,001,199.63
OTHER REAL ESTATE OWNED	1,744,244.02
CUSTOMERS' LIABILITY FOR ACCEPTANCES	167,143,137.67
OTHER RESOURCES	1,311,198.83
TOTAL RESOURCES	**$10,779,846,808.97**

LIABILITIES

CAPITAL	$ 160,000,000.00	
SURPLUS	290,000,000.00	
UNDIVIDED PROFITS	139,406,340.14	
RESERVES	6,246,440.92	
TOTAL CAPITAL FUNDS		$ 595,652,781.06
RESERVE FOR POSSIBLE LOAN LOSSES		95,485,915.95
DEMAND	$4,450,084,439.60	
DEPOSITS		9,812,411,535.59
SAVINGS AND TIME	5,362,327,095.99	
LIABILITY ON ACCEPTANCES		169,534,573.64
RESERVE FOR INTEREST RECEIVED IN ADVANCE		67,848,726.04
RESERVE FOR INTEREST, TAXES, ETC.		38,913,276.69
TOTAL LIABILITIES		**$10,779,846,808.97**

Figure 7–5. Balance sheet of a large banking company.

STANDARD OIL COMPANY (NEW JERSEY)

STATEMENT OF FINANCIAL POSITION

DECEMBER 31, 1955-1954

	1955	1954
CURRENT ASSETS		
Cash	$ 63,805,720	$ 61,040,954
Marketable securities, at lower of cost or market	971,380,707	1,002,422,344
Accounts receivable	7,191,930	18,316,102
Total current assets	1,042,378,357	1,081,779,400
LESS—CURRENT LIABILITIES		
Indebtedness to companies consolidated	439,859,599	507,877,599
Accounts payable and accrued liabilities	9,630,710	10,660,669
Income taxes payable	34,800,598	24,531,728
Total current liabilities	484,290,907	543,069,996
WORKING CAPITAL	558,087,450	538,709,404
INVESTMENTS AND LONG-TERM RECEIVABLES, at cost or less		
Stocks of companies consolidated	1,732,715,871	1,593,241,287
Receivables from companies consolidated	173,633,390	165,260,591
Other investments and long-term receivables	213,594,370	217,406,336
PREPAID CHARGES AND OTHER ASSETS	22,745,553	10,914,446
Total assets less current liabilities	2,700,776,634	2,525,532,064
DEDUCTIONS		
Long-term debt	315,796,631	316,002,631
Deferred credits	508,483	530,511
Annuity and other reserves	6,082,942	5,877,659
NET ASSETS	$2,378,388,578	$2,203,121,263
SHAREHOLDERS' EQUITY		
Capital:		
Stock issued—$15 par value	$ 981,532,110	$ 981,532,110
Amount in excess of par value	364,828,659	364,828,659
Earnings reinvested and employed in business	1,032,027,809	856,760,494
	$2,378,388,578	$2,203,121,263

Figure 7-6.   A comparative type of balance sheet.

accounts, he will find that most of them are due to revenue which is received from the sale of goods or services or to the expenses which are incurred in the production of the goods or services. These items of income and expense, such as sales, purchases, salaries, wages, sales expense, taxes, insurance, and depreciation expense, are recorded in appropriate income sheet accounts.

The transactions recorded in the income sheet accounts are those which normally produce the increase or decrease in the value of an investment of capital. Therefore it is these items which management attempts to control so as to obtain favorable results. They represent the expenses and revenues that occur after capital has been invested. For this reason they are of particular interest to the engineer. They record the actual occurrence of events which he predicts and estimates in making economy studies. It is desirable for the engineer to be acquainted with the terms and methods which the accountant uses in handling these items so that he may treat them in the proper manner when they must be considered in an economy study.

A few words are in order regarding some of these terms. When the accountant speaks of *gross revenue,* he refers to all of the proceeds which are received by the business as the result of the sale of goods or services. *Net revenue* or *net income* is defined as the amount by which the equities of the proprietors or owners are increased because of successful conduct of the business. One hopes that a portion of gross revenue will be net income.

Accountants define expense as the cost of producing revenue. Obviously many different expenses arise. These include the usual items, such as expense for materials, labor, taxes, insurance, sales, and shipping. An additional expense which is of great importance to the engineer is that due to depreciation.

Income statements may vary in form to an even greater extent than do balance sheets. The very different natures of the many types of business make it necessary to adapt the income statement to the particular enterprise in order to show the information to the best advantage. The only requisite is that the statement should show the information in a clear, concise, and complete manner. Figure 7–7 shows the income statement for The Brown

THE BROWN MANUFACTURING CO.

Statement of Income and Expense

January 1, 1959, to February 28, 1959

Income from Sales			$1,755.00
Less Cost of Goods Sold			
Materials			
Inventory January 1	$_____		
Purchases	480.00		
	$480.00		
Inventory February 28	250.00		
Total Materials		$ 230.00	
Labor		1,000.00	
Burden		354.55	
Cost of Goods Sold			1,584.55
Gross Profit			$ 170.45
Other Expenses			
Interest			8.17
Net Profit			$ 162.28

Figure 7–7.   Income statement for The Brown Manufacturing Co.

Manufacturing Co. for the period January 1 through February 28, 1959. This statement is much less complicated than the form shown in Figure 7–8, which is one required by the Internal Revenue Department for filing corporate income tax returns.

Though the statement shown for The Brown Manufacturing Co. is relatively simple, it is entirely adequate for this particular company, whose business is small and whose operations are not extensive. An examination will show that the statement is divided into four sections. The first section shows the revenue or receipts from the major operations of the business—from the sale of goods.

The second section presents the cost of producing these goods. The cost of the materials used in the goods produced must be determined in this section. Obviously, the total material available for use during a period is the sum of the materials on hand at the beginning of the period plus those purchased during the same time. If the inventory of materials remaining on hand at the close of the period is then subtracted from this total, the difference is the amount used in production during the period. To the cost of materials must be added the productive labor costs and items of manufacturing overhead or burden. By subtracting from sales income the cost of the goods or services produced, the gross profit from sales is obtained.

In the third section of the income statement the costs of selling the goods and management expenses are listed. These are expenses which are the result of administration and are subtracted from the gross profit to obtain the net profit. In the case of The Brown Manufacturing Co., selling and administrative salaries were negligible and were included in the overhead. The item "interest" is a management expense, since it arose through a particular method of financing the purchase of equipment. It is therefore included in this section of the statement.

The fourth section shows the net profit or loss and indicates whether there has been any distribution of these funds. Thus it would show if the profits had been used to pay dividends or had been set aside as surplus.

From an income statement in this form one may determine whether the expenses of one phase of the business, such as sales, are out of line with other items. The statement also shows the effect of any unusual financial methods which may have been used. Not only are the sources of income revealed, but the extent and distribution of income may be determined. If one wishes to make a detailed study of the financial structure of an enterprise, a comparative income statement, showing the values for two or more periods, is very useful. Thus the income statement reveals cost information which is necessary and useful in controlling the operations of a business.

ADJUSTED NET INCOME COMPUTATION

GROSS INCOME

Item No.			
		Less returns and	
1. Gross sales (where inventories are an income-determining factor)...... $ ....; allowances...... $..........			$..........
2. Less cost of goods sold (from Schedule C)...........			
3. Gross profit from sales (item 1 minus item 2)............			
4. Gross receipts (where inventories are not an income-determining factor)... $..........			
5. Less cost of operations (from Schedule D)............			
6. Gross profit where inventories are not an income-determining factor (item 4 minus item 5)............			
7. Interest on loans, notes, mortgages, bonds, bank deposits, etc. (See Instruction 18—(1))............			
8. Interest on obligations of the United States (from Schedule P, line 19 (a) (4)). (See Instruction 18—(2)).			
9. Rents. (See Instruction 19)............			
10. Royalties. (See Instruction 20)............			
11. (a) Capital gain (or loss) (from Schedule E). (If a net loss, do not enter over $2,000)............			
(b) Gain or loss from sale or exchange of property other than capital assets (from Schedule F)......			
12. Dividends (from Schedule G)............			
13. Other income (state nature of income)............			
14. Total income in items 3, and 6 to 13, inclusive............			$..........

176

DEDUCTIONS

15. Compensation of officers (from Schedule H)
16. Salaries and wages (not deducted elsewhere)
17. Rent. (See Instruction 23)
18. Repairs. (See Instruction 24)
19. Bad debts (from Schedule I)
20. Interest. (See Instruction 26)
21. Taxes (from Schedule J). (Do not include Federal excess-profits tax)
22. Contributions or gifts paid (from Schedule K)
23. Losses by fire, storm, shipwreck, or other casualty, or theft. (Submit schedule, see Instruction 29)
24. Depreciation (from Schedule L)
25. Depletion of mines, oil and gas wells, timber, etc. (Submit schedule, see Instruction 31)
26. Other deductions authorized by law (from Schedule M)
27.   Total deductions in items 15 to 26, inclusive
28. Net income for excess-profits tax computation (item 14 minus item 27)
29.   Less: Federal excess-profits tax. (See Instruction 33)
30. Net income (item 28 minus item 29)
31.   Less: Interest on obligations of the United States (item 8, above)
32. Adjusted net income (item 30 minus item 31)

Schedule C.—COST OF GOODS SOLD. (See Instruction 17)
(Where inventories are an income-determining factor)

1. Inventory at beginning of year
2. Material or merchandise bought for manufacture or sale
3. Salaries and wages
4. Other cost perbooks. (Attach itemized schedule)
5.   Total (lines 1 to 4)
6. Less inventory at end of year
7.   Cost of goods.   (Enter as item 2, page 1)

Figure 7–8.   Income statement required by the Internal Revenue Bureau from corporations.

177

THE SOURCE OF DATA FOR FINANCIAL STATEMENTS

In order to obtain the data shown on balance sheets and income-and-expense statements, it is necessary to set up and maintain records in which are recorded all financial events. This involves the routine procedures of bookkeeping. These procedures have been quite standardized and, with few exceptions, are not of much importance in relationship to economy studies.

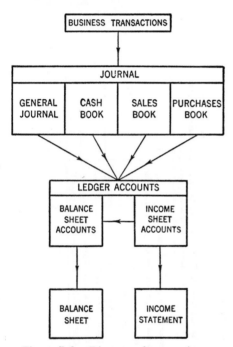

In general, various "accounts" are set up, and each transaction is recorded in the accounts affected, in order to show the increase or decrease in the value of the account. In each case the procedure is adapted to fit the needs of the particular organization involved.

When the preparation of a balance sheet or income-and-expense statement is desired, each account is "balanced" to determine the net result of the plus and minus entries. The "balances" of several similar accounts may, for convenience, be grouped together under one heading, such as *Accounts Receivable, Sales,* or *Accounts Payable.* The items shown on a balance sheet are thus the net summations of all of the various accounts denoting assets,

Figure 7–9. Diagram of accounting procedure.

liabilities, or ownership. Similarly, the items on an income-and-expense statement are the net summations of the accounts in which have been recorded all matters of income or expense over a period of time. Figure 7–9 is a simple diagram of accounting procedure.

DEPRECIATION ACCOUNTING

In Chapter 5 mention was made of the fact that the money set aside from income as the depreciation expense is retained and used in the business. The method of handling these depreciation funds in accounting practice is very frequently misunderstood. The misunderstanding appears to arise from the fact that, as shown in Figure 7–4, an item called *Reserve for Depreciation* appears on balance sheets as a *deduction* from the fixed assets. Since a reserve is normally thought of as something of value, the subtraction of this item on a balance sheet seems contradictory. In accounting practice, however, the term has a somewhat different significance, as may be seen from the following simple example.

Assume that John Doe invests $1,000 to buy some equipment with which to carry on a business enterprise. The simple balance sheet to show the relationship between assets and ownership would be that shown in Figure 7–10.

BALANCE SHEET A

Assets		*Liabilities and Ownership*	
Equipment	$1,000	John Doe, Ownership	$1,000
	$1,000		$1,000

Figure 7–10.   Balance sheet of John Doe immediately after investment in equipment.

Mr. Doe estimates that the equipment will have a useful life of five years and decides to compute depreciation on a straight-line basis for accounting purposes. Out of the first year's income produced by the equipment he therefore sets aside $200 as depreciation expense. In accordance with the necessity for using this money to the best advantage and with the usual need of a growing business for more capital with which to operate and to buy additional facilities, he uses it in the business. Some of it may be retained as cash for day-to-day operations, while some is used to purchase other needed fixed assets. As a result, the balance sheet at the end of the year must reflect two facts: (*a*) the original equipment has decreased in value by $200, and (*b*) $200 worth of new assets have been added. The second fact has been made possible through the depreciation funds which accounted for the first. Both facts are made evident by the balance sheet for the end of the first year shown in Figure 7–11. Thus the *Reserve for Depreciation* item on the balance sheet is a *contra entry* against the fixed assets to show the decrease in value, and it is balanced by the amount of cash or other assets that have been acquired through the depreciation funds.

It is true that, through the use of the customary depreciation reserve, it is possible for equipment to become worn out and for no funds to be available for replacement, although the correct depreciation has been charged at all times. This merely means that the management has not maintained the proper ratio between cash and other assets. No one would expect all the in-

BALANCE SHEET B

Assets			Liabilities and Ownership	
Equipment	$1,000		John Doe, Ownership	$1,000
Less Reserve for Depreciation	200			
		$ 800		
Cash or Other Assets		200		
		$1,000		$1,000

Figure 7–11.   Balance sheet of John Doe after one year of operation.

vested capital of a business to be kept in the form of cash. It is no more reasonable to expect that depreciation reserves should all be in the form of cash. Management must be foresighted and provide funds for replacement. However, this is no greater responsibility than is placed on management for the conduct of the other affairs of a business. No one would question giving management the responsibility of keeping enough of the assets in the form of cash so that the payroll can be met. If the executives are capable of managing a business, they should also be capable of having the necessary cash available when fixed assets must be replaced.

OBJECTIVES OF COST ACCOUNTING

Cost accounting, in simple terms, is the determination of the cost of producing a product or rendering a service. In order to accomplish this, one must determine what expenses are incurred in a business undertaking. An accounting system must then be established so that these expenses may be recorded in such a manner that the various costs of production can be found. While the basic objective of cost accounting is simple, the exact determination of costs usually is not. As a result, some of the procedures used are arbitrary devices which make possible the obtaining of answers that are reasonably accurate for most cases, but which may contain a considerable percentage of error in others.

More and more the paths of engineers cross and parallel those of the cost accountants. As the engineer takes over responsibility for making economy studies of proposed projects, plants, equipment, and methods, he frequently sets up cost estimates which will be similar to the production or operating costs which the cost accountant establishes after the project is in operation. Many, if not all, of the disputes that have taken place between cost accountants and engineers (and there have been many) are due to a lack of understanding on the part of one group of the objectives and methods of the other. In reality, each group has much that is of benefit to the other, and when the objectives and purposes are thoroughly understood, there usually is excellent cooperation.

To a considerable extent the engineer has been responsible for the high degree of development of cost accounting. As the engineer has assumed a greater responsibility, he has constantly demanded more and better cost data so that decisions regarding processes and equipment could be decided upon the basis of fact. The cost accountants, in many instances aided by engineers, have responded with highly effective cost procedures which now are important managerial aids.

Modern cost accounting may satisfy any or all of the following objectives:

1. Determination of the actual cost of products or services.
2. Provision of a rational basis for pricing goods or services.
3. Provision of a means for controlling expenditures.
4. Provision of information on which operating decisions may be based and by means of which operating decisions may be evaluated.

As cost accounting developed, it was found that not only could it be used to determine costs, but, more importantly, it also provided a means for controlling costs. As a result, several types of cost accounting have been developed.

TYPES OF COST ACCOUNTING

Cost accounting has developed in three phases, resulting in three types of cost data. After an article has been produced, one wishes to know what costs were incurred in its production. Without such information a business is in the same position as the college student on Saturday morning after a big Friday night date; he knows that his wallet is considerably depleted but doesn't have an accurate knowledge of just where the money went. Cost accounting was originated to supply business with a knowledge of where the money went. By carefully accounting for all of the expenses of every type during the period of production, the actual cost of manufacture may be determined. However, with this method the cost is not known until production of the goods or service is finished. This method of obtaining cost figures is often called *post-mortem* cost accounting. Costs are determined after they occur. Accounting of this type is used to a considerable extent and fills a very real need. It is essential that costs be known. Even if they are not determined until after they have taken place, this is better than never knowing what they were. In small industries which produce only small lots of goods of the same kind, it is often not feasible to use more advanced methods of cost analysis than are found in post-mortem cost determinations.

The second type of cost accounting attempts to make it possible to know what costs will be before production takes place. The advantage of knowing what future costs will be is very evident. Such costs must, of course, be based upon experience, careful specification of materials and processes, and detailed analysis and distribution of overhead expenses. These costs are estimates, but with intelligent preparation they can be given a high degree of accuracy and thus made to approximate actual values very closely. Because of this, they are sometimes called *predicted costs*.

Well-prepared predicted costs are ideal figures. They are somewhat like the estimate which the college student might prepare before taking his co-ed friend to dinner the next weekend. He determines how much he wants to spend and plans his activities accordingly. However, the girl friend does not know that the predicted costs did not include filet mignon, and the actual costs turn out to be very different from those that were predicted. The realization that this might happen and the desire to make actual costs match the ideal gave rise to the third type of cost accounting. It is a broader and extra use of the second type of cost figures. Costs are predetermined as before, with as much accuracy as possible. These are set up as *standard costs*. All operations are then performed in the manner which was specified for these standard costs. Thus the cost-accounting system becomes not only a means of determining costs, but also an aid to control.

This use of cost accounting as an instrument of control is peculiarly adapted to the needs of the large scale, standardized production that characterizes modern industry. With such production, the standard costs can be more accurately determined, and, at the same time, the need for a means of controlling costs becomes more essential. The importance of the cost-accounting system becomes apparent.

THE ELEMENTS OF COST

One of the first problems in cost accounting is to determine the elements of cost which arise in producing an article or rendering a service. A study of how these costs occur then gives an indication of the accounting procedure which must be established in order to give satisfactory cost information.

As stated by the economist, the three factors that contribute to production are land, labor, and capital. From an engineering and managerial viewpoint it is suitable to consider the general elements of cost of production to be

materials, labor, and *overhead*. It may readily be seen that the latter grouping includes the factors as given by the economist. The cost accountant,
however, ordinarily uses a somewhat more detailed classification of costs, as
shown in Figure 7–12. Illustrative amounts are shown in this diagram for a
product having a selling price of $10. The determination of these various
classifications of cost will now be considered.

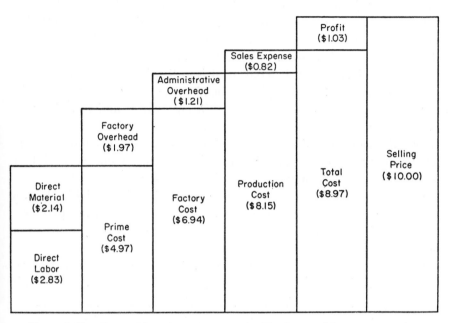

Figure 7–12. Composition of common cost classifications used in cost accounting.

DIRECT AND INDIRECT MATERIALS

Ordinarily, the cost of materials that are used directly in making a product are called *direct materials* and are charged directly to the cost of the
product. However, it is at once apparent that this is not a precise definition
and that arbitrary decisions must be made in such matters. Several guiding
principles are used in deciding whether a material is classified as a direct
material. In general, direct materials should be readily measurable, be of
the same quantity in identical products, and be used in economically significant amounts. Those materials which do not meet these criteria are classified
as *indirect materials* and are a part of the charge for *factory overhead*. For
example, the exact amount of glue used in making a chair would be difficult
to determine. Still more difficult would be the measurement of the exact
amount of coal which was used to produce the steam which generated the

electricity which was used to heat the glue. Some reasonable line must be drawn beyond which no attempt is made to measure directly the material which is used for each unit of production.

As the extent of a business increases, the importance of determining the exact cost of as many of the materials as possible increases proportionately. It is not uncommon for large companies to compute material costs to four or five decimal places. It should always be remembered, however, that there is little advantage in knowing that the cost of a certain material is $0.04562 per pound when it is impossible to determine whether one sixteenth or one quarter of a pound is used in each unit produced.

A record of the direct materials used is ordinarily obtained through the use of inventory cards and requisition blanks. The inventory cards are maintained in connection with the perpetual inventory of materials in the storeroom. These cards appear in many forms, but their primary purpose is to record the amount and cost of material brought into the storeroom, the amount and value of the material taken from the storeroom on requisition, and the amount of the material remaining in the storeroom.

One of these cards is kept for each type and size of material in the raw materials stores. A sample card is shown in Figure 7–13. On this particular type of card the average cost of the material on hand is kept, so the value of any material sent from the storeroom may be computed.

Other types of stock cards may carry less or more information than the one illustrated in Figure 7–13. Some of the more elaborate cards show the

		INVENTORY CARD				
Article		3/4" brass collar		Stock Number		786A
Date	Received	Cost	Balance on Hand	Average Cost	Delivered	Requisition Number
9/2	5,000	$0.0400	5,000	$0.0400		
9/4			2,000		3,000	B 475
9/20	3,000	$0.0420	5,000	$0.0412		

Figure 7–13. Stockroom inventory card.

department to which the material was issued, the maximum and minimum quantity to be kept on hand, the name of the supplier, and any other information which may be thought necessary. The more elaborate the card is, the more the amount of labor required to maintain the card system. As simple a form as possible helps to prevent neglect and carelessness in recording essential information.

The pricing of materials raises one of the troublesome problems encountered in cost accounting. As mentioned, using the average cost of material on hand is one method. Another is to assume that the oldest material is always used first. Thus, in this "first in-first out" (the so-called "FIFO") method, each lot of a particular material is carried at its actual cost. The oldest lot is assumed to be used first, and the operation is charged with the cost of the material assumed to be used. In this manner the value of the inventory tends to reflect latest market value. Such a procedure is quite satisfactory for ordinary accounting purposes, or even for setting the standard cost of performing current operations. However, such material cost data may be of no value in making an economy study which deals with *future* costs, which may be considerably different from the past costs.

Another procedure for pricing direct materials is the "last in-first out" method. By this "LIFO" method cost data tend to reflect current prices. A third procedure is to use the average cost of the materials on hand. This obviously requires extra calculations.

It is apparent that since the ordinary direct materials' costs as supplied by the usual cost accounting procedures may involve a number of arbitrary and empirical decisions, the engineer in making economy studies should not use material costs as shown by the cost accounting records without ascertaining whether they are applicable to the conditions being considered.

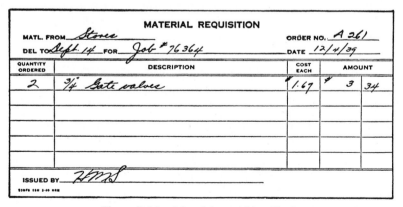

Figure 7-14. Material requisition blank.

Materials are usually ordered from the storeroom by a requisition blank. Such a blank is shown in Figure 7–14. The essential information includes the name, amount, and stock number (if any) of the material required and the work-order number or department to which the material is to be charged. The value of the issued material is computed from the cost figures shown on the stock card and entered on a copy of the requisition. This copy is then sent to the accounting department. In this manner the cost of materials which are placed in production is obtained. Material requisition forms often provide the best source of information as to the actual amounts and cost of direct materials used in a product.

DIRECT AND INDIRECT LABOR

Labor costs also are divided into *direct* and *indirect*. Here again the division must be somewhat arbitrary. Normally, the wages and salaries of those people who actually process the material, changing its form, are charged directly to the cost of the product. Such cases are rather clearly and easily defined. Likewise, the salaries of foremen and supervisors are rather clearly indirect labor costs and are therefore charged to factory overhead. However, in many cases, such as stock movers and warehouse employees, there can be no definite rule. As a result, one must make certain what is included in direct labor and prime cost data before attempting to use them in economy studies.

Where the workers are paid a fixed weekly or monthly salary, determination of post-mortem unit cost is simple. An effort to predetermine unit labor costs presents a much more difficult task. After the work is completed, the unit cost may be found by dividing the total salaries of the production period by the number of units produced during that period. However, there is seldom any guarantee that the same workers will produce the same number of articles in an equal future period. Precise predetermination of labor costs is usually impossible with this system of wage payment.

Where wages are based on an hourly rate, approximately the same difficulties are encountered as with payment of fixed salaries. The exact amount of time consumed by an operation may be found after the task is completed if suitable means are provided. This is usually accomplished through the use of some kind of time clock and job card. Samples of two types of records, obtainable by the use of two types of time clocks, are shown in Figures 7–15 and 7–16. From these records and the known hourly rates of pay, the labor cost is determined. With this method of wage payment, accurate predetermination of labor costs is still difficult, even though each task is given an *allowed time*.

The piece-rate system of wage payment was originated not only to provide a method that would pay the worker in proportion to the work accomplished, but also to ensure constant labor costs for the performance of a given operation. In this system the wage paid for the performance of a set task is based upon a scientific study of the actual labor required. Whenever the same task is performed the wage paid is the same amount. With piece rates established, the labor cost for a given operation is known before or after the operation is performed. This method of wage payment is widely used by progressive companies, and its use is increasing rapidly. A more detailed discussion of the various wage payment methods is given in Chapter 17.

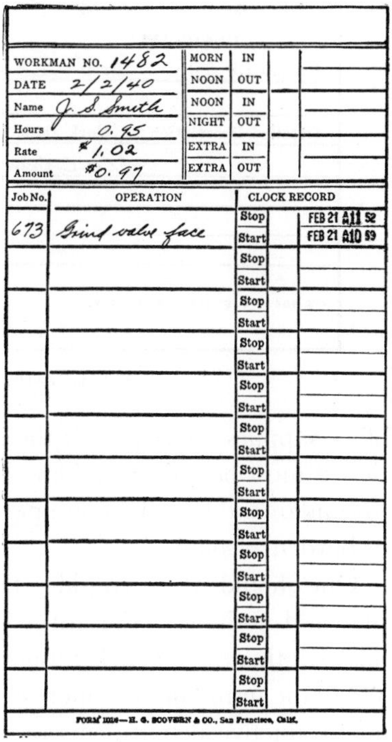

WORKMAN NO. 1482	MORN IN
DATE 2/2/40	NOON OUT
Name J. S. Smith	NOON IN
Hours 0.95	NIGHT OUT
Rate $1.02	EXTRA IN
Amount $0.97	EXTRA OUT

Job No.	OPERATION	CLOCK RECORD	
673	Grind valve face	Stop	FEB 21 A11 52
		Start	FEB 21 A10 59

Figure 7–15. Ordinary job clock time card.

New techniques have recently been developed by which the time required to perform a given operation may be determined before it actually takes place in production. These new procedures, the best known of which is called Methods-Time Measurement,[3] are applicable in the majority of cases and are very helpful in estimating labor costs for the purposes of both cost accounting and engineering economy study.

In recent years such items of cost as social security, pensions, and health and accident insurance, which are approximately proportional to direct labor costs, have increased considerably. It is now common practice to include these as a part of direct labor costs, whereas in earlier years they often were considered to be indirect costs.

THE ELEMENTS OF OVERHEAD COST

In order to produce an article or render a service, a business must pay for services and supplies that do not add directly to the value of the product. For example, it is necessary to have janitor service; taxes must be paid;

[3] Maynard, H. B., G. J. Stegemerten, and John L. Schwab: *Methods-Time Measurement,* McGraw-Hill Book Company, Inc., New York, 1948.

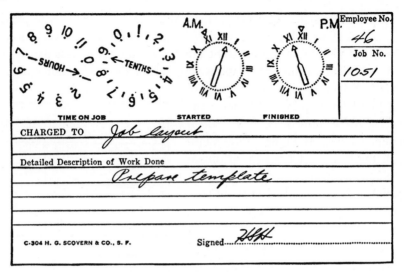

Figure 7–16.   Calculagraph time card.

office supplies are required; the indirect labor and materials previously mentioned must be paid for. Thus any expense that can not readily be charged to fundamental production operations ordinarily is charged to the overhead or burden account.

One should never consider that these expenses are nonproductive—that they add nothing to the utility or value of the product. In a well-managed business there is no such thing as a nonproductive department or expense. While the term "nonproductive" is often used, what is actually meant is that nonproductive departments or expenses add to the total value of products in an *indirect* manner. "Service departments" would be a more satisfactory and descriptive term than "nonproductive departments," since in reality they render service to the productive departments.

Included under overhead will be indirect labor, indirect materials, rent, depreciation, taxes, insurance, supervision, maintenance, and many other such items.

ADMINISTRATIVE OVERHEAD

Administrative overhead expenses are incurred for salaries of executives, accounting personnel, legal expense, etc., which are related to the over-all direction of an enterprises and thus not directly related to production activities. By considering them apart from factory overhead it is possible to determine and control them more readily. They usually are charged as a percentage of factory cost.

SALES EXPENSES

Sales expenses include all items of expense incurred in disposing of the finished products or services: salesmen's salaries and commissions, office and supervisory expenses of the sales staff, travel expenses, entertainment of customers, advertising, market surveys, etc. Where several products are involved, an attempt is usually made to allocate the proper amount of sales expense to each. Ordinarily sales expense is assigned as a percentage of production cost.

METHODS FOR DISTRIBUTING OVERHEAD COSTS

Since overhead is a real part of the cost of producing goods or services, it is essential that some method be used whereby the correct proportion of the total overhead may be charged to each unit produced in order for the true cost of production to be known. Because overhead is made up of many different items of expense, arising from different sources, exact distribution is not easy. This results in the typical problem of trying to find a procedure that is simple and easy to use and that will produce reasonably accurate and satisfactory results. To meet this problem, several methods for allocating overhead costs have been devised and are used. As might be expected, each gives approximate results, the degree of accuracy depending upon how closely actual conditions coincide with the assumptions upon which the method is based.

Five methods of allocating factory overhead costs commonly are used. These are

1. Direct-labor-cost method.
2. Direct-labor-hours method.
3. Direct-material-cost method.
4. Sum-of-direct-labor-and-direct-material-costs (prime-cost) method.
5. Machine-hour-rate method.

In each of these methods it is necessary to know what the total of the overhead costs have been if post-mortem costs are being determined, or to estimate what the total overhead costs will be if predicted or standard costs are being determined. In either case, the total overhead costs will be associated with a certain level of production. This is an important condition that should always be remembered when dealing with unit-cost data. They can only be correct for the conditions for which they were determined.

The direct-labor-cost method assumes that factory overhead of all types is incurred in direct proportion to the cost of the direct labor used. With this method the direct-labor-cost rate (overhead per dollar of direct labor) and the overhead cost per unit would be

$$\text{direct-labor-cost rate} = \frac{\text{annual overhead in dollars}}{\text{annual direct labor in dollars}}$$

$$\text{overhead per unit} = \text{direct-labor-cost rate} \times \text{direct labor cost per unit.}$$

This method obviously is simple and easy to apply. In many cases it gives quite satisfactory results. However, in many other instances it gives only very approximate results since some items of overhead, such as depreciation and taxes, have very little relationship to labor costs.

By the direct-labor-hours method, the rate for allocation (overhead per hour of direct labor) and the overhead per unit are

$$\text{direct-labor-hour rate} = \frac{\text{annual overhead in dollars}}{\text{annual direct labor hours}}$$

$$\text{overhead per unit} = \text{direct-labor-hour rate} \times \text{direct labor hours per unit.}$$

This method also is simple but is of limited accuracy. It usually is somewhat better than the direct-labor-cost method in allocating supervision expenses.

By the direct-material-cost method, the cost rate and the overhead cost per unit are

$$\text{direct-material-cost rate} = \frac{\text{annual overhead in dollars}}{\text{annual direct material in dollars}}$$

$$\text{overhead per unit} = \text{direct-material-cost rate} \times \text{direct material cost per unit.}$$

This method also gives satisfactory results in some cases but in others is quite inaccurate. For example, two products might require the same amount of floor space and equipment, yet one might be made from very expensive materials and the other from very inexpensive materials. Use of the direct-material-cost method would assign considerably different amounts for building space and equipment overhead costs when actually the same amount should be assigned in each case.

The sum-of-the-direct-labor-and-direct-material-costs method is an obvious attempt to take both factors into account in overhead distribution. The allocation rate and the overhead per unit are

$$\text{prime-cost rate} = \frac{\text{annual overhead in dollars}}{\text{annual prime cost in dollars}}$$

$$\text{overhead per unit} = \text{prime-cost rate} \times \text{prime cost per unit.}$$

While in many cases the prime-cost method gives somewhat more accuracy than any of the previous methods, there is no assurance that this will be true. The procedure is quite widely used in job shops.

The machine-hour-rate method is coming into wider use. In simple terms, the allocation rate and the overhead per unit are

$$\text{machine-hour rate} = \frac{\text{total annual overhead assigned to the machine}}{\text{hours machine is used per year}}$$

$$\begin{aligned}\text{overhead per unit} = \Sigma \text{ machine-hour rate}_1 \times \text{ hours on machine}_1 \\ + \text{ machine-hour rate}_2 \times \text{ hours on machine}_2 \\ + \ldots \text{etc.}\end{aligned}$$

Once accurate machine-hour rates have been established, the method is quite simple to use and is quite accurate. However, the task of assigning the correct amount of overhead to a given machine, or class of machines, may be quite extensive. In general, the procedure is to consider each item of overhead, such as depreciation, supervision, or space charges, and assign the cost by some method that fits the individual item. Some of the commonly used methods of allocation are

1. Building expense (rent, depreciation, taxes, insurance, etc.); proportional to floor area used.
2. Heat; proportional to floor area or volume of space.
3. Light; proportional to connected lighting load.
4. Power; proportional to connected power load.
5. Depreciation on equipment; proportional to value of equipment used.
6. Personnel department expense; proportional to number of employees.
7. Supervision expense; proportional to number of employees.

Other expenses, such as stores and accounting, must be distributed by special arbitrary methods that fit the existing conditions. It is to be expected that such a procedure should usually produce more realistic results than one of the simpler methods. However, this does not obviate the fact that the resulting distribution of overhead costs is tied to an assumed set of operating conditions and volume of output.

RESULTS BY DIFFERENT METHODS OF ALLOCATION

It should be apparent that quite different total costs may be obtained for the same product when different procedures are used for the allocation of overhead costs. The magnitude of the difference will, of course, depend on the extent to which each method produces or fails to produce results which are in accord with the facts. Table 7–1 shows the factory cost for a product

TABLE 7–1   Factory Costs Determined by Four Methods of Overhead Cost Allocation

	Direct-labor-cost method	Direct-materials-cost method	Prime-cost method	Machine-hour-rate method
Direct Labor	$ 8.24	$ 8.24	$ 8.24	$ 8.24
Direct Materials	14.60	14.60	14.60	14.60
Factory Overhead	7.31	14.80	10.82	4.02
Factory Cost	$30.15	$37.64	$33.66	$26.86

when computed by four different allocation procedures. This was one of eighteen products made by a company. Overhead costs had been computed by the direct-labor-cost method and the company had almost decided to discontinue production of the item, believing that the costs were too high to permit a satisfactory profit to be made. As may be noted, when a careful machine-hour allocation analysis was made, it was found that the actual overhead costs for this product were considerably less than had been thought. While this is a rather extreme case, it illustrates the importance of correct distribution of overhead cost. This does not mean, of course, that if one of the simpler methods of allocation is being used the results are necessarily incorrect.

As the investment per worker increases, the ratio of overhead costs to direct labor costs, or to direct material costs, usually increases considerably. This situation increases the importance of the problem of correct allocation of overhead costs.

INTEREST AS AN ELEMENT OF COST

There has been considerable discussion among accountants and engineers as to the handling of interest (profit) on owned capital as an element of cost. As has been pointed out in earlier chapters, this form of interest must be considered in nearly all economy problems. It is apparent, however, that cost figures which include interest on owned capital will be considerably different from similar figures in which interest has not been included.

The manner in which the minimum profit on owned capital is considered is not of prime importance. It is important that the method used be correct and that the figures which result be understood.

In most cost determinations for economy studies, it appears to be good practice to omit minimum profit as a cost item and consider it as a separate factor. However, in numerous instances, including minimum profit as a cost item makes comparisons somewhat easier. In such cases minimum profit may be included as a cost element, but this should be clearly indicated so there will be no doubt as to what the item is.

When minimum profit is included as a cost, one should keep in mind the fact that the resulting cost is affected by the rate of profit used. Thus total costs may be made abnormally high by using a high rate of profit. Similarly, costs will be low if low rates of profit are used. Since there is no exact method of determining what rate of return should be used, it is evident that one should exercise considerable care in selecting the rate which is to be used in a particular problem.

It is apparent that if an interest (profit) charge is included in computing *Total Cost* in the procedure shown in Figure 7–12, there would already be a profit on the investment included in the total cost before the *Profit* is added to determine the selling price. Unless this fact were taken into account, there would be a double profit included in the selling price.

When one wishes to compare the production costs of one company with those of another, it is clear that some method of considering the amount of capital required, and the cost of obtaining it, is desirable. The obvious method is to consider interest upon invested capital as an element of cost.

One finds that many of the uniform accounting systems recommended by various trade associations consider interest on owned capital as a cost of production. In this way the association can make a valid comparison of the true costs of the various members, since the amount of capital utilized is reflected in the cost figures.[2] With all the member companies figuring their costs in the same manner, the cost figures of the various producers yield much more significant information. If such figures are used only for legitimate control purposes, there is no harm and much good in considering interest as a cost in computing them.

It is apparent that the handling of profit on owned capital as a cost is a debatable subject. In most ordinary business transactions it is not considered to be a cost and is not included in standard cost figures.

CONTROL THROUGH STANDARD COSTS

If a product to be produced is standardized, is to be made by a specified series of operations, and is to be produced in a certain volume, it is fairly

[2] There is evidence that one reason trade associations recommend inclusion of interest on capital as a cost is to influence small marginal producers not to cut selling prices. Such producers tend not to consider the cost of obtaining capital and thus sell their output at prices which may yield less than a reasonable return upon their actual investment.

easy to determine the standard costs that should be encountered. Under such conditions, the only reason why *actual* costs should vary from the standards would be that actual operations differed from the theoretical procedures which were assumed and specified in establishing the standard costs. This situation provides a means for controlling operations in order to assure that all activities and expenditures are occurring in the desired manner. Using a system of reports on current expenditures and production, the actual costs can be compared with the standard costs. Deviations of the actual from the standard indicate where corrective action is needed.

Knowledge of production difficulties through deviations of actual costs from the standards permits corrective action to be taken while production is in progress, rather than after production is finished and costs have become badly out of line. The situation is somewhat like that which would occur if two trains were sent simultaneously from Chicago to Los Angeles, the engineer of one being told only to start and make certain that he arrived in 39 hours while the engineer of the other was given a complete schedule, and all sections and operations of the railroad were operated according to this schedule. It would be only by chance that the first train arrived on time, or at all. On the other hand, using reports on the progress of the second train, the proper sections of track could be cleared so that it could proceed on schedule.

In setting up standard costs, it is important that they be practical as well as theoretical standards. For example, in nearly all cases there will be some unavoidable waste in material and labor. Certain excess overhead expenses will occur which can never be anticipated. These items should be considered carefully and a reasonable allowance provided when a standard cost is computed. Unless they are included, after careful consideration, much grief is likely to result.

In using standard costs for control purposes the department foremen and managers should be held accountable only for those items of expense over which they can exercise some control. For example, depreciation rates, wage rates, and other such items are usually established by persons outside the operating departments. It is obviously unfair to expect a foreman to be concerned over variations in these expenses, over which he has absolutely no control.

EFFECT OF CHANGES IN PRODUCTION RATE

Standard costs must be established for a particular set of conditions. If actual conditions, under which production is carried out, vary from those assumed, it is only logical to expect that the actual costs will differ from the standards. Such differences may occur in material cost, labor cost, or overhead expense. It is natural to expect certain variations under ordinary operating conditions. Provision for such variations is made in the standard costs by including reasonable allowances. These common deviations are charged to *Variance Accounts*. A variance account is usually provided for each cost element—material, labor, and overhead. Under normal conditions the deviations should, over a period of time, be in line with the allowances which have been provided in the standard costs. The balances of the variance accounts are periodically charged to Profit and Loss.

The greatest problem in handling the variations from the standards arises when the volume of production is different from that assumed in establishing the standards. The problem may be clarified by a simple illustration. Assume that a man has driven his car, *on the average,* 6,000 miles per year. He pays $2.50 per month ($30.00 per year) as rent on a garage for storing his car. He thus figures that it costs him $0.005 per mile for garage rent. He considers this to be his "standard cost" for garage rent. During the following year he drives his car only 1,000 miles. According to his cost standard he should pay only $0.005 × 1,000, or $5.00, for garage rent. Obviously the results are in error, because his operating "volume" was different from the standard. His standard costs failed to absorb $25.00 of his actual expense. Similarly, if he should drive the car more than 6,000 miles per year, the actual cost of garage rental would be more than absorbed by the standard costs.

In connection with industrial production, under- and overabsorbed costs present serious difficulties. If a plant is forced to operate at less than normal capacity, the total unit cost will nearly always exceed the standard cost. This would indicate that the products would have to be sold at a higher price to obtain a reasonable profit. Yet at such times higher selling prices are usually out of the question. It is more likely that the goods would have to be sold at lower prices. If the inventory value of finished goods were based upon the actual unit cost, inventories would tend to have higher values, although from the standpoint of profit possibilities they would actually be worth less.

From the viewpoint of control, further difficulties are encountered. Actual costs would exceed the standards. Pressure would be put upon the operating personnel to reduce costs. Yet most of the increased costs would be due to increased overhead, over which the operating staff would have little or no control. Similarly, when production is greater than normal, the actual costs would be less than the standards. This would make it appear that the operating departments were more efficient than usual, which would not be the case.

It is apparent that such variations in unit costs are due, not to production methods, but to the extent to which the production facilities are utilized. Before a comparison of standard and actual costs can be significant, the actual costs must be adjusted to account for the difference between actual output and the assumed normal.

For control work a satisfactory result is obtained either by using an output factor or allowance which is applied to actual costs before they are compared with the standard costs or by supplying new standards each month, these being adjusted for the scheduled output for the period. In this manner the production departments are held accountable for those production costs which they can control.

For accounting and managerial purposes it is customary to base inventories and production costs upon the standards, regardless of volume. The over- or underabsorbed costs are charged to profit-and-loss accounts. They are considered the costs resulting from managerial policy and efficiency. Thus, since they can be controlled by the management, it is up to the management to adjust policies so as to keep them at a minimum.

Obviously, over- or underabsorbed costs will, to a great extent, depend on the volume assumed for computing the standard costs. By assuming a small enough volume, underabsorbed costs would be eliminated. However, this would result in high standard costs, making higher selling prices probable and increased operating efficiency unlikely. On the other hand, if too large volume is assumed, too low selling prices may result, and the operating departments may lose all respect for standards which can never be attained. Thus, as in all cases where standards are being established, great care must be taken that they will be reasonable, workable figures which will be useful for both accounting and control purposes.

THE USE OF STANDARD COSTS IN ECONOMY STUDIES

When one recognizes that standard costs are linked to a definite set of conditions, it is apparent that they should not be used in cases where the conditions are different from those for which they were determined. Similarly, it should be kept in mind that standard costs ordinarily are based upon the assumption that something *is to be done*. For many economy studies, therefore, standard cost data cannot be used, at least in their usual form, since such studies may be concerned with a change in conditions, or with the cost of *not doing* something. Likewise, many economy studies deal with activities which have not yet been carried out. It can not be expected that there will be cost accounting data available for such activities.

An understanding of what is included in cost-accounting data will enable the engineer to know what needed and useful data may be available to him from the cost-accounting records. Such understanding will also prevent him from attempting to use cost data for purposes for which they were never intended or in cases to which they do not apply. While the cost accountant may not have cost data in the exact form desired by the engineer, he may be able to provide the desired data and thus be of great help in supplying information for an economy study.

PROBLEMS

7–1   Explain the fundamental difference in the viewpoint of the accountant and that of the engineer making economy studies.

7–2   Into what two categories are equities usually divided on a balance sheet?

7–3   What determines whether an asset is "current" or "fixed"?

7–4   Through what accounting procedure are fixed assets normally converted into cash?

7–5   What is a comparative balance sheet, and why is it used?

7–6   What are two basic uses for an income-and-expense statement?

7–7   Explain the relationship between the "balances" of the various ledger accounts and the balance sheet and the income-and-expense statement.

7–8   Explain what is meant by *Reserve for Depreciation* as shown on a balance sheet.

7–9   The following are the balances of the personal ledger accounts of John Doe. Make a balance sheet and determine his net worth.

Cash in bank	$ 970	House (at cost)	$12,000
Balance owed on car	1,100	Car (present trade-in value)	2,200
Account at department store	40	Furniture	3,000
Mortgage on house	6,000	Taxes due	75
Government savings bonds	500		

7–10   Explain the effect of including the *Reserve for Depreciation* entry on the liability side of a balance sheet.

7–11   Give three objectives of cost accounting.

7–12   What are the three usual elements of costs?

7–13   Explain how the "LIFO" method of valuing inventory helps keep production costs current.

7–14   What are five commonly used methods of allocating overhead costs?

7–15   In a job-type machine shop which of the three following methods of overhead cost allocation would be most likely to give best results, and why?

    (*a*)   Direct-labor-cost method

    (*b*)   Machine-hour-rate method

    (*c*)   Prime cost method

7–16 A company was found to be charging 200 per cent of direct labor cost as overhead on an operation requiring a group of workers, three of whom were receiving $1.70 per hour and one $2.40 per hour. The equipment involved cost $3,000.00 when new and had an estimated life of ten years. The only power requirements were for a ½-horsepower motor. Floor space occupied was 450 square feet. The workers worked as a group and required very little supervision. Does the overhead charge appear reasonable? Why or why not?

7–17 The plating solution in an automatic plating unit is renewed once each week, during which thousands of parts of several different designs are put through the solution.

a. Would this solution be charged as a direct material, and why or why not?

b. How would the plating metal be charged?

7–18 Explain how standards costs are used for control.

7–19 What is a "variance" account?

7–20 Give a logical basis for distribution of the following overhead cost items:

(*a*) Depreciation on equipment

(*b*) Night watchmen's salaries

(*c*) Fire insurance

(*d*) Supervisory salaries

CHAPTER 8

Read

Basic
Economy
Study Patterns

Just as there usually are two or more alternatives to consider in making an economy study, there are several procedures available for making such studies. Each procedure or pattern has certain advantages and limitations. There is no one pattern that will provide a categorical answer in all cases without the necessity for interpretation. The variety of conditions and viewpoints for economy studies is too great to permit this.

Six basic patterns are frequently used. While one of these seems to be a somewhat more basic approach than the others, one can not truly say that any one of the methods produces better or more accurate results than the others. Instead, it is a matter of the results produced by the various patterns having different significance and therefore requiring different interpretation in order for correct decisions to follow. Because of this situation, one may expect to use and/or encounter all of these patterns. It is therefore imperative that each be thoroughly understood so that they may be used and interpreted correctly.

It also is important to recognize that economy studies may be made from different viewpoints. For example, one may make an economy study in which he is concerned only with the potential profitability of a venture, without any consideration of the source of the investment funds that would be required, thus not considering whether owned capital or borrowed capital is to be used. For some purposes, primarily for preliminary analyses, such a viewpoint is quite satisfactory. A procedure of this sort assumes that after the inherent feasibility of the project has been determined, one will then consider the additional problems related to the acquisition and ownership of the required capital.

A little thought makes it apparent that one can not make a complete economy study without considering the source of the required capital. If borrowed capital is used, there will be interest to be paid and deducted from earnings before income taxes can be determined. Also, when borrowed capital is used, one must consider the requirements for repayment of the founds at the agreed-upon time.

Another possibility is to make economy studies from the viewpoint of the owners of the capital utilized. In the vast majority of situations, except in the case of publicly-financed projects which will be discussed in detail in Chapter 20, most, if not all, of the capital used in business ventures is owned capital. For this reason, most economy studies are made from the viewpoint of owned capital, borrowed capital being considered as a separate item when necessary. The patterns discussed in this chapter are based upon this concept.

RATE-OF-RETURN-ON-THE-REQUIRED-INVESTMENT METHOD

Since the most commonly used method of measuring the effectiveness of an investment of capital is to determine the financial efficiency or annual rate of return obtained from the capital, it is to be expected that one basic method for making economy studies would follow this pattern. As expressed in Equation (1.3), this rate of return is

$$\text{rate of return} = \frac{\text{annual net profit}}{\text{capital invested}}.$$

As was pointed out in Chapter 1, this rate of return may be either before or after income taxes.

The usual accounting procedures that are used to record and determine the effectiveness of financial investments provide results in terms of profit before and after taxes, profit per share of stock, or rate of return per unit of invested capital. Thus managers and investors are accustomed to measuring financial effectiveness in these terms. It is to be expected that a procedure for an economy study which provides results in these terms will have the very considerable advantage of being easily understood by management and investors. Such is the case of the *rate-of-return-on-the-required-investment method*.[1] Just as rate of return is a measure of financial effectiveness that is used in almost all types of investment situations, so can this economy study pattern be used in virtually all types of situations. However, this obvious

---

[1] This method is commonly called simply *rate-of-return method*.

advantage does not mean that other procedures can not or should not be used in situations where their advantages may be important.

The basic pattern for the rate-of-return-on-the-required-investment method is as follows:

Annual revenue = gross receipts = ' G

Less: Annual expenses

Out-of-pocket expenses for operation and
maintenance = $O + M$
(Direct labor)
(Direct materials)
(All overhead, including property taxes,
except depreciation)

Interest on borrowed funds (if any) = I

Depreciation = $(C - C_L)/s_{\overline{L}|} = D$

Net profits before taxes = $E_b = G - (O + M + I + D)$

Annual rate of return on required investment, C (before taxes) $= \dfrac{E_b}{C} \times 100$

Net profits after taxes = $E_b - T = E_a$

Annual rate of return on required investment (after taxes) $= \dfrac{E_a}{C} \times 100$

In this pattern the required investment, C, obviously is owned capital. There are, of course, many situations where all of the capital is borrowed. Such cases can be handled within the basic pattern by treating this capital as though it were owned and then determining whether the computed rate of return is adequate to cover the interest costs on the borrowed capital plus the risk factors. Because of the income tax situation, the owned and borrowed capital must be treated separately.

Examination of the basic pattern for this method makes it apparent that this procedure may be applied to a single project or to any number of alternatives. Likewise, the fact that the incomes from various alternatives may be different offers no difficulty in its use. These advantages contribute to its wide use.

All of the income and expense, or cost, items in this method are treated in the same manner as in the other basic patterns. The interest or profit rate included in the depreciation calculation requires some special consideration. If, as is the usual case, the capital recovered through depreciation is retained and used in the enterprise, the interest rate in the depreciation calculation should be the profit rate which these funds will earn. In using the sinking fund depreciation method the earnings of the depreciation funds belong to the sinking (depreciation) fund. This is essential in order to meet the requirements of the sinking fund assumption and provide for complete recovery of the invested capital. These earnings are thus part of the cost of depreciation and as such are not subject to income taxes. Therefore the profit rate used in the sinking fund depreciation calculation (or in using a capital recovery factor, as will be discussed later) should be the rate *before* income taxes. In an existing enterprise, since depreciation funds from a specific project can not be considered to be reinvested in a particular item of property, the profit rate will be the average rate earned by all of the capital invested in the business.

The profit rate used in the depreciation calculation may be different from the rate that is anticipated, or considered as a necessary minimum, from the project considered in the economy study. This is due to the fact that there usually is no assurance that the depreciation funds can be reinvested in the particular project being considered, or even in future projects that are of equal profitability. Of course, it always is hoped that all new projects will be more profitable than existing operations. However, reality forces one to recognize that this can not always be true. In addition, investment in new projects that are more favorable than existing operations helps to increase the average rate of return of the entire enterprise.

DETERMINATION OF THE SUFFICIENCY OF AN ANTICIPATED RATE OF RETURN

When the rate-of-return method is used, it is necessary to decide whether the computed rate of return is sufficient to justify the investment. This often is not a simple matter and can not be reduced to a simple, numerical procedure. However, the same problem must be faced whenever the other basic economy study patterns are used, although in some of them it may appear, at first glance, that such is not the case. In the rate-of-return procedure the rate of return upon the required investment, which usually is the most important single factor to be considered in any investment decision, appears as a separate and distinct item and may be considered along with the related factors upon which the investment decision will be based. Trying to set up a single rate of return such that any greater rate will justify investment is rather like trying to define a tall man. Thus in order to determine whether the predicted rate of return is sufficiently great to justify the investment of capital, one must consider a number of factors.

It will perhaps be helpful to review briefly just what is involved when money is invested in an ordinary industrial enterprise. First, the capital is used to buy certain properties which are to be utilized to produce goods or services. One expects to obtain income from the sale of such goods or services. If the income so derived is greater than the cost of producing and selling, a profit will remain. In this process of obtaining a profit in an industrial enterprise, one usually has no guarantee that he will be able to sell the products. Neither is there any *absolute* knowledge of what the cost of production will be. In addition, there is no assurance that the original capital will be recovered. Thus there is usually a considerable element of uncertainty as to whether the expected profit and recovery of capital will occur. The very fact that time must elapse before the capital will be recovered causes uncertainty. In nearly every case uncertainty exists, regardless of what care has been used in making the study. In some cases this uncertainty will be very great, while in others it may be rather small. But in practically all cases, risk is involved. In the end, one must decide whether the anticipated rate of profit is sufficient to offset whatever risk may exist, and whether the proposed investment is the most satisfactory possible for the capital involved.

Since it is not possible to obtain an absolute measure of the risk element in any enterprise, the most logical method of solution is to compare the possible profit with that which could be obtained from other investment possibilities where risk factors are known or are comparable. One basis for such comparison may be the rate of return which is obtained if capital is invested in some conservative manner, in savings banks, government bonds or the bonds of some well-established corporation, for example. In such investments the element of risk still exists but is very small. As long as the economic structure of the nation is at all sound, the risk might be said to be the minimum which is possible for any type of investment. On the other hand, in most cases the capital which is available for investment in a business venture would not be utilized in such conservative investments even if it were not to be risked in the particular venture being considered, but would be invested or used in some other business opportunity. Thus, one usually must decide between two or more possible uses for the capital. Since the capital is very probably being used in some manner at the time the advisability of a venture is being considered, the basis for comparison ordinarily is the rate of return expected from the capital if it is not used in the new project being considered. Such a rate may be quite different from those which correspond to conservative investment yields.

If capital is placed in a very conservative investment, such as those which have been mentioned, the rate of return is rather small, usually varying anywhere from 2 to 4%. This rate of return will change with time. During the years prior to 1928 it was possible to obtain a 5 or 6% return on conservative and sound investments. Since about 1930 one has been fortunate if he could obtain 2 to 4%. Thus the rate of return which may be obtained with a minimum of risk will vary from time to time.

Next in line would be the rate which could be obtained from a high-grade bond. This rate is usually about 1 to $1\frac{1}{2}\%$ higher than going rates of interest. Thus, when bank interest rates are 3%, highest-grade bonds yield 4 to $4\frac{1}{2}\%$. The risk involved in such investments is definitely greater than is associated with insured bank deposits, but is still very small. Such investments would fail to pay their interest and become insecure only in case of a national disaster.

As the next example, one might consider high-grade preferred stocks which yield a return somewhat more than highest grade bonds. Thus such stocks pay about 5 to 6%. The risk is here greater, especially the possibility of the capital value of the investment being lessened or wiped out in time of severe business depression.

Common stocks of well-established companies usually may be purchased to yield returns of $1\frac{1}{2}$ to 2% above those of preferred stocks. Thus a return of 6 to 7% *may* be realized. At times such stocks *may* even yield returns as high as 8 or 9%. The word "may" is emphasized advisedly. These stocks ordinarily yield such returns only when business conditions are good. Their market value fluctuates from day to day, so there is no assurance of receiving the purchase price if the stock is sold. Of course, they may increase in value. Obviously, there is quite a bit of risk involved in such investments. However, many such stocks are those of large and well-established corporations whose histories are well known. They would not be considered highly speculative.

Where a comparison is to be made with the earning rate of typical business ventures, fairly high rates may be expected. For example, the average return on stockholders' equity for all manufacturing companies reporting to the Securities Exchange Commission during 1951–1955 was 22.9% before taxes and 11% after taxes. Obviously there is considerably more risk in such business ventures than in some of the types of investments mentioned in previous paragraphs. This is particularly true when entirely new business ventures are being considered. Thus it is apparent that capital will seldom be invested in an industrial undertaking unless an economy study indicates the possibility of receiving a profit, after taxes, of more than 8%. And such a low profit figure would correspond only to an enterprise about which there was a great amount of accurate information. In the average business, a prospective return in the neighborhood of 10 to 15% is required to justify the uncertainties which exist in the facts revealed by well-prepared economy studies. A little cold consideration of the risks actually attendant in many proposed investments makes required returns of 20 and 25% seem well justified.

Thus the only satisfactory answer to the question, "How great a return is enough?" is that the return should be commensurate with that which can be obtained from other investments in which there is the same amount of risk. The answer is best obtained by the method of comparison which has been discussed. It is a common rule in business that money should not be invested in ordinary business enterprises unless the prospective return is at least two or three times the rate which can be obtained from conservative investments such as high grade bonds. Thus from 7 to 10% would usually be considered a minimum required return. These figures would hold only when the enterprise was considered to involve no more than moderate risk.

It is also quite apparent that a rate of return which would be satisfactory to one investor may be entirely too low to satisfy another. Thus, personal opinions and other items, such as the amount and availability of capital, may influence the final investment decision.

It should be mentioned that whether or not one should invest in very risky enterprises, even when they offer the prospect of very high rates of profit, is an entirely different question.

ANNUAL-COST METHOD

The annual-cost method is similar to the rate-of-return method, with one important exception. This exception is that a minimum required profit on the invested capital is included as a cost. The basic pattern for this method is as follows:

Annual revenue $=$ gross receipts $=$ G

Less: Annual costs

    Out-of-pocket costs for operation and
    maintenance $=$ $O + M$
      (Direct labor)
      (Direct materials)
      (All overhead, including property taxes,
      except depreciation)

    Interest on borrowed funds (if any) $=$ I

    Depreciation $= (C - C_L)/s_{\overline{L}|} =$ D

    Minimum required profit $= C \times i = P_{bt}$ or P_{at}
Excess of revenue over costs (before taxes) $= G - [O + M + I + D + P_{bt}]$
Excess of revenue over costs (after taxes)
$$= G - [O + M + I + D + P_{at} + T]$$

In using this method it is apparent that an evaluation of the risks connected with a proposed investment must be made at the time that the minimum required profit is computed. If this is done correctly, the basic premise of the method—that if the excess of revenue over costs is not less than zero the proposed investment is justified—is valid. It is obvious that if the minimum required profit does not properly reflect the risks, the results will be incorrect. This means that the use, occasionally found in practice, of some average rate of return unrelated to the specific case involved is incorrect.

Very often the costs for depreciation and minimum required profit are combined, when using the annual cost method, by making use of the capital recovery factor, CRF. Using this procedure the cost items are:

Capital recovery with minimum profit $= (C - C_L) \times \text{CRF} + C_L \times i = CRP$
Excess of revenue over costs (before taxes) $= G - [O + M + I + CRP]$
Excess of revenue over costs (after taxes) $= G - [O + M + I + CRP + T]$

Unfortunately, two difficulties arise in attempting to use this capital-recovery-factor procedure. The first is that, as explained previously, it does not necessarily follow that the rate of return that will be earned by the reinvested depreciation funds is the same as the minimum profit rate that must be required to justify the particular investment being considered. This difficulty is avoided if capital recovery is separated from minimum required profit.

The second difficulty arises from income taxes. As was discussed previously, in computing the cost of depreciation by the sinking-fund method, which is a part of the capital recovery factor, CRF, the rate of profit *before* taxes must be used. However, the rate involved in the minimum required profit is dependent upon whether the study includes income taxes. If a study is to determine the excess of income over costs *before* income taxes, as very often is the case, the minimum required profit rate is the rate before taxes and no difficulty is encountered. On the other hand, if the study is to determine the excess of income over costs *after* income taxes, the minimum required profit rate is the rate after taxes, and there would thus be two rates involved in the capital recovery factor. Therefore, when using the annual cost procedure for conditions where income taxes are considered, it is desirable to use separate calculations for capital recovery and for minimum required profit. It is true that in some economy studies of this type the error resulting from the use of the capital recovery factor may be less than those errors resulting from other factors, but this does not seem to be a valid excuse for its use.

The annual-cost method sometimes appears to be somewhat easier to use and interpret than the rate-of-return procedure, since if the total costs are equal to or less than the revenue, the investment is supposedly justified. It thus appears that one can avoid the necessity for determining the adequacy of a rate of return. However, this is not quite the case, since one must analyze the conditions and risks in order to decide what minimum rate of profit to include as a cost. The method is very convenient for use in comparing several alternatives which produce the same revenue. However, when the revenues of the several alternatives are not the same, it is not as easy to use as the rate-of-return procedure. It has the further weakness of not making obvious the significance of the excess of revenue over costs when such an excess exists, and this often is the case. Any such excess, of course, represents a profit *in addition* to that included as a cost. When income taxes are to be considered, this added profit will also be subject to income tax if the income tax included as a cost was computed only on the minimum required profit.

The annual-cost method is useful in comparing the effectiveness of similar operations in different companies, which require different amounts of investment. The inclusion of a minimum required profit takes the different amounts of capital into account for comparison purposes and thus emphasizes these differences.

This method, of course, suffers a certain disadvantage in that it includes the item of profit as a cost, although it will not be included as such for either accounting or tax purposes. Also, it sometimes is necessary to do some explaining of the inclusion of this profit item to those who are not accustomed to seeing profit included as a cost. Probably the most important fact to remember when using and understanding the annual-cost method is that a profit has been included as one of the cost elements; this always must be kept in mind in interpreting the results.

THE PAYOUT METHOD

In the payout method a calculation is made to determine how much time would have to elapse after an investment is made until the capital could be recovered through depreciation (capital recovery) and profits. Basically the pattern is as follows:

Invested capital $=$ C

Portion recoverable through scrap
or salvage at end of life $=$ C_L

Annual revenue $=$ gross receipts $=$ G

Annual out-of-pocket expenses
for operation and maintenance $= O + M$
  (Direct materials)
  (Direct labor)
  (All overhead, including property
  taxes, except depreciation and
  interest)

Income taxes $=$ T

Number of years for payout (without profit) $= \dfrac{C - C_L}{G - [O + M + T]}$

The portion of the denominator of this equation within the brackets represents all of the annual disbursements which must be paid out of pocket. Whatever remains after these expenses are paid out of income can be applied toward the recovery of the invested capital. Obviously this formula does not consider possible earnings from reinvested capital that is recovered during the payout period. It is thus not an exact expression.

Some engineers and managers include an annual profit as one item of cost. Such a practice makes the expression for payout period

$$\text{Number of years for payout (including profit)} = \frac{C - C_L}{G - [O + M + P + T]}.$$

Including profit in this manner makes it possible to take into account interest which must be paid if the invested capital is borrowed. In this case I is substituted for P in the equation. However, including profit also raises a number of complications. In the first place, profit on owned capital is not an out-of-pocket cost. However, more serious difficulties are the matter of what rate of profit should be used and the great effect a change in the profit rate can have on the payout period. By varying the profit rate the payout period may be made of almost any length desired. Certainly if profit is included, it should be at a rate no greater than the *actual* cost of the capital used.

A further serious weakness of the payout-period method is the fact that it does not take into account the actual or probable life of the depreciable property that is involved. As will be discussed more fully in Chapter 11, this can easily lead to erroneous decisions when the procedure is used to compare two or more alternatives.

Because of the several weaknesses of this method, it probably should be used only for making a check on a proposed investment to determine what length of time would have to elapse before actual income will have exceeded actual out-of-pocket expenses by an amount equal to the capital investment—in other words, how long it will be before the investors can abandon the enterprise without losing any of their capital, but also without receiving any interest on their funds.

PRESENT-WORTH-COST METHOD

A fourth basic pattern for economy studies is based on the concept of present worth. Present-worth cost may be computed in two ways. The first determines the present worth of the annual costs. In this case depreciation, taxes, operation and maintenance costs, and amortization of nonrecurring expenses are included. This procedure is most advantageous when the annual costs will be uniform throughout the life of the project or study period. For these conditions the basic pattern is

$$\text{Present-worth cost} = (D + O + M + I)\,a_{\overline{L}|}.$$

More generally expenditures are not uniform each year. For this condition the present worth of all lump expenditures plus the present worth of any recurring annual expenditures is determined. It is customary to include the first cost of all assets, thus eliminating the consideration of depreciation or amortization costs. Similarly, any consideration of the cost of money is eliminated, since the inclusion of first cost provides for recovery of capital plus a return on the investment. Using this very general concept, the basic pattern for present-worth cost is

Present-worth cost =

$$C + (O + M + I)_1 v^1 + (O + M + I)_2 v^2 \cdots + (O + M + I)_L v^L.$$

For comparing two or more alternatives which produce the same revenue, it theoretically is only necessary to determine the present-worth cost of each and select the one having the minimum cost. For studying the feasibility of an individual project, or several alternatives which produce different incomes, the present worth cost must be subtracted from the present value of all of the future revenue. Since the present value of all future revenue is equal to

$$G_1 v^1 + G_2 v^2 \cdots + G_L v^L + C_L v^L,$$

by subtracting the present-worth cost from this value, the desired difference can be found. If the present value of the future income exceeds the present-worth cost, the project is satisfactory.

The present-worth-cost procedure is used quite extensively in making economy studies involving long-lived structures in the civil engineering field. Alternative structures such as bridges, dams, and roads produce the same service or income and there is considerable assurance of their continued use throughout their long lives. For such conditions the present-worth-cost method is satisfactory. However, for more modern conditions of dynamic private enterprise the method has several serious disadvantages.

First, it is apparent that the interest rate is a very important item in this method, since it enters into each term except the first cost. It is therefore essential that the rate used must be considered very carefully. If the selection between alternatives, or the decision regarding a single project, is to be based solely on the present-worth-cost data without considerable interpretation, the interest (profit) rate must include a full consideration of all of the risk factors.

A second disadvantage of the present-worth procedure is that it appears to assume that the present value of all of the future expenses is to be paid at one time. This, of course, is not the case, but the assumption frequently seems to cause some difficulty in the minds of engineers who attempt to use this method.

A third difficulty is that the present-worth cost usually is an amount of considerable magnitude, being the summation of a number of annual costs. This sometimes results in figures of such magnitude that they may be misleading. If the number of years involved is fairly large, a relatively small annual cost can result in a quite large change in the present-worth cost. For example, in comparing several alternatives, it must be remembered that any differences in present-worth costs represent the sum of the present value of all of the annual differences. It frequently is helpful to convert a difference in present-worth cost into the equivalent annual difference in order to obtain a value that has somewhat more meaning when attempting to make a decision.

RECEIPTS vs. DISBURSEMENTS METHOD

A fifth economy study procedure that may be used is one in which the receipts and disbursements, made in connection with a venture, are related by means of suitable interest factors. This method is particularly useful in

cases where, in order to finance a venture, several investments of capital are made at different times. Such a problem is worked by this method in Chapter 10.

The receipts vs. disbursements technique is illustrated in Figure 8–1. Here an initial investment (disbursement) D_0 is made at the beginning of the first year. Profit (or interest) increases the worth of the disbursement during the year. At the end of the year receipts amounting to R_1 are received, reducing the amount remaining invested in the venture. Similarly, receipts of R_2 are received at the end of the second year. At the end of the

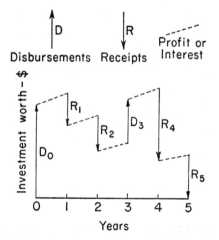

Figure 8–1. Representation of the relationship between receipts and disbursements to determine rate of return.

third year there is a net disbursement, D_3. This might be the result of additional investment greater than the receipts of the year, or be due to annual disbursements being greater than the annual receipts. Receipts R_4 and R_5 are indicated at the ends of the fourth and fifth years, respectively.

It is apparent for the set of conditions shown, or for any set of disbursements-receipts relationships, that there is some rate of return (profit) which will exactly reduce the worth of the investment to zero at the end of the time period. For the case shown in Figure 8–1 the relationship may be written

$$D_0 s^5 - R_1 s^4 - R_2 s^3 + D_3 s^2 - R_4 s^1 - R_5 = 0$$

Unfortunately, the value of i, the profit rate, which will fulfill this relationship can not be computed directly. However, it usually is not very difficult to determine the rate by trial and error, and thus to find the actual rate of return.

The above expression relates the relationship of the receipts and disbursements at the end of the fifth year. However, Figure 8–1 also represents the present worth, or *discounted cash value,* of the cumulative receipts and disbursements at the beginning of the first year. The mathematical expression for this relationship is

$$D_0 v^0 - R_1 v^1 - R_2 v^2 + D_3 v^3 - R_4 v^4 - R_5 v^5 = 0$$

From this expression it is evident that the present worth of the disbursements is equal to the present worth of the receipts, at some particular rate of profit or interest.

It will be recognized that this economy study method is closely related to the present-worth-cost procedure, except that the rate of profit is determined instead of relating the revenues and costs by an assumed rate of profit.

This method, which represents the discounted value of the cash flow of a venture, is applicable to virtually any situation. It also determines the rate of return of the particular venture being considered without any reference to other portions of a business of which it may be a part. However, except in cases where there are several investments of capital at different times, other methods of analysis are usually easier to employ. The method may be used to determine the rate of return after income taxes by treating all receipts and disbursements on an after-tax basis.

CAPITALIZED-COST METHOD

The capitalized-cost method is a modification of the present-worth-cost procedure. As was discussed in Chapter 4, capitalized cost is the immediate cost of providing a given property and its service in *perpetuity.*

In the early years of economy study history the capitalized-cost concept was used quite extensively. Studies usually involved such structures as dams, bridges, sewers, or railroad rights-of-way, which were thought to have perpetual life and/or use. Most modern structures and projects, even some of those above, are not considered to have such extensive lives. Further, there is very little difference between the capitalized cost of a structure and the present-worth cost based on fifty or seventy-five years, unless the interest rate is quite high, and this is seldom the case for projects of the type where an unlimited life might possibly be realistic. As a result, most modern economy studies assign limited, and more realistic, lives to structures, and the capitalized-cost procedure has given way to the present-worth-cost or other methods. However, the capitalized-cost method is used occasionally, but ordinarily only for cases where the original structure, such as a dam, will not need to be replaced in the foreseeable future. In such instances the capitalized cost is the sum of the first cost and an amount sufficient to provide, from the interest on it, for operation and maintenance in perpetuity. Since most projects for which the capitalized-cost method might be used are governmentally financed, so that no taxes are involved, the expression for capitalized cost becomes

$$\text{Capitalized cost} = C + (O + M)/i.$$

The capitalized-cost procedure has all of the disadvantages of the present-worth method.

STEPS IN MAKING ECONOMY STUDIES

In making economy studies it is helpful to have an over-all plan of attack so that important factors may not be overlooked. A ten-step procedure usually can be used. The sequence in which the steps must be considered is not always as listed since the particular economy study pattern used will dictate the sequence for those after Step 7.

STEP 1. *Determining the objectives.* Although the broad purpose of economy studies is the assurance of the best use of capital, not all have identical objectives. In some cases one is concerned with an entirely new venture. Other cases may involve a selection between equivalent alternatives for accomplishing the same results, or the possibility of replacing an existing structure or machine by a new one, or the economy of a change in operations to meet a temporary change in demand. Obviously it is easier to make an economy study if one knows exactly what type of decision must be based on the results. The degree of accuracy which must be achieved and the thoroughness of the study are also determined by the objectives. Further, the basic pattern to be used may be determined by the objective to be accomplished.

STEP 2. *The number of alternatives to be studied.* In many cases the number of alternatives which might be considered may be quite large, or in some instances might be almost unlimited if time and money are not important. Since economy studies do cost time and money, the number of alternatives which should be studied may be restricted. There obviously is no advantage in studying additional alternatives if the cost of making the study is greater than any possible saving that might result, or if during the additional time consumed possible income or savings are lost which exceed the possible benefits that might be achieved through the additional alternative. Such a practice is about like that of the man who drove his car to an adjacent city to buy gasoline, using a gallon in so doing, because he could fill his fourteen-gallon tank for 30 cents per gallon instead of the 31 cents he had to pay in his own community. Whether a particular additional alternative should be considered can usually be determined quite easily and quickly by a brief comparison of the approximate probable differences in income or expenses that might exist for it with those for other alternatives being considered.

STEP 3. *The basis for decision.* Before the basic pattern for making an economy study is selected and the study started, one should decide what the basis for decision is to be. In some cases the rate of return on the required investment will be most useful. In other cases a comparison of annual costs or present-worth costs may be more revealing. Sometimes one is concerned primarily with keeping the amount of required investment at a minimum. Occasionally it may be essential that the amount of labor required be minimized. While one must make certain that the information developed by the study will provide the results that are needed for decision making, one must be equally certain that no facts are overlooked because they do not appear at first glance to have a direct bearing on the situation.

STEP 4. *Handling differences in time.* Very frequently two or more alternatives being considered in economy studies do not have the same economic lives and/or involve different amounts of income or expenses which occur at different times. When different lives are involved, one must first make certain that the extra years of life of an alternative having a longer life are actually needed and therefore of value. A study pattern must then be used which will give proper consideration to the differences in life and to any differences in capital requirements. Time differences in occurrences of income and expense items can be handled by the use of the proper present-value and annuity factors, once the time basis for the study has been determined.

STEP 5. *Basic pattern to be used.* As has been discussed previously in this chapter, the various basic patterns produce results which have somewhat different meanings and which therefore must be interpreted differently. The pattern to be used will be determined by the objectives of the study, the basis for decision, the time factors, and by the financial sophistication and understanding of those who are to read and use the economy study. When practicable, the study should be presented in a pattern which contains language and procedures that are familiar to the users. If they are accustomed to making all decisions on the basis of rate of return on required investment, certainly the study should not be made by the annual-cost procedure, unless by so doing it would be possible to bring out pertinent information that could not otherwise be shown. On the other hand, if those who are to make the ultimate decisions are more accustomed to dealing with annual-cost studies, it would be proper to use this pattern with suitable interpretation.

Step 6. *Determining what needs to be known.* Before starting on the detailed work of a study, it is desirable to consider what facts need to be known in order to provide the basis for decision. This should be an obvious step, but unless it is considered as a definite item, one may easily waste considerable time in considering insignificant details or fail to obtain and use information which is pertinent.

Step 7. *Determining what is known.* This step is one which should logically follow Step 6. It, of course, leads to the next step, that of determining what information is not known and thus must be obtained. However, it also has other significance in that a knowledge of the degree to which all the required information is known is very helpful in evaluating the risks involved in a proposed undertaking.

Step 8. *Handling the unknowns.* When it has been determined that certain information is not known, several courses of action are possible. First, the majority of such information can be determined to varying degrees of accuracy if the expenditure of adequate amounts of time and/or money is justified. In some instances it may require very little time or money to obtain the desired information when what is desired becomes apparent. It may only be a matter of going to the source that has the required information. When needed information is not readily available but could be obtained, one must decide whether the cost of obtaining it will be repaid by the increased accuracy of the study.

The second method for handling unknown factors is to make estimates of their amounts and effects. Obviously the accuracy of the estimates will depend upon the nature of the item, the experience and judgment of the person making the estimate, and the amount of historical information available. All information available should be utilized in making such estimates.

A third procedure, and actually a variation of the estimating technique, is to consider a range of assumed values and determine the resulting effects. Thus one might assume "probable," "minimum possible," and "maximum possible" values.

Step 9. *Evaluating the risks.* Some of the factors which must be considered in evaluating risk are (*a*) source of the data, (*b*) present state of technological progress in the field involved, (*c*) the length of time involved in the write-off period, (*d*) general economic conditions, and (*e*) type of equipment, structure, or industry involved. As has been mentioned previously, the evaluation of risk must primarily consider all of the facts and compare them with conditions existing in other situations.

STEP 10. *Making the decision.* The final decision must take into account all factors, both monetary and intangible. Such factors as economic conditions, competition, probable price trends, availability and sources of capital, etc., should be considered. In evaluating intangibles it frequently is helpful to classify them according to whether or not they tend to favor the proposed project.

When the economy study is to provide information or recommendations for others who will make the final investment decision, it usually is desirable to provide a complete evaluation of the reasons which justify the recommendation. This provides those who must make the final decision with valuable information beyond the mere recommendation.

Occasionally those who must make detailed economy studies are given instructions as to certain assumptions or procedures which should be used. For example, companies frequently specify certain arbitrary write-off periods for equipment within given price ranges, regardless of type. The findings of a particular study may make it clear that such assumptions or procedures are not sound or applicable for the situation involved. In such circumstances it is the obligation of the person making the study to report such facts and their effect upon the results. This can often be done by reporting two sets of data, one based on the specified assumptions and the other using more realistic values.

Finally it should be remembered that the decision reached should be the one most practicably feasible, although it may not be ideal. Most business decisions, and indeed most engineering decisions, are of this type.

PROBLEMS

8–1   What are the six basic patterns that commonly are used in making economy studies?

8–2   Why are the results obtained by the rate-of-return procedure often preferred by business managers over those obtained by the other methods?

8–3   Explain why the profits earned by the money in the sinking fund should not be subject to income taxes when the sinking fund method of depreciation is used for accounting purposes. Is there a limit to such tax-exempt profits?

8–4   Explain how it is determined whether a given prospective rate of return is adequate.

8–5   How does the annual-cost method of making economy studies differ from the rate-of-return procedure?

8–6   What is the danger in using an average profit rate in making economy studies by the annual-cost procedure?

8-7 What are two difficulties which may arise when a capital recovery factor is used in making economy studies by the annual-cost method?

8-8 Two alternatives, *A* and *B*, were compared by the annual-cost procedure in which a 10% capital recovery factor was used. Alternative *A* required an investment of $40,000 and Alternative *B* an investment of $52,000. Alternative *B* was found to have a total annual cost which was $4,000 per year less than that of Alternative *A*. Explain the significance of the $4,000 difference.

8-9 Why do economy studies made by the annual-cost method often require some explanation when they are used by persons accustomed ordinarily to dealing with accounting data?

8-10 Explain why the payout procedure is not preferred for most economy studies.

8-11 What is a good use of the payout method?

8-12 How does the present-worth-cost procedure differ basically from the capitalized-cost method?

8-13 What is the significance of the difference in present-worth costs of two alternatives obtained in making an economy study by this procedure?

8-14 For what types of structures might the capitalized-cost procedure be suitable?

8-15 What are ten steps in making an economy study?

8-16 What are two factors which should be considered in deciding the basic pattern to be used in making an economy study?

8-17 Name four factors which must be considered in an economy study in evaluating risk.

CHAPTER 9

Handling
Income and Cost
Data

All of the basic patterns used in economy studies involve income and cost data in some manner. It is therefore essential that all such data be collected, used, and analyzed properly so that accuracy will be obtained, due implications understood, and correct conclusions reached. Certain items of income and cost are usually handled in more or less standardized manners. Following such practices, insofar as they apply to a given situation, tends to reduce the work of making economy studies and also the possibility that important data may be omitted. In addition, it tends to promote a certain amount of uniformity which makes it easier for users to understand and interpret economy studies. It is the purpose of this chapter to present and discuss the handling and significance of these various income and cost items.

IMPORTANCE OF INCOME DATA

Economy studies nearly always are concerned with an increase in profit, which is defined as the excess of income over expenses. Such an increase may result either (a) from the sale of additional goods or services or (b) through a saving, or reduction in expenses. In the first of these situations, either new or additional amounts of goods or services are to be produced and/or sold. In the latter case, existing facilities are to be operated more economically, or more than one possible means for producing the same goods or services are to be considered. These various possibilities will be discussed in detail in later chapters. At this point, however, it should be noted that the fact that the income item usually occurs as a single figure frequently results in insufficient consideration of its source, importance, and accuracy. One should remember

218

that the single income figure usually is as important as all of the expense or cost items taken together.

REQUIRED INVESTMENT

At some stage in virtually all economy studies it is necessary to determine the amount of capital which must be invested in order to place a proposed project into operation. Likewise, the source of the capital, whether borrowed or owned, is a pertinent item to be considered. This usually must be done before the production costs can be determined, since depreciation and interest costs are dependent upon the amount of capital and its source. In addition, some of the other expenses, such as maintenance, may depend indirectly on the amount of capital that is utilized.

When the rate-of-return method is used one must determine the rate of return upon the required investment. With the annual cost method a minimum required profit on the investment is computed as a cost.

The amount of capital required can usually be determined with some accuracy. If the exact amount of output is decided upon, the productive facilities can be estimated with little difficulty. Of course, if the product is something entirely new and involves equipment of a new type, there may be some uncertainty regarding the output which can be expected. However, a reasonable amount of study should yield a satisfactory answer in nearly all instances.

Once the type and amount of physical equipment have been determined, the cost of acquisition may be determined by a straightforward method of estimation. Prices for buildings may be obtained from experienced construction engineers and contracting firms. Similarly, the cost of various types of equipment may be obtained from the producers of the equipment or, in the case of new types of equipment, by obtaining bids for its construction. Thus, so far as the physical plant is concerned, little difficulty is usually found in determining the amount of capital necessary.

The amount of capital that will be required for certain intangibles is more difficult to determine. Usually many expenses besides those for a physical plant must be incurred before any product can be sold. A certain amount is necessary as working capital to provide for the purchase of raw materials, to pay salaries, and to permit the organization of all the necessary factors of production. Such items as legal and acquisition fees, and investigation, exploratory, and promotional costs, require capital and must not be overlooked. It is just as necessary to have capital for these items as it is to provide funds for the physical plants. In many cases the capital for these items is neglected, and an attempt is made to start an enterprise with insufficient capital. The result is usually disaster.

Obviously it is not easy to determine the amount of capital which should be on hand for these intangible factors of production. In most cases the amount is underestimated. This is especially true in cases of small concerns or entirely new enterprises. This phase of a study concerning the advisability of investment should receive very careful consideration and application of all the experience which is available.

The impracticability of an enterprise sometimes becomes apparent as soon as the amount of required capital is determined. If the amount is far above that which is available through any legitimate method of finance, there is little need to make further investigation. Many persons and companies would have been much better off financially if they had determined carefully the entire amount of capital which was required before they embarked upon rather risky enterprises. One might as well admit that what may be a good investment for persons possessing adequate capital may be an extremely poor investment for those without it.

It must be recognized that a particular investment possibility may be entirely sound and advisable in spite of the fact that the person considering it does not have sufficient capital. In other words, the situation may be one in which the required amount of capital would earn a very satisfactory return. The only difficulty is the fact that the persons considering the enterprise do not have adequate capital. A detailed ecoonmy study may show the soundness of the proposed investment and enable the facts to be presented so that the required capital may be obtained by legitimate borrowing or through the sale of stock. Such methods of obtaining capital are entirely legitimate provided the possibilities of profit are sufficiently large to balance the additional liabilities which such financing may involve.

HANDLING OUT-OF-POCKET COST DATA

After the capital and equipment requirements and the volume of production are known, one may make estimates of production costs. These costs are composed of numerous items, as discussed in the previous chapter on accounting. In making economy studies one must be sure that all of the expenses which will be incurred after the investment is made are included and that the estimates are accurate. Material costs can be determined without much difficulty. If the details of the product are known, the amount of material required can be determined and its value computed.

One problem that frequently causes trouble in estimating material expense is the amount which should be included as an allowance for scrap and waste, since few operations are performed without these. Accurate estimation of the proper allowances requires experience. If they are not included, an appreciable error may result, particularly where expensive materials are involved.

As mentioned previously, an accurate estimate of labor cost is more difficult to make. If a product is to be manufactured, or some process is involved where labor is paid on the basis of units produced, the problem is quite simple. On the other hand, where fixed salaries are involved one may have to rely on past experience or upon estimate. The accuracy of such estimates will of course depend upon the conditions and the experience and judgment of the person doing the estimating. If labor costs are estimated in this manner, the final cost figures will, in turn, contain an element of doubt.

Overhead expenses other than maintenance and depreciation may be estimated with a fair degree of accuracy for any proposed amount of output. Of course, this requires experience in such matters. However, such expenses are subject to a considerable degree of control and, once the estimates have been made, operations may often be regulated within the estimated figures. Thus it usually is possible to assume that the estimate of these expenses is quite accurate *if it has been made by competent persons in a scientific manner.*

In attempting to predict maintenance costs, one usually must be guided by past experience and judgment. It is nearly impossible to anticipate just what the maintenance expense for any particular piece of equipment will be. However, one may usually obtain worth-while information by comparing the equipment and the anticipated operating conditions with similar equipment with which he has had experience. Studies have indicated that there usually is a tendency to underestimate maintenance costs but that the effect is often offset by unforeseen operating economies.

The determination of fuel and power costs must also be based to a considerable extent upon comparison and past experience. There are considerable data available regarding power consumption for various types of plants and equipment. These may be consulted whenever necessary and will be found very helpful. Most of these data appear to give rather high values, so their use will give conservative results. Such data may be found in various handbooks.

MISCELLANEOUS PAYROLL EXPENSES

There are a number of overhead expenses which are related to labor and frequently are proportional to labor expense. Some of these are

Vacation pay,
Sick leave,
Social security taxes,
Unemployment insurance,
Accident compensation insurance,
Retirement benefits payments,
Health and hospitalization insurance.

In earlier years most of these did not exist and the amounts involved were small; thus they constituted only a small percentage of the total if they were included as a part of overhead. However, in recent years such items often are equal to 25 per cent of the direct labor cost. Since they usually are nearly proportional to the direct labor cost, they quite frequently are added to, and included as a part of, the direct labor cost. In other cases they are listed separately from direct labor cost or overhead cost but as a percentage of direct labor cost. Either procedure is quite satisfactory, or they, of course, may be included as a part of overhead. However, the important thing is that one should make certain that they are included, since they are an appreciable part of total costs where labor is involved.

DEPRECIATION EXPENSE

In determining depreciation expenses, one must estimate what the economic life of the physical plant and equipment will be. It is usually impossible to know exactly how long any property can be operated on an economical basis. There are two possible ways of handling this situation. One is to make every effort and use all the available information and experience to determine what the probable economic life will be. In most cases such a determination, in spite of all effort, will still be subject to some error. It is impossible to predict what new developments in the future may affect the economic life of any property. Therefore, it is often the practice in economy studies to assume a write-off period which is considerably less than what one might reasonably expect the actual economic life to be. In other words, the depreciation is based on a period considerably shorter than what the physical life might be expected to be and somewhat shorter than a reasonable expectation of economic life. The result of this procedure is that production cost estimates will tend to be high, but the amount of time which must pass before the invested capital will be recovered under the proposed setup will be shortened. Both of these results tend to make the study more conservative. Any error resulting from this practice tends to make production costs high and predicted profit correspondingly less, and there is the probability that the actual economic life will be greater than the one which has been used in the study. Thus the error tends to prevent investment in doubtful enterprises.

The use of such shortened write-off periods is, of course, an entirely arbitrary matter. Most large companies have established arbitrary write-off periods for various classes of plants and equipment. Surveys have shown that these companies tend toward the use of shorter write-off periods, especially when considering new equipment. Most plants now are written off within five or ten years, and equipment in much shorter times. A very common write-off period for equipment in economy studies is five years.[1] However, one should use care in arbitrarily establishing a fixed write-off period which must be used in all economy studies. Such a practice is not in accordance with sound engineering. Each case should be considered in the light of the facts, giving due consideration to the past experience of the persons or companies involved. Undue shortening of the write-off period, when such is not justified by the facts, is just about as bad as using periods which are too long. It may be just as bad not to make an investment that is economically justifiable as it is to make one that is unsound.

TAXES AND INSURANCE

It is common practice in economy studies to express the cost for property taxes and insurance as a percentage of the original cost of the property involved. This is sometimes objected to, on the basis that as the value of the property decreases with age the taxes and insurance should also diminish. While this view is theoretically sound, in actual practice the total tax bill seldom decreases. As the value of the property decreases, the tax *rate* usually increases sufficiently to offset the change in value. Insurance costs may actually decrease during the later years of the life of a property. However, since insurance expense is ordinarily such a small proportion of total production expense, the refinement of taking into account the decrease in this item is seldom justified. Therefore, the usual practice of assuming that the expense for taxes and insurance is constant throughout the life of the project will probably continue.

---

[1] Quite often the write-off period used for an economy study will be different from that which may be used for accounting purposes. This is due to the fact that the income tax authorities will not allow certain types of equipment to be written off in less than a definite period of time.

INCOME TAXES

The existence of income taxes means that their effect must be considered in economy studies. Fortunately, however, in most cases the effect of income taxes on each alternative being considered is virtually the same, so that there is no necessity or advantage in including them as a part of the study; the study can usually be made on a "before-income-taxes" basis. There are, however, seven distinct types of situation in which income taxes must be considered if correct answers are to be obtained. It is therefore essential that these situations, although they are encountered rather infrequently, be thoroughly understood and recognized, so that due consideration be given to income taxes. The seven types are

1. Economy studies making use of the minimum-payout-period procedure: As has been explained previously, tax money paid to the government is not available for payout.
2. Economy studies in regulated public utilities: As will be discussed at length in Chapter 19, the rates which such companies are permitted to charge for their services are set so as to provide for earning a certain rate of return *after* income taxes. Therefore, for exact answers economy studies in such companies should give proper consideration to income taxes. However, even in this case it often is possible, and satisfactory, to use an equivalent before-taxes rate of return.
3. Situations where one alternative will produce taxable income while the other(s) produce tax-free income: Such a situation usually arises from the possibility of investing in tax-exempt securities. Such securities invariably produce rates of return which are considerably below the normal after-tax earning rates of successful businesses. Therefore economy studies of proposed business ventures almost never involve this situation. This possibility, however, frequently is encountered in studies relating to investments of individuals.
4. Situations where one alternative involves investment in depreciable property while another involves using capital to produce income through increased nontax-deductible expenses: For example, by increasing inventories of finished goods available in a new market area, increased sales income may be produced.
5. Situations where one wishes to determine the true cost of the capital used in an enterprise when a portion of the capital is borrowed and the remainder is owned. Since the interest paid for the use of borrowed capital is a deductible expense, no income tax is paid on the

cost of borrowed capital. On the other hand, income taxes must be paid out of profits before stockholders receive their payment for the use of owned capital. Thus the total cost of owned capital is the sum of the profits paid to stockholders plus the income tax paid on these profits. Therefore, income taxes must be considered in determining the actual cost of capital under the conditions stated.

6. Situations where income is derived in part, or entirely, from foreign subsidiaries: This is a complex, and rather exceptional, instance. Since such cases usually involve the tax laws of the foreign country concerned, and thus are usually complex, a competent tax lawyer ordinarily should be consulted when such situations are encountered.

7. Situations where accumulated tax money that has been set aside from income, but is not yet due for payment, serves as financing: This situation primarily provides for the availability of a certain amount of low-cost capital and thus is not a matter for ordinary economy studies.

A consideration of these seven situations leads to the conclusion that few economy studies of business projects, outside the public utilities field, fall within the categories stated. Therefore most economy studies can be made without the necessity of including income taxes, provided the minimum-payout-period method is not used. As will be pointed out in later chapters, this method is not a recommended one for most studies.

The fact that income taxes may be omitted in most economy studies does not mean that any error is introduced by including them. However, neither is any accuracy gained by including them in the vast majority of cases. In numerous studies which have been made of such cases it has been found that, although the inclusion of income taxes will obviously change the figures upon which the investment decision must be based, the relative merits of the alternatives and the decision itself will not be changed. Therefore, in the chapters which follow basic economy study procedures will be presented without the inclusion of income taxes, except for the cases involving public utilities and the other six tax-subject situations mentioned. These exceptions will be dealt with in another chapter.

EVALUATING RISK

At some point in virtually every economy study the risks or uncertainties existing must be considered and evaluated. The factors that may affect the risk involved in any investment are many and varied. It would be almost impossible to list and discuss them all. There are four, however, which are nearly always present.

The first factor, which is always present, is the possible inaccuracy of the figures used in the study. If exact information is available regarding the items of income and expense, the resulting accuracy should be good. If, on the other hand, little factual information is available, and nearly all the values have to be estimated, the accuracy may be high or low, depending upon the manner in which the estimated values are obtained. Are they sound scientific estimates or merely guesses?

The accuracy of the income figures is difficult to determine. One can usually be guided only by the method by which they were obtained. If they are based upon a considerable amount of past experience or have been determined by adequate market surveys, a fair degree of reliance may be placed on them. On the other hand, if they are merely the result of guesswork, with a considerable element of hope thrown in, they must of course be considered to contain a sizable element of uncertainty. Thus, to a great degree the amount of risk resulting from uncertainty in the income figures must be determined by exercising good judgment. Evaluation of this risk requires mature judgment and experience.

If the income is in the nature of a saving in existing operating costs, there should be less risk involved. It is usually easier to determine what the exact saving will be, since one has considerable experience and past history on which to base the estimates.

In most cases the income figures will contain more error than any other portion of a study, with the possible exception of depreciation costs. If short write-off periods are used for computing depreciation, the element of uncertainty in the depreciation figure is reduced, and the income figure will then probably be the most uncertain of all those in the economy study.

There should be no large error in estimates of capital required, except perhaps in the amount allowed above the actual cost of plant and equipment. If one can feel confident that the amount allowed for this purpose is on the high side, the resulting study is apt to be conservative. This element again requires careful study and experience to be certain that one is not underestimating the amount of required capital.

Among the cost figures depreciation is undoubtedly the element which should be considered most carefully. It is seldom that the actual physical life of the plant or equipment can be used in determining depreciation. It must always be remembered that only through providing for depreciation is the capital recovered. Obviously it is better to err on the side of too short a depreciation period than to make the period too long. Of course this process can be carried to an extreme. In determining the amount of risk which results from depreciation estimates, one should be guided by past experience of the company involved as well as that of other companies which have operated similar properties. The important thing is to be certain that the period selected is short enough to assure that the invested capital will be recovered.

The accuracy of the other cost elements will depend to a great degree upon how carefully the estimates have been prepared. If thorough investigations have been made and all of the items considered in detail, it is reasonable to assume that the estimates will not be in great error.

Another element of risk is the type of business involved. Some lines of business are notoriously less stable than others. For example, most mining enterprises are more risky than large retail food stores. However, one can not arbitrarily say that an investment in any retail food store always involves less risk than investment in mining property. Whenever capital is to be invested in an enterprise, the nature and past history of the business should be considered in deciding what risk is present. In this connection it becomes apparent that investment in an enterprise which is just being organized, and thus has no past history, is usually rather uncertain.

A third factor affecting risk is the type of physical plant and equipment involved. Some types of structures have rather definite economic lives and second-hand values. Little is known of the physical or economic lives of others, and they have almost no resale value. A good engine lathe can always be used for many purposes in nearly any shop. Depreciation on such a lathe can be estimated fairly accurately. Quite different would be a special type of lathe which was built to do only one unusual job. Its value would be dependent almost entirely upon the demand for the special task which it can perform. Thus the type of physical property involved will have a direct bearing upon the accuracy of the depreciation figures and thereby affect the risk. Where money is to be invested in specialized plant and equipment, this factor should be considered carefully.

The fourth, and very import, factor which must always be considered in evaluating risk is the length of time that must pass before all the conditions of the study become fulfilled. The conditions which have been assumed in regard to income and expense must exist throughout the write-off period in order to obtain the predicted profit. In other words, not only must the plant or equipment have an economic life equal to that of the write-off period, but all of the others items, such as income, material, and labor costs, must remain relatively the same or the resulting profit will change. A particular piece of equipment might operate satisfactorily and be able to produce at as low a unit cost as is indicated in the economy study, but market conditions might have changed so that the product can no longer be sold. Similarly, material costs might have increased to such an extent that profit would be eliminated. In other words, one must remember that *all of the factors involved in the study must continue throughout the write-off period as predicted, or the predicted profit will not be obtained.* A long write-off period naturally decreases the probability of all of the factors remaining as estimated. Therefore a long write-off period, even though justified by the probable life of the equipment involved, always increases the risk in an investment. One simply can not prophesy exactly what the future will bring.

PROBLEMS

9–1   What are two basic ways in which "profit," in an economy study sense, may be obtained?

9–2   Explain the relative importance of the income figure and the various cost items in an economy study.

9–3   What are some of the cost items which are functions of the amount of investment?

9–4   What are some elements of required investment other than the cost of buildings and equipment?

9–5   Assume alternative *A* requires $10,000 in invested capital, while alternative *B* requires $100,000. In what ways might the difference in amounts of capital affect the cost of obtaining the money?

9–6   What are some factors that determine the accuracy of estimates of labor costs? of material costs?

9–7   What items usually are included under "Miscellaneous Payroll Expenses"?

9–8   How are miscellaneous payroll expenses usually handled in economy studies?

9–9   What are the dangers involved in using write-off periods that are too short?

9–10   Why is it customary to base the cost of property taxes and insurance on the first cost of assets even though it is known that their value will decrease during their life?

9–11   Why may income taxes be omitted from most economy studies?

9–12   What are the seven cases which require the inclusion of income tax effects?

9–13   What is the basic procedure for evaluating risk?

9–14   List four factors which determine risk.

CHAPTER 10

R vol

Economy Studies
of New
Projects

Perhaps the most basic situation in which economy studies are made is that involving possible investment in a new project, or the extension of an existing operation. Only two alternatives are available here: One is to invest in the project being studied; the other is not to invest. The second alternative means not diverting available capital from where it currently is being used. It would thus continue to be used as it is at present, or would be available for investment in some project other than the one being considered. Thus this type of economy study supplies the answer to the question, "Should this project be undertaken?" Other types of studies, to be considered in later chapters, deal with such questions as, "Which alternative should be used in carrying out this project?" and, "Should existing properties be replaced with new ones?"

It should be noted that a new project may involve the organization of a new business, or it may be undertaken by an existing business. While the economy study procedure is the same in either case, some of the factors to be dealt with will be affected differently. For example, where a company is considering adding new facilities to increase the output of an existing product, much more is known about probable income and cost data than would be the case if a group of investors were considering starting an entirely new company to produce and sell the same product. Yet the basic factors to be considered and the type of economy study are the same for both conditions.

New projects have certain inherent advantages and disadvantages which must be considered, either in monetary or nonmonetary terms, when economy studies are made. These advantages and disadvantages frequently are of considerable importance in the decision which must be made.

ADVANTAGES OF NEW PROJECTS

A completely *new* project, not being a part of an existing enterprise, is usually not restricted by established policies or existing practices. This permits greater freedom in planning, both as to product and organization, than would be the case if an existing organization were involved. For example, when a large automobile manufacturer recently planned to produce an entirely new line of cars, it was necessary to make the new car resemble the existing lines in certain respects and to restrict the body sizes so that the body shells of two of the existing makes could be used. These limitations would not have existed if the line of cars had been produced by a new manufacturer.

Another advantage of a new project, and one which may be present for even an existing organization, is that it usually involves a new product or service. If the product or service has previously not been available, it can be designed to fill the specific current needs. Thus the design of the product or service is not hampered by previous trends or practices. It may be completely unique. Such conditions may provide unusual sales possibilities and superior competitive standing. Sometimes patents are involved which assure an opportunity to develop markets with little or no competition for some period of time. Such a situation is of extreme value during the early years of a project, when production and marketing organizations must be built and perfected.

Another advantage of a new project by a new organization is the extra enthusiasm of those engaged in the venture because of their association with it during the developmental and growth stages. This, of course, can be a disadvantage if their enthusiasm prevents their seeing realities.

When a new project is an extension of the activities of an existing organization, it usually is the result of a well-demonstrated need—either for a new product or service, or for a remedy for some established difficulty in present operations. If a new product or service is involved, the organization usually either has data regarding the need or is in a position to determine the need more readily than could a new organization or an individual or group not yet organized. If a proposed project is to permit a reduction in existing costs, there ordinarily are considerable data available regarding the conditions and costs which must be considered in an economy study. Such advantages are obvious and important.

DISADVANTAGES OF NEW PROJECTS

Unfortunately, new projects also have several important disadvantages. Probably the foremost is that little or nothing in the way of historical information may exist and the unforeseen events of the future are of extreme importance. The future always is difficult to predict, and where the success of a project is dependent upon future income from sales the uncertainties of the future are of utmost importance. Since there is no way of knowing whether future events will actually be as assumed in an economy study, this uncertainty must always be kept in mind.

If a product or service has not existed previously, there probably is very little information available as to what future demand will be. Modern market research makes it possible, in many cases, to obtain fairly reliable information regarding the sales possibilities for new products or services. However, such research is quite costly and often can not be afforded by new or small business organizations. In some cases prospective sales possibilities can not be determined without actually placing the product or service on the market. Thus, in making an economy study of a proposed new project, the source and probable accuracy of income data must be reviewed carefully.

Another disadvantage, and one that too often is overlooked, is that income from new products or services lags the investment and many of the costs by a considerable period. Plants and equipment must be built or purchased, materials bought, production organizations perfected, and sales made before income is received. Further, a new product or service usually does not reach its full sales potential immediately. Unless this time lag is taken into account and an adequate amount of capital is provided with which to pay the operating expenses during the interval of reduced income, a new project is bound to fail. Inadequate financing is one of the most frequent causes of business failures.

Another disadvantage which sometimes exists is that some types of new projects can not be started on small scale. In projects which involve new and untried features it usually is advantageous to start on a small scale and expand as demand is increased. This permits mistakes to be made on a small scale, and correct actions on a large scale. Where technology does not permit a small-scale operation, as in the case of a blast furnace, or where a small-scale operation is economically unfeasible, as in the case of automobile manufacture, one must either venture large amounts of capital or not engage in the activity.

Another inherent disadvantage of a new project by a new organization is that it is difficult to obtain credit. Lending agencies do not want to loan money to a new venture until it can furnish proof of future success. This situation often prevents a new business from taking full advantage of opportunities for expansion. On the other hand, an existing business can start and exploit a new project much more readily because of its established credit standing.

The competition which exists is another disadvantage that may be faced by a new project. Existing producers seldom welcome another supplier into the market. Price reductions, in compliance with the law of supply and demand, and stepped-up sales activity are apt to occur. These factors must be considered carefully in estimating probable sales income.

Another factor that can be particularly serious in the case of a new venture is the matter of economic or seasonal cycles. If a new project is started during a downward economic trend, or after the peak of a seasonal cycle, it may not have sufficient financial resources to survive until income increases. Thus, if a new venture is apt to be affected by such variations in activity, this fact should be taken into account in timing the initiation of the project. Sometimes it may be advisable to operate temporarily under conditions resulting in somewhat higher production costs if this will enable earlier income to be obtained and sales to be made during peak periods of demand.

A final important factor is the abilities of those who manage and operate a new enterprise. Frequently their abilities are unproved. A corollary disadvantage is that the loss of a key staff member, through death or resignation, can be disastrous to a small organization that is just getting started. These factors add a degree of uncertainty which increases the risks attendant to such a venture.

AN ECONOMY STUDY OF A NEW ENTERPRISE

The following is a typical example of an economy study of a new project wherein there is no existing organization, and income and expense data can be assumed to be uniform throughout the life of the project. It thus represents a rather simple set of conditions.

Mr. Jones is considering buying a newly built apartment house in a fairly large city, within walking distance of a large university. The apartment, which is already 80 per cent rented, can be purchased for $75,000, of which $5,000 is considered to be the value of the land. The building consists of ten four-room apartments, a small apartment for a caretaker, and garage space for eleven automobiles. From a study of similar apartments it is estimated that each apartment and garage can be rented for $100 per month and that at least 95 per cent of the units will be rented, on the average, at all times. Heat and water are included in the rental.

The operating expenses are estimated as follows:

Caretaker	$175 per month
Fuel	$400 per year

Water $150 per year

Maintenance and repair   equal to one month's rental on each unit per year

Taxes $4 per $100 of assessed value, which value will be approximately 30% of the cost of the building and land

Insurance   0.5% of the first cost of the building

Agent's commission $2\frac{1}{2}$% of gross revenue

At present Mr. Jones' capital is invested in bonds which yield approximately 5% before taxes and 4% after taxes. He estimates that the economic life of the apartment house will be at least forty years and wishes to recover his capital within that period. There is a shortage of suitable apartments in the area, and this condition has existed for many years.

Since Mr. Jones is accustomed to the return from his present investment being measured in terms of the per cent return on the investment, the rate-of-return pattern is most appropriate for this study. The annual income to be expected from the apartment building will be

$$10 \times \$100 \times 12 \times 0.95 = \$11,400.^{[1]}$$

The required investment will be

Land	$ 5,000
Building	70,000
Total	$75,000

Since the apartments are already rented, there will probably be no need for additional working capital. Annual expenses will be

Depreciation $= \$70,000/121.0 \ (i = 5\%)$	$= \$\ \ 578$
Fuel	$=\ \ \ \ 400$
Water	$=\ \ \ \ 150$
Caretaker $= \$175 \times 12$	$=\ \ 2,100$
Agent's commission $= \$11,400 \times 0.025$	$=\ \ \ \ 285$
Maintenance & repairs $= 10 \times \$100$	$=\ \ 1,000$
Taxes $= \dfrac{\$75,000}{\$100} \times 0.3 \times \$4.00$	$=\ \ \ \ 900$
Insurance $= \$70,000 \times 0.005$	$=\ \ \ \ 350$
Total	$= \$5,763$

The net profit will be

$$\$11,400 - \$5,763 = \$5,637.$$

The rate of return on the investment, before income taxes, will be

$$\$5,637/\$75,000 = 7.5\%.$$

[1] Slide-rule results are used in this and other economy studies which follow in this text. The error introduced by this instrument is considerably less than that due to the impossibility of predicting future results exactly.

Mr. Jones thus must decide between leaving his capital invested in bonds, which provide a return of 5%, and buying the apartment building, which offers the prospect of a return of 7.5%.

In order to arrive at a decision Mr. Jones would have to consider a number of factors, somewhat as follows. The first item to be considered would be the income estimate. Some questions to be answered would be

1. Is the assumed rental rate reasonable, particularly in relationship to other similar apartments?
2. Is the assumed occupancy rate a reasonable one for this type of housing?
3. How will possible changes in economic conditions affect the rentals, both as to price and occupancy rate?

It is evident that it would be quite easy to obtain reliable answers to the first two of these questions. Answers to the third would be less precise. However, it would be possible to predict the general effect of changing economic conditions. One would also have to take into account the other types and classes of rental housing available in the area. There would also be the fact that if changing economic conditions forced a reduction in the monthly rental charge, some of the expenses would also probably be reduced. By such an analysis the validity of the estimated income data can be determined in any economy study. In this particular case it should be possible to obtain income data that are quite accurate.

In this study the amount of investment required is known exactly, since the finished and already rented building is to be purchased at a stated price.

Among the expense items, all can be determined without difficulty, and with some accuracy, except those for depreciation and maintenance. Obviously the important factor in connection with depreciation is whether the assumed write-off period is reasonable. From the viewpoint of physical depreciation the assumed life of forty years is very conservative if the building is well built. With respect to functional depreciation there would appear to be little doubt that people will still be living in apartments for forty years. Since the building is located near a fairly large city, and also near a large university, there would be little doubt as to the need for apartments continuing indefinitely. Thus, while forty years is a rather long period of time, with respect to the economic life of the apartment building in question it appears to be a quite conservative write-off period. Obviously considerable uncertainties exist with respect to any such period, but it must also be remembered that many or most of these long-range uncertainties would also apply to any use to which capital might be put. In evaluating this type of risk one must, in general, be concerned only with those risks involved in the project being considered which do not exist in the alternative investment opportunity.

Maintenance and repair expenses are difficult to estimate unless historical data are available from similar projects. Such data are readily available for apartment buildings. In the absence of such data, it is well to remember that estimates of these expenses are frequently too low and that the expenses usually increase as time passes. This may be of considerable importance when long write-off periods are involved.

It thus appears that in this case all of the income and expense data can be determined with accuracy. The primary element of risk is due to the rather long, but not excessive, write-off period. There is also the added factor that investment in the apartment would provide a hedge against inflation that does not exist in the bonds which Mr. Jones now owns. Thus he has an opportunity of obtaining a before-tax return of 7.5% instead of the 5% he is now getting, without a great increase in risk. If he is certain that the data have been determined carefully, he probably will make the investment.

ANALYSIS BY THE ANNUAL-COST METHOD

If the annual-cost method were to be used to make an economy study of the apartment house purchase, Mr. Jones would have to decide what minimum rate of return he would require before he could add the minimum required return to the list of costs. In this case it is clear that he would require a rate of return greater than the 5% he is now getting, since the write-off period is rather long and there would be more uncertainty regarding the income than at present. If he decides that he will not invest unless the return is at least 7%, the list of costs would be as follows:

Depreciation $= \$70,000/121.0$ $(i = 5\%)$	$= \$$	578
Fuel	$=$	400
Water	$=$	150
Caretaker	$=$	2,100
Agent's commission	$=$	285
Maintenance and repairs	$=$	1,000
Taxes	$=$	900
Insurance	$=$	350
Minimum required profit $= \$75,000 \times 0.07$	$=$	5,250
Total cost	$=$	$\$11,013$

Since the total annual cost of $11,013 is less than the estimated annual income of $11,400, the investment is justified.

In this case the annual income is estimated to exceed the annual costs by $387. This excess is a return of 0.5% on the required capital in addition to the 7% included as a cost. Thus the total rate of return is $7\% + 0.5\% = 7.5\%$, the same as computed by the rate-of-return method.

EXAMPLE OF A NEW PROJECT WITH NONUNIFORM INVESTMENT, INCOME, AND COSTS

In many new projects the amount of capital invested is not the same throughout the life of the venture, and the income produced and the costs incurred also vary. The relationship of the investment, income, cost, and profit data for such a project are shown in Table 10–1. In this project additional investment is required during the second, third, and fourth years for working capital. Most of the required capital is owned, but some borrowed capital is used during the first five years.

Economy studies of projects of this type can be made in either of two ways. One method is to determine the actual rate of return on the invested capital by considering the relationship between the disbursements and the receipts. The determination of the actual rate of return by this procedure involves a trial-and-error solution.

The relationship of the disbursements and receipts is as follows (values from Table 10–1):

Beginning of year	Disbursements Column (3)	Receipts Column (11)	Net Difference Disbursements	Net Difference Receipts
1	$ 8,000		$8,000	
2	8,500	$ 8,100	400	
3	10,000	9,090	910	
4	9,500	11,520		$2,020
5	9,000	11,410		2,410
6	9,000	10,940		1,940
7	8,000	11,000		3,000
8	6,000	9,900		3,900
9	4,500	7,700		3,200
10	3,800	5,800		2,000
11		4,700		4,700

The present value of the disbursements is equal to the present value of the receipts *when the interest rate used in the present value calculations is the actual rate of return.* Thus,

$$\$8,000 + \$400\,v^1 + \$910\,v^2$$
$$= \$2,020\,v^3 + \$2,410\,v^4 + \$1,940\,v^5 + \$3,000\,v^6 + \$3,900\,v^7$$
$$+ \$3,200\,v^8 + \$2,000\,v^9 + \$4,700\,v^{10}.$$

TABLE 10–1   Relationship of Investment, Income, Costs, and Profits for a Proposed New Enterprise

(1) Year	(2) Total investment required during year	(3) Owned capital	(4) Borrowed capital	(5) O + M costs	(6) Depreciation	(7) Interest paid	(8) Total costs	(9) Gross income G	(10) Net profits $G-(O+M+D+I)$	(11) Owner's equity at end of year
1	$10,000	$ 8,000	$2,000	$4,000	$1,000	$120	$5,120	$5,220	$ 100	$ 8,100
2	12,000	8,500	3,500	4,700	1,000	210	5,910	6,500	590	9,090
3	13,000	10,000	3,000	5,100	1,000	180	6,280	7,800	1,520	11,520
4	11,000	9,500	1,500	5,000	1,000	90	6,090	8,000	1,910	11,410
5	10,000	9,000	1,000	4,800	1,000	60	5,860	7,800	1,940	10,940
6	9,000	9,000	0	4,700	1,000	0	5,700	7,700	2,000	11,000
7	8,000	8,000	0	4,600	1,000	0	5,600	7,500	1,900	9,900
8	6,000	6,000	0	4,300	1,000	0	5,300	7,000	1,700	7,700
9	4,500	4,500	0	4,000	1,000	0	5,000	7,000	1,300	5,800
10	3,800	3,800	0	3,500	1,000	0	4,500	5,400	900	4,700

By trial and error the rate of return is found to be approximately 15%. While this method of making the economy study may be somewhat laborious, it is a procedure that can be used in virtually any situation.

The usual rate-of-return method can be used in making economy studies of projects of this type, provided the nonuniform data are converted to equivalent uniform values. This, of course, requires that some rate of interest be assumed for use in making the equivalence calculations. The rate assumed is that which is considered to be the minimum that will justify investment in the proposed project. If a rate of 10% is assumed to be adequate for this project, the necessary calculations for determining the equivalent uniform investment are as follows:

Year	Investment [2]	v^n	Present Value
1	$ 8,000	1.00	$ 8,000
2	8,500	0.91	7,740
3	10,000	0.83	8,300
4	9,500	0.75	7,170
5	9,000	0.68	6,120
6	9,000	0.62	5,580
7	8,000	0.56	4,480
8	6,000	0.51	3,060
9	4,500	0.47	2,120
10	3,800	0.42	1,600
		Total	$54,170

$$\text{Equivalent uniform investment} = \frac{\$54,170}{a_{\overline{10}|}} = \frac{\$54,170}{6.75} = \$8,030$$

The equivalent uniform annual profit is found in the same manner.

Year	Profit [2]	v^n	Present Value
1	$ 100	0.91	$ 91
2	590	0.83	490
3	1,520	0.75	1,140
4	1,910	0.68	1,300
5	1,940	0.62	1,204
6	2,000	0.56	1,120
7	1,900	0.51	969
8	1,700	0.47	798
9	1,300	0.42	546
10	900	0.39	351
		Total	$8,009

$$\text{Equivalent profit} = \frac{\$8,009}{a_{\overline{10}|}} = \frac{\$8,009}{6.14} = \$1,303$$

[2] Note that the investment is assumed to be made at the beginning of each year, and the profit received at the end of the year. This is in accord with the usual practice. In computing the equivalent values an annuities due factor is used to preserve this relationship. Values for $a_{\overline{n}|}$ for rates of interest above 10% can be obtained by using the reciprocal of the capital recovery factor, $1/a_{\overline{n}|}$, given in Table XXV.

Using these values of investment and profit the prospective rate of return is $1,303/$8,030 = 16.3%. This is greater than the minimum rate of 10% which was assumed to be necessary; therefore the investment is justified.

It is obvious that the yield rate computed in this manner is different from the 15% obtained by computing the relationship of the disbursements and receipts. This is due to the fact that a rate of 10% was used in the equivalence calculations, whereas the actual yield was 15%. If a rate of 15% had been assumed for the equivalence calculations, the computed rate of return would have been close to 15%. However, the discrepancy does not detract from the usefulness of the method, since it provided the desired answer—that the prospective rate of return was greater than the minimum required to justify the investment.

PROJECTS INVOLVING OWNER'S SERVICES

In economy studies of individually owned organizations the owner's services frequently are involved. This raises a question regarding the proper method for including this item, since from the usual accounting viewpoint and in computing income taxes, nothing paid to the owner for his services can be deducted as an expense. Yet the value of such services is frequently an important item to be considered in economy studies of this type. The method of handling owner's services is illustrated in the economy study of the following problem.

John Handy is considering investing $20,000.00 to open a semiautomatic auto-washing laundry in a city of 90,000 population. The equipment can wash one car in five minutes, with only two men required to operate the equipment and to do a small amount of handwork on the cars. He figures he would have to hire two men, in addition to himself, and operate the station on an eight-hour basis, six days per week. He would have to pay these men $1.90 per hour and time and one-half for all hours over forty in a given week. He expects to charge $1.50 for a car wash. Other expenses would be as follows:

Social Security and other payroll taxes	5% of labor cost
Insurance	$400.00 per year
Taxes	$400.00 per year
Rent	$1,200.00 per year
Operating expense, water, power, etc.	$3,000.00 per year

Because of the length of his lease, he must write off his investment within five years. John plans to operate fifty weeks of the year but will pay his employees for fifty-two weeks. His capital is now returning about 5% before income taxes and 4% after taxes. He is now employed at a steady job which pays him $450.00 per month. Should John invest in the business?

The income would be dependent upon the volume of business. If operated at 100 per cent of capacity, 96 cars could be washed each day. However it is unlikely that such utilization of the equipment could be achieved. It is therefore helpful in such cases to determine what would result at several assumed percentages of capacity. For example, at 60, 75, and 90 per cent of capacity the income per year would be as follows:

60%	$96 \times 0.60 \times 6 \times 50 \times \$1.50 = \$25,900.00$
75%	$96 \times 0.75 \times 6 \times 50 \times \$1.50 = \$32,400.00$
90%	$96 \times 0.90 \times 6 \times 50 \times \$1.50 = \$38,800.00$

Since any salary paid to himself would not be a tax-deductible expense, it will not be included with the usual expenses but will be considered later. The expenses at the three percentages of utilization are assumed to be virtually the same.

Depreciation	$20,000/5.53 (5% S.F.)	=	$ 3,620
Hired labor	$2 \times \$1.90 \times 52 \times 52$	=	10,280
Payroll taxes	$\$10,280 \times 0.05$	=	510
Insurance		=	400
Taxes		=	400
Rent		=	1,200
Operating expenses		=	3,000
	Total	=	$19,410

Thus, if John invests in the automobile washing business and in addition gives his services, at the three assumed load factors he would receive before-tax profit as follows:

60%	$ 6,490
75%	12,990
90%	19,390

If he does not invest in this business, his before-tax income will continue to be as follows:

Present salary	450×12	= $5,400
Interest from capital	$20,000 \times 0.05$	= $1,000
	Total	= $6,400

Therefore the actual net rate of return that would result from the *changed* use of his capital and services would be as follows:

$$60\% \qquad \$90/\$20,000 = 0.45\%$$
$$75\% \qquad \$6,590/\$20,000 = 33\%$$
$$90\% \qquad \$12,990/\$20,000 = 65\%$$

It is obvious that at a volume of business equal to 60 per cent of capacity the investment would not be desirable. At 75 per cent it appears to be very good. Thus the final decision would depend upon a careful investigation of the load factor which might be expected.

This method of considering the owner's salary in a separate step seems somewhat more desirable than the frequently used procedure of including it with the ordinary expenses. The latter procedure, combining tax-deductible and nontax-deductible items, makes correct interpretation difficult.

AN EXAMPLE WITH IMPORTANT INTANGIBLES

In many economy studies the final decision is determined primarily by the intangibles which exist in the situation. The following case illustrates this type of problem.

The management of a hotel in a city in an inland valley of California was considering the installation of an air-cooling system for all of the rooms. This hotel had 150 guest rooms and was considered to be one of three "first-class" hotels in the city. One of the other hotels had installed such a system the previous year. A bid of $18,000 had been received for installing the system. It was estimated that the cooling system would have to be operated at full capacity for fourteen weeks of each year, and at reduced capacity for six weeks. Operation costs at full capacity would be $17 per day, and at reduced capacity, $12 per day. The annual maintenance expense was estimated to be $125, and taxes and insurance to be $200. The life of the installation was estimated to be not less than fifteen years.

If the cooling system were installed, it was estimated that 90 per cent of the rooms would be rented during the twenty weeks of the hot weather, whereas only 80 per cent of the rooms could be rented if no air cooling was available. These estimates were based on results of similar hotels in other cities. The existing average profit on each room that was rented was $2 per day. The owners had capital invested in stocks, paying about 6% before taxes, which could be used to finance the project.

The study was made as follows:

Income $150 \times (0.9 - 0.8) \times \$2.00 \times 7 \times 20 =$ \$4,200

Expenses
  Depreciation = \$18,000/23.3   = \$ 772
  Operation = \$17 × 7 × 14   = 1,666
            \$12 × 7 × 6   =   504
  Maintenance   =   125
  Taxes and Insurance   =   200
    Total   \$3,267

Profit   \$ 933

Return on the investment = \$933/\$18,000 = 5.5%

This predicted rate of return was less than that currently being received on the capital. It thus might appear that the investment should not be made. However, there was an important intangible in the situation. It was feared that unless the cooling system was installed, customers of the hotel who came to the city at various times during the year might not patronize it during the hot season, thus establishing a habit which they would follow during cold weather. The hotel might be thought of as a second-class hotel and lose a considerable amount of the patronage it now enjoyed. It was believed that the income and expense estimates were accurate and the write-off period conservative. The owners decided to invest in the cooling system, even though the predicted return as shown by the economy study was less than they were then receiving from their capital. The intangibles pointed toward greater loss if the investment were not made.

EXAMPLE OF A PROPOSED INVESTMENT TO REDUCE EXPENSES

A manufacturer of jewelry is contemplating the installation of a system which will recover a large portion of the fine particles of gold which result from the various manufacturing operations. At the present time a little over \$6,000 worth of gold per year is being lost. This figure has been determined accurately from the known weights of incoming and outgoing material. The proposed recovery system would involve a network of exhaust ducts and separators. The complete installation would cost \$8,000. It is known from the history of other installations of equipment of this type that at least two thirds of the gold lost at present could be recovered. The best estimates available are that it would cost $1,000 per year for operation expense and $300 per year for maintenance and repairs and that taxes and insurance would be approximately 2%. The company demands that all equipment be written off within five years. The average earnings of the company before taxes have been about 10%. Should the gold recovery system be installed?

Such an investment is made to reduce some of the operating expenses; in this case, the cost of material used. Thus the saving (income) to be obtained by making an investment is almost entirely within the control of the investors. The company knows exactly what expenses have been. If the efficiency of the proposed equipment is known, the only factors which should affect the saving are the variation of production, operation, and maintenance expenses of the proposed equipment and depreciation expense. In most cases of this type these items are known or may be predicted quite accurately. The company would have a good idea of how its volume might vary. Operation and maintenance expenses can usually be estimated accurately, especially if historical data are available on the proposed equipment. Depreciation costs can be placed on the safe side by using a write-off period shorter than actual physical life.

For the gold-recovery system the total annual operating costs would be

Depreciation (10% S.F.)	$1,310
Operation	1,000
Maintenance	300
Taxes and insurance	160
Total	$2,770

Since the resulting saving in recovered gold would be two thirds of $6,000, or $4,000, the actual net saving resulting from the investment of $8,000 would be

$$\$4,000 - \$2,770 = \$1,230.$$

This is a return of 15% on the invested capital.

In deciding whether or not this possible return of 15% is sufficient to justify investment, each factor which might contribute to risk must be examined so that a measure of the total risk may be obtained. In this case it appears that the factors are quite well controlled or known. There is little reason to believe that much more risk would be involved than is present in all of the normal operations of the company. Thus the company has its own experience to use as a basis of comparison. If the company is sound and its business quite stable, certainly a return of 15% should be satisfactory, since the average capital invested in the company is earning only 10%.

Thus it may be seen that when capital is invested in a going concern in order to bring about reduction in expenses, or when company funds are used for the same purpose, the risk is usually easier to determine and is often much less than when entirely new enterprises are involved. As a result, the rate of return required for such investments is often lower, being only a little more than the existing rate of earning of the company.

INVESTMENT WHERE INCOME IS UNKNOWN

Decisions to invest or not to invest capital often must be made when it is impossible to know or evaluate the return. In some cases it is not particularly necessary to know what the income will be. This often occurs when public or governmental improvements are made. The returns are often in non-monetary form, yielding convenience and satisfaction to the public. When companies spend large sums of money to create customer or employee good will, a precise measurement of the return is impossible. Yet such investments must often be made.

Probably the only rule that can be established for such cases is that no more should be invested than is required to give a satisfactory result. Obviously this rule can not be followed rigidly. In building public roads, for example, it may be advisable to spend more than a bare minimum in order to assure permanence and low maintenance cost. In such cases the rule of least annual cost becomes important. The income (or at least a large part of it) resulting from many projects that at first thought do not appear subject to the type of analysis under discussion can be measured if the undertakings are analyzed fully. Whenever this can be done, it should not be neglected. Greater efficiency in the use of capital is bound to result. Some of these cases will be discussed in later chapters.

PROBLEMS

10-1   The prospectus of a uranium exploration and mining company states that "investors may obtain a return of 200% on their money." Only one small uranium find has been made, by another company, in the state where the company expects to operate. Only one of the officers of the company has had any mining experience, and this one a very limited amount. Extensive geological surveys of the state have been available for several years. What are some of the factors you would consider in deciding whether to invest money in this company?

10-2   Two men are considering establishing a company to produce and sell a soap product for household use. It is a highly competitive but stable industry. An investment of $120,000 will be required for the plant and equipment, and an additional $30,000 for working capital. It is believed that ten years is a conservative estimate of the economic life of the property. Operating expenses are estimated to be as follows:

Materials $42,000 per year
Overhead $21,000 per year
Selling expense $10,000 per year
Labor $78,000 per year
Taxes and insurance   4% of the first cost

Sales are estimated to be $180,000 per year. No market survey was made, but the estimated sales volume was determined by studying sales data of other companies in the field. The men have the necessary capital available and are now receiving a before-tax return of 7%. Would you advise making the investment?

10–3   Joe Doaks has an opportunity to buy out the proprietor of a "Hot Dog, Doughnut, and Coffee Emporium" adjacent to the entrance of an office building in a small city. It is a one-man establishment and has not been very successful. However, Joe believes that if additional equipment is added and the business run properly it should be very profitable. The nearest competitor is about one half block away and across the street.

Joe will have to pay the present owner $1,000.00 and spend an additional $1,000.00 for new equipment and alterations. He estimates he can sell 200 hot dogs per day, 100 doughnuts, and 300 cups of coffee. The estimated operating costs are

Wieners $0.06 each
Buns $0.03 each
Doughnuts $0.04 each
Coffee $0.70 per pound (30 cups per pound)
Cream and sugar $0.01 per cup
Mustard, napkins, etc. $2.00 per day
Electricity $12.00 per month.

Selling prices will be

Hot dogs $0.15 each
Doughnuts $0.05 each
Coffee $0.10 per cup.

Joe plans to operate six days per week, fifty weeks per year. Monthly rent will be $75.00 on a five-year lease.

Because of the terms of the lease, he feels he must recover his capital in five years. Insurance will cost $175.00 per year. He is now employed at a job which pays $2.75 per hour. His capital is in a savings and loan association and earns 4% interest.

Should Joe invest in the business?

10–4   A company must decide whether to install a system to control the fly ash from its power plant. Such a system would cost $50,000 and have an estimated life of at least ten years. Experience at other companies indicates that such a system will effect an annual saving of 2½% of the annual fuel bill in addition to solving a serious air pollution problem. The annual fuel bill has been $420,000. The estimated annual operation and maintenance cost will be $2,200, and the sum of taxes and insurance 2% of the initial cost. It appears likely that local legislation will require the installation of such equipment within five years. The company's capital earns about 10% before taxes. Should the installation be made?

10–5   A chemical manufacturer is considering expanding his operations by entering the plastics field. He has developed a new plastic which has properties equal or superior to another widely used plastic. A plant of capacity sufficient to produce 1,000,000 pounds per year will cost $1,000,000.00 for buildings and equipment and $30,000.00 for the necessary land. Operating costs for producing 1,000,000 pounds per year would be $40,000.00 for labor, $100,000.00 for raw materials, and $20,000.00 for operational overhead. Taxes and insurance are estimated to be 1½% of first cost per year. It is believed that the entire output can be sold for $0.32 per pound, since the competing product sells for $0.38 per pound. Present earnings of the company are about 4% after income taxes, and its tax rate is 50%. The company wishes to recover its capital in ten years. Would you advise the investment?

10–6   A manufacturer is preparing to produce a new product which will require one die casting. A company, specializing in this work and having excess capacity in equipment required for producing the casting, offers to manufacture the castings for the cost of the material, plus labor, plus $0.01 per casting for power, heat, and increment overhead, plus a profit of 25%, based upon the mentioned items of expense. They quote material and labor costs per casting of $0.11 and $0.04 respectively. The quoted prices are to be good only if they are allowed to produce the required number of castings at off-peak intervals. This will necessitate the manufacturer's carrying an average stock of $550.00 worth of castings on hand. His capital is worth 10% before taxes.

The manufacturer dislikes the idea of paying the die-casting company a profit of 25%. He therefore buys die-casting equipment for $4,000.00. As he uses only a relatively small amount of material, his material costs are $0.12 per casting. Labor costs are the same as quoted by the die-casting company. He must write off his investment in the die-casting equipment in four years. Other overhead costs will amount to $0.02 per unit.

If he produces 10,000 castings per year, has he made a wise choice?

10–7   Tom Freshman has an opportunity to buy a business operating twenty candy-vending machines located in fraternity houses and cooperative dormitories on his college campus. He must purchase ten of the machines at $200.00 each and can obtain the remaining ten on a 48-month lease-purchase plan under which he would pay interest on the unpaid balance at the rate of $\frac{1}{2}\%$ per month. He estimates that, on the average, each of 1,000 students will purchase six items per week during the 39 weeks of the school year, each item selling at $0.10. Tom will have to pay $0.06 for each item and will also pay $0.02 per item to each fraternity or dormitory as space rental. Servicing of the machines will require twenty hours per week and require him to drive his car fifty miles per week. He estimates the cost of operating his car at $0.05 per mile. In addition to buying the ten machines, he will have $500.00 invested in a supply of candy at all times. He must insure the machines, and the annual insurance premium will cost 1% of the initial value of the machines. Maintenance on the machines is estimated by the company selling them at $10.00 per machine per year.

Tom has the required $2,500.00 invested in U.S. Treasury savings bonds which pay him 3% interest. Part-time jobs in the vicinity of the campus pay about $1.50 per hour. Because he is uncertain that he will be able to sell the machines at the end of his expected four-year stay in college, he feels he must recover his capital within four years.

Should Tom invest in the business?

10–8   The Dippo Manufacturing Company is building a new plant in a new location. In its present location all incoming and outgoing shipments are by truck. A spur track can be built at the new location at a cost of $40,000; a study has indicated that at least forty tons of freight per day could be brought to the plant and the same amount taken away over this spur track without the necessity for rehandling, resulting in a saving of $0.45 per ton. A conservative life for the spur track is estimated to be ten years, with annual maintenance costs of $250.00. Property taxes would amount to 1% of the first cost per year. The plant operates 250 days per year. Sufficient capital is available, and average earnings are about 15% before taxes. Should the spur track be built?

10–9   Assume that the Dippo Manufacturing Company would have to borrow $30,000 of the required $40,000 for building the spur track, paying 6% interest. Would this affect the decision?

10–10 A three-inch fill of rock wool insulation in the ceiling is estimated to reduce the annual fuel bill for a certain type of house by 20%. If the cost of such an installation for a six-room house is $175 and the annual fuel bill has been $92, how many years would be required for the installation to pay for itself, assuming money is worth 4% to the home owner?

10-11 The ABC Company recently began making a new product in addition to two others it has been producing for several years. One of the major parts of this new product is now being purchased from another company at a cost of $5.00 per unit. One of the officers of the ABC company believes it would be advisable to purchase the required equipment, at a cost of $7,000.00, which would permit making this component. This equipment would have a capacity of 7,000 units per year and an economic life of at least five years. It could be installed in the existing plant, but a small storage shed must be built, at a cost of $2,000.00 to make the necessary floor space available.

Material costs would be $1.10 per unit, and direct labor costs $2.40. Overhead, exclusive of depreciation, is charged at 50% of prime cost. There would have to be an added annual charge of 2% of the first cost of the storage shed to cover taxes and insurance.

The company now is purchasing 4,000 of the parts per year.

a. If capital is worth 8%, should the part be purchased or made in the plant?

b. What volume would be required to justify purchasing the equipment?

10-12 An insurance company is investigating the possibility of investing in a large housing project to consist of 1,000 apartment units. Each unit would rent for $80 per month and would consist of a living-dining room, a kitchen, a bathroom, and two bedrooms. Covered storage area for one automobile would be provided for each apartment. The project would cost $8,000,000. Annual upkeep is estimated to be $150 per apartment. Annual operational costs for supervision, rental expense, etc., would amount to $45,000. Taxes and insurance would total 2% of the first cost per year. Investigation of similar projects leads to the belief that at least 95 per cent of the units would be occupied at all times. The company must obtain at least a 6% return on an investment of this type and recover its capital within forty years. Would you advise investing in the project?

10-13 Two men have designed a "rocket" which gives its occupants a simulated trip to the moon through the use of a motion-picture screen and suitable sound effects. They can obtain a permit to build and install the rocket in a children's amusement park which is maintained by a city of 300,000 population.

Construction of the rocket, which will hold 30 persons, will require an investment of $17,000.00. Operation will require the services of both men, plus one woman to sell tickets. They will have to pay her $2,700.00 per year. Insurance and taxes will cost $500.00 per year. Other operating and maintenance costs are estimated at $2,000.00 per year.

They can obtain a ten-year franchise from the city, which provides that the maximum admission price that can be charged is $0.15 and that 5% of the gross revenue must be paid to the city. There is a further provision that at the end of the franchise period ownership of the rocket reverts to the city.

From surveys of similar amusement features in the park and in other cities they believe they can operate six days per week during thirteen weeks of the summer at 60 per cent of capacity, and on Saturdays and Sundays during the remaining weeks of the year at 75 per cent of capacity. Each trip takes twelve minutes, including loading and unloading time. The rocket would operate eight hours per day. The two men now have jobs which pay each of them $5,200.00 per year.

If capital is worth 4% to them, should they make the investment?

10–14 A company is considering making a product which now is produced by three other large companies. It is a fairly stable product in terms of demand, and there is evidence that the domestic market will increase gradually and that a decrease in selling price would increase the market only slightly. The present selling price is $0.50 per pound; over a period of years the price has varied about plus or minus 10 per cent from this price.

An investment of $250,000.00 will be required to build a plant which could produce 500,000 pounds of the product annually. This amount would constitute 20 per cent of the present annual domestic consumption. Annual costs for labor for this volume of output would be $70,000.00 and for materials $90,000.00. Advertising, sales expense, and administrative overhead would amount to $40,000.00 per year. Taxes and insurance would total 2% of the cost of the plant.

The company would expect a before-tax return of at least 10% on its capital and would write off the plant in twenty years.

a. Would you advise the investment under the conditions stated?

b. What would be the minimum selling price which would permit the investment to be acceptable?

10–15 A certain business venture will require the immediate investment of $80,000, and additional investments of $5,000 in one year and $3,000 in two years. Operational costs and income are expected to be as follows, all considered as year-end amounts:

Year	Costs	Income
1	$30,000	$20,000
2	25,000	30,000
3	30,000	35,000
4	32,000	53,000
5	32,000	53,000
6	32,000	53,000
7	32,000	53,000
8	32,000	48,000
9	25,000	40,000
10	18,000	25,000

The assets will have a scrap value of $5,000 at the end of the tenth year. Does this appear to be a satisfactory investment?

10–16 A women's clothing shop is investigating the advisability of installing two unit-type air conditioners. The units would cost $3,000 each, installed. Operating costs for each unit are estimated to be $2 per day. It is estimated that they would have to be operated 200 days per year. They carry a five-year guarantee on maintenance, and it is estimated that maintenance costs would not exceed $100 per year on each unit during the remainder of their anticipated ten-year life.

The shop has been earning about 15% return on capital before taxes, which corresponds to a profit of 10% on sales. A number of other shops of this type in the city are already air-conditioned. In addition to the probability that sales will be increased by the installation, it is believed that there will be a saving of at least $200 per year in cleaning and decorating costs. Taxes and insurance will amount to 2% of the first cost per year.

What increase in sales will be required in order to justify the installation?

10–17 A small chemical plant has its own power plant but requires "stand-by" service from a utility company so that continuous service will be available. The company is paying $125 per month for this stand-by service. In addition, it pays $300 per year for power purchased while its plant is being overhauled.

A Diesel stand-by plant is being considered. The installation would cost $28,000. Maintenance of this plant under these conditions would not exceed $250 per year, and operational costs during the shut-down of the main plant would not be more than $400 per year. Taxes and insurance would cost $375 annually. While the plant would be expected to last at least thirty years under these conditions, the company feels it must recover its capital in twenty years. The estimated salvage value of the plant at the end of twenty years is $5,000. Average before-tax earnings of the company have been approximately 20%.

Should the installation be made?

10–18 In designing a new warehouse the installation of a sprinkler system for fire protection is being considered. The warehouse will cost $600,000, and a sprinkler installation would cost an additional $22,000. Insurance companies have advised that they will grant a decrease of 20% on the insurance rate on the building and a decrease of 35% on the rate for the merchandise stored in it if a sprinkler system is installed. The insurance rates without a sprinkler system will be 0.75% on the building and 0.6% on the contents. Taxes are 1% per year. The owners demand that any such equipment be written off within thirty years. Annual maintenance for the system should not exceed $100. It is expected that on the average $750,000 worth of merchandise will be stored in the warehouse, and the insurance premium will be based on this amount. The owners expect to receive a return of at least 10% on their investment in the warehouse, before taxes. Should the sprinkler system be added?

10–19 Two men are considering investing money to open a new pre-mix concrete company in a suburban area that is expanding rapidly. A large amount of business and residential construction is expected to take place in the area during the next ten years, and many streets and some new highways will be built. There is no such plant in the area, and concrete now is brought in from a city about four miles distant.

The materials handling and batching plant will cost $18,000 and will have a capacity of three batches of three cubic yards each per hour. To handle the mixing and distribution will require four mixer trucks costing $7,000.00 each and having an estimated life of four years, with a salvage value of $500.00 each at the end of that time. The batching plant will have an estimated economic life of ten years. The plant would operate 250 days per year, eight hours per day, and it is believed that it probably can operate at about 75 per cent of capacity.

Operating costs will be as follows:

Labor	Two men at $18.00 per day
	One woman at $11.00 per day
	Four truck drivers at $21.00 per day

Power $7.00 per day
Miscellaneous office overhead $2.00 per day
Truck maintenance $5.00 per day per truck
Truck operation $9.00 per day per truck
Taxes & insurance on plant   2% of first cost per year
Insurance and taxes on trucks $320.00 per year each
Materials (per cubic yard of concrete)   Cement $5.30
                                             Sand $1.60
                                             Rock $2.50
                                             Water $0.02

Payroll taxes   7% per year
Vacations and fringe benefits   5% per year

The present selling price of pre-mixed concrete is $16.00 per cubic yard.

The investors will not contribute any labor to the project. A manager will be hired at $8,000.00 per year to manage the company and solicit business. He will also receive a bonus of 5% of the net profits before taxes. The investors demand a return of at least 15% before taxes.

Would you recommend the investment?

CHAPTER 11

Alternative
Investments

Chapter 10 dealt with economy studies made to determine whether a specific project should be undertaken. In many cases, after it is decided that it is advisable to undertake a project, one is faced with the fact that there is more than one way in which the project may be carried out. Typically, the various available methods or plans require the investment of different amounts of capital, and usually they involve different annual disbursements for operation, maintenance, taxes, etc. They may produce different revenues and frequently have different lives. Thus one must make economy studies to determine which available alternative should be used. Such studies answer the question, "How much should be invested?"

The decision regarding several investment alternatives, or levels, is simplified if one remembers that the purpose of investment is to obtain the greatest possible return from *each* dollar of capital. Theoretically, one should consider each unit of capital separately before investing it. In actual practice, there are usually only a limited number of choices. The problem of deciding which alternative should be used is made easier if one adopts a simple policy which can be stated as follows: *The alternative which requires the minimum investment of capital and will produce satisfactory functional results, will always be used unless there are definite reasons why an alternative requiring a larger investment should be adopted.* Under this policy one would consider the alternative which required the least investment of capital to be the basic plan. All other alternatives would then be compared with it. Additional amounts of capital would not be invested unless some distinctively advantageous results would be obtained.

The investment of additional amounts of capital in various alternatives

253

usually results in increased capacity, increased revenue, decreased operating expenses, or increased life. One expects through these means to obtain greater profit. Any change in profit which occurs is obviously the direct result of the additional capital which was invested. Thus one may measure the effectiveness of the investment of additional increments of capital beyond the minimum which would be required to obtain the desired results. If the additional return obtained by investing an additional amount of capital is better than could be obtained from investment of the same capital elsewhere, the investment should probably be made. If such is not the case, one obviously would not invest more than the minimum amount required. Thus, in determining how much should be invested, each possible increment of investment must be considered as a separate investment possibility. Of course, along with this, one must consider any possible effect of a change in the total amount invested on the investment as a whole.

ALTERNATIVES HAVING IDENTICAL REVENUES AND LIVES

Many economy studies must be made where the revenue from the various alternatives will be identical, or may be assumed to be the same. If it is already known that the project is to be undertaken, one is interested only in determining the manner in which it is to be done.

In such studies it is ordinarily assumed that the physical output from each method will be the same and that the revenue will be the same for each and may thus be neglected. Different levels of investment will result only in different operating expenses. Thus the result of investment beyond the minimum will be an increase or decrease in operating expense. Obviously, if the operating expense increases with increased investment, the additional amount of capital should not be invested. If increased investment, however, results in decreased operating expenses, one must decide whether the decrease in expenses is sufficient to justify the additional investment. Such a case may be illustrated by the following example.

A company is going to install a new plastic-molding press. Four different presses are available. The essential differences as to cost and operating expenses are as follows:

	A	B	C	D
Cost (installed)	$6,000	$7,600	$12,400	$13,000
Power (per year)	680	680	1,200	1,260
Labor (per year)	6,600	6,000	4,200	3,700
Maintenance (per year)	400	450	650	500
Taxes and insurance	2%	2%	2%	2%
Life (economic)	5 years	5 years	5 years	5 years

Each press will produce the same number of units. However, because of different degrees of mechanization, some require different amounts and classes of labor and have different operation and maintenance costs. The capital invested in this company has earned about 10% before taxes. Which press should be chosen?

Since each press will produce the same output, the only justification for investing more than the $6,000 required to buy press A is the possibility that use of the additional capital will produce a greater return than could be obtained for the use of the same capital elsewhere. To determine whether the resulting savings will justify the additional investment, examine Table 11–1, where the operating expenses of each press are tabulated. It will be

TABLE 11–1   Comparative Total Annual Costs of Four Molding Presses

Item	A	B	C	D
Power	$ 680	$ 680	$1,200	$1,260
Labor	6,600	6,000	4,200	3,700
Maintenance	400	450	650	500
Taxes and insurance	120	152	248	260
Depreciation (10% S.F.)	984	1,245	2,030	2,130
Total expense	$8,784	$8,527	$8,328	$7,850
Saving over next lowest investment		$ 257	$ 199	$ 478
Necessary increment investment		$1,600	$4,800	$ 600
Return on added investment		16%	4.1%	80%
Return on added increment beyond next lowest *acceptable* investment		16%	4.1%	12.5%

noted that the investment of an extra $1,600 in order to buy press B would result in an annual saving of $257. This constitutes an annual return of 16% that could be obtained by investing an increment amount of $1,600. This is thus an investment opportunity and problem essentially like those discussed in Chapter 10. The decision as to whether the investment should be made must be arrived at in the same manner as before, by determining whether the prospective return is adequate. If one assumes that the capital now is earning only 10%, the investment of the additional $1,600 appears to be justified.

Now consider press C by comparing it with press B. One finds a *further* saving of $199 can be obtained by investing an additional increment of $4,800. This saving, however, represents a return of only 4.1% upon the capital required to produce it. Obviously this rate of return does not justify the investment of the additional $4,800.

From this example and the previous discussion, it can be seen that where no revenue data are given each increment of capital above the minimum must be considered as a separate investment possibility. By this method of analysis, the same procedure and reasoning that are used for deciding whether an investment should be made can be used to determine the amount that should be invested. It should be recognized, however, that the risk factors, and consequently the rate of return which should be demanded, may be somewhat different for alternatives of investment than they would be for the original investment.

A DANGER OF MISINTERPRETATION

The method just presented for analyzing alternative investments, using the rate of return of the increment required investment, is relatively simple and has several advantages. In using it, however, one must be certain to avoid one pitfall. This may be illustrated by considering the case of press *D*. In Table 11–1 it is shown that when this press is compared with *C* a return of 80% is obtained on the added increment of $600. However, *such a comparison is not a valid one, since press C would not be a satisfactory investment*. This is a type of error which sometimes is made in such economy studies. Since press *C* was *not* found to be an acceptable alternative, it should not be used as a basis for comparison. The correct comparison is shown in the last line of Table 11–1, where press *D* is compared with press *B, the one which offers the next lowest acceptable investment level*. In this case the return offered by the increment investment of $5,400, required to purchase press *D* instead of press *B*, is 12.5%. Although this rate of profit is just a little greater than that which is being received from capital invested in the business, one would have to decide whether it is adequate to justify the investment of the additional $5,400. It is apparent that this increment will not earn as high a rate of return as the $1,600 increment that could be invested in press *B*. One would probably decide to try to find a more favorable use for the capital, thus providing increased diversity and, at the same time, avoiding putting unnecessary amounts of capital in molding presses.

COMPARING ALTERNATIVES BY MINIMUM ANNUAL COST

The annual-cost method may also be used for comparing alternatives. The alternative which has the minimum annual cost is assumed to be the most desirable. However, the use of this method requires careful interpretation with special attention to the rate used in the "Minimum Required Return" which is included as an expense.

For the case of the four molding presses the solution by the minimum annual cost method would be as follows:

	A	B	C	D
Power (per year)	$ 680	$ 680	$1,200	$1,260
Labor (per year)	6,600	6,000	4,200	3,700
Maintenance	400	450	650	500
Taxes and insurance	120	152	248	260
Depreciation (10% S.F.)	984	1,245	2,030	2,130
Minimum required return (10%)	600	760	1,240	1,300
Totals	$9,384	$9,287	$9,568	$9,150

According to this method of analysis, press D has the least annual cost and thus would be the one to select. However, as was revealed by the rate-of-return analysis, there is considerable doubt as to whether one would want to buy press D instead of press B. It should be noted that the annual-cost method does not tell, without further computations and interpretation, what the *actual* return on the investment will be for each press. Neither does it show the rate of return to be obtained from each increment of investment. The method, in effect, assumes that unlimited capital is available and that alternatives which require larger amounts of capital will be justified by the same rate of return that would be demanded for those which might require the investment of much smaller sums. Such a situation is contrary to the demands of many companies and investors. In this case, for example, the *total* rate of return which would be received if press D were used would be less than if press B were selected. It usually is necessary, when using the annual-cost method, to make further calculations to determine the rate of return from each increment of capital before a sound decision can be reached.

If the rate of minimum required return is set to include a proper consideration of possible differences in the value of different amounts of capital, the above difficulty can be avoided. However, such differences are rather difficult to evaluate. Perhaps the best rule to follow when using the annual-cost method is to re-examine carefully alternatives which are found to have nearly equal annual costs and give further consideration to such factors as important differences in capital required.

PLANT LOCATION STUDIES

Economy studies of alternative sites for plants usually are of the form that has been discussed in the previous paragraphs. Ordinarily, if a plant of a given capacity is to be built, the income from sales will be the same for each location being considered. The investment, operating, and selling costs will be different for the various locations, because of land and building costs, wage rates, taxes, transportation expense, and availability of materials. The following is an example of this type of problem.

A company was going to build a new plant and was considering three locations. Site B was in the center of a large city. Site A was at the edge of a smaller city. Site C was in a small community, a short distance from a medium-sized city, where land was quite inexpensive but a considerable sum of capital had to be invested to provide access roads, power facilities, etc.; wage rates also were somewhat lower in this community.

Table 11–2 shows the investment, income, and cost data and the total and increment rates of return for the three locations. Site B was rejected on

TABLE 11–2   Comparison of Three Locations for a Plant

	Site A	Site B	Site C
Required investment			
Land	$ 75,000	$105,000	$ 10,000
Buildings	535,000	550,000	665,000
Total	$610,000	$655,000	$675,000
Income from sales	$856,000	$856,000	$856,000
Production costs			
Materials	$130,000	$130,000	$120,000
Labor	245,000	245,000	200,000
Transportation	38,000	30,000	42,000
Power & Miscellaneous	45,000	45,000	50,000
Overhead	210,000	220,000	200,000
Total	$668,000	$670,000	$612,000
Selling expense	$ 87,000	$ 84,000	$130,000
Profit	$101,000	$102,000	$114,000
Rate of return on total investment	16.6%	15.6%	16.9%
Rate of return on increment investment (Site A as a base)		2.2%	20%

the basis of the figures shown, since the increment rate of return was too low, and all other factors were considered to be equal for sites A and B. Site C offered an attractive increment rate of return on the required capital and had certain other advantages in respect to living conditions for the employees. However site A was finally selected because of two factors. The more important was that it was necessary for customers to come to the plant at frequent intervals. It was felt that the remote location, as compared with site A, would be a considerable disadvantage. The second factor was that it was believed there was much greater probability of wage rates and taxes increasing at site C than at A.

ALTERNATIVES HAVING DIFFERENT LIVES

In many cases the lives of various alternatives may be different. The investment of a larger amount of capital may purchase longer life and lower operation and maintenance costs. In order to make economy studies of such cases, some method must be adopted which will put the alternatives upon a comparable life basis. Neither the rate-of-return nor the annual-cost procedure is completely satisfactory for such cases. The present-worth method provides a procedure for comparing such alternatives.

This method of comparing two alternatives having different lives and operating costs may be illustrated by the following example, in which two structures are compared.

	Structure M	Structure N
First cost	$12,000	$40,000
Economic life	10 years	25 years
Salvage value at end of life	0	$10,000
Annual maintenance and operation expense	$ 2,200	$ 1,000

Minimum worth of capital = 5%

Since the structures have different lives, ten and twenty-five years, it is necessary to adopt a study period of such a length that a number of structures of either type will provide the desired service throughout the same period. It also is desirable that the study period be the shortest that will meet this requirement. In this case fifty years of service can be provided by building structure M and replacing it four times—a total of five structures. The same length of service can be obtained by building structure N and replacing it once—a total of two such structures. The present worth of all of the costs of providing fifty years of service with structure M would be:

Present worth of 1st structure $= \$12,000$
Present worth of 2nd structure $= \$12,000 \times v^{10} = \$12,000 \times 0.614 = 7,350$
Present worth of 3rd structure $= \$12,000 \times v^{20} = \$12,000 \times 0.377 = 4,520$
Present worth of 4th structure $= \$12,000 \times v^{30} = \$12,000 \times 0.231 = 2,770$
Present worth of 5th structure $= \$12,000 \times v^{40} = \$12,000 \times 0.142 = 1,700$
Present worth of O & M $= \$ 2,200 \times a_{\overline{50}|} = \$ 2,200 \times 18.26 = \underline{40,170}$
Present worth of total costs $= \$68,510$

For structure N the present worth of the costs would be:

Present worth of 1st structure   = $40,000
Present worth of net cost to obtain 2nd structure
$$= (\$40,000 - \$10,000)\, v^{25} = \$30,000 \times 0.295 = \underline{8,850}$$
$$\$48,850$$
Less present worth of salvage value of 2nd structure
$$= \$10,000 \times v^{50} = \$10,000 \times 0.087 \qquad = \underline{-870}$$
$$\$47,980$$
Present worth of O & M
$$= \$1,000 \times a_{\overline{50}|} = \$1,000 \times 18.26 \qquad = \underline{18,260}$$
Present worth of total costs $= \$66,240$

Thus, if capital is worth 5%, structure N will be more economical.

This method of analysis also has certain weaknesses which should be considered. Probably the most critical is the very great effect that the interest rate may have. A quite modest change in interest rate may reverse the relative standings of the alternatives. For example, if a 6% minimum acceptable return is used, the present worth of the total costs for structures M and N would be:

	Structure M	Structure N
Present worth of total costs	$60,290	$62,210

On this basis, structure M would be more economical.

The critical importance of the interest or profit rate in this method of analysis does not mean that it should not be used. It only means that in using the procedure one should select the interest rate with great care, and also understand the effect of variations in interest rate. In general terms,

1. Increased interest rates make long-lived alternatives less attractive.
2. The existence of interest tends to discount the value of future services from long-lived alternatives.

One also must make certain that the additional life to be provided by the longer-lived alternative(s) is truly needed or usable. For example, in comparing two alternatives having lives of ten and twenty-five years, one should make certain that life beyond ten or twenty years, as could be provided by the ten-year alternative, is really needed and valuable before considering the other alternative, particularly on the basis of a fifty-year study period. From this viewpoint the shorter-lived alternative usually has some advantages, since the need and general conditions can be predicted with greater certainty for a shorter period than for a longer one. Therefore, unless there is a substantial difference in the present worth of the future costs, preference would usually be given to the shorter-lived alternative.

The fact that the same interest rate is used for all alternatives in a given study also offers some difficulty. It is common practice to require a somewhat higher interest rate from a prospective investment that has a long life and write-off period than from one having a shorter life. Yet it is very difficult to include this consideration in studies of short-lived versus long-lived alternatives by the present-worth method. If a higher interest rate is used for the longer-lived alternative, it actually reduces the present worth of the total costs because of the higher discount effect. Thus the net effect is exactly opposite to what was intended. Therefore the most feasible solution is to use the same interest rate for each alternative and to give proper consideration to such factors as the normally expected differences in profit rates for different-lived alternatives by proper analysis of the total cost figures.

As was discussed in a previous chapter, it must be remembered that the differences in the present worth of the total costs of the various alternatives is the present worth of the sum of the annual differences throughout the entire study period. Thus, what appears to be a rather substantial total difference may easily be the sum of a considerable number of quite small annual differences. It frequently is helpful, in analyzing the significance of the differences in total costs, to compute the equivalent equal annual differences.

COMPARISON OF ALTERNATIVES HAVING DIFFERENT LIVES BY THE RATE-OF-RETURN METHOD

It is possible to compare alternatives having different lives by the rate-of-return method. This method, of course, does not directly take into account the difference in lives, except with respect to depreciation. However, proper interpretation of the results will provide satisfactory information upon which decisions can be based.

By the rate-of-return method the analysis of structures M and N would be as follows:

	Structure M	*Structure N*
Depreciation	$\dfrac{\$12,000}{12.58} = \$\ 955$	$\dfrac{\$40,000 - \$10,000}{47.7} = \$\ 630$
O + M	2,200	1,000
Total	$3,155	$ 1,630
Annual saving		$ 1,525
Increment investment		$28,000
Rate of return		5.4%

These results indicate that structure N will produce a rate of return on the increment capital that is slightly greater than the required 5%. Obviously, these figures require some interpretation. If the structure is required for more than ten years (and it must be if an economic life of twenty-five years is valid for structure N), it must be recognized that structure M will have to be replaced after each ten-year period. As in other cases, one must decide whether the rate of return is adequate in view of the write-off period involved, risk, etc. However, such interpretation is required in virtually all economy studies. This situation again brings out the necessity of examining and interpreting the conditions and results of any economy study if sound conclusions are to be reached.

COMPARING ALTERNATIVES BY THE CAPITALIZED-COST METHOD

Obviously, the capitalized-cost method can be used for comparing alternatives having different lives. The only basic difference is that an infinitely long study period is assumed, and such an assumption is very unrealistic for most projects. About the only types of projects for which such an assumption is even reasonably realistic are governmentally financed projects involving such structures as dams, large bridges, and irrigation canals. However, the differences resulting from using an infinitely long study period or one of fifty or seventy-five years are so small that there is virtually no advantage to be gained from the perpetual-use concept. As a result, there has been a marked trend in recent years away from the capitalized-cost procedure and toward the use of the present-worth method and more realistic study periods.

COMPARING ALTERNATIVES BY THE PAYOUT-PERIOD METHOD

Alternatives may be compared by the payout-period procedure. If the life of each alternative is the same, this method rates the alternatives relative to each other. Obviously, such a study gives no information as to the rate of return obtained from any alternative and assumes that ample capital is available.

Consider the case of two alternatives, X and Y, which are estimated to have the same economic life and to produce the same income. Zero scrap value is assumed.

	X	Y
First cost	$5,000	$7,000
Estimated annual income minus out-of-pocket costs	$2,200	$3,400
Payout period $(1 \div 2)$	2.27 years	2.06 years

By this type of analysis, alternative Y would be assumed to be the more desirable.

As might be expected, this very simple type of analysis is apt to produce misleading results when it is applied to more complex situations. Yet it is used rather frequently without a realization that incorrect results may be obtained. For example, a recent study [1] revealed that small companies make rather extensive use of the payout period method in comparing alternatives which have different expected lives. The following is a typical case.

	A	B	C
Required investment	$5,000	$5,000	$6,000
Estimated useful life	8 years	5 years	10 years
Available for payout (Annual income minus out-of-pocket costs)	$2,250	$2,500	$3,000
Payout period	2.2 years	2.0 years	2.0 years

By this analysis, alternative B undoubtedly would be selected, since it has a shorter payout period than A and requires less capital than C. If, however, the three alternatives are compared on the basis of the rate of return, giving proper consideration to the estimated lives, the results are:

	A	B	C
Income minus out-of-pocket expense	$2,250	$2,500	$3,000
Less depreciation (8% S.F.)	470	853	414
Profit (before taxes)	$1,780	$1,647	$2,586
Rate of return on investment	35½%	33%	43%

By this analysis, alternative B is found to be the least desirable of the three, and, if capital is available, alternative C is much more desirable than either A or B.

The reasons for the extensive use of the payout method of analysis were found to be

1. It is a very simple procedure.
2. No consideration of depreciation is required.
3. The company managers desired to recover their capital as soon as possible so they could use it to undertake other projects.

One company owner expressed the third reason quite clearly by saying, "I have only a very limited amount of capital available. There are a dozen opportunities available to me for using any spare capital I have. I want to put my funds into that alternative which will enable me to get my capital back most quickly, so I can reinvest it in another opportunity."

As shown by this example, there is no advantage in two successive shorter-lived alternatives which will each produce a return of 30% when one

[1] Gonzales, F. M., "Evaluation of Investment in Production Facilities," M.S. Thesis, University of California, 1953.

longer-lived alternative will produce a 40% return. Therefore, since the payout-period method does not take expected life into account, its use is not recommended for comparing alternatives having different lives.

MORTALITY DISPERSION EFFECT

Occasionally economy studies of long-lived versus short-lived alternatives involve considerable numbers of units in each case. For example, one may be considering untreated telephone poles versus chemically treated poles. It is common practice to assume an average life in each case. Actually, of course, the poles will not all go out of service at the same time. Some will last longer than the average life, while others will not last as long as the average.

This actual mortality dispersion will result in some error if average-life values are used in computing depreciation or capital recovery with interest or profit. This is, of course, due to the effect of compound interest in such calculations. The effect may be illustrated by a simple example, assuming that five units are involved, each costing C dollars and having lives of eight, nine, ten, eleven, and twelve years. If a 6% interest rate is used, the following will be the total depreciation cost computed by considering the actual mortality dispersion:

Life of unit		$d = C/s_{\overline{n}|}$
	8 years	$0.101C$
	9	$0.087C$
	10	$0.076C$
	11	$0.067C$
	12	$0.059C$
Average	10 years	Total $0.390C$

If an average life of ten years is used, the total depreciation is $5C/13.2 = 0.379C$. Obviously the amount by which depreciation, or capital recovery, costs will be greater if actual mortality dispersion data are used will depend upon the dispersion and the interest rate. In most cases the error introduced by using average-life values is not great enough to justify the added complication involved in using actual mortality distribution data. However, it is well to keep the situation in mind, so that when conditions warrant, the more exact procedure may be used.

LOW FIRST COST AND HIGH ANNUAL COSTS VERSUS HIGH FIRST COST AND LOW ANNUAL COSTS

In many instances, particularly in small businesses where available capital is limited, selection must be made between two (or more) alternatives, one of which requires less investment but will have higher annual operating and/or maintenance costs, while the other requires a larger investment of capital but will have lower annual operating and/or maintenance costs. Frequently the alternative requiring greater investment also will have a longer economic life. The procedures that have just been discussed are, of course, adequate for such economy studies. There are, however, several special factors which should be considered in such cases.

First, it should be recognized that what may be a sound investment for an organization with ample capital may not be sound for a small business with limited capital. This means that it may be advisable, and sometimes necessary, for a small company to favor an alternative that calls for somewhat greater unit or total cost but less capital investment. The day-to-day variable operating costs may thus be somewhat greater, but there is some possibility of controlling them as conditions change, which can not be done with high fixed costs. The use of an alternative requiring a minimum of capital may permit an organization to get started in a new field of endeavor and then to take advantage of a lower total-cost method at a later date, when the volume of business has increased and the future is more certain.

Second, the matter of flexibility usually is very important in small businesses. For this reason, an alternative which has a shorter write-off period and requires less investment usually is preferred, even though the current costs may be slightly higher, since it permits a change in plans at an earlier date.

A third consideration is the fact that where capital is limited, the selection of an alternative requiring a smaller amount of capital may make it possible to engage in several projects, whereas the number would be reduced if projects requiring larger investments of capital were selected. While greater diversification usually is desirable, it should be remembered that if greater profit can be obtained by fewer projects, this may be more important than flexibility.

A fourth factor, which tends to favor low initial investment, is the economic state of business at the particular time. If times are difficult and the state of business uncertain, it may be advisable to operate with slightly higher costs rather than tie up larger amounts of capital than are absolutely necessary. Such a decision must, of course, be made with all the facts and results in mind.

Finally, if the necessity for replacement will cause considerable inconvenience to the owner or the general public, or loss of needed protection, this favors the selection of an alternative having a long life. In some cases one must also consider whether the replacement for a short-lived alternative will be available when needed. This particular consideration ordinarily exists only when national crises, such as wars, impend; their occurrence is difficult to predict.

ALTERNATIVES HAVING DIFFERENT REVENUES

There are many cases where the alternatives being considered produce different incomes. In some the results obtained by one method are considerably different from those obtained by another. All but the main objective may be quite different. Where the magnitude of the results, as well as the operating expense, is changed by varying the method and the amount of the investment, the economy study must consider all of these facts. While such studies are usually somewhat more complex, the main purpose still is to determine whether the proposed investment offers the best use for the capital.

When a change in the method, or amount invested, causes a difference in output or revenue, several possibilities result. Among these are the following.

1. Additional investment above a required minimum may increase the rate of return on the total investment above that which can be obtained by minimum investment. This means that the added increment of invested capital will earn a higher rate of return than can be obtained from the minimum investment. Because of certain circumstances, the added increment of capital is more productive than the basic investment. Where the return from the minimum amount of capital is not quite sufficient to justify investment, the investment of an added amount of capital may remove a proposition from the doubtful or undesirable class to the satisfactory or advisable level.

If the rate of return should continue to increase with added increments of capital, one would like to invest as much capital as possible, assuming that unlimited funds are available and that the soundness of the investment does not decrease. These conditions, of course, seldom exist. Funds are usually somewhat limited, and increased size, resulting from increased investment, usually results in greater risk. Moreover, it is very seldom that added increments of capital continue to earn rates of return equal to or greater than the preceding amounts which have been invested.

2. Investment of an additional increment of capital may cause the rate of return on the total investment to decrease. This means that the rate of return resulting from the added increment of capital is less than that which can be obtained from the original amount. For example, assume that from the investment of A dollars, X dollars of profit will result. X/A is the rate of return resulting from the investment of A dollars. If $A + B$ dollars were

invested, the profit would be $X + Y$ dollars. Since Y dollars of profit resulted from the investment of B dollars of additional capital, the rate of return upon the additional capital would be Y/B. If Y/B is less than X/A, the investment of the additional amount of B dollars was not as good a proposition as was the investment of A dollars.

When such a situation exists, the decision as to the correct amount to invest is not always simple. For example, consider the following data regarding two investment alternatives, A and B.

	A	B
Cost	$3,500	$5,000
Total annual expense	1,400	1,240
Annual receipts	1,900	1,920
Annual profit	500	680

Alternative B shows an annual profit of $180 more than alternative A. However, it would be necessary to invest $1,500 of additional capital in order to obtain this additional profit. This means that the actual annual rate of return on this $1,500 of additional capital would be 12%. While this is a fairly good rate of return, one should consider that the investment of $3,500 in alternative A would produce a return of 14.3%. Considering the entire $5,000 which would be invested if alternative B were used, one finds that this choice would result in a return of 13.6% upon the total investment. Thus in a case of this type one has several factors to consider before arriving at a decision as to the method which should be used.

It is entirely logical and proper to want to accomplish any undertaking with the investment of as little capital as possible. There should be a good reason for utilizing any method which requires more than the minimum amount of capital. If the rate of the additional return that will result from the added investment is greater than the rate produced by the minimum investment, this may be a satisfactory reason for increasing the size of the investment. Such a condition results in a rate of return on the entire amount invested greater than the rate which would be earned by the investment of only the minimum amount.

If, however, the rate of return from the added increment of investment is less than that which would be obtained from the minimum amount of capital, the decision must be made by considering all the possibilities for investment of the increment of capital *and* the effect upon the minimum amount of capital. For example, in the illustration just discussed, the added increment of $1,500 which would be required for alternative B would earn a return at the rate of 12%. If this amount of capital were on hand and no other investment opportunity of a similar risk were available which offered as great a return, the use of this capital to employ alternative B would be the best available investment for this money. While the additional $1,500 would not be invested as effectively as the basic $3,500, it would be earning at a rate that would satisfy its owner and might thus be called a *contentment* rate. However, when such a decision is made, one must keep in mind the fact that the entire amount which is invested becomes a single investment and thereafter earns a rate of return determined by the revenue produced by the entire investment. Thus, in the previous problem, while from a theoretical view the basic $3,500 earns 14.3% and the incremental $1,500 earns 12%, actually the entire investment of $5,000 earns 13.6%. Therefore, not only must one determine what return the added investment will produce, but he must also consider the effect which the added investment will have upon the minimum investment which would secure the desired results.

3. Added investment may have no effect on the rate of return which the total investment would earn. This means that the rate of return earned by the added increment of capital is the same as that earned by the basic investment. Under such circumstances, the only limit to the amount that should be invested is the amount of capital that the owners have available and wish to tie up in one enterprise. However, one should always keep in mind the hazards which result from investing too much capital in a single enterprise. Actually this third possibility is seldom encountered.

AN EXAMPLE OF INCREASING INVESTMENT
AFFECTING THE RATE OF RETURN

An excellent example of the conditions which may arise when added increments of investment produce unequal rates of return is found in a study which was made several years ago by W. C. Clark and J. L. Kingston.[2] This study grew out of experience related to the Empire State Building, whose height was uneconomical at the time at which it was constructed, resulting in great financial loss to the owners.

The study was made for various heights of a theoretical office building which was to be built on a plot of ground in New York City where land was worth $200 per square foot. Data were compiled for the cost of erecting buildings of the heights indicated in the chart of Figure 11–1. Estimates were made of the expected income and expenses of each structure. From

[2] Clark and Kingston, *The Skyscraper,* American Institute of Steel Construction, Inc., New York.

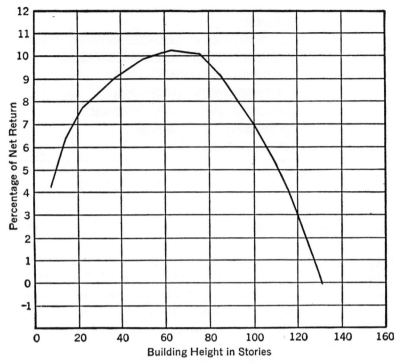

Figure 11–1. Return from the investment required for building skyscrapers of various heights.

these data the expected return on the total investment was computed and plotted as shown in Figure 11–1. In addition, it was possible to determine what return could be expected from the investment necessary to add a certain increment to the height of the building. These results are shown in Figure 11–2.

In Figure 11–1 it will be noted that a building of 8 stories would yield a return of only slightly over 4%. This would not be sufficient to justify investment in such a structure. As the height of the building is increased, the probable return is also increased, until a maximum of 10.2% is indicated for a structure of 63 stories. Increasing the height beyond 63 stories would result in an actual decrease in the rate of return. The projected curve indicates that for a building of 131 stories the rate of return would be zero.

The bar chart of Figure 11–2 presents some significant points of this situation. The bars represent the rate of return which would result from the investment necessary to provide each additional increment to the height of the building. Additional investment used to increase the height from 8 to

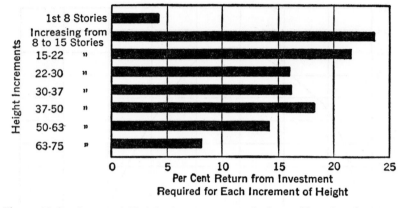

Figure 11–2. Return yielded by investments required to add various increments to the height of a proposed skyscraper.

15 stories would yield a return at the rate of 23.69%. Each successive increment of approximately 7 stories, up to a total height of 50 stories, yields a decreasing rate of return. The increase from 37 to 50 stories would produce a larger rate of return, but this is due to the lessened effect of the set-back ordinance. Beyond 63 stories, the increases in investment would yield a rate of return less than the maximum of 10.2% shown in Figure 11–1. As a result, the rate of return on the total investment is decreased with each additional increment of height beyond 63 stories. A point is reached, beyond 100 stories, where each additional amount invested has a negative rate of return.

This study points out a number of the important conditions which may arise in alternative investment studies. First, the investment of an amount beyond the minimum may be necessary in order to make a project sufficiently effective to provide enough return to be financially sound. Second, it is necessary to know how far the investing of additional capital should be carried. The amount of investment that will bring a maximum rate of return upon the total investment is theoretically the best. However, from a practical view, if no better opportunity for investment of additional amounts of capital exists than is offered by the increase above the point of maximum total rate of return, it is logical to invest the additional increment and obtain this contentment return. This process could continue as long as the return from each additional increment is greater than the contentment rate. Third, the risks may increase with each increment of investment due to decreased flexibility of the invested capital as more and more is tied up in a single property.

EFFECT OF PRICE CHANGES

The possibility of future price changes can be a factor in the selection of alternatives. Such effects must be based upon an assumption of considerable certainty as to what future prices will be. Usually only a general realization of what has occurred in the past, and of what general trends appear to exist, is available. Thus it usually is not wise to give a great deal of weight to price changes in making investment decisions. It must be remembered that other factors also change along with price levels.

It is evident that the probability of higher price levels in the future tends to favor long-lived alternatives, since replacements of shorter-lived alternatives would have to be made at a cost higher than that of the initial property. Thus, if higher costs seem definitely to be in prospect, they should be taken into account by assigning higher prices to future replacements of a short-lived alternative.

Should there be the likelihood of increasing annual out-of-pocket costs, due to increased labor rates and increased prices, an alternative having higher initial investment costs, but lower operating and maintenance costs, would be more attractive than if prices were going to remain constant. Here, again, anticipated changes in price levels should be included in the study or considered in making the decision.

Historically prices have shown an almost continuous and steady increase. There have, of course, been some notable but relatively short periods during which prices declined. However, the general trend of rising prices is a fact worthy of consideration in many economy studies.

PRINTED COMPARISON FORMS FOR STUDYING ALTERNATIVES

It sometimes is convenient to make use of printed forms on which to record the cost data for the alternatives being studied. Such forms are particularly useful when the decision regarding the alternative to be used is to be made by someone other than the person who collects and tabulates the cost figures. Figure 11–3 shows a form used by a large automobile manufacturing company for economic evaluation of alternatives. Such forms are of real value in many cases, but one must be certain that the form does not prevent consideration of pertinent data simply because it does not fit into the pattern of the form.

PRODUCTION DATA

Net Hourly Production Requirement	1100
Shifts per day	2
Daily Production Requirement	17,600

Project **Adjustable Tie Rod Socket Assembly** No. **5600**

Division **Motor Car**

Project Engineer **John Jones** Date **June 1956**

Index Volume (Annual) **4,065,600**

Average Labor Cost $**2.40**/Hour

MANUFACTURING COST		Existing Method	*Best Manual Method	Alternate Plan 1	Alternate Plan 2	Alternate Plan 3	Alternate Plan 4	Alternate Plan 5
	Net Hourly Production	950	1100	1100	1100	1100		
	Direct Material (If affected)	--	--	--	--	--		
	Direct Labor Operators	16	13	8	6	5		
	Hours/Unit	.0168	.0118	.0073	.0055	.0045		
Manufacturing Expense	$/Unit	$.0403	$0283	$.0175	$.0132	$.0108		
	**Indirect Labor Operators	--	--	--	--	--		
	Hours/Unit							
	$/Unit	.						
	Maintainance Operators	--	--	1/2	1/2	1		
	Hours/Unit			.00045	.00045	.0009		
	$/Unit			$.0011	$.0011	$.0022		
***	Hours/Unit	--	--	--	--	--		
	$/Unit							
	Total Cost $ per Unit	$.0403	$.0283	$.0186	$.0143	$.0130		
	Total Cost Index Volume	$163,844	$115,056	$75,620	$58,138	$52,853		
	Annual Improvement Potential	$48,788	Debit →Existing Method	$39,436	$56,918	$62,203		

(Annual Improvement Potential is based on "Best" manual method)

ESTIMATED IMPROVEMENT COST

	Existing Method	*Best Manual Method	Alternate Plan 1	Alternate Plan 2	Alternate Plan 3	Alternate Plan 4	Alternate Plan 5
Capital Expenditure (Details not affected by model change)			176,000	299,000	356,000		
Special Tooling Expenditure (Details affected by model change)			22,000	19,000	33,000		
Installation Cost			4,000	6,000	9,000		
TOTAL IMPROVEMENT COST			202,000	324,000	398,000		

AMORTIZATION PERIOD							
(Improvement Cost divided by Savings Potential)	--		5.1	5.7	6.4		

IN - PROCESS INVENTORY							
20,000	18,850	14,000	13,000	4,000			

Flexibility

AFFECT ON:	PRODUCT QUALITY	OR	MACHINE RELIABILITY—FLEXIBILITY		OR	FLOOR SPACE	
	Good	Excel.	Good	Good	Poor		

* "Best" manual method is the improvement that can be made with existing facilities.
** Labor not included on standard routing such as; inspection, material handling, tool set-up, etc.
*** Add items that affect the cost comparison such as; scrap, expense tools, operating supplies, etc.

Figure 11–3a & 3b. Printed forms used by a large automobile manufacturing corporation for making economic comparisons of alternatives.

ECONOMIC COMPARISON RECAP

Process Development Section

Project _Adjustable Tie Rod Socket Assembly_ _____ No._5600_

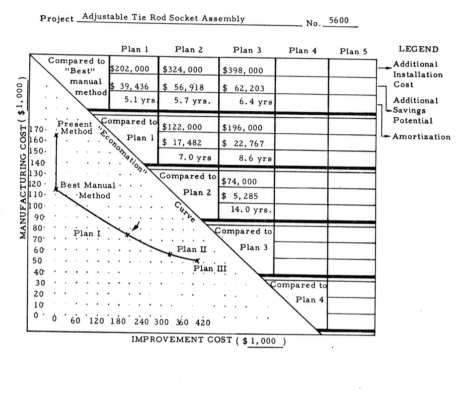

	Plan 1	Plan 2	Plan 3	Plan 4	Plan 5	LEGEND

Compared to "Best" manual method
$202,000 $324,000 $398,000
$ 39,436 $ 56,918 $ 62,203
5.1 yrs.   5.7 yrs.   6.4 yrs

Present Method
Compared to Plan 1
$122,000 $196,000
$ 17,482 $ 22,767
7.0 yrs   8.6 yrs

Best Manual Method
Compared to Plan 2
$74,000
$ 5,285
14.0 yrs.

Plan I
Compared to Plan 3

Plan II
Plan III

Compared to
Plan 4

MANUFACTURING COST ($1,000)
170 160 150 140 130 120 110 100 90 80 70 60 50 40 30 20 10 0
0 60 120 180 240 300 360 420

IMPROVEMENT COST ($1,000)

LEGEND
— Additional Installation Cost
— Additional Savings Potential
— Amortization

REMARKS _Plan I is recommended for action,_
_____ Plan II requires an additional investment of $122.000 which amortizes
_____ in 7.0 years and might be considered. However, Plan II includes a
_____ revision to part design which is questionable by Division.
_____ Plan III is considered uneconomical because of the long amortization
_____ period of the additional investment.

John Jones
Project Engineer

Figure 11-3b. (See 11-3a)

273

CONCLUSION

Any investment of an increment of capital greater than the minimum required to obtain satisfactory physical results may be considered as a separate investment possibility. In this manner the rate of return can be determined and weighed against the risks and other investment possibilities.

However, the effect on the return earned by the minimum possible investment must also be examined. Once an increment of capital is invested, it becomes a part of the whole and must be considered as such. Consideration should always be given to the possibility of attaining a satisfactory result with the investment of a minimum amount of capital.

If added increments of capital are invested, although their rate of return is less than that of the basic capital, the return is in the nature of a contentment return. Such investment may be justified when extra capital is available and no other investment possibility is as satisfactory.

PROBLEMS

11-1 Under what conditions may alternatives be compared on the basis of the added required increment of investment when it would not be possible to do so by considering the return on the total required investment for each alternative?

11-2 What important precaution must be observed when comparing several alternatives by the increment-investment procedure?

11-3 A company is considering two types of punched-card equipment to be used for inventory control purposes. Type A will cost $10,000, require $2,000 per year for power, supplies, and maintenance and $20,000 annually for labor. Type B will require an investment of $100,000 and require $4,000 annually for power, supplies, and maintenance, but will cost only $6,000 per year for labor. Insurance and property taxes total 1% of first cost per year. Payroll taxes are 4% annually. The company maintains an average inventory of $500,000. Estimated life of each type of equipment is ten years, and capital is worth 15% before taxes. Which equipment should be purchased?

11-4 In designing a small office building, two types of heating systems are under consideration. A system burning natural gas would cost $25,000 to purchase and install. The cost of fuel is estimated to be $1,000.00 per month. Operational and maintenance costs would amount to $1,500.00 per year.

A considerable saving in fuel costs could be made if the owners installed an oil-burning system. Such a system would burn 45,000 gallons of fuel oil per year at a cost of $0.16 per gallon. Annual operational and maintenance costs would amount to $4,000.00.

The building will cost $750,000.00. Capital is expected to earn 12% before taxes. Property taxes and insurance will amount to 2% of the first cost per year.

If both heating systems have an estimated life of 25 years, how much could the owners afford to pay for the oil-burning installation?

11-5 The increased popularity of outdoor barbecuing over a charcoal fire has made the igniting of the charcoal a major problem. Assume that a consumer advisory service has asked you as a consultant to make cost comparisons and recommendations concerning three available procedures.

The first method utilizes a paper cup filled with a wax-like material which is lighted with a match and placed in the bed of charcoal. The units sell for $0.50 per dozen. Normally one cup is adequate to start the fire if some care is used to prevent pieces of the charcoal from falling down on the cup when first lighted and smothering the flame.

A second method is to use a device called a "Char-lighter." This is a 600-watt electrical heating element, with cord and handle, which is placed on the charcoal until it is properly ignited. Normally about fifteen minutes are required. The unit costs $7.95 and should last for at least five seasons with average use. Investigation indicates that a typical home would also have to purchase an electrical extension cord at $1.19. It is estimated that the average increment cost for electrical power would be $0.025 per kw.-hr. Typical use has been found to be seventy times per year.

The third method is to buy and use kerosene at $0.40 per gallon. A half-pint is required for each lighting.

Insurance costs are the same with each method. All purchases are subject to a 4% sales tax. Assume that the average homeowner's investments are conservative, earning an average of 4% before taxes.

Which method is most economical, and which would you recommend and why?

11-6 An oil refinery must install a new pipeline from a pier to storage tanks. The initial costs and the hourly pumping costs to provide the same discharge rates for three sizes of lines are as follows:

Diameter	Initial cost	Pumping cost
6″	$4,200.00	$4.50
8″	6,500.00	2.10
10″	9,000.00	1.50

Assume the pipeline would have an economic life of five years and 4,000 hours use per year. Three grades of oil will be pumped through the line. Taxes and insurance on the pipeline will amount to $2\frac{1}{2}$% of the first cost per year. If a before-tax return of 12% must be received, which size pipe should be installed?

11-7   A gray iron foundry is considering the advisability of installing a glass-
        lined smokestack on its cupola, since the ordinary steel stack now in
        use must be replaced. Past experience has shown that the ordinary steel
        stacks must be replaced each ten years and require painting and inspec-
        tion, at a cost of $330, at the end of three and six years. The present
        installed cost of an unlined steel stack is $6,000, and it is estimated that
        the replacement cost for each succeeding stack will increase by 15 per
        cent over the cost of the previous one.
            A glass-lined stack will cost $10,000 and have an estimated life of
        thirty years. Maintenance cost on this stack will be $100 at the end of
        each five-year period for inspection.
            Annual taxes and insurance on each stack would be 2% of first cost.
        Capital is worth 15% to this company.
            Which type of smokestack should be installed?

11-8   A company is going to purchase a new boiler. Boiler A will cost
        $27,000 and consume $4,000 worth of oil per year. It will require an
        attendant twenty-four hours per day during the seven days of the
        week. For this four men will be required; each will receive $425 per
        month. Maintenance is estimated at $1,000 per year and the economic
        life at fifteen years.
            Boiler B is semi-automatic and will cost $44,000. However, it can be
        operated with two men, who will be paid $450 per month. It is esti-
        mated that this boiler would consume 10 per cent more fuel than
        Boiler A, and its estimated life would be only ten years. Maintenance
        costs would probably be about $1,500 per year.
            Taxes and insurance on either boiler would be 2% of the first cost
        per year. Payroll taxes and benefits cost 6% per year.
            If capital is worth 10%, which boiler would you recommend?

11-9   A decision must be made whether to install incandescent or fluorescent
        lights in a new office being built at a factory. The following data are
        available regarding fixtures that would provide equivalent illumination.

	Incandescent	Fluorescent
First cost of fixture, installed	$24.00	$60.00
Lamps, per fixture	$2.40	$8.00
Life of lamps, in hours	1,000	3,500
Watts per fixture	500	100
Starters per fixture		$1.20
Starter life, in hours		2,000

        If electricity costs $0.022 per kw.-hr. and the lights would be on 10
        hours per day, 280 days per year, which type of lights should be
        selected? Assume a ten-year write-off period and average earnings of
        10% on capital.

11-10   In designing a new department store, elevators and electric stairways
        are being considered. It has been found that if elevators are used, twelve

[handwritten at top: Cost = Dep + Interest on investment, or USE CRF]

will be required at an initial cost of $41,000 each; this price includes the necessary building modifications. If electric stairways are used, eight would be required at an installed cost of $24,000. With this installation it would also be necessary to have two elevators, one of which would be primarily for service use. Operational and maintenance costs would be:

	Elevators	Stairs
Operators	$2,800 per year each	
Starter (1)	$3,000 per year	
Power	$ 500 per year per elevator	$ 75 per year per stairs
Maintenance	$1,200 per year per elevator	$650 per year per stairs

If the eight electric stairs and two elevators are used, no starter will be required; also, 7,400 square feet of merchandise area will be saved. Information available shows that such area will produce $80 worth of sales per square foot per year in the type of store involved and yield a profit before taxes of 8% on sales.

Annual taxes and insurance would amount to 2% of first cost in either case, and a 30-year amortization period would be used.

a. Which installation should be used?

b. What type of economy analysis would you use to present the case to the owners for their decision? Assume capital is worth 15% before taxes.

11–11 A company requires a large amount of steam per month for processing and for heating a plant containing 500,000 square feet. In addition, the plant uses 100,000 kw.-hrs. of electricity each month. It is building a new power plant and must decide whether to generate or purchase the power. The costs in each case would be:

	Steam only	Steam and power
First cost		
Power plant	$175,000.00	$200,000.00
Generating equipment		65,000.00
Annual costs		
Operation, maintenance, and labor	60,000.00	70,000.00
Taxes and insurance, % of first cost	2%	2%

The electric power now is being purchased at an average cost of $0.015 per kw.-hr. The investment in either case would be written off over a twenty-five-year period. Earnings of the company, before taxes, have been about 15%. Which alternative should be adopted?

11–12 In order to assure a constant flow of water at the proper pressure, a chemical plant is considering three alternatives. The first is to build an elevated tank on a tower at a cost of $20,000. The second is to build a tank of the same capacity on the roof of an existing plant building some distance from the area where the water is needed. This installation would cost $12,000 but would require additional pumping equipment costing $2,700 and having annual pumping and maintenance costs of $800. The third alternative is to install a separate booster pump which would cut in automatically when required. Such an installation would cost only $7,000 but would have estimated annual operating and maintenance costs of $3,200 per year. Annual taxes and insurance on all installations would be 1½% of first cost per year. Daily consumption of water is 700,000 gallons. While it is conceded that each installation will meet the requirements, the plant supervisors have expressed some preferences, rating the tank on the tower first, the tank on the building second, and the pumping plant third. Assuming a thirty-year life for each installation and capital worth 20%, which installation would you recommend?

11-13 An auto-supply chain store guarantees its "first-line" tires for 25,000 miles, covering wear and damage. A 7.60–15 tire of this brand sells for $24.50. A top quality tire of the same size, produced by a nationally known manufacturer, retails for $29.00. This tire does not carry an all-inclusive guarantee but has the reputation of often giving more than 30,000 miles of trouble-free service. Determine which tire is the better buy for the average motorist as a replacement for the original equipment tires, assuming he drives an average of 10,000 miles per year, expects to replace his car in 3 more years, and that the condition of his tires will not affect the trade-in value.

11-14 A consolidated school district is planning a new school building, to be located in a fairly remote area. A power-and-light company has proposed that the building, to house 300 students, be heated by electricity rather than by the oil-burning system originally planned. The electric plant would consist of individual thermostatically-controlled units in each room. Each would contain a small fan to provide adequate ventilation. This installation would cost $8,700.00 and would consume 120,000 kw.-hr. of power annually at a cost of $0.025 per kw.-hr. No attention of any kind would be required, and annual maintenance costs are estimated not to exceed $200.00.

The oil-burning plant would cost $11,000.00 to install and would require the additional expenditure of $4,000.00 for a small boiler room and stack. This system would be semi-automatic and would require employing a caretaker at an annual salary of $3,200.00. Fuel costs with this type of heating plant would not exceed $400.00 per year. Annual maintenance costs are estimated to be $400.00. If the electric system is used, $50.00 per year will be saved in insurance costs. The school is to be financed by a fifteen-year 5% bond issue.

Which heating system should be installed?

11-15 A manufacturer of aluminum truck trailers is making a study to determine what maximum selling price could be established on his product to have them competitive with steel trailers. Conventional steel trailers of the same size sell for $8,000.00 and weigh 12,000 pounds. The aluminum trailers weigh only 9,000 pounds. State regulations limit the total load on the road (trailer plus load) to 30,000 pounds. His survey indicates that such trailers operate, on the average, about 80,000 miles per year and that the revenue, less handling costs, is about $0.02 per ton mile. Taxes and insurance on such trailers would total 4% of first cost per year. To sell the trailers, their potential savings would have to be based on an economic life of four years; a return of at least 15% on capital, before taxes, would be required. What would be the maximum selling price?

11–16   A company is considering two alternatives, A and B. The basic information is as follows:

	A	B
First cost	$8,000	$14,000
Scrap value	0	$ 2,000
Annual operation and maintenance costs	$4,200	$ 3,400
Annual taxes & insurance, % of first cost	1½	1½
Estimated life	10 years	15 years

Alternative B is considered to be somewhat more dependable than A, but is manufactured in a foreign country. The service from the equipment is expected to be needed for at least thirty years. Which alternative should be selected if capital is worth at least 10%?

11–17   A city is increasing the capacity of its municipal power plant by the addition of another generating unit. Two alternatives are being considered. The first is a conventional steam plant, consisting of a modern boiler, steam turbine, and generator. This installation would cost $500,000. It is estimated that the annual fuel consumption would be $14,000 and the annual maintenance costs $5,000 over an estimated life of thirty years. Labor costs with this type of installation would be $30,000 per year.

The second alternative is installation of a gas turbine and generator. This would cost $375,000 and have an estimated life of twenty years. Annual costs for fuel would be 10% greater than for the steam installation. It is estimated that the annual maintenance costs will be $6,000, but there are few data available regarding maintenance costs on plants of this type. Labor costs with this installation will be the same as for the steam plant.

The expansion will be financed by a 6%, twenty-year, tax-exempt bond issue.

Which installation would you recommend?

11–18   An overseas air line must provide a fresh water supply for a Pacific island base. One proposal is to install a distillation plant which will have a capacity of 2,000 gallons per hour. This installation will cost $7,500.00 and can be operated at a cost of $0.45 per 1,000 gallons for fuel and maintenance.

Another method would be to install ion-exchange equipment. This type of equipment costs $0.90 per gallon per hour rate for the initial installation. The resins used in this equipment cost $0.40 per pound, and 1.2 pounds are required per 1,000 gallons of output. Other operating costs will be $0.25 per 1,000 gallons.

It is expected that the equipment will be operated 7,500 hours per year. Either type of installation is expected to have a ten-year life. Because of the location, there will be no property taxes, but annual insurance costs will be $1\frac{1}{2}\%$ of first cost. Annual earnings of the company have been about 10% before taxes. Which installation should be installed?

CHAPTER 12

Fixed, Increment, and Sunk Costs

Many economy studies, instead of dealing with a new project which requires the investment of capital, involve only a change in an existing activity which will result in altered costs or income. If some investment is involved, it affects directly only a portion of the business, many other portions and costs remaining unchanged. In many cases the change in activity is considered to be only temporary. Therefore, the economy study in reality is concerned with the decision relating to the immediate and temporary problem. However, in many instances it also is necessary to consider the effects which would be experienced should the more or less temporary situation development into a permanent one.

When such temporary situations arise, a careful study of the costs that will result, or the change in costs that will occur, is necessary in order to evaluate the financial effects. Unfortunately, much of the cost information which is normally available is not directly usable in such situations, and, as a result, erroneous thinking and decisions frequently occur.

A typical problem of this kind arose in the southwestern part of the United States just prior to World War II. One group of cities, several years before, had constructed a large aqueduct system to bring water from the distant mountains. This aqueduct, consisting of tunnels, open canals, and pumping plants, was much larger than needs at the time it was built demanded in order to take care of the requirements for many years in the future. An adjacent city had a great temporary increase in the need for water because of a national defense project. Officials of the latter city approached the directors of the aqueduct, asking permission to build a pipeline connecting with the aqueduct and to purchase water. These officials pointed out that more water could easily be put through the aqueduct system and offered to pay the cost of delivering the water plus a small profit. They indicated that the only cost which would be incurred would be for the small amount of pumping that would be necessary, since the remainder of the system operated by gravity and already was in existence. The directors of the aqueduct system refused this offer and stated that, although they did not expect to make a profit, the city which wanted the water should pay a part of the cost of the aqueduct, since it would be used in delivering the water.

Obviously, the two groups reasoned in entirely different manners. In this case the change which was proposed involved a going operation. No new investment was involved, but certain costs were going to be altered by the change in operation. If a valid solution was to be reached, a correct analysis of the costs had to be made. In such studies one must consider costs which fall under one of the three following headings: *fixed costs, increment costs,* and *sunk costs.* These classifications are the natural results of a factual examination of their natures. Fixed- and increment-cost economy study problems constitute a distinct and basic type. One of the first steps in considering any economy study problem is to determine whether it can be handled by the fixed-and-increment-cost procedure. Once one has a clear understanding of fixed and increment costs, as they relate to engineering economy, such problems are relatively easy to handle.

FIXED AND INCREMENT COSTS

Fixed costs are those which will continue, unchanged, whether or not a given change in operations or policy is adopted. In other words, a proposed change will have no effect upon fixed costs. It should be kept in mind, however, that when one uses the term "fixed costs" he means "fixed" only with respect to the particular proposal or change being considered and the span of time involved. A cost which would not be affected by a certain change in operations might be altered greatly by some other change. For example, suppose Mr. Jones drives to his bank and parks his car, putting a nickel in the parking meter to gain the privilege of parking one hour. He concludes his business at the bank in fifteen minutes and, passing a haberdashery, decides to purchase a tie which he happens to see displayed in the window. This added transaction requires only ten minutes, and he returns to his car and drives away, leaving time remaining on the parking meter. In this case the decision to purchase the tie involved no increased cost for parking. So far as this transaction was concerned, the cost for parking was fixed. On the other hand, had Mr. Jones, upon leaving the bank, stopped at his club, engaged in a card game, forgot about the time, and returned to his car after the hour had expired and found a citation for violation of parking regulations on his car, his cost for parking would not have been fixed.

Similarly, a cost which may be fixed for a certain interval of time, regardless of how operations vary, may change if the revised operating procedure becomes permanent. For instance, a contractor who is to make a cut through a large hill, in connection with building a new highway, makes a subcontract to sell the dirt to a company for $1 per load to be used to fill in some swamp land. The $1 charge exactly covers the cost of hauling the dirt. As long as he obtains the dirt from the cut being made in the hill, the contractor may correctly assume that the dirt costs him nothing. However, if after the cut were completed he were still obligated to supply additional dirt to the company at the same price, but no longer had any free source of supply, his cost situation would not be fixed. Thus temporarily he could correctly consider the cost of the dirt to be zero; on a longer basis he could not.

It should also be noted that *fixed costs* do not necessarily have any relationship to what are often referred to as *fixed charges* in ordinary accounting procedure. For example, bond interest is usually classified as a fixed charge. However, a change in operations might conceivably result in increased or decreased total bond interest. Similarly, certain expenses that ordinarily are thought of as variable, such as labor cost, may remain constant when a proposed change is made; thus they may be considered as fixed costs.

It is important to remember that so-called fixed costs usually are not completely fixed, particularly if the magnitude of activity change is very great. Over small ranges of change, frequently sufficient to cover a proposed

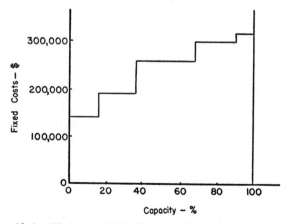

Figure 12–1.   Variation of "fixed" costs with volume for a company.

activity, they may be substantially, if not completely constant. Figure 12–1, for example, shows how fixed costs varied in one company as volume varied from 0 to 100 per cent of capacity. It may be seen, for example, that if a proposed change in activity involved increasing the capacity utilization from 15 to 20 per cent, there would be an increase in the so-called fixed costs. On the other hand, these costs would be unaffected by a change in capacity utilization from 70 to 85 per cent. Thus the term "fixed costs" must be considered in relation to a specific proposal.

INCREMENT COSTS

Increment costs are those which arise as the result of a change in operations or policy. Thus they represent the actual increases or decreases in cost resulting from the change.[1] They are the costs that must be considered in determining the true cost of carrying out the added operations. Like fixed costs, they are applicable only to the specific change from which they result. They may be either positive or negative in amount. Like fixed costs, they should be determined by fact.

From the nature of fixed and increment costs it follows that economy studies of this type involve a short-term viewpoint. Where a long-term viewpoint must be adopted, other factors become important. Such cases will be considered in Chapter 16.

UNIT COSTS VERSUS FIXED AND INCREMENT COSTS

Much confusion has resulted from attempts to use unit costs in economy studies where fixed and increment cost analysis was required. It has been pointed out in a previous chapter that unit costs are essentially accounting and control items and are valid only for the particular set of conditions for which they were determined. It is sometimes possible to use unit cost data in economy studies *if the correct unit costs are available.* However, in most cases the conditions for which the economy study must be made are not the same as those for which the unit costs were established, and, as a result, the unit costs available are not those that are needed. It is not always realized that many expenses are not affected in direct proportion to a change in output. A little thought should make this apparent. For example, one would not expect the salary of the president of the American Telephone and Telegraph Company to be affected by the fact that fifty phones were discon-

---

[1] Such costs sometimes are called "*differential* costs." However, because of the mathematical connotation of the word, meaning an extremely small change, this term is not as appropriate as "increment costs," and thus is less frequently used.

nected from the Bell System. Yet it is theoretically possible to determine the unit cost of operating each telephone in the Bell System, and a portion of this unit cost would be a fractional part of the president's salary.

This same situation, to a more closely connected degree, exists in most businesses. It is customary to determine the unit cost of producing an article or rendering a service. It is necessary to do this in order to know the cost of production for each article. To obtain this unit cost, all expenses of labor, material, and overhead are determined and apportioned among the various units produced. They are thus based upon *existing* operating conditions and represent actual costs under those conditions. They may thus be used for determining profits or as aids to control.[2] Attempting to apply them to a different set of conditions, or to use them for some purpose for which they were not intended, is much the same as saying that a Cadillac should cost the same as a Ford because both are automobiles. An economy study is an entirely different process from routine accounting. While many of the same items of expense may be involved and many of the same things considered in both, all items must be used in the light of the conditions that actually exist or will exist.

An excellent example of how a wrong decision may result from improper use of unit costs in an economy study is found in the following case. A large manufacturing plant consisted of 11 departments. In one of these automobile batteries were produced. The equipment for producing the hard-rubber covers for the cells of these batteries occupied about 100 square feet in one corner of this department. This operation required only one workman per shift and was under the supervision of a man who also supervised a number of other operations. The daily production of cell covers was 576. The costs of operation were as follows:

Labor	$12.00
Material	8.64
Overhead	8.20
Total	$28.84

Unit cost = $28.84/576 = $0.05 per cover

The cell cover operation was the cause of considerable noise, and the percentage of defects was high. It required considerable attention by the foreman and was a general source of grief.

A new foreman was appointed for this department, and he soon became aware of the troubles connected with the making of the cell covers. He happened to have a friend who was the manager of another company which

[2] See chapter on accounting.

specialized in the production of hard-rubber and plastic products. In discussing their problems together, the new foreman mentioned his troubles with the cell cover operation and the fact that it cost $0.05 to produce each cover. His friend thought the price seemed rather high and later made an offer to produce the cell covers from the existing molds for $0.035 each. The department manager computed that the saving involved through having the cell covers manufactured outside the plant would be as follows:

Present cost for 576 cell covers	$28.84
Cost if made outside (576 × $0.035)	20.16
Daily saving	$ 8.68

This appeared to him to be a very worth-while saving, since it could be obtained with no investment of additional capital. As a result the change was made, and the cell covers were made by the outside company.

After the change had been in effect a little over a month, the cost department made a check upon the savings that actually resulted from the change. The investigation showed that the actual saving in overhead was only $0.30 per day, which represented a saving in insurance. The molding press had to be kept available, since it served as a stand-by for a second press which was required for another operation. It was further found that a portion of the material which had been used for the cell covers was a waste product of another operation in the factory and that the actual saving in material was only $6.10 instead of $8.64. This waste product had been included in the unit-cost determination at $2.54 per day, since it would have cost this much to produce this material if it had not been available as scrap. As a result the company was now paying for the 576 cell covers the following:

Remaining overhead	$ 7.90
Waste material	2.54
To outside company	20.16
Total	$30.60

Instead of a saving of $8.68 per day there was actually a loss of $30.60 − $28.84, or $1.76. Arrangements were made immediately to have the molds returned to the plant, and cell covers were again produced within the factory.

A little thought makes it apparent why the use of unit costs failed to give correct results. The unit cost of $0.05 per cover was based upon the assumption that 576 cell covers *were to be produced* each day. If the covers were not produced, the unit cost had no meaning, since it did not apply to this set of conditions. One might even do a bit of computation and say that the unit cost of *not producing* 576 cell covers each day would be

$$\frac{\$7.90 + \$2.54}{576} = \$0.018 \text{ per cell cover.}$$

It becomes apparent from the above example that serious errors may result from using unit costs in economy studies. For economy studies of this type one must determine the increment cost of producing the products. The actual (increment) costs which were incurred when the cell covers were produced, but which would not exist if they were not manufactured, would be as follows:

Labor	$12.00
Material	6.10
Overhead (insurance)	0.30
Total	$18.40

Dividing $18.40 by 576 gives a unit increment cost for producing the cell covers of $0.3194. In other words, the actual cost of producing each cell cover, *compared to not making any cell covers,* was slightly less than $0.032. This result makes it obvious that an actual loss would result from paying $0.035 each for cell covers produced by an outside company. The department foreman had made the common mistakes of using unit costs for a purpose for which they were never intended and of failing to determine the facts which would reveal the differential cost for the alternatives of producing or not producing the cell covers.

TWO METHODS FOR INCREMENT-COST STUDIES

The example of the molded cell covers illustrates two basic methods which can be used for making increment-cost studies. The first is to consider only the increment costs, revenues, or savings. For example, for the cell covers the increment costs were found to be $18.40. By comparing this amount with $20.16, the cost of the alternative of having the cell covers produced by an outside company, it could easily be concluded that the existing program for producing them was more economical. This method of analysis, considering only the increment values, usually involves fewer data and sets forth the pertinent facts very clearly. One must, however, be certain that all increment costs are correctly separated from the fixed costs.

The second method is to compare the total of all costs for the two alternatives being considered. Thus, for the cell covers the total cost of making them had been $28.84. The total cost of having them manufactured by an outside company, including those portions of the existing costs which would continue, was $30.60. This procedure requires a careful determination of the fixed costs. It may thus be seen that the first method deals, essentially, with increment costs, while the second deals with the total costs.

PROBLEM OF NEW OR BY-PRODUCTS

One of the industry's great problems is keeping all of its production facilities operating at capacity throughout the entire year. By thoroughly understanding the principles of fixed and increment costs and applying them to this problem, it is often possible to lessen the effect of slack production. In many companies, because of increased use of heavy and expensive equipment and machinery, overhead costs are becoming a considerable proportion of the total cost of production. These expenses continue through periods of slack production. A great proportion of them are fixed costs; they do not change with temporary variations in production. If, during idle periods, the unused production facilities are used for the production of some new product, there is no need to charge this new product with more than a very small amount of overhead, since the major portion of the plant overhead has already been charged to the existing production. Thus, if no overhead expense has to be paid for the new product, it can be produced at a relatively low cost. In many cases it may be possible to produce this new article at a considerably lower cost than could be obtained in plants where it is the main article of production and must, therefore, bear its share of the overhead. By producing an additional product in this manner, the company may be able to market it at a price below the usual market price and still make a very substantial profit. Such a practice is obviously advantageous.

An example of this type of application of fixed- and increment-cost principles is found in the case of a company manufacturing blowers of various sizes. During the depression years the sales of large blowers were very low. As a result, the company was faced with the necessity of operating at very low output and of laying off a number of its employees. A study of the situation revealed that it had all the facilities necessary for the production of small kitchen-ventilating fans. It was found that there would be no fixed costs involved and that the men could work on this product at odd times when they were not employed on the production of blowers. The cost of producing each fan under these conditions was

Material	$4.80
Labor	1.08
Total	$5.88

Other fans of this type were sold at about $18.00 retail, and the dealers were given a 40% discount from this price. This company placed its fans on the market at a retail price of $15.00 and allowed the dealers a discount of 50%. With this pricing, the dealers were able to make more profit on a $15.00 fan than they had previously obtained from an $18.00 sale. The manufacturer obtained $7.50 from each fan. The profit to the manufacturer was

Selling price to retailers	$7.50
Cost to manufacture	5.88
Profit per fan	$1.62

As the sales of the fans at $15.00 were considerably greater than had been anticipated, the company was able to show a profit throughout the entire depression. At the same time, the entire working force was kept at nearly full employment. Thus, by taking advantage of the fact that the additional product could be produced for only the amount of the increment costs, the company was able to avoid a serious loss of profits and to maintain employment. Such a policy is of obvious advantage.

UTILIZATION OF SCRAP

In almost all plants where materials are processed there is accompanying waste and spoilage. Many companies have made profitable progress in converting these waste materials into income-producing goods, either by reclaiming them as salable materials or by using them in producing other products. It may or may not be necessary to incur additional overhead in utilizing or reclaiming such materials. Where the overhead costs go on, unchanged, regardless of whether the materials remain as useless waste or have a small amount of labor expended on them, the only actual expenses are the increment costs.

A case of this kind existed in a tire factory where a special grade of canvas was used as "liner" between the layers of calendered fabric in order to prevent the layers from sticking to one another. This liner was subject to hard usage and wore out quite rapidly. Previously the scrap liner had been sold as useless rags for $0.75 per hundred pounds. The foreman of the scrap department found on investigation that if this grade of canvas were cleaned and cut into certain sizes, it could be sold to a furniture factory, for use in making upholstered furniture, at a price of $6.00 per hundred pounds. He found that the material could be laundered for $0.75 per hundred pounds and that the necessary labor for cutting to the required sizes would be $2.00 per hundred pounds. Examination showed that 80 per cent of the scrap liner could be made useful by this procedure. The profit to be obtained from each 100 pounds of scrap liner would be

> Income from sale of 80 pounds of reclaimed liner $4.80
> Expense of reclaiming
>   Laundering $0.75
>   Labor   2.00   2.75
> Profit per hundred pounds of scrap $2.05

In this case the advisability of reclaiming the scrap liner is obvious.

Where some overhead costs are incurred in manufacturing a product which includes some scrap material, care must be taken to make certain that the correct amount of overhead is charged. An example of this may be seen in the case of a company which was planning to add a by-product to its line. Each unit of the by-product would utilize one pound of a waste material, resulting from the company's main operation, which cost $0.50 per pound according to the cost records. If this same material were purchased on the open market it would have cost $2.50 per pound. The direct labor required to produce the by-product would amount to $4.50 per unit. This company had found that on the average its annual overhead was equal to

$$\$50,000.00 + 50\% \times (\text{direct materials} + \text{direct labor}).$$

What would be the true cost of producing the by-product?

In cases of this type the major problem is to determine the correct amount to charge for overhead. From an increment-cost viewpoint, the cost for materials and labor was $0.50 + $4.50 = $5.00. Also the increment cost of overhead was stated to be 50% of the sum of materials and labor cost. On this basis the charge for overhead would appear to be 0.50 × $5.00 = $2.50. However, a more careful analysis shows that this is incorrect. Whether the materials are purchased on the open market for $2.50 or happen to be available as scrap at a cost of $0.50 would make no difference in the overhead costs incurred for processing them into the by-product. Therefore if the increment cost of overhead is 50 per cent of the cost of labor and materials, the normal cost of materials should be used in calculating the overhead charge. Thus the cost of producing the by-product would be calculated as follows:

> Material $0.50
> Labor   4.50
> Overhead = 0.5($4.50 + $2.50) =   3.50
>   Total $8.50

This matter of the correct increment overhead cost to be charged, when scrap materials are further processed into by-products, is one that must be considered carefully.

The possibilities for utilizing waste or scrap materials for producing salable by-products through increment-cost pricing are very great. Many companies have taken advantage of such situations. One notable example is a paper mill which, through research, has been able to produce synthetic vanilla flavoring, a chemical for tanning hides, a chemical for improving cement, and a lignin plastic from waste sulphite liquor which previously was dumped into streams, thereby causing serious pollution.

LONG-RANGE PROBLEMS ASSOCIATED WITH INCREMENT-COST BY-PRODUCTS

While the immediate advantages to be derived from using increment-cost pricing for by-products are apparent, one must keep certain possible long-range effects in mind. The increment-cost analysis usually is correct only if the new product is, and will continue to be, a true by-product. When a new product is to be produced in this manner, it is assumed that the existing main products are the principal source of income and will therefore continue to pay the fixed costs of the company. It is expected that the new products are to be more or less temporary items, or are to be considered as side lines. Considered in this way, they are the tail of the dog, but in numerous cases the tail has wagged the dog.

A classic example of this occurred some years ago in a large sash-and-door mill in the northwest. The company was an old established manufacturer, and its various kinds of doors were well known throughout the trade. In an effort to use some of the pieces of scrap wood which resulted from the manufacturing processes, it was decided to produce a cheap door made by glueing these scrap pieces together to give the necessary thickness. It was thought that by selling these laminated doors at a price considerably below that of their other doors, the company might be able to sell enough to use up the waste pieces of wood. After a number of these "cheap" laminated doors had been sold and used, it was found they were superior to any of the ordinary doors the company produced, principally because the laminated structure prevented warping in damp climates. In a short time the main product of the plant was laminated doors which sold at a premium price because of their superiority. The company had reached the unacceptable condition where it was necessary to cut up large pieces of lumber in order to obtain small pieces which could then be glued together to make large pieces from which the doors could be made. Since the by-product had become the main product, it was obvious that it would have to bear the true cost of the material being used and the proper share of the fixed costs of the business. It was necessary to revise the cost figures of the entire plant to fit the new conditions.

Such situations have occurred in numerous industries. One must be particularly careful about adding equipment and facilities in order to expand the output of by-products which are priced upon the basis of increment production costs. Such a procedure results in fixed costs being incurred which may seriously affect the over-all cost situation if it should become desirable to reduce the volume of output of the by-product.

Another example of what may happen when a company attempts to expand the sale of by-products is found in the borax industry in this country. In former years a by-product of the borax industry was potash, used for the manufacture of soap and in producing glass and fertilizer. In recent years there has been an increasing demand for potash, which has principally been imported from Europe, mainly from Germany. The European producers, through their syndicates and cartels, attempted to maintain high prices for potash. As a result, the borax producers in this country began to experiment with methods of obtaining a greater yield of potash from borax. They were so successful that they were able to obtain two tons of potash from each ton of borax. The demand for potash had become so great that it was necessary to find some means of disposing of the excess borax which was produced, although this had originally been the main product. This problem was solved by halving the price of borax between the years 1926 and 1930 and introducing a number of new borax products. This is another, and somewhat extreme, example of how fixed costs may have to be shifted from the main to the by-product.

Such examples illustrate the fact that fixed and increment costs must be related to a given set of conditions. Temporary changes of policy may be based upon such cost figures without further consideration. However, if the policy becomes permanent, or if the results affect the conditions considerably, honest accounting demands that the situation be restudied and the cost distribution be adjusted. The difficulty occurs in determining the line between temporary and permanent conditions. It is also true that many companies knowingly maintain a policy of cost distribution for many years which is contrary to the facts. Certain products are allowed to bear more than their share of the fixed costs in order to allow other products to be marketed at lesser prices than they would normally have to bring. The wisdom of such a course is open to question.

ECONOMY OF SHUTTING DOWN PLANTS

The principle of fixed and increment costs is of prime importance in decisions regarding shutting down plants during seasons of slack production. This situation was encountered by most companies following the crash of 1929. In some companies the situation was more acute than in others, but most were compelled to restudy their positions. A small manufacturer of specialized chemicals furnishes an example of this condition. This company produced a special line of chemicals which were used principally by one industry. In the year before the depression its net sales were $141,200. Operating expenses had been approximately as follows:

Raw materials	$ 42,500
Labor	27,600
Taxes, depreciation and maintenance	18,200
Managerial and sales expense	14,000
Total	$102,300

With these conditions, the net profit was as follows:

Income from sales	$141,200
Expenses	102,300
Profit	$ 38,900

Because the industry which it served was affected seriously by depressed business conditions, the company estimated that its sales for the following year would be only $46,000. Examination made it estimate that its expenses for operating under these conditions would be as follows:

Raw materials	$10,600
Labor	19,800
Taxes, depreciation and maintenance	16,000
Managerial and sales expense	12,000
Total	$58,400

The loss which would be incurred by operating under these conditions would be calculated as:

Expenses	$58,400
Income from sales	46,000
Loss	$12,400

An alternative to operating the plant under these conditions was to close the manufacturing plant and maintain only the sales offices. Its products would be manufactured by a large general chemical plant. It was estimated that it could buy its products from the larger producer at prices which would enable it to resell them to its customers and break even on the individual transactions; that is, there would be no profit or loss from not producing the chemicals. Under these conditions its expenses for the year would be as follows:

Taxes, depreciation, maintenance	$12,800
Managerial and sales expense	12,000
Total expense and loss	$24,800

After these figures were assembled, it was at once apparent that from a purely financial viewpoint it was much better policy for the company to operate its chemical plant and produce its own goods even though a loss would follow. The loss would be only $12,400 from this method of operating, whereas there would be a loss of $24,800 if the plant were closed. Even though a loss could not be avoided if the company were to remain in business, it would be much better to have a small loss than a larger one. In addition to the purely monetary side of the question, the costs of rehiring and training new workers that would follow later, the possible loss of customers to the larger company from which it was going to purchase its products, and the effect of unemployment on its workers were factors which had to be considered but upon which a monetary value could not easily be placed. It was decided that the plant should be operated at reduced capacity and considerable effort made to develop additional products and new markets for its existing products.

Many companies found themselves in similar positions in the years following 1929 and continued to operate at a loss instead of closing their plants. The effect of fixed costs is clear in such cases. If there had been no fixed costs, it would have been possible to operate at reduced output without experiencing large losses. Obviously, unit costs were of no value in making such decisions, since they would indicate that if there were no production there would be no expense. The information for a correct decision can be obtained only by breaking all the expenses up into fixed and incremental components.

BALANCING OUTPUTS BETWEEN PLANTS

A modification of the problem involved in possible shutting down of plants frequently occurs where more than one plant of a company produces the same product, although no one plant is operating at maximum capacity. If operating costs are not identical in all plants, it is necessary to determine the proper amounts to produce in each plant to assure maximum economy.

This may involve a reduction in the output of a plant, but not complete shutdown. This situation is illustrated in the following example.

A company having its main factory in Illinois produces a by-product in a separate factory adjacent to its main plant. It also produces this same product in a California plant, where it is the sole product. The Illinois plant has a capacity of 15,000 tons per year and is currently producing at the rate of 10,000 tons per year. At this output the unit cost of production is $110.00 per ton. Included in this unit cost is a charge for material A, which is a waste product of the main Illinois plant and for which the by-product plant pays $5.00 per ton used. Any excess of this waste product not used in the by-product plant is sold for $2.00 per ton. The by-product plant is currently using 2,000 tons per year of this waste product. The fixed expenses of the Illinois by-product plant are $850,000.00 per year.

At the California plant the capacity is 10,000 tons per year, with a current output of 7,000 tons. At this output the unit cost is $94.75 per ton with the fixed expenses being $500,000.00 per year. At this plant all materials have to be bought at regular market prices. Would any change in the output of either plant be desirable?

Since neither plant can produce the total output, both will have to continue in operation. Therefore the fixed costs of each plant will continue, and the decision should be based on the increment costs.

To determine the true increment costs at the Illinois plant, the $3.00 per ton bookkeeping profit being made on waste material A, must be taken into account. The unit variable cost for the by-product at this plant would then be as follows:

        Total annual cost = $110.00 × 10,000   = $1,100,000.00
        Less profit on material A = $3.00 × 2,000 =   6,000.00
        Actual total annual cost   = $1,094,000.00
        Less fixed costs   =   850,000.00
        Variable costs   = $ 244,000.00
        Unit variable cost = $244,000.00/10,000 = $24.40 per ton

At the California plant, at the existing load

        Total annual cost = $94.75 × 7,000   = $663,250.00
        Less fixed costs   =   500,000.00
        Total variable costs   = $163,250.00
        Unit variable costs = $163,250.00/7,000 = $23.32 per ton

Therefore, if there are no difficulties regarding extra shipping costs, etc., it appears that the output should be shifted so that the California plant operates at capacity and only 7,000 tons are produced by the Illinois plant.

UTILIZING EXCESS CAPACITY BY DUMPING

Another method is often resorted to by companies with a problem of excess plant capacity, particularly those which export a portion of their products. In a number of industries, especially the heavy equipment industries, there is an absolute maximum number of units of production which can be used by the domestic market during a given period. Reduction of the selling price would bring few, if any, additional sales. The only outlet for additional products lies in foreign markets. In such situations, sales can often be made in foreign markets only if the selling price is considerably reduced so as to compete with foreign-produced goods. This price at which the product must be sold on the foreign market may be considerably less than is obtained from the same product on the domestic market. When goods are produced and sold in this market, the procedure is known as "foreign dumping." [3]

The economy of dumping is based upon the fact that fixed costs are present in nearly all enterprises. When a plant is operating at reduced output, a moderate increase in output will not affect the fixed costs. As a result, these additional increments of production will actually cost less to produce than the others. This situation is illustrated best by an example.

Consider the case of the ABC Company which has plant capacity for the production of 100,000 units annually. Owing to depressed business conditions, only 60,000 units can be sold in the domestic market at a price of $2.27 each. The unit cost for these products, on the basis of 60,000 annual production, is $2.34. Under these conditions there is obviously a loss of $0.07 on each unit, or a total loss of $4,200.00 on 60,000 units. The costs of producing 60,000 units, and other quantities between 60,000 and the plant capacity of 100,000 are shown in Table 12–1.

In Table 12–1 it will be noted that none of the costs are actually fixed costs in the strict sense that they are not affected by changes of output. However, factory overhead and selling expense are almost fixed, varying only slightly with changes of production. Material expense is not exactly proportional to output, since increased production makes it possible to obtain some economy in purchasing materials in larger quantities. This is a

[3] The term "dumping" is also applied to cases where governments acquire surplus agricultural commodities and export them to foreign countries at prices which are often less than those paid to the producer. Many question whether, in the long run, dumping of manufactured goods is ever a sound economic practice. This is especially true in the case of heavy producers' goods. There is always the danger that the foreign purchasers will use these goods, bought at low prices, to produce consumers' goods which will eventually compete with those of domestic manufacturers. In this manner the domestic market for producers' goods might be destroyed.

TABLE 12-1   Variation in Unit Costs with Output

(1)	(2)	(3)	(4)	(5)	(6)	(7)	(8)
Output	Material	Labor	Factory overhead	Selling expense	Total	Unit cost	Cost per unit of last increment
60,000	$31,200	$ 75,600	$22,800	$10,800	$140,400	$2.34	
70,000	35,700	88,200	24,000	10,950	158,850	2.27	$1.845
80,000	40,000	100,800	25,200	11,200	177,200	2.22	1.835
90,000	44,100	113,400	26,400	11,350	195,250	2.17	1.805
100,000	48,000	126,000	27,600	11,400	213,000	2.13	1.775

situation which usually occurs in economy studies of this type. There are actually very few fixed costs in the strict sense of the term. They usually vary slightly. Similarly there may be other costs which do not vary quite in proportion to production but are more nearly incremental than fixed. In this case only labor expense varies in direct proportion to output.

From Column (6) of Table 12–1, one may see that the total cost of producing 60,000 units is $140,400.00. The total cost for producing 70,000 units is $158,850.00, an increase of $18,450.00. Thus the cost of producing each of these additional 10,000 units is only $1.845, whereas each of the first 60,000 units cost $2.34 to produce. If 60,000 units are all that can be sold in the domestic market, any price above $1.845 that could be obtained for the additional 10,000 units in the foreign market would be profitable. From Table 12–1 it will be seen that successive increases of production above 70,000 units are accompanied with still lower unit costs for the additional increments of production. If the production were increased to plant capacity, the unit cost of the entire 100,000 units would be $2.13, while the increment cost of each of the 10,000 above 90,000 would only be $1.775. In this particular case it is estimated that 30,000 units could be sold annually on the foreign market for $2.05 each. This is less than the unit cost of $2.17 for producing *all* of the 90,000 total production. The net effect upon the profits of the company is shown, however, by the following figures:

Income from sales	
60,000 units @ $2.27	$136,200.00
30,000 units @ $2.05	61,500.00
Total income	$197,700.00
Cost of producing 90,000	195,250.00
Profit	$ 2,450.00

Thus, although 30,000 units of production would be sold at less than the unit cost of the entire output, there is an actual gain of $6,650.00 by selling these goods on the foreign market, this gain being represented by the sum of the $2,450.00 profit on total sales and the loss of $4,200.00 which would be incurred if only 60,000 units were produced and sold on the domestic market. The immediate advantages of dumping become apparent from such an illustration. The practice is one which has been successfully followed by numerous companies, while others have later suffered bad effects from such a procedure.

BLOCK AND OFF-PEAK POWER RATES

Many of the earliest accurate studies of fixed and increment costs were made in electrical utilities. In these industries a large portion of the installed capacity of generating and distributing equipment is not used during much of the day. Under these conditions much of the total expense of a company is fixed, and the cost of producing and selling an increased amount of power can be computed on an increment-cost basis. This has resulted in so-called block schedules whereby larger amounts of power can be purchased at lower cost. For example, the rate schedule of one company for domestic power is as follows:

First 40 kw.-hr. per month	$0.05 per kw.-hr.
(Minimum monthly charge, $1.50)	
Next 200 kw.-hr. per month	$0.02 per kw.-hr.
All above 240 kw.-hr. per month	$0.01 per kw.-hr.

In order to set up such a rate schedule, the company had to determine the fixed and increment costs of producing and distributing power.

Another situation that exists because of fixed and increment costs is that of off-peak power rates. Figure 12–2 shows a typical load curve of an elec-

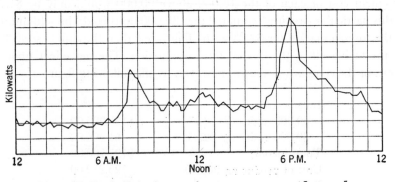

Figure 12–2. Daily load curve of a power company on January 5.

tric power company for its peak winter day. It will be noted that the peak demand occurring between 4:30 and 9:30 P.M. is approximately twice that of any other time during the day. During the remaining nineteen hours of the day much of the generating and distributing equipment is idle.

Since a great portion of the expense of delivering electric power to the consumer is due to the fixed charges resulting from heavy investment in plant facilities, any additional power which can be generated and sold during the nineteen off-peak hours will not increase the fixed costs to any extent. These will have been borne by the customary load. As a result, the increment cost of producing and distributing off-peak power will be very low. If the demand for such off-peak power can be stimulated by low rates which will yield some return above the increment cost of production, such a policy is of obvious advantage to the power company. Most power companies offer extremely favorable rates to consumers who will buy power only during the off-peak hours. For example, one company in the Pacific Northwest has built up a very good off-peak load by establishing a rate of $0.0075 per kw.-hr. for power used for domestic water heating during the nineteen off-peak hours. The water heaters are equipped with electric clock controls which turn the power on at 9:30 P.M. and off at 4:30 P.M. Sufficient hot water storage is provided for the five peak hours by using a larger tank than would otherwise be needed and providing insulation. Although the average rate received by this utility for its power is about $0.023 per kw.-hr. the $0.0075 rate for off-peak power is very satisfactory from a revenue standpoint.

Off-peak rates should not be considered in the same category as dumping. In dumping there is no difference in the goods that are sold in the domestic and foreign markets at different prices. Off-peak power, on the other hand, is different from ordinary power, since certain limitations are placed upon its use. The consumers of off-peak power obtain lower rates than those who buy ordinary power because they abide by those limitations. Thus the consumer benefits because he adjusts his demands to the requirements of the power company.

For the utilities companies these problems always have long-term implications. Once the rates are established they can not be changed readily. As a result, matters of installed capacity, and its utilization, and of long-range investment are involved. These problems will therefore be considered in Chapter 19. For the consumer and for other types of industries however, these conditions present problems which are of a pure fixed- and increment-cost nature.

As an example of this type consider the case of Richard Roe who wishes to buy a new kitchen range for his home. He has a gas range and finds he can buy either a new gas or an electric range, installed, for the same price. His average monthly gas bill has been $3.50. He buys electric power under the block rate schedule shown on page 298, and his average monthly bill has been $5.00. He estimates that the electric range will consume 260 kw.-hr. per month. Which type of range would be more economical?

Here the problem is to determine the increment cost of the power that will be consumed by the range. His present power bill of $5.00 per month represents the following:

$$40 \text{ kw.-hr. at } \$0.05 \text{ per kw.-hr.} = \$2.00$$
$$150 \text{ kw.-hr. at } \$0.02 \text{ per kw.-hr.} = \underline{3.00}$$
$$\text{Total bill} \qquad\qquad\qquad = \$5.00$$

While this shows that Mr. Roe now is paying an average of approximately $0.0263 per kw.-hr. for the power he is using, this is not applicable to the problem at hand. The additional power consumed by the electric range must be purchased in accordance with the rate schedule, starting in the $0.02 per kw.-hr. block, from which 50 kw.-hr. must be bought before any is obtained at the $0.01 per kw.-hr. rate. Therefore the monthly cost of the power for the range will be as follows:

$$50 \text{ kw.-hr. at } \$0.02 \text{ per kw.-hr.} = \$1.00$$
$$210 \text{ kw.-hr. at } \$0.01 \text{ per kw.-hr.} = \underline{2.10}$$
$$\text{Total bill} \qquad\qquad\qquad \$3.10$$

These figures show that the electric range will be more economical than the gas range. It is apparent that the amount now being paid for power is a fixed cost and unrelated to the purchase of the new range.

In industries other than public utilities the possibilities for utilizing off-peak capacity are varied and numerous. This is especially true in seasonal industries. Certain large manufacturing companies possess large and well-equipped machine shops which are used to capacity only a few months of the year for the production of jigs and dies for each year's models. Some of these companies are now turning out similar work for other concerns during the slack season. Since the differential costs of such production are low, the manufacturers are able to contract for such work at a low figure and still make a good profit. By keeping these departments operating at a much higher level than would otherwise be the case, they are able to maintain their equipment at a much more modern standard and at the same time earn more money.

Another practice is that of giving purchasers special discounts on goods that can be produced during off-peak seasons, or on especially large quantities for which the sales, packing, and shipping expense per unit may be considerably less than normal. Obviously, competent studies of increment costs are required in order to carry through such programs effectively.

SUNK COSTS

A third type of cost which often must be considered in economy studies of going concerns is *sunk cost*. Sunk costs are different from other costs considered in economy studies in that they are costs of the past, rather than of the future. Since virtually all economy studies deal with future costs, this fact should immediately indicate that sunk costs have no place in them. Yet many misconceptions have existed, and still do exist, concerning sunk costs, and there is a necessity for recognizing them so that they may be handled properly.

"Sunk cost" may be defined in several ways. It is the unrecovered balance of an investment. It is a cost, already paid, which is not relevant to the decision concerning the future which is being made. Capital already invested, which for some reason can not be retrieved, is a sunk cost.

HOW AND WHY SUNK COSTS OCCUR

In any business venture capital is invested or expended because of assumptions and beliefs that certain events will result which will permit the capital to be recovered and a profit obtained. As has been pointed out previously, one can never know for certain that the capital actually has been recovered and what the true profit has been until the property purchased with the capital has reached the end of its economic life and is retired from service. It should not be surprising that events do not always turn out exactly as originally anticipated, or that new conditions may call for a change in operations from those initially planned. If such situations do arise, it should be recognized that the old cost data, unit or annual, were based on certain estimated conditions and that if the assumed conditions are subsequently found to be wrong, the costs have been and are wrong. It should be equally clear that such errors may arise in spite of completely sound decisions at the time the investment or costs were incurred. It also should follow that such errors of the past should not be a part of decisions regarding the future. Unfortunately, such reasoning does not always prevail.

The principle of sunk costs may be illustrated by the following simple example. John Jones had purchased one quart of anti-freeze for $1.00 and put it into the radiator of his car. A few days later he planned to make a trip to a colder locality and decided he would need three additional quarts of anti-freeze to prevent the radiator from freezing during the trip. When he got to the service station, he found that the anti-freeze was obtainable in quart cans costing $1.00 or in one-gallon cans for $2.75. The service-station attendant suggested that he drain his radiator, purchase a gallon of anti-freeze for $2.75, and refill the radiator with this gallon and the additional water as required. However, Mr. Jones insisted that he couldn't afford to throw away the quart of anti-freeze which was already in the radiator and for which he had paid $1.00. So he bought three quart cans of anti-freeze for $1.00 each.

It is apparent in this case that Mr. Jones spent $3.00 for the necessary amount of anti-freeze which he required, while if he had followed the service-station attendant's suggestion he could have acquired approximately the same amount of anti-freeze in the radiator of his car for only $2.75. The $1.00 which John Jones had previously spent for anti-freeze was a sunk cost insofar as the immediate problem was concerned. What he had spent *in the past* had no bearing upon the proper choice between two possible methods of acquiring three additional quarts of anti-freeze; one by purchasing three one-quart cans for $3.00, the other by purchasing a gallon for $2.75. John Jones' reluctance to forget about the $1.00 which he had spent previously, in order to make a correct immediate decision, is shared by many, including some who make economy studies and business decisions. In many cases past expenditures are pertinent to a situation being studied. In many others they represent sunk costs which, like water gone over the dam, can not be recovered. In such cases they have no place in an economy study and must be completely, though perhaps regretfully, forgotten.

SUNK COSTS AND DEPRECIABLE ASSETS

Sunk costs frequently arise in connection with depreciable assets. Such a situation may be seen in the case of a small company which purchased an ABC dictating and transcribing machine for $350. At the time of purchase it was estimated that this machine would have a life of at least five years, and depreciation was charged on the accounting records on this basis, using the straight-line method. Upon being used, it was found that the machine contained certain design defects which could not be corrected and that it did not give satisfactory service. At the end of three years a new XYZ dictating machine, using magnetic tape and costing only $220, came on the market. The distributor who had sold the original machine wanted to sell the company a new model of the ABC machine for $375 and offered in his sales proposal to ". . . allow $100 for the old machine on the price of the new model. This will make it possible for you to recover $100 of the price originally paid for the old machine." The XYZ machine was judged to be at least as good as the new ABC machine, and the two were estimated to have equal lives. So far as could be determined, if the XYZ machine were purchased, nothing could be obtained for the ABC machine.

Figure 12–3 shows what had happened to the value of the ABC machine. According to the accounting records, the value of the machine was $140.

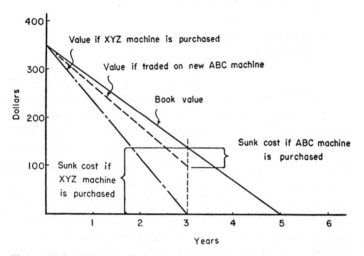

Figure 12–3. Effective of time on value of the ABC dictating machine.

Actually the machine had decreased in value at a faster rate than had been assumed when the depreciation account was established. The rate of depreciation and the value at the end of three years depended upon which new machine was to be purchased. If a new ABC machine were bought, there would be a sunk cost of $140 — $100 = $40. If the XYZ machine were purchased the sunk cost would be $140 — $0 = $140. However, the most significant fact was that neither of these sunk cost values had any relationship to the decision that had to be made regarding the purchase of the new dictating machine. The only relevant factors were the costs of providing the *future* service. These were as follows:

ABC Machine		XYZ Machine	
List price	$375	List price	$220
Less trade-in value of old		Less trade-in value of old	
machine	100	machine	0
Net cost	$275	Net cost	$220

This example illustrates the manner in which sunk costs may arise and that their magnitude may depend upon both previous assumptions and current decisions. At the same time, it shows that they have no relevance to decisions regarding future actions.

When depreciable assets are involved, sunk costs may arise through below-normal activity, an error in estimated salvage value, or an error in estimating the economic life. It should also be remembered that above-normal activity, higher than expected salvage value, and longer than antici-pated life may result in an extra profit. Such a profit, like a sunk cost, has no relevance to decisions related to the future.

RESULTS PURCHASED BY SUNK COSTS MAY BE PERTINENT

While sunk costs themselves are not relevant in economy studies, the bene-fits or results which have been obtained through them may be of considerable importance. For example, assume you have an automobile which is four years old. It has just developed differential trouble which will require a complete rear-end overhaul and considerable expense. You must decide whether it would be more economical to have the necessary repair work done or to trade the car in on a new one. Three months previously you paid $200 for a complete engine overhaul job. Obviously the $200 paid for the engine overhaul is a sunk cost with respect to the decision at hand. Yet the fact that the engine has been overhauled and will probably give very good and economical service for some time is a factor of considerable importance in deciding whether to keep the old car or to buy a new one. Thus the sunk cost of $200 is not relevant, but the possible effect of this expenditure upon future costs is pertinent.

This relationship of sunk costs to future disbursements is encountered quite frequently. For example, should more money be spent on a research project which has not yet produced positive results but still is promising? Should an oil well be dug 1,000 feet deeper or abandoned? In such cases it is apparent that what has been done must be considered in terms of the conditions from which future disbursements may be made. To neglect what has taken place would be a gross error.

PROBLEMS

12-1   One year ago a manufacturer of machine tools put a line of small power tools on the market for home-shop use, planning to utilize some of the unused capacity of his plant, and to cash in on the "do-it-your-self" market. The new line of tools was priced on an increment-cost basis. He now finds that his plant is operating at 90 per cent of capacity, and that 75 per cent of the plant capacity is being utilized for the production of the new line of tools, whereas a year ago 50 per cent of the capacity of the plant had been used for producing the large machine tools. Discuss the problems faced by this manufacturer with respect to his unit costs.

12–2 A plant having a capacity of 1,600 units per year is operating currently at 1,200 units. The sales income at this level is $864,000. Variable costs are $416 per unit. The fixed costs of the plant are $365,000 per year. A modernization plan is being considered which would increase the fixed costs by $58,000 per year, but would reduce the variable costs by $56 per unit.

a. Would this be a good program to follow?

b. If a reduction in selling price of $50 per unit would increase sales by 300 units per year, would this be a better procedure than the modernization program?

12–3 A manufacturer has considerable excess capacity. He has a chance to obtain a contract on a cost-plus basis to produce a product that will use for each unit produced two pounds of a material which now exists as waste from the manufacture of his major product. He has been selling a small portion of this waste material on the market for $0.50 per pound. The major portion of it, however, is being sold as scrap for $0.10 per pound. There is a sufficient amount of the waste material to supply the needs of the new product and still permit the sale of the amount at present being sold at the market price.

Other materials for the new product will cost $0.25 per unit. Direct labor will cost $1.02 per unit. The overhead costs of the company are equal to $75,000.00 per year plus 50 per cent of the sum of direct labor and direct material costs. The buyer offers to purchase 10,000 units per year at cost plus 20% profit. The company operates as a corporation, with all of the stock held by three people.

What should be the selling price for the new product?

12–4 Tom Jones owns and operates a shop which specializes in the repair of electronics equipment. He has $30,000 invested in the business and has been writing off the investment on a straight-line basis, using a ten-year write-off period. He estimates that most of the depreciation is functional and is almost independent of the actual usage of the equipment involved. He has one employee whom he pays $425 per month. Monthly rent on the shop is $150. Taxes and insurance are $300 per year. Miscellaneous expenses amount to $10 per week, mostly for power, light, and heat.

Tom has followed the practice of closing for two weeks each year for a vacation, and he pays his employee during this period. Business has been slow this year, and Tom estimates that instead of the usual $6,000 per month on which he makes an average profit of 50% before charges for labor and overhead, he probably will not take in over $600 per week during the two-week period following the vacation shutdown. His employee is not greatly averse to taking an extra two weeks vacation without pay, and Tom thinks an extra two weeks to go fishing might be in order. He therefore is considering closing the shop for four weeks this year instead of the usual two.

Make an economy study relating to the decision he must make.

12–5   A company has an old plant, A, and a newer plant, B, in the same city, each having a capacity of ten units per month of the same product. Fixed costs at plant A are $10,000 per month and at B are $20,000 per month. Variable expenses per month at A are $1,000 \times N - \$10N^2$ and at B are $1,200 \times M - \$5M^3$, where N and M are the number of units produced. At present the sales are stable at fourteen units per month, with each plant producing seven units. Should the production volume at the plants be changed, and to what extent?

12–6   Because of a merger, a corporation now has two plants which produce the same product. The plants are located in the same state and utilize different processes. At plant A, which has a capacity of 200 tons per month, the present output is 140 tons and the unit costs are $48.00 per ton. It is computed that $2,500.00 of the total monthly costs would remain fixed even if the output were changed considerably.

The capacity at plant B is 150 tons per month, and the present output is 100 tons. At this plant the unit cost is $55.00 per ton. The fixed costs are $2,800.00 per month. Any increase in output at this plant would involve an additional cost of $0.50 per ton to pay for night-shift wage premiums.

Should the corporation make any shift in the outputs of the two plants, and if so, what?

12–7   In preparing to produce a new model of its product a company wishes to use a die casting instead of several small stampings and machined parts. However, the company has no die-casting equipment, so it must either purchase such equipment or have the part made by an outside contractor. A company specializing in this work and having some excess capacity offers to manufacture the castings for the cost of the material, plus labor, plus $0.02 per casting for power, heat, and increment overhead, plus a profit of 25% of the sum of these cost items. This company quotes $0.22 and $0.08 for the cost of materials and labor respectively. It also is specified that the quoted prices are to be good only if the castings can be produced at off-peak intervals. This will necessitate the purchasing company's carrying an average inventory of $1,000.00 worth of the castings at all times.

An influential member of the board of directors of the company insists that they should not pay another company a 25% profit; die-casting equipment has therefore been purchased for $7,500.00 so that the part can be manufactured. Material costs turn out to be $0.24 per unit, and labor costs the same as quoted by the die-casting company. The equipment is to be written off over a five-year period. Overhead costs are found to be $0.03 per unit.

If 10,000 castings are produced per year and capital is worth 15%, was the decision to produce the castings a wise one?

12–8 A manufacturer of small pumps has estimated costs as follows:

Output	Labor	Materials	Overhead	Selling Costs	Total Costs
0			$72,000	$20,000	$ 92,000
5,000	$ 40,000	$ 70,000	75,000	22,000	207,000
10,000	80,000	135,000	76,000	23,000	314,000
15,000	120,000	200,000	77,000	24,000	421,000
20,000	160,000	260,000	78,000	24,500	522,500
25,000	200,000	320,000	79,000	25,000	624,000
30,000	240,000	365,000	80,000	25,500	710,500

A survey of domestic sales indicates that not more than 15,000 pumps can be sold during the current year at $28 per pump. An exporting company makes an offer to purchase 5,000 pumps for export at $22 each, or 10,000 at $20 each. There would be no sales expense on these pumps. Should the manufacturer accept either of these offers, and if so, which one?

12–9 A company has a one-year contract with a mail-order house to manufacture a special model of its product which could be produced on the existing equipment during off-peak periods. During the year 10,000 units were produced and sold. The increment costs, including material, labor, supervision, and all overhead except building and equipment costs, were $10 per unit. The selling price was $14 per unit.

Near the end of the year the mail-order house has offered a contract for 20,000 units for the second year at the same price. In order to produce this many units, the company will have to build a new building at a cost of $100,000 and spend a similar amount for equipment. The building and equipment would normally have a ten-year life. The building probably could be sold at any time for its book value, but the equipment would have very little salvage value. Aside from its use for the proposed contract, there would be little possible use for the new plant. Taxes and insurance on the new assets would amount to 2% of first cost per year. It is known that several other similar companies have excess capacity available and could manufacture the units, or at least a portion of them, should the contract be refused. Capital is worth at least 10% to the company.

What would you recommend, and why?

12–10 A factory has a power plant which furnishes space heating, process steam, and electric power. The annual operating costs have been as follows:

Fuel	$ 2,800.00
Labor	8,900.00
Maintenance	1,600.00
Depreciation	1,900.00
Miscellaneous overhead	1,800.00
	$17,000.00

134,000 kw.-hr. of electric power are generated annually. The salesman for a local power company has told the company president that it would be cheaper to purchase the required power and has stated that the factory could save at least $0.01 per kw.-hr. by doing so.

A careful analysis of the annual costs shows that no more than 11 per cent of the fuel cost is attributable to the generation of power. Repair and maintenance on the generating equipment has cost only $250.00 per year. Power generation has been charged with 40% of the miscellaneous overhead of the power plant. No labor would be saved if power were not generated. It was found that if the power-generating equipment were sold, the salvage price would approximately equal the cost of removal and repair of the power-plant floor; it was therefore decided that the equipment would be retained for stand-by use even if power were purchased. Company capital is worth 12%.

Should the power be purchased?

12–11   The domestic rate schedule under which Mr. Householder purchases electric power reads as follows:

For all power used for residence purposes:

Meter charge	$1.00 per month
0–40 kw.-hr. per month	0.05 per kw.-hr.
Next 200 kw.-hr. per month	0.02 per kw.-hr.
Excess above 240 kw.-hr. per month	0.01 per kw.-hr.

Mr. Householder's monthly bill for electricity has been $4.20, giving an average cost of $0.042 per kw.-hr. He installs an electric range which consumes 320 kw.-hr. per month.

a. What will be his monthly power bill after installing the range?

b. What will be the average cost per kw.-hr. of the power used by the range?

12–12   A chemical plant has a waste product which, according to the cost records, is worth $600.00 per month. The material now is being dumped into a river adjacent to the plant and is the subject of some local controversy. The material could be processed to produce fertilizer, but this would require the investment of $4,500.00 in equipment and the use of other materials costing $750.00 per month. One worker would have to be employed at $470.00 per month. The company figures that miscellaneous payroll expenses and taxes amount to 4%. Taxes and insurance on equipment amount to 2% of first cost per year. The company requires that all equipment of the type involved must be written off within five years and earn a return of 20% before taxes. Overhead expense for power, heat, etc., will cost $800.00 per year. If thirty tons of fertilizer are produced per month, which can be sold for $0.02 per pound, should the company make the investment?

12–13   Four college students wish to go home for Christmas vacation, a distance of 400 miles each way. One has an automobile and agrees to take other three if they will pay the costs of driving the car. When they return from the trip he presents each of them with a bill for $17.07, stating that he has kept careful records of the cost of operating his car and has found that, based on his average yearly mileage of 15,000 miles, his cost per mile is $0.064. The three students declare they feel the charge is too high and ask to see his cost figures. He shows them the following list:

	Cost per mile
Gasoline	$0.0200
Oil and lubrication	0.0035
Tires	0.0045
Depreciation	0.0250
Insurance and taxes	0.0040
Repairs	0.0050
Garage	0.0020
	$0.0640

Was the bill presented computed correctly, and if not how much should each student pay?

12–14   The ABC Company manufactures electric refrigerators. It is considering adding a line of home food-freezer-and-storage units. It can produce up to 1,000 units per month by operating an extra shift and without having to add more factory space or equipment, but it would have to rent additional warehouse space at a cost of $500 per month. The annual overhead costs of the company are equal to $800,000 + 20% of prime cost. Labor cost for each freezer unit would be $60, and the cost of materials $30. In addition, a compressor unit costing $18 would have to be purchased.

a. If the company desires to make a profit of 20% of the selling price on its products, before income taxes, what should the selling price of the freezer units be, priced on an increment-cost basis?

b. What adjustment in selling price of the freezers would have to be made in order for them to assume their share of the total overhead, assuming that the dollar sales volume of freezers becomes one half that of the refrigerators?

12–15 An adding-machine company is considering production of a small, light-weight model to be sold by a national chain-store organization. This organization has made an offer to purchase 200 adding machines per month for one year at a price of $50.00 each less a 35% discount. This volume would increase the utilization of the company's plant from 75 per cent to 85 per cent of capacity.

To produce the new model would require an investment of $20,000 for new dies and tooling. While the sales contract on the new line would only be for one year, the company, is willing to make the write-off on the dies and tooling on a two-year basis, being willing to gamble that if the contract is not renewed, some additional sales outlet can be found. Labor costs for the small adding machines would be $12.10, and material costs $8.20 each. The overhead costs of the company are computed to vary by a straight-line relationship from $250,000.00 per year at zero output to $450,000.00 at 100% capacity.

The company obtains a return, before taxes, of 12% on its capital, and a profit of 10% on sales.

Should it accept the order from the chain-store organization?

12–16 An asset was purchased six years ago at a cost of $7,000. It was estimated to have a useful life of ten years, with a salvage value of $500 at the end of that time. It is now of no further use and can be sold for only $800. Determine the sunk cost if depreciation has been computed by

(a) The straight-line method.

(b) The sum-of-the-years'-digits method.

12–17 The XYZ Company purchased a machine for $20,000. Estimating that it would have a five-year life, straight-line depreciation was charged on this basis. Profits resulting from the use of the equipment during the first three years were computed at $4,500, $4,900, and $4,200. Because of a change in demand, there was no use for the machine after three years, and it was sold for $500.

a. What was the sunk cost?

b. Assuming the cost of capital to be 8%, what was the true profit from the machine during the first, second, and third years? (Straight-line depreciation plus average interest may be used.)

CHAPTER 13

Replacement
Studies

One of the problems which individuals and businesses encounter frequently is deciding whether existing equipment or property should be replaced with new and more modern facilities. Wear and tear of equipment, coupled with rapid technological progress which results in new and improved devices, make this an ever-present problem. The impossibility of always being able to predict what technological progress will bring forth often requires replacement decisions at times when one had not expected to make them. Many businesses have found themselves in serious difficulty, from both a financial viewpoint and a competitive position, because of incorrect thinking about replacement. The facts that must be dealt with in replacement studies sometimes are unpleasant in that they reveal that a previous decision was unsound. Yet correct solutions require that all the factors be dealt with realistically and honestly.

REASONS FOR REPLACEMENT

There are four basic reasons for replacing or retiring existing equipment or properties. These are

1. Physical impairment: The existing equipment or property is completely or partially worn out and will no longer function satisfactorily without extensive repairs.
2. Inadequacy: The equipment or property does not have sufficient capacity to meet the present demands that are placed on it; no physical impairment is necessarily implied.

3. Obsolescence: This may be caused either by a lessening in the demand for the services rendered by the equipment or by the availability of more efficient equipment which will operate with lower out-of-pocket costs.

4. Rental possibilities: It is possible to rent identical or comparable equipment or property, thus freeing capital for other and more profitable use. (Such cases usually involve income tax considerations and therefore will be discussed in Chapter 18.)

EXAMPLE OF A REPLACEMENT SITUATION

The following is a typical replacement problem which may be used to illustrate a number of the factors which must be considered in replacement studies.

A company, five years ago, purchased for $1,700 a pump, including the driving motor, with a capacity of 700 gallons per minute. At the time it was purchased it was estimated that it would have a useful life of ten years and a salvage value at the end of that time of 10% of the initial cost. Depreciation has been charged in the accounting records on this basis, using the straight-line method. The annual operating costs have been $325. Maintenance costs have turned out to be more than originally anticipated but have leveled off at about $175 per year. It appears that the pump will continue to operate for a considerable number of years if the present level of maintenance is continued. Annual taxes and insurance are about 2% of present book value.

The addition of new processing equipment will increase pumping requirements to 1,000 gallons per minute. Two alternatives are available for meeting this requirement. The first is to purchase a new pump having a capacity of 300 gallons per minute to supplement the existing pump. This pump would cost $750, installed, have an estimated useful life of ten years and a salvage value of 10% of the first cost. Operation costs for this pump are estimated to be $110 per year, and annual maintenance costs to be $50.

The second alternative would be to replace the existing pump with one having 1,000-gallons-per-minute capacity. This pump would cost $2,000, installed, have a useful life of ten years, and an ultimate salvage value of 10% of first cost. If this pump were purchased, the company would receive a trade-in allowance of $75 for the old pump. Operation costs for this larger pump are estimated to be $375 annually, and the maintenance costs not to exceed $100.

Annual taxes and insurance on either of the new pumps would amount to 2% of first cost. If the old pump is continued in service, it is estimated that the ultimate salvage value would not be less than $20. A decision must be made as to which pump to purchase. Annual profits of the company have been about 8% before income taxes.

This example will be recognized as one in which both physical impairment and inadequacy are factors. However, the physical impairment can apparently be overcome by continuing an established maintenance program.

FACTORS WHICH MUST BE CONSIDERED IN REPLACEMENT STUDIES

The problem of the pump illustrates most of the factors which must be considered in replacement studies. These are

(a) Recognition of a past error.
(b) The possible existence of a sunk cost.
(c) Remaining life of the old property.
(d) Write-off period for the proposed replacement.
(e) Method of handling unamortized values.

Once a proper viewpoint has been established with respect to these items, replacement studies are not basically different from other studies of alternatives.

RECOGNITION OF PAST "ERRORS" AND SUNK COSTS

In the case of the pump three factors have turned out not to be in accord with conditions assumed at the time the pump was purchased. First, the required pumping demand is greater than was predicted. Second, the maintenance costs are greater than estimated. Third, the apparent salvage value has decreased more rapidly than was anticipated and provided for by the depreciation accounting. According to the straight-line depreciation which was used, the salvage value at the end of five years of service should be $935. Yet it appears that the company can get only $75 for the old pump. If it should sell the pump there would be an unamortized value of $935 − $75 = $860.

Such differences frequently have been designated as past "errors." Such a designation is unfortunate since in most cases, as in this one, the differences are not the result of errors, but of honest inability to foresee future conditions. This distinction is important in establishing a proper state of mind which will accept two very important facts, namely

(a) The "errors" or discrepancies are related to the *past* and have no relevance to the replacement decision which must be made, and (*b*) Unamortized values are sunk costs with respect to the decision at hand.

Once these facts are recognized and accepted, a major stumbling block has been removed from replacement studies.

Some have found that acceptance of these facts may be made easier by posing a hypothetical question, "What will be the costs of my competitor whose similar property is completely amortized and who therefore has no past 'errors' to consider?" In other words, one must decide whether he wishes to live in the past, with its errors and discrepancies, or to be in a sound competitive position in the future. A common reaction is, "I can't afford to take the loss in value of the existing asset which will result if the replacement is made." Of course, the fact is that the loss already has occurred, whether or not it could be afforded, and it exists whether or not the replacement is made.

REMAINING LIFE OF THE OLD PROPERTY

Since in every replacement study one alternative is to retain the existing property, one must assign some probable additional life to this asset. The assumed life must be realistic, yet, at the same time, it should be that life which will result in the lowest realistic annual cost for extending the service through the use of the old asset. Ordinarily the old property should not be replaced unless the proposed replacement will provide service at an annual cost, including profit on capital, which is less than the best that can be obtained with the old asset. Similarly, the old asset should not be retained unless, at its realistic best, it is more economical than the proposed new asset.

If the old asset requires substantial rebuilding or rehabilitation in order to be continued in service, it is probable that the most economical write-off period will be the length of time before a similar rehabilitation will again be necessary.

When the salvage value of the existing asset is zero but the annual outlay for operation and maintenance will increase each year, it is apparent that one year is the most economical life which can be obtained. On the other hand, where the salvage value decreases each year while the operation and/or maintenance costs increase each year, a set of year-to-year calculations must be made to determine the most economical life.

In establishing the remaining life for the old asset, it should be remembered that the fact that a replacement is being considered casts some doubt on its probable life. Unless there is some definite fact, such as rehabilitation, to warrant contrary action, it seldom is reasonable to assign a remaining life to the old equipment which is longer than the estimated economic life of the new equipment. In some cases a company may have adopted a recent write-off policy which requires new equipment to be written off in a period which is less than the originally estimated remaining life of the old equipment. If such a rule is applied to the new equipment, it is logical that it also should be applied to the old. When there are no clear facts to indicate what remaining life should be assigned to the old equipment, a satisfactory rule is to use (a) the life remaining as determined by the original estimate made when the equipment was new or (b) the life assigned to the new equipment, whichever value is shorter. It should be remembered, however, that this rule does not eliminate the possibility of using a life which is less than either of these values if the facts justify such a procedure.

If a decision is made not to replace an existing asset, it is based upon information available at the time. Additional time may produce different information. Therefore the decision to continue the asset in service should be restudied periodically.

WRITE-OFF PERIOD FOR REPLACEMENTS

Obviously, the write-off period for the proposed replacement asset is of great importance. As has been discussed previously in this book, companies frequently demand rather short, and frequently arbitrary, write-off periods for new investments. In connection with replacement assets they sometimes are even more conservative. Such attitudes appear to stem from one or more of several bases:

1. A realization that an unamortized value has arisen in connection with the old asset may lead to a natural desire to make certain that no such sunk cost will occur in the future if a replacement is made.
2. It may be reasoned that if a new asset has appeared which makes the old one obsolete, later improvements may, at a later date, make the replacement asset obsolete.
3. In many cases the replacement asset is more specialized than the old one, and it is therefore believed that an increased possibility of obsolescence exists.

While all of these are valid lines of reasoning, it must be remembered that most factors which tend to support a short write-off period for the replacement asset apply with equal force to the old asset. Failure to recognize this fact sometimes results in some rather illogical practices. For example, a zero salvage value will be assumed for the replacement asset, thus requiring 100% write-off, while the old asset is assigned an ultimate salvage or scrap value because its value can be determined at the time the replacement study is made. Another such erroneous practice is assigning an arbitrarily short write-off period to the replacement asset while using a longer one for the old asset. Replacement, should, of course, not be made unless it is economically justified, but failure to replace when it is justified can be dangerous. Therefore one should make certain that realistic write-off periods are applied to both the old and the replacement assets.

STUDY PERIOD FOR REPLACEMENT STUDIES

When a single new asset is being considered for replacement of an old asset, as is the case in most replacement studies, it is not necessary that the life of the old and the new be the same, provided the service is needed throughout the anticipated life of the new asset. One is merely concerned with whether the replacement should be made now or later. If, however, there are two or more alternatives which can be used for replacement, it is desirable to adopt the same study period for the alternatives, as is done in ordinary alternative investment studies.

If an asset has value beyond the period when it is needed, this may be handled by subtracting the present value of its worth at the end of the study period from the costs of the asset.

METHODS OF HANDLING LOSSES DUE
TO UNAMORTIZED VALUES

There can be no question that, although unamortized values are sunk costs and have no place in replacement studies, they do cause considerable concern on the part of business owners and managers. Therefore an understanding of how they are handled may provide some peace of mind to those making economy studies. Several methods have been and are used for dealing with unamortized values. Some are sound; others are incorrect.

One incorrect method is, in effect, a pretense that no unamortized loss has occurred. This is accomplished by using book value for the old equipment in the replacement study. People who do this usually justify their action by saying that if the old equipment is kept, they can continue to charge depreciation on it until the entire amount of capital that has been invested is recovered. Actually, such wishful thinking could only be realized if one had no competition. If a competitive situation exists, one's competitor may obtain the more economical new equipment and be able to sell at lower prices and thus prevent any further recovery of capital, since capital can be recovered only through the sale of goods or services produced by the old equipment. It must always be remembered that the value of any property is determined by the profits that can be obtained through its use. Thus attempting to recover or prevent unamortized values in this manner is entirely erroneous.

A second incorrect method of handling unamortized values involves adding them to the cost of the replacing equipment and then computing future depreciation costs, if the replacement is made, with this total. Users of this procedure believe that they can thus require the replacing property to repay the unamortized value "which the replacement has caused." This line of reasoning is fallacious on two counts. First, the unamortized value is a fact, regardless of whether the replacement is made or not. Second, if one has competition, he probably will not be able to make the replacing equipment pay the sunk cost. Again, a competitor who did not have an old machine, and thus had no unamortized value to recover, would have much lower costs with a new machine and could thus sell at a lower price. One's selling price usually is dictated by competition and not by one's desire to recover a sunk cost.

The correct handling of unamortized values requires that they be recognized for what they are—losses of capital. One of the most common procedures is to charge them directly to the profit and loss account. This considers them a loss of the current operating period and thus deducts them from current earnings. This is a satisfactory procedure except for the fact that unusually large losses will have a serious effect upon the profits of the current period.

A more satisfactory method is to provide a surplus against which such losses may be charged. Thus, a certain sum is set aside each accounting period to build up and maintain this surplus. When any losses occur from unamortized values, they are charged against the surplus account and current profits are not affected seriously. The periodic contribution to the surplus account is in the nature of an insurance premium to prevent profits from being affected by losses from unamortized values.

Other methods which are used might be described more accurately as methods of avoiding unamortized values altogether. These consist, essentially, of writing off investments in equipment in a very short time. This practice is becoming more prevalent throughout industry. For example, a recent study of 200 business firms revealed that over 60 per cent of them expected an investment to pay for itself within three years. Five per cent expected the pay-out period to be a year or less. By requiring very short payout periods (high rates of depreciation) the likelihood of any unamortized values arising becomes less and less. One can readily appreciate this attitude when the rapid changes of industry are considered.

A further example of the tendency of industry to shorten the write-off period of investments is illustrated by the chart of Figure 13–1. This repre-

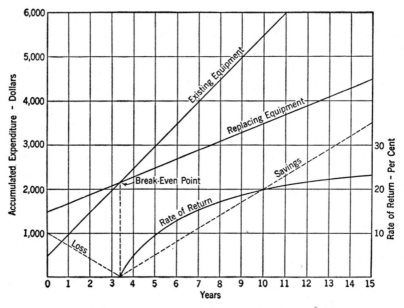

Figure 13–1. Graphical representation of the economy of a proposed replacement.

sents the method used by the engineering department of a large oil company for considering the advisability of replacing equipment. The new equipment is not considered to yield any profit until it has paid for itself out of the savings it brought about. After the equipment has paid for itself, the company considers that it is commencing to receive some profit from the replacement. The great difficulty with this method is that it is impracticable, if not impossible, to keep a record of each investment in this manner and to pay profits to the stockholders only after each item of equipment has paid for itself. Applied to an entire enterprise, it would mean that no profits could be paid until all the investment has been written off. The resulting accounting system would be amazingly complicated.

It is apparent that none of the procedures discussed actually provides for recovery of the lost capital. The only way the capital can be restored is, in effect, to obtain it from the owners through capital assessments or by withholding from them some of the profits in the future. Quite frequently such capital losses place companies in serious financial difficulty. One nationally known company, for example, at the close of World War II found that many of its plants, worth many millions of dollars according to book value, were obsolete as the result of technological advances that had taken place. No provision for this decline in value had been made, and the company was in a very poor competitive position. Its situation was such that obtaining new capital would be very costly. As a result, a five-year rehabilitation program was established, during which time no profits were paid to stockholders but were used to build new plants. It was hoped that such a program could be carried out, but it was recognized that some of the company's competitors were in a position to reduce prices to a point where there might be very little hope of profit on certain lines of products. Subsequent to the decision it was found that the competition was not as favorably situated as had been thought and that demand for the product was sufficient to keep prices high enough to permit the operation of some of the old plants. This permitted the rehabilitation program to be completed without complete retention of profits.

THEORETICAL PATTERNS OF COSTS IN REPLACEMENT STUDIES

There are a number of theoretical patterns into which the year-to-year operation and/or maintenance costs of an asset may fall. These are (a) constant, (b) constantly increasing, (c) combination of physical impairment and obsolescence, and (d) sporadic. If certain idealizing assumptions are made it is possible to set up equations which may be solved to determine the most economical time for replacement of a given asset under the first three of the above conditions. As a result, numerous replacement formulas have been derived. Such formulas suffer two major difficulties. First, if a formula is reasonably simple, the assumptions behind it are so idealized that one seldom encounters such a case in actual practice. Second, if the formula attempts to take most of the possible factors into account, it becomes complex while remaining subject to some limitations due to the assumptions made.

The most common assumption used in deriving replacement formulas is that history will repeat itself—that the replacement asset will have the same cost experience as the existing asset has experienced. Another assumption frequently used is that the replacement asset will be exactly the same as the old asset. In view of normal technological advances, it may be seen that neither of these assumptions is realistic in most cases. Therefore most replacement formulas are of little value in replacement studies. However, they do yield some general conclusions which are of some value.

Based on the assumptions of repeated history and identical replacements, some common generalizations are

1. Where operation and/or maintenance costs are constant, replacement is never justified as long as the old asset operates satisfactorily and meets the demand.
2. Where costs increase by a constant amount each year, there is a theoretical replacement life which gives maximum economy. However, the cost curve is quite flat, so a variation of a relatively moderate amount from the theoretically correct time produces rather small differences.
3. For combinations of constantly increasing maintenance (due to physical impairment) and obsolescence, the optimum life tends to decrease as obsolescence, in proportion to maintenance, increases.

The most elaborate replacement formula is the one supported and advocated by the Machinery and Allied Products Institute. This formula, commonly known as the MAPI formula, is based on the work of George Terborgh [1] and is discussed in Appendix A. It has been widely publicized but is used relatively seldom, except by companies which are members of the sponsoring institute. The original formula has been replaced by a new MAPI procedure which is presented in Appendix A. As is the case with other replacement formulas, actual replacement problems usually can be handled more readily, and with somewhat greater clarity, by ordinary economy study procedures than by the MAPI procedure.

BASIC PATTERNS FOR REPLACEMENT STUDIES

Replacement economy studies may be made by any of the basic procedures which have been discussed previously. However, in most cases either the rate-of-return method or the annual-cost method is used. Both will be used in the examples which follow.

REPLACEMENT BECAUSE OF INADEQUACY

The pump problem, stated on page 312, is a typical example of a common situation where replacement must be considered because of the inade-

---

[1] Terborgh, George, *Dynamic Equipment Policy*, McGraw-Hill Book Company, Inc., New York, 1944.

quacy of the existing asset. If the pump is kept it must be supplemented by a smaller pump having a capacity of 300 gallons per minute. For this combination the annual costs, without profit, would be as follows:

For old pump:

Depreciation	$\dfrac{\$75.00 - \$20.00}{s_{\overline{10}|(8)}} = \dfrac{\$55.00}{14.5}$	= \$ 3.80
Operation		= 325.00
Maintenance		= 175.00
Taxes and insurance	\$935.00 × 0.02	= 18.70

For new 300-gallons-per-minute pump:

Depreciation	$\dfrac{\$750.00 - \$75.00}{s_{\overline{10}|(8)}} = \dfrac{\$675.00}{14.5}$	= 46.50
Operation		= 110.00
Maintenance		= 50.00
Taxes and insurance	\$750.00 × 0.02	= 15.00
Total		= \$744.00

For the new 1,000-gallons-per-minute pump the annual costs would be as follows:

Depreciation	$\dfrac{\$2,000.00 - \$200.00}{s_{\overline{10}|(8)}} = \dfrac{\$1,800.00}{14.5}$	= \$124.00
Operation		= 375.00
Maintenance		= 100.00
Taxes and insurance	\$2,000.00 × 0.02	= 40.00
Total		= \$639.00

It is thus indicated that if the new 1,000-gallons-per-minute pump were purchased, an annual saving of $744.00 − $639.00 = $105.00 could be obtained. However, in order to obtain this saving, additional capital, to the extent of $2,000 − $750.00 − $75.00 = $1,175.00, would have to be invested. The annual rate of return on this capital would be

$$\$105.00/\$1,175.00 = 8.94\%.$$

Since capital is worth 8% to the company, it appears that the old pump should be replaced with the new 1,000-gallons-per-minute pump.

Several items should be noted regarding this study. First, future depreciation on the old pump was based on the present realizable salvage value. Since there was no definite evidence that the actual worth of this pump was greater than the salvage value, $75.00 − $20.00 was the *minimum* decrease in value (depreciation) that could be experienced in the future. Therefore the use of the present salvage value placed the old pump in the most favorable situation. Since it could not compete with a new pump on this basis, it is obvious that it could not compete if any larger value were used in computing the depreciation. This reasoning leads to the general principle that *the future depreciation expense of existing equipment should be based upon actual present value.*

The second item to be noted is that for all new equipment the full cost must be used in computing depreciation costs. An error which sometimes is made is the deduction of the salvage value of the old asset from the cost of the new one in computing depreciation. This must never be done, since it is the actual full cost of the new asset which will depreciate through future use.

A third item relates to the computation of the rate of return when this method is used. The amount of capital investment required is the cost of the new asset *less* any amount received from the sale of the old asset. This is the amount of new capital which must be invested to bring about the expected saving.

If the annual-cost method were used for the pump-replacement study, the same cost figures would be used with the addition of an 8% minimum required profit.

For old pump and new 300-gallons-per-minute pump:

Out-of-pocket and depreciation costs		= $744.00
Minimum required profit (8%)	($750.00 + $75.00)0.08	= 66.00
Total annual cost		= $810.00

For new 1,000-gallons-per-minute pump:

Out-of-pocket and depreciation costs		= $639.00
Minimum required profit (8%)	$2,000.00 × 0.08	= 160.00
Total annual cost		= $799.00

This method of analysis thus indicates the advisability of buying the 1,000-gallons-per-minute pump.

The evaluation of the adequacy of the rate of return in replacement studies, or the setting of the minimum required profit when the annual-cost method is used, is essentially the same as for alternative investment studies. In the case of the old asset the cost items should be known with considerable certainty. Proper consideration should be given to the source of cost data for the replacement asset.

REPLACEMENT WITHOUT RETIREMENT

The case of the inadequate pump, just discussed, raises the common possibility of replacement without retirement. In many instances, although the old asset will not operate as economically as the new one, its very low value makes it possible to retain it for stand-by purposes or for diversion to some secondary use. Thus, the annual cost of retaining the old pump, assuming that there would be no problem of space, would be

Depreciation	$ 3.80
Taxes and insurance	18.70
	$22.50.

The operation and maintenance costs, of course, would be dependent upon its actual use.

Because of such realistic cost analyses, old equipment frequently is diverted to one or more secondary uses before actually being retired from service.

REPLACEMENT DUE TO OBSOLESCENCE

One of the most frequent causes of replacement studies is the advent of new equipment which, due to technological improvements, tends to make existing assets obsolete. Such situations ordinarily involve one or more factors which may have psychological as well as real effects upon the person who must make the decision regarding replacement. First, the existing asset is usually in satisfactory operating condition. Second, there is a natural reluctance to invest new capital when it apparently is not necessary. Third, and tending to offset the previous factor, a new and better piece of equipment sometimes has a certain glamorous appeal. It is therefore essential that proper replacement studies be made in such cases.

Where the existing asset is becoming obsolete, its salvage value usually will decrease in future years, and sometimes there is a decrease in the income which will be derived from its use.

A typical example of a study involving obsolescence is found in the case of a company which made products of molded plastic. Three years before it had purchased for $2,000 a certain mold which had an estimated life of five years. A zero scrap value had been assumed, and depreciation had been charged on a straight-line basis. Labor costs for operating this mold had been $4,900 per year, taxes and insurance $25 per year, and maintenance costs $30 annually.

A new type mold was available for $3,600 which would permit easier loading of the cavities and would eject the finished parts automatically.

With this improved mold the annual labor costs would be only $3,400 per year. Maintenance was estimated to be $75 per year, and taxes and insurance $35 annually. It was estimated that the life of the new mold would be at least three years, and that it would be needed at least that long. The output from each mold would be the same, and overhead expense, except that for depreciation, would be approximately the same for either mold. The old mold could be sold for $300. The company was earning about 10% profit before income taxes and would not invest in any new or replacement equipment unless a return of this magnitude could be obtained. Should the new mold be purchased?

Using the annual-cost method, the costs with the old mold would be:

Depreciation (10% S.F.)	$300/2.1	= $ 143
Labor		= 4,900
Maintenance		= 30
Taxes and insurance		= 25
Minimum required profit	$300 × 0.10	= 30
Total annual cost		= $5,128

Since there was no doubt that the old mold would operate satisfactorily during the remaining two years of the original life estimate, this period was used in computing the depreciation cost. For the new mold:

Depreciation (10% S.F.)	$3,600/3.31	= $1,088
Labor		= 3,400
Maintenance		= 75
Taxes and insurance		= 35
Minimum required profit	$3,600 × 0.10	= 360
Total annual cost		= $4,958

It was evident that the new mold should be purchased.

REPLACEMENT DUE TO EXCESSIVE OPERATION AND MAINTENANCE COSTS

One of the most frequently occurring reasons for considering replacement of existing property is increasing operating costs, usually because of excessive maintenance expense. Ordinarily in such cases the maintenance costs are becoming larger at an increasing rate, so that it is apparent that the total annual costs will increase with each additional year that the property is continued in operation. At any given time one is faced with the necessity of deciding whether it is more economical to continue to operate the old equipment for an additional period of time or to replace it. Since the cost of operating the existing equipment will increase from year to year, it is apparent that the relative economy of the two alternatives also will change from year to year. Thus, if a study is made today, based on the next year's predicted operating costs, it will be valid only with respect to what course should be followed during the next year. If the replacement study reveals that the old equipment should be continued in service during the year being considered, it would tell nothing about what should be done with respect to the following year. Thus, in such cases a year-to-year analysis must be made. The following example is one of this type.

A construction company owns a tractor that was purchased two years ago for $2,200. The machine was estimated originally to have a useful life of five years and to have no scrap value at the end of that time. During the past year the repair costs for the tractor have become quite high, and there are indications that they will be even higher during the coming years. Also, the machine has broken down twice during the past year, each time causing a loss of $25 because of delay, in addition to repair costs. The construction foreman believes it would be cheaper to replace the tractor at the end of its second year of service and buy a new one every two years. A new tractor of the same or slightly better type could be purchased for the same amount as was paid for the old machine. The various expenditures for operating the old tractor during the past two years, and the estimates for the next three years of its life, are shown in Table 13–1.

TABLE 13–1   Operating Expenses of a Tractor During the First Five Years of Its Life

Expense	Year				
	1	2	3	4	5
Fuel	$1,100	$1,180	$1,290	$1,450	$1,650
Repairs	120	200	325	450	500
Breakdown	25	50	100	175	275
Total	$1,245	$1,430	$1,715	$2,075	$2,425
Trade-in value at end of year	$1,300	$ 850	$ 600	$ 400	$ 250
Book value at end of year	$1,760	$1,320	$ 880	$ 440	$ 000

The problem is to determine what saving, if any, would be made if the tractor were turned in at the end of the second year instead of being kept during the third year. It is therefore necessary to determine what the total cost would be in each case. In determining such costs, it is the usual practice to assume that the various expenses would be paid at the end of the year. Thus, if the tractor were kept during the third year, the cost would be

Depreciation = \$850 − \$600	= \$ 250
Operation	= 1,290
Maintenance	= 325
Breakdown loss	= 100
Total	= \$1,965
Less profit earned by depreciation fund = \$880 × 0.07 =	62
Net cost during third year	= \$1,903

These calculations assume that the company had charged depreciation expense during the previous years on the basis of estimated future trade-in values. If the tractor were kept for the third year, the \$880 which had been charged as depreciation during the first two years would remain in the business and would thus earn profits the same as any other capital. This profit of \$62 is therefore deducted from the total of the other costs. It should be noted that such a deduction is necessary only when the actual yearly depreciation, such as obtained by the difference in year-end trade-in values, is used. When sinking fund depreciation over the life of the asset is used, the earnings from the depreciation funds are automatically taken into account.

If it is found cheaper to replace the existing tractor at the end of two years than to keep it during the third year, it is reasonable to assume that the new tractor, if it is of the same general type and will be used in about the same manner as the old one, will also be replaced at the end of two years of service. Thus, if a new tractor is to be purchased every two years, the equivalent annual cost would be

$$\text{Depreciation (2 years, 7\% S.F.)} = \frac{\$1,350}{2.07} \qquad = \$ \ 652$$

$$\text{Operation} = \frac{\$1,100 \times 0.935 + \$1,180 \times 0.873}{1.81} = \ 1,139$$

$$\text{Maintenance} = \frac{\$120 \times 0.935 + \$200 \times 0.873}{1.81} = \ 159$$

$$\text{Breakdown} = \frac{\$25 \times 0.935 + \$50 \times 0.873}{1.81} = \ 37$$

$$\text{Total annual cost}\ [2] \qquad\qquad\qquad = \$1,987$$

It is clear from these calculations that the tractor should not be replaced at the end of the second year, since a loss of \$84 would result.

If the replacement of the tractor were considered again at the end of the third year, the values would be as follows:

[2] The exact method of equivalent uniform annual costs has been used in this example. Actually, the error which would result from using *average* annual cost figures is so small, because of the short time involved, that it ordinarily would be used.

If tractor is kept the fourth year:

Depreciation ($600 − $400)	= $ 200
Operation	= 1,450
Repairs	= 450
Breakdown	= 175
Total expense for fourth year	= $2,275

Less profit from depreciation fund = $1,320 × 0.07	= 92
Net cost during fourth year	= $2,183

If new tractor is bought each three years:

Depreciation (3 years, 7% S.F.) = $1,600/3.21	= $ 498
Operation (average of 3 years)[3]	= 1,190
Repairs (average of 3 years)	= 215
Breakdown (average of 3 years)	= 58
Average total annual cost	= $1,961

From these calculations it is seen that there would be a saving of $2,183 − $1,961 = $222 during the fourth year if the replacement were made. In order to produce this saving it would be necessary to invest $1,600 in the new tractor—the difference between the purchase price and the trade-in value of the old one. The rate of return on this investment would therefore be

$$\$222/\$1,600 = 13.9\%.$$

At the end of the third year it would therefore be economical to replace the old tractor.

Obviously, the annual-cost method can also be used for this type of study. For the study regarding the fourth year, the use of this method would include a minimum required profit of $600 × 0.07 = $42 for the old tractor, giving total annual costs of $2,225. For the new tractor the minimum required profit would be $2,200 × 0.07 = $154, and the total annual costs would amount to $2,115. These figures would show the replacement to be justified, and the difference between the two totals ($2,225 − $2,115 = $110) represents a return of 6.9% upon the required investment of $1,600, in addition to the 7% minimum required profit included as a cost.

Replacement studies of this type, where future expenses of the old equipment will increase from year to year and where the depreciation expense during any ensuing year is determined from differences in resale values,

[3] The average annual cost method is used in this calculation to show a comparison between it and the equivalent equal annual cost method which was used in the previous case.

must be made on a year-to-year basis and take account of the profits which will be earned by accumulated depreciation funds if they are not used to purchase the replacing equipment.

The operation and maintenance costs of both the old and new asset should be considered carefully with respect to what may happen in the future. If these costs for the old asset have been high, it is more likely that they will increase rather than decrease in future years. This probability tends to favor early replacement. On the other hand, one must consider the possibility that the operation and maintenance costs for the new asset also may increase in future years. If this is the case, and it is not taken into account, replacement may be made at too early a date.

REPLACEMENT DUE TO DECREASING EFFICIENCY

Replacement frequently has to be considered because the existing asset decreases in efficiency as time passes. The decreasing efficiency may produce various results, such as decreased income because of lessened output or decreased reliability, increased scrap or spoilage because of wear of tools, or loss of product, as in the case of leaky pipelines. In such cases one must determine the proper time for replacement, balancing the cost of the losses against the cost of replacement. It usually is assumed in such studies that the experience with the new asset will repeat the history of the old one.

A simple but typical example of this type involved the tooling on a special production machine. This tooling cost $500. During the first month of its use very few defective products would be produced. However, during subsequent months increasing amounts of defective products would be produced which would require reworking, as shown in Column (C) of Table 13–2. It was necessary to determine how many months the tooling should

TABLE 13–2   Cost Analysis for Determining the Most Economical Replacement Period
for Special Tooling Which Decreases in Efficiency

(A) Month number	(B) Tooling cost	(C) Cost of rework required during month	(D) Total cost for month	(E) Total cost to end of month ΣD	(F) Average monthly cost to end of month (E/A)	
1	$500	$ 25	$ 525	$ 525	$525	
2		75	75	600	300	
3		175	175	775	258	
4		300	300	1,075	269	
5		450	450	1,525	305	

be operated before being replaced in order to achieve maximum economy. The results of the cost study are shown in Table 13–2. For purposes of simplicity, and since the time is short, all considerations of interest are omitted. These data show that for maximum economy the tooling should be replaced at the end of three months, if it is required for that long an additional period.

If studies of this general type involve more than two or three years, interest should be considered. Such studies can be made in the manner which is introduced in the next paragraph.

REPLACEMENT DUE TO A COMBINATION OF CAUSES

In certain cases a combination of reasons may lead to consideration of replacement. Typically, the salvage or trade-in value of the old asset is declining with the passage of time, while the annual operation and/or maintenance costs are increasing. Where it is known that such conditions will persist, it often is desirable to determine, in advance, the date at which the old asset should be replaced in order to achieve maximum economy.

To facilitate such a determination it is helpful to make certain assumptions. The most common, and important, of these is that the history of the old asset—its first cost, annual operation and maintenance costs, and salvage value—will be repeated in the new asset. In addition, the conditions of operation, maintenance, etc., must be assumed throughout the life of the property. Also, it usually is assumed that the asset can be maintained in such condition that satisfactory operation and dependability will be obtained throughout its life; this is not a necessary assumption, however, and decreased dependability can be accounted for by suitable cost charges. Some of these assumptions are somewhat contrary to ordinary operating conditions, yet their use enables a satisfactory solution to be obtained. The results can then be interpreted in the light of the deviation of actual conditions from those assumed.

The proper time for replacement of an ordinary truck may be used to illustrate the procedure for making such a study. The tabulated data for such a study are shown in Table 13–3. For this study the following conditions were assumed:

First cost	$3,000.00
Mileage per year	30,000
Gasoline	$0.32 per gallon
Tires	$275.00 per set, replaced each 20,000 miles
Lubrication	$1.75 each 1,000 miles
Interest	6%

Repairs, oil, taxes (license), trade-in value, and insurance are as shown in Table 13–3.

TABLE 13–3 Determination of Most Economical Replacement Period for a Truck

		Year				
		1	2	3	4	5
A	Value at beginning of year	$3,000	$2,000	$1,200	$ 750	$ 450
B	Depreciation	1,000	800	450	300	200
C	Gasoline	960	1,065	1,200	1,370	1,600
D	Oil	91	100	110	120	130
E	Lubrication	58	60	60	60	60
F	Repairs	250	400	600	450	700
G	Tires	275	275	550	275	550
H	Insurance	110	105	100	100	100
I	Taxes	75	70	67	65	65
J	Gross operating cost	$2,819	$2,875	$3,137	$ 2,740	$ 3,415
K	Amount in depreciation fund at beginning of year		1,000	1,800	2,250	2,550
L	Interest from depreciation fund		60	108	135	153
M	Net operating cost	$2,819	$2,815	$3,029	$ 2,605	$ 3,262
N	Interest factor $(1 + i)^n$	1.0	1.06	1.12	1.19	1.26
O		$2,819	$2,985	$3,155	$ 3,370	$ 3,550
			2,815	2,982	3,150	3,350
				3,029	3,210	3,395
					2,605	2,760
						3,262
P	(All operating costs)	$2,819	$5,800	$9,166	$12,335	$16,317
Q	$s_{\overline{n}\rceil}$	1.0	2.06	3.18	4.37	5.64
R	$Q/s_{\overline{n}\rceil}$	$2,819	$2,815	$2,885	$ 2,820	$ 2,900

The problem is clarified if one realizes that the sum of $3,000 must be invested to own a truck. One then wishes to determine what annual expenditures will be required to operate the truck and maintain the investment. In other words, it is assumed that the truck is to be operated continuously. Thus, the investment must always be equal in value to the purchase price. If all depreciation and operations costs are met annually, there will be no need for further consideration of the amount of the original investment. The return which can be obtained through replacement should be compared to the return which would be obtained through the necessary capital remaining in the invested depreciation fund.

Line A of Table 13–3 gives the trade-in value of the truck at the beginning of the year indicated at the top of each column. Lines B through I inclusive list the annual expense items for operating the truck. Line J gives the gross operating cost for each given year.

The money which is set aside each year as the cost of depreciation is assumed to be invested at 6% interest. Thus the interest earned by the depreciation fund during any year would be available at the end of that year to help pay for a portion of the operating cost. The amount in the depreciation fund at the beginning of each year is shown in line K. Line L indicates the interest earned during each year.

Line M gives the net operating cost for each year, being the gross operating cost less the interest received from the depreciation fund.

In order to be able to determine annual cost, which may be compared when trucks are kept for different lengths of time, it is necessary to have equivalent annual costs. These are determined by assuming that all of the expenses occurring in any one year are paid at the end of that year. Interest is then computed on these amounts up to the time the truck is replaced. Line N gives the interest factor, $(1 + i)^n$, for the number of years indicated. Each net annual expense, as given in line M, is then multiplied by the interest factor corresponding to the number of years which have elapsed between the time the annual expense was paid and the time a truck is replaced. For example, at the end of the third year the value at the end of that year of all the costs which had been paid up to that date would be as follows:

$$
\begin{aligned}
\text{First year's cost} &= \$2{,}819 \times (1+i)^2 = \$2{,}819 \times 1.12 = \$3{,}155 \\
\text{Second year's cost} &= \$2{,}815 \times (1+i)^1 = \$2{,}815 \times 1.06 = \$2{,}982 \\
\text{Third year's cost} &= \$3{,}029 \times (1+i)^0 = \$3{,}029 \times 1.00 = \underline{\$3{,}029} \\
\text{Total value at end of third year (line } P) & \qquad\qquad\qquad\quad = \$9{,}166
\end{aligned}
$$

The summation of all of the annual cost items, with interest, is given in line P.

Line Q gives the values of $s_{\overline{n}|}$ for the various years. The interest rate used in this study was 6%, corresponding to the rate earned by other capital used by the company.

Line R gives the equivalent equal annual operating cost if the truck were kept for the number of years indicated at the top of each column. For example, if the truck were kept for four years the operating costs for the various years would vary from a maximum of $2,885 to a minimum of $2,815, with the equivalent equal annual cost being

$$
\$12{,}335/s_{\overline{4}|} = \$12{,}335/4.37 = \$2{,}820.
$$

From Table 13–3 it may be seen that replacement at the end of each two-year period would theoretically be most economical. However, the economy of replacement at the end of one year or four years would be almost as great. In view of the greater uncertainty regarding reliability, replacement at the end of four years undoubtedly would be ruled out. Similarly, in view of the very slight difference in annual costs, very probably it would be decided to make the replacement at the end of one year, $4 per year being considered as a small premium to pay for greater reliability and freedom from repairs.

It should be kept in mind that studies of this type can be no more accurate than the assumptions behind them. Deviation of actual conditions from those assumed will produce more or less error in the theoretical replacement period. Proper procedure requires that, in actual practice, a year-to-year analysis be made prior to the theoretical replacement time, using the procedures presented on page 326.

REPLACEMENT WHERE SALVAGE VALUE IS ZERO OR UNKNOWN

Quite frequently replacement studies must be made where the scrap or salvage value of the existing property is zero or very uncertain. The following is an example of this type.

In a certain process in an oil refinery, several types of crude stock are put through a particular piece of equipment. When a change is made from one stock to another, this portion of the plant must be shut down so that the equipment can be cleaned before the next stock is processed. This cleaning requires twenty hours, during which no production is obtained from this portion of the refinery. A manufacturer has developed a new piece of equipment which makes it possible to change from one stock to another in two hours.

The management estimates that it costs them $50 for each hour this portion of the refinery is not in operation. The existing equipment was installed two years previously at a cost of $20,000. Depreciation has been figured by the straight-line method, based upon an expected life of five years. The new equipment would cost $32,000. Although it would undoubtedly last at least five years, the refinery managers have decided that, because of recent rapid changes in the industry, any new equipment at this time must be fully depreciated within two years.

During the past two years the system has been changed from one stock to another twice each month. This is expected to continue. Capital is worth 8%. Should the change in equipment be made at this time

What one wishes to determine by the replacement study is whether the existing equipment can compete with the new equipment. If not, it should be replaced. Obviously, the most favorable conditions for the old equipment would be those in which the depreciation charge assessed against it as a cost of operation would be zero. If it can not compete with the new equipment under these conditions, it is apparent that it can not compete when its operating costs are increased by the addition of depreciation expense. Thus the replacement study would be made as follows:

Old equipment:

Depreciation	$= \$ \quad 0$
Cost of making stock changes $= 20 \times \$50 \times 24$	$= \underline{24,000}$
Total cost per year	$= \$24,000$

New equipment:

Depreciation (8% S.F.) $= \$32,000/2.08$	$= \$15,390$
Cost of making stock changes $= 2 \times \$50 \times 24$	$= \underline{2,400}$
Total cost per year	$= \$17,790$

Annual saving $= \$24,000 - \$17,790 = \$6,210$

% return $= \$6,210/\$32,000 = 19.4\%$

It is clear that the old equipment should be replaced. If the study had shown that the return on the required investment under these conditions was not sufficient to justify making the investment, or if the annual operating costs of the old equipment were less than for the new equipment, this would have meant that *as an operating unit,* in competition with the new equipment, the value of the old equipment was greater than zero.

REPLACEMENT WHERE SALVAGE VALUE IS GREATER THAN BOOK VALUE

Occasionally a replacement study involves an existing asset which is found to have actual salvage value greater than the book value. An extreme form of this situation is the complete amortization of the value of the old asset resulting in a zero book value. Under such conditions, it might be argued that no problem exists concerning the equipment, since the invested capital has been fully recovered and it can therefore be disposed of without loss. Actually, however, such is not the case. Again, if one recalls that depreciation is the decrease in value which will be experienced as the property is used, the fact that the old equipment can be sold for a certain amount shows that it has value, and continuing it in service will cause this value to decline. This situation is illustrated by the following problem.

A small factory, making a single product, has utilized a casting as the main body of the article. This is the only casting in the product. It has been making its own castings, having a small electric furnace and other necessary foundry equipment. The furnace cost $4,000.00 when new four years ago. Straight-line depreciation has been provided to write off this equipment over a ten-year period. The other foundry equipment has been entirely written off the books. The owners now find that the casting can be eliminated by welding rolled shapes. The resulting saving in labor, material, maintenance and power will be $0.50 per article. The annual output is 600 machines. The necessary welding equipment will cost $2,000.00 and will have an estimated life of eight years. The electric furnace can be sold for $1,000.00, and the remainder of the foundry equipment for $250.00. Capital in the company earns 6%. Should the change in methods be made?

This situation is somewhat different from the previous problems in that the "other foundry equipment" has been completely depreciated on the books. Thus it appears that the company has no capital invested in this equipment. However, if one compares what the financial situation would be if the company continues to use the existing equipment with what it would be if this equipment were replaced, it is seen that in the latter case $250.00 could be realized from the sale of the miscellaneous equipment; if its use continues, on the other hand, it will be worn out and its resale value will decrease. The further use of the equipment will result in a decrease in value, or depreciation. Therefore correct procedure requires that this depreciation expense be included as a cost of continuing this equipment in use when the replacement study is made. The replacement study in this case would be

To continue using castings:

Depreciation (6%, six year S.F.) = $1,250.00/6.98 = $179.00
Excess cost = 600 × $0.50   =   300.00
      Total annual cost   = $479.00

To use welding:

Depreciation (6%, eight year S.F.) = $\dfrac{\$2,000.00}{9.9}$ = $202.00

      Total annual cost   = $202.00
Saving = $479.00 − $202.00 = $277.00 per year.
Return on the required investment = $277/$750   = 36.9%

This rate of return would undoubtedly justify the replacement of the foundry equipment.[4]

[4] Other expenses, such as taxes and insurance, have been neglected in this problem in order to simplify it and focus attention on the primary factors.

Considering the resale value of the equipment, even though it had been written off the books, is consistent with the practice indicated in the previous examples. This case differed from the others only in that some of the property had been written off at too rapid rather than at too low a rate. In this instance a perfectly honest mistake had also been made. However, the fact that the mistake resulted in a book value which was less than the actual value of the equipment does not alter the fact that what had happened was past history and had no place in the replacement analysis which had to be based only on existing facts.

CONSIDERATIONS OF FAVORABLE TRADE-IN OR DISPOSAL PRICE

In cases where the trade-in or disposal value of an existing asset is likely to vary in the future, adequate consideration must be given to this fact. If an economy study shows that the most economical disposal date is a considerable number of years distant, moderate changes in the assumed disposal value are not likely to make any substantial change in the calculated date. On the other hand, if only a few years are involved, prospective changes in the salvage value can have a considerable effect on the year-to-year economy.

Where the trade-in or disposal value is changing rapidly, one must be certain that a sufficient number of years is considered in determining the economy of the old asset. For example, on the basis of keeping the old asset one more year, it might appear to be more economical to make the replacement now. If, however, a three- or four-year retention period were used, in order to gain the smaller amounts of depreciation during the additional years, the old asset might be more economical than a new one.

Thus, in general, slow rates of decrease in salvage value, with increasing operation and/or maintenance costs, tend to favor early replacement, while rapid rates of decrease in salvage value favor later replacement.

CONSIDERATIONS OF FUTURE GROWTH

The probability of future growth of a business is sometimes an important factor in a replacement study. If it is evident that growth is imminent which will require increased output unobtainable from the existing asset, it is obvious that replacement or augmentation will have to be made in the near future. The resulting problem is basically to determine whether replacement or augmentation is cheaper, and at what time either should occur. The only complicating factor is the possibility that the desired equipment may not be available when needed if replacement is deferred, or that the increased demand may develop earlier than anticipated. In order to avoid these possibilities, companies sometimes prefer to make the replacement somewhat earlier than necessary and then attempt to develop the market.

EVALUATING EXCESS CAPACITY

Replacement frequently results in excess capacity, since new machines usually are more efficient than those which they replace. If there is no actual use for such excess capacity, it has no value and thus should not be given any consideration. On the other hand, if the excess capacity can be used for some function not rendered by the old asset, this should be considered in the replacement study. This can easily be done by deducting the annual net profit *after income taxes* derived from the added service from the annual costs for the new machine.

CONSIDERATIONS OF FUTURE PRICE CHANGES

While it is difficult to predict what price changes will occur in the future, the long history of price increases that have occurred cause many to believe that the trend is apt to continue. This possibility therefore should not be overlooked in replacement studies. Such a condition almost always favors earlier replacement, which decreases the initial cost of the new asset. However, this practice should not be followed blindly, particularly where the need for the service is expected to continue for many years. Two additional facts must also be considered. First, the earlier the replacement, the sooner the new asset will have to be replaced—at higher first cost. Second, it is likely that technological improvements will occur, and by deferring replacement it is possible that a more efficient asset may be obtained. Therefore, before too much emphasis is given to probable price increases, other possible and probable future changes also should be considered.

BUDGETARY AND PERSONNEL CONSIDERATIONS

Replacements frequently must be timed according to budgetary and personnel considerations, rather than solely in accordance with economy study data. Most companies do not have unlimited funds, and many projects are usually competing for the funds that they do have. In such cases replacement studies supply information on the basis of which decisions can be made regarding the timing of replacements as funds become available.

Similarly, in the case of governmental agencies, where financing is done through bond issues, replacements may have to be timed in accordance with bond-market conditions. In some instances a governmental unit may have reached the limit of its legal indebtedness, and replacements must wait until further financing can be done.

More and more replacements are timed with due consideration to personnel factors. Replacement equipment frequently involves a temporary reduction in labor requirements, or a change in skills required. In order to avoid undesirable layoffs of working personnel or unnecessary tensions among employees, replacements are timed to coincide with upswings in business activity; thus temporarily displaced workers may be retained for other activities. The usual turnover in working force ordinarily can be counted on to absorb a temporary excess of personnel within a short period of time.

DETERMINING VALUE BY REPLACEMENT THEORY

As was pointed out in Chapter 5, it frequently is necessary to determine the value of old assets, often a considerable number of years after their acquisition. During the years since the assets were acquired price levels will have changed and technological progress have occurred. As a result, the valuation process is difficult.

A common practice is to use the reproduction-cost-new-less-depreciation procedure. This method contains a serious defect in that, even if the cost of reproducing the asset with proper inclusion of the results of price changes and technological progress can be determined accurately, arbitrary depreciation methods must then be applied. Since the usual depreciation methods are not intended to give accurate salvage values at intermediate intervals in the life of an asset, but are merely empirical accounting devices, the resulting value obtained will be accurate only by chance.

If proper cost data are available, a more accurate value of old assets can be obtained by applying replacement theory. As has been pointed out in this chapter, an asset has economic value only if it can be operated profitably in competition with the most economically efficient asset available. The economic value of an existing asset is the maximum amount on which depreciation and interest can be charged while permitting it to compete on an even basis with the most efficient new asset. With V representing value, such a comparison may be illustrated as follows, using straight-line depreciation and average interest and five years of remaining life:

		Old Asset		New Asset
Depreciation	$V/5$	$= 0.2V$	$\$50,000/10$	$= \$ 5,000$
Annual out-of-pocket costs		$= \$17,000$		$= 14,000$
Average interest, 8%	$V \times 6/5 \times 1/2 \times 0.08$	$= 0.048V$		$= 2,200$
Total cost (equal for both)		$= \$21,200$		$= \$21,200$

Solving for V gives a value of $\$16,950$ for the old asset.

In this illustration it was assumed that the old asset had a remaining life of five years, and that the annual costs would remain at a constant level throughout this period. A more common situation is one in which the out-of-pocket costs for the old asset are increasing and will continue to do so. In this case the number of years, if any, the old asset should be kept in service is determined by the time at which its annual cost *without any charge for depreciation and interest* exceeds the annual costs for the new asset. For example, suppose it is found that the annual out-of-pocket costs for the old asset are increasing at a rate of 10% each year over those of the previous year, while those of the new asset will, for the next few years, increase at only a 1% rate. Table 13–4 shows the results. It is evident that the old asset should not be kept more than three additional years and that its economic value at the beginning of the first year is $7,270.

TABLE 13–4 Determination of Economic Value of an Old Asset Having Operation and Maintenance Costs Increasing 10% per Year versus New Asset with Same Cost Items Increasing 1% per Year

Year	Old Asset Out-of-pocket costs	New Asset Out-of-pocket costs	Total costs	Difference	v^n (8%)	Present Value
1	$17,000	$14,000	$21,200	$4,200	0.926	$3,890
2	18,700	14,140	21,340	2,640	0.857	2,260
3	20,570	14,281	21,981	1,411	0.794	1,120
4	22,627	14,424	22,124	Negative		
			Economic value of old asset			$7,270

Thus where adequate cost data are available the use of replacement theory makes possible a sound determination of the economic value of an old asset without recourse to empirical depreciation methods; and price changes and technological advances are automatically included if the asset considered as a replacement is the best available.

PROBLEMS

13–1 A company has been generating its electric power with equipment that cost $18,000.00 when new. When the equipment was purchased ten years ago, it was believed that the future demand for power would not increase, and a fifteen-year life estimate for the equipment was made for depreciation purposes. A straight-line depreciation reserve has been maintained. Each month 15,000 kw.-hrs. of power are used. The cost of producing this power, exclusive of depreciation, has been $0.012 per kw.-hr.

The company now can purchase power for $0.015 per kw.-hr. for the first 1,000 kw.-hr. per month, and $0.008 for each additional kw.-hr. To use the purchased power $3,000.00 must be spent for new distribution panels, etc. The old generating equipment can be sold for $1,500.00. The company has an established policy that any new equipment must be written off within five years. Capital is worth at least 8% to the company.

Should the company continue to generate its own power or change over to purchased power?

13–2   A contractor has ten pneumatic-tired concrete buggies which he purchased three years ago for $80.00 each. He has maintained a straight-line depreciation reserve based on an estimated five-year life and believes the buggies are entirely satisfactory for the next two years' service. When these buggies are used, each requires a laborer who receives $1.95 per hour.

A salesman has proposed the use of power-driven buggies. These would cost $650.00 each, would have an estimated life of at least five years, and would consume two gallons of gasoline per hour. An operator (laborer) is required for each buggy, but, because of its greater capacity and speedier operation, each power buggy is equivalent to two regular buggies. Maintenance costs on each of the powered buggies is estimated at $75.00 per year.

Records show that the present equipment has been used 800 hours per year. Taxes and insurance in each case would be 3% of the first cost annually. The old buggies can be sold for $5.00 each. Gasoline costs $0.25 per gallon.

If capital is worth 8% to the contractor, should the powered buggies be purchased?

13–3   In a certain railroad switching yard two steam locomotives are now being used which are ten years old. The hourly operating costs for each of these locomotives are $6.00, including the costs for fuel, water, lubrication, and repairs, and engine-house expense. New Diesel switchers can be purchased for $100,000.00 each and would have corresponding hourly operating costs of $3.10. Each locomotive must operate 5,000 hours per year. Each steam locomotive cost $70,000.00, has a present salvage value of $8,000.00, and is estimated to have an ultimate scrap value of $4,000.00. Taxes and insurance on both types would amount to 2% of present values per year.

Capital is worth not less than 10%, and capital recovery on any new investment would have to be on a fifteen-year basis. It is believed that the steam locomotives would operate satisfactorily for a minimum of five more years without maintenance costs becoming excessive. Estimated scrap value of the Diesels is 5% of first cost.

Should the replacement be made?

13–4   All of the printing equipment of a large daily newspaper operates on direct current. Because of gradual changes, this plant is the only direct-current load of the local power plant. The power company wishes to eliminate its direct-current power lines and has filed a notice of an increase of 20 per cent in all direct-current power rates. The newspaper's average annual power bill has been $17,420, and it finds that if it could use alternating current its power bill would be 10 per cent less than in the past. Conversion of the entire plant to alternating current is therefore being considered.

Investigation reveals that sale of all the old direct-current motors would bring only $750. This would still leave an unamortized loss of $3,800 on the direct-current equipment. Complete installation of the new alternating-current equipment would cost $21,000. Capital is worth 12%. No surplus account for adjusting unamortized values has been provided.

Another alternative would be to purchase new rectifier equipment which would supply direct-current output from alternating-current input. This equipment would cost only $10,000 but would have to be written off within five years, since the probability is that most of the existing direct-current equipment would be replaced with alternating-current equipment within that time. Such equipment would have an efficiency of 90 per cent.

If the new alternating-current equipment is installed, a ten-year depreciation period will be used. Taxes and insurance on all equipment would be 2% of present book value or cost.

What would you recommend?

13–5   Five years ago a sugar refinery purchased for $3,000 a direct-connected centrifugal pump and motor which would provide an output of 3,000 gallons per minute. The pump was estimated to have a life of ten years, with a salvage value of 10% of the first cost at the end of that time. At its rated output the pump consumes 50 kw. of power, and it is operated sixteen hours per day, 250 days per year.

A change in the process has reduced the output requirements to 1,000 gallons per minute. At this reduced load the pump consumes only 30 kw. of power, and it is estimated that the annual maintenance costs will be only $150 per year.

A new pump and motor having a capacity of 1,000 gallons per minute can be purchased for $2,000, and a trade-in allowance of $250 would be made for the old pump. The new pump would require only 20 kw. of power and is estimated to have a life of ten years and a 10% salvage value at that time. Annual maintenance costs should not exceed $100. For either pump the annual costs for taxes and insurance would amount to 3% of the first cost. Power costs $0.01 per kw.-hr. Capital in the company earns about 10% before taxes.

Should the new pump be purchased?

13-6   A company which rents limousines for sight-seeing and special tours has five vehicles that cost $5,800 each when purchased three years ago. As the result of straight-line depreciation, based on an assumed life of five years and a salvage value of $800, their total book value now is $14,000. The company also has two older limousines which have been completely depreciated but which it believes can be used for another two years, provided their motors are overhauled at a cost of $275 each. The annual operational and maintenance costs for the seven vehicles have been $14,000, and it is believed they would continue at this level if the two older cars were overhauled. Each vehicle requires a driver who receives $4,700 per year.

Six new limousines can be purchased which, it is believed, would handle all of the load now served by the seven older ones. These would cost $6,200 each, but the dealer would give a trade-in allowance of $1,200 for each of the five newer cars and $1,000 for each of the two older ones, provided all are traded at the same time for the six new limousines. Another dealer has offered a trade-in of $750 on each of the older limousines, each car being traded in on a new one. It is believed that if the two older limousines were replaced, so that seven reasonably reliable cars would be available, only six would have to be operated at any one time, permitting one to be held in reserve for repairs and maintenance.

If six new limousines are purchased, it is estimated that the operational and maintenance costs will be $1,500 per year. However, if only two new cars are purchased, the average operation and maintenance costs for the seven cars will be only $1,300. Each new vehicle purchased will increase the annual cost for taxes and insurance by $120.

Assuming the new cars will have a useful life of six years, with a salvage value of 10% of the first cost at that time, and that capital is worth 10% before income taxes, what would you recommend?

13-7   Because of earth slides in a rural area a gas company has found that one of its transmission lines has developed some leaks. The line was installed 22 years ago at a cost of $7,800. Depreciation has been computed on a 35-year straight-line basis. The line has no realizable salvage value. Measurements have shown that the leakage is at the rate of 3,500 MCF per year. The county involved has taken steps to correct the earth slippage problem, and if no further slides occur, it is believed that the increase in gas leakage will not be greater than that normally experienced on aging gas lines. Gas costs $0.35 per MCF.

A replacement line would cost $22,000 and would have a depreciable life of thirty years, but it probably would last for an additional five to ten years without excessive leakage. A new line would involve $120 per year in additional taxes.

If capital is worth 8% before taxes, would you recommend replacement of the present gas line?

13-8   A company has maintained a small gray-iron foundry to produce castings, each of which comprises the main body of its product. In order to maintain its competitive position in the market, it is considering redesigning the casting to make it by the shell-molding process. This will save a considerable amount of weight and allow substantial savings in machining costs.

All of the existing foundry equipment has been fully depreciated, except an arc furnace which was purchased five years ago at a cost of $20,000.00 and estimated to have a life of fifteen years. Annual maintenance expenditures will maintain the general equipment in satisfactory condition for an indefinite period. Labor costs have been $14.20 per casting, and material costs $8.10. Other overhead costs, exclusive of depreciation, have been $2.20 per casting. In each year 10,000 castings are produced.

If the castings are to be made by shell molding, new equipment costing $8,000.00 will be required. Such equipment would have an estimated life of ten years. Utilizing shell molding would reduce the unit labor costs by $2.40 per casting. Other costs would be unchanged. There would also be a saving of $3.40 per unit in machining costs.

An alternative to purchasing the new equipment is to buy the castings from a local foundry which produces excellent castings by the shell-molding process and will supply them for $22.50 each. The existing foundry operation would then be discontinued, and the building torn down. Investigation shows that the arc furnace can be sold for $6,000.00, and the other foundry equipment for $2,000.00; the scrap value of the building would just meet the cost of demolition. An analysis of the overhead costs shows that $3,000 of the annual cost would remain if the foundry operation is discontinued.

If capital is worth 10% before taxes, what should be done?

13-9   A construction company has a bulldozer that was purchased four years ago for $8,000. Repair and maintenance costs have been increasing, and when the machine breaks down, a substitute bulldozer must be rented at rather high rates. Trade-in values and operating and maintenance costs have been, and for the next two years are estimated to be, as follows:

	Year					
	1	2	3	4	5	6
Trade-in at end of year	$5,600	$3,900	$2,750	$1,900	$1,350	$ 950
Fuel oil	600	650	725	825	950	1,100
Lubrication	75	80	85	90	100	110
Repairs	50	75	125	200	300	450
Taxes	40	38	35	30	23	15
Rental equipment	0	100	200	400	800	1,200

Assuming that a new bulldozer could be purchased at any time for $8,000, that capital is worth 8%, and that the cost experience with a new bulldozer will be the same as the old, should the equipment be replaced at the end of the fourth year?

13–10　A set of Kirksite forming dies for use on a drop hammer costs $1,750. The scrap resulting from the operation amounts to $50 per month during the first month of use, and increases at the rate of $50 per month. The labor required for hammering out wrinkles and for trimming costs $300 per month during the first month of use and increases by $75 per month as the dies are used. If capital is worth 10%, how long should a set of dies be used before being replaced?

13–11　On a certain short stretch of city pavement, records show that the following expenditures have been made for repairs over a ten-year period:

1950	$ 250	1955	$1,800
1951	600	1956	2,000
1952	1,000	1957	2,100
1953	1,300	1958	2,100
1954	1,600	1959	2,100

In a heated political campaign a local politician has asserted that the city could have had new pavement for less than was spent in repairing the old. The new pavement would have cost $10,000. The work would have been financed as part of a ten-year bond issue which bore 4% interest. It has been estimated that annual maintenance on the new pavement would not have exceeded $350 per year over the same ten-year period. Was the politician correct?

13–12　A factory has been producing a certain article on two turret lathes. In previous years these lathes, which were acquired ten years ago for $7,000 each, were used to produce several different articles, but at present the lathes are used only for making this one part. Since it appears probable that the requirements will continue at the existing level, consideration is being given to replacing the two lathes by a single screw machine. The essential facts are as follows:

	Turret Lathes	Screw Machine
Cost	$7,000.00 each	$24,000.00
Production	44 pieces per hour each	100 pieces per hour
Labor	One man for each at $2.85 per hour	One man at $2.20 per hour
Maintenance	$350.00 per year each	$100.00 per year each
Power	$220.00 per year total	$175.00 per year
Taxes and insurance	1% of first cost	1½% of first cost
Annual requirement	100,000 pieces	100,000 pieces

The cost of the turret lathes has been completely written off the books. However, they can be sold for $300.00 each. It is believed that they can be operated for another three years without an appreciable rise in maintenance costs. All new equipment of the type proposed is written off within five years for economy study purposes. A surplus account is maintained for absorbing unamortized values. Capital is worth 15% before taxes.

    a. Should the replacement be made?

    b. Compute the "use value" of the lathes to the company.

13–13   A certain two-lane highway bridge must either be replaced or reinforced in order to meet increased loads. Reinforcement would cost $11,000 and would make the bridge adequate for another five years. The present realizable salvage value of the bridge is $7,000. If reinforced, its salvage value at the end of five years would be $8,000.

A new bridge of adequate capacity to handle all foreseeable requirements for forty years will cost $70,000. Because it would be built of reinforced concrete, it would have no scrap or salvage value. It is estimated that maintenance costs on the reinforced bridge would be $1,800 per year above those for the new bridge.

Assuming money is worth 5% to the state involved, what would you recommend?

13–14   To obtain fresh water, three years ago a plant manufacturing woodpulp products installed, at a cost of $14,000, a pipeline from a mountain reservoir. The growth of the plant has been much greater than was anticipated, and the flow of water now is inadequate. Three solutions are being considered.

The first would be to install a pump and operate the existing line at a higher pressure. The pumping equipment would cost $8,000; annual operation and maintenance costs would be $1,100 and $300 respectively.

The second alternative would be to duplicate the existing pipeline at a cost of $20,000. Annual maintenance costs on the existing line are $150 per year and probably would not increase.

The third alternative is to build a new pipeline large enough to supply all of the needs, at a cost of $28,000. The maintenance costs on this line probably would not be more than $50 per year greater than on the smaller line. If this line is built, the existing pipeline would be removed. Since most of it is above ground, it would have a salvage value of $3,000.

Assume that taxes and insurance on all pipe lines amount to $1\frac{1}{2}\%$ of first cost per year, that each alternative would last thirty years, and that capital is worth 10%. Which alternative should be used?

13–15 A processor of livestock feed must improve his methods for handling grain in order to meet increased sales. One method would be to invest $25,000 in additional steel bins and retain all existing equipment, all of which has been fully depreciated and has no salvage value. This procedure would take care of the demands for the next five years at least. A second procedure would require conversion to semiautomatic handling equipment at a cost of $600,000. Two existing buildings would be abandoned and torn down, and one new building built. The new building would cost $200,000 and have an estimated life of forty years, and the equipment would cost $400,000, with an estimated life of twenty years.

The industrial engineers have estimated that the semiautomatic plant would produce the following annual savings:

Labor	$61,000
Reduction in loss of grain	1,800
Cleaning of equipment	2,200
Supervisory labor	12,000

Fringe benefits and payroll taxes amount to 10% of payrolls. An annual benefit of $700 in property taxes and insurance would result from tearing down the buildings, but corresponding costs on the new assets would be $11,000 per year. It also is believed that with the semiautomatic equipment there would be at least a $1,300 per year benefit from the new assets through the improved handling of customers' orders and resulting increases in sales. Power and maintenance costs for the new equipment will be $5,200 per year greater than with the old equipment.

Ample land is available for building the new facilities without interrupting operations. Capital is worth 15% before taxes, and the company has a 50% income tax rate.

Should the new facilities be built?

13–16 In a factory, castings are moved from the foundry to the machine shop on hand trucks. Five trucks, each operated by a laborer who receives $12 per day, are used. These trucks may be replaced by an overhead motor-driven crane requiring an investment of $18,200. The crane will require an operator at $16 per day and one helper at $12 per day.

Power and lubrication costs for the crane will be $30 per month, and maintenance costs are estimated at $20 per month. Annual taxes and insurance will amount to 2% of first cost. The hand trucks have been fully depreciated but can be sold for $20 each. Installation of the crane would require thirty days, and the investment would have to be written off in five years. The plant operates 200 days per year. If capital is worth 15%, should the investment be made?

13-17   Twelve years ago a smelter installed an electric locomotive and track to haul waste material to a dumping area. The original installation cost $22,000. The annual operating costs, including the required moving of portions of the track each year in order to dump in new locations, has been $4,700. In addition, an operator is required who is paid $4,900 per year. Maintenance costs on the locomotive are increasing; during the past year they were $1,200. It is expected that they may increase at the rate of about $200 each year for the next five years that the loco-motive is expected to last. The original life estimate for the locomotive was twenty years, and a straight-line depreciation reserve has been maintained.

The plant engineer has suggested replacing the locomotive and track with a conveyor belt, at a cost of $40,000. This installation would require no labor, but would involve an annual expenditure of $4,100 for maintenance and moving the end sections to various dumping areas. Estimated annual power costs would be $2,800. A write-off period of ten years would be used.

Annual taxes and insurance on all equipment amount to 1½% of first cost. The locomotive and track now will bring a total of $2,800 as scrap.

If capital is worth 10% before taxes, should the locomotive be replaced now? At a later date?

CHAPTER 14

Break-Even and
Minimum-Cost
Studies

It is a common experience that the costs of procuring or operating a property or piece of equipment are affected by one or more variables. Thus the costs are *functions* of one or more variables which may be defined. This situation leads to two types of economy studies of considerable importance in the selection of alternatives or the operation of equipment or properties to obtain maximum economy.

When a common variable affects the costs of two methods, there may be a certain value of the variable for which the costs for both methods will be equal. This value of the variable is known as the *break-even point*.

Where the costs of a given operation or venture are a function of a single, definable variable, some value of the variable will result in lower costs than any other value. This *minimum-cost point* is of considerable economic importance in the operation of many assets.

Many cases involving break-even points and minimum-cost points can readily be expressed by mathematical equations, and the desired answers can be obtained through the solution of these equations. On the other hand, the conditions sometimes are such that the functional relationships between the variables are not continuous, or require uneconomical amounts of time to determine. In such cases graphical solutions are more feasible. In addition, graphical solutions often yield information not shown by mathematical solutions. Therefore both mathematical and graphical solutions will be illustrated in the presentation which follows.

347

BREAK-EVEN-POINT THEORY

Break-even studies involve two or more situations which are affected by a common variable. Considering the costs of two situations, A and B,

$$C_A = f_1(x) \quad \text{and} \quad C_B = f_2(x)$$

where C_A and C_B = certain specified costs for situations A and B respectively. (These costs may be first costs, annual costs, costs per piece, etc.)

and $\quad\quad\quad\quad x$ = a variable which affects C_A and C_B.

The break-even point is where C_A and C_B are equal,

$$C_A = C_B.$$

For this condition,

$$f_1(x) = f_2(x).$$

Thus, by solving this functional relationship for x, the break-even point may be determined.

In real situations the independent variable x may be any of a large number of factors. Some of the more common are output volume, sales volume, hours of operation per year, material cost, labor cost, fuel cost, power cost, and size. Several of these will be illustrated.

MATHEMATICAL SOLUTION FOR BREAK-EVEN POINT

An example of a situation involving a break-even point may be found in a comparison of two 100-horsepower electric motors. The *Alpha* motor can be purchased for $1,250, has an efficiency of 87 per cent, an estimated life of ten years, and estimated maintenance costs of $50 per year. A *Beta* motor will cost $1,600, have an efficiency of 92 per cent, a life of ten years, and annual maintenance costs of $25. Taxes and insurance costs on either motor will be $1\frac{1}{2}\%$ per year. If capital is worth 8%, how many hours per year would the motors have to be operated at full load for the annual costs to be equal?

For the *Alpha* motor the annual cost, Y, would be as follows:

$$D = \text{depreciation and minimum profit on capital}$$
$$= \$1{,}250 \times \text{CRF} = \$1{,}250 \times 0.149 = \$186$$

$$O = \text{operating cost for power}$$
$$= (100 \times 0.746 \times N \times \$0.012)\, 1/0.87 = \$1.03N$$

where N = number of hours of operation per year

M = maintenance cost = \$50

$T + I$ = taxes and insurance = \$1,250 $\times$ 0.015 = \$18.75

Similarly, the annual cost, Y', for the *Beta* motor will be as follows:

$$D' = \$1,600 \times 0.149 = \$238$$
$$O' = (100 \times 0.746 \times N \times \$0.012)\,1/0.92 = \$0.973N$$
$$M' = \$25$$
$$T' + I' = \$1,600 \times \$0.015 = \$24$$

For the break-even point, $Y = Y'$. Thus,

$$D + O + M + T + I = D' + O' + M' + T' + I'$$
$$\$186 + \$1.03N + \$50 + \$18.75 = \$238 + \$0.973N + \$25 + \$24$$
$$N = 566 \text{ hours.}$$

GRAPHICAL SOLUTION FOR BREAK-EVEN POINT

There are many situations in which the relationship between the dependent and independent variables is not continuous and can not therefore be expressed readily in mathematical terms. In other cases the relationship may be so complex that the time required to develop a mathematical formula would be so great that it would be uneconomical to do so. In such cases a graphical solution may be used to determine the break-even point. The following is a case where a graphical solution is used to advantage.

Products ordered from a wholesale drug company are collected in large wire-mesh baskets and taken to the shipping department for packing. Two methods of packing are used—one with heavy paper bags and the other with cartons. Figure 14–1 shows the packing costs for the two methods as a function of the volume of the merchandise. It is apparent that the relationship of volume and cost is not a simple one and that for shipments whose volume is less than approximately 3,500 cubic inches the bag method should be used, while shipments whose volume is larger should be packed in cartons. In this instance, since the sides of the baskets are nearly vertical, the packers are able to determine which packing method to use and the correct size of bag or carton merely by checking the height of the merchandise in the basket against a colored vertical scale on the end of the packing table.

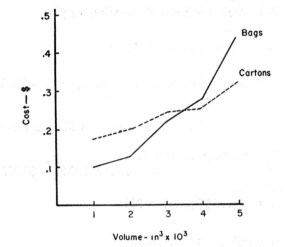

Figure 14-1. Packing costs for paper sacks and cartons shown as a function of the volume of the merchandise.

BREAK-EVEN POINT FOR JIGS AND FIXTURES

One common use of break-even formulas is the determination of the economic use of jigs and fixtures, adjuncts of machining or assembly operations which permit the use of less-skilled labor, increase output, provide greater accuracy and uniformity, etc. Two types of determinations are made. The first involves selection between two jigs or fixtures of different design. The other is determining the volume of production required to justify the use of a given jig or fixture.

Typically, the economic life of jigs and fixtures is quite short, frequently from six months to two years. This is due to the fact that they are specialized tools associated with one size or model of a product. When a change is made in the design of the product, the specialized tooling usually becomes obsolete. When the life is short, simplified break-even formulas can be used, since interest can be neglected and certain maintenance costs are negligible. However, in some instances the life may be five or more years, the first cost considerable, and maintenance costs appreciable, so that formulas which account for all the cost elements are necessary. Such complete formulas will be developed, and it then will be shown that the simplified formulas result from the dropping of unimportant terms.

Most break-even formulas for jigs and fixtures are developed with the number of pieces produced, N, as the independent variable. The useful life of the fixture is expressed in terms of the number of units that it will aid in producing. The formulas will be developed for the following case:

$N =$ number of pieces per year to break-even
$N_1 =$ number of pieces to be made per year
$\quad = 12,000$
$I =$ interest or profit on invested capital, expressed as a decimal
$\quad = 0.10$
$T =$ taxes and insurance, as a per cent of investment, expressed
$\quad$ as a decimal
$\quad = 0.02$

Since the same procedure applies for jigs, fixtures, or other specialized tooling, the general term "fixture" will be used in developing the formulas. For fixture A

$C_f =$ cost of the fixture $= \$3,000.00$
$N_f =$ life of the fixture, expressed in terms of the number of pieces
$\quad$ made $= 36,000$
$L =$ life of the fixture in years $= \dfrac{N_f}{N_1}$
$D =$ annual depreciation cost, on a straight-line basis
$\quad = C_f/L = C_f \times \dfrac{N_1}{N_f}$
$F =$ annual fixed cost of the fixture $= C_f(N_1/N_f + I + T)$
$V =$ variable cost of the fixture per hour (such as power, maintenance, etc.) $= \$0.10$
$R_m =$ cost of machine used per hour $= \$2.50$
$R_f =$ labor cost per hour $= \$2.00$
$K =$ cost per set-up $= \$120.00$
$N_s =$ number of pieces made per set-up $= 3,000$
$t =$ processing time per piece $= 0.08$ hour
$C_p =$ cost per piece
$S_p =$ savings per piece over condition where no fixture is used
$\quad =$ saving due to fixture A
$Q =$ material cost per piece $= \$0.80$.

For fixture B, or no fixture

$C'_f =$ cost of the fixture $= \$1,600.00$ (none used $= 0$)
$N'_f =$ life of the fixture, in terms of the number of pieces made
$\quad = 24,000$ (omitted when none used)
$L' =$ life of the fixture in years $= \dfrac{N'_f}{N_1}$ (omitted when none used)

D' = annual depreciation cost, on a straight-line basis

$$= C'_f/L' = C'_f \times \frac{N_1}{N'_f} \text{ (none used} = 0)$$

F' = annual fixed cost of the fixture = $C'_f(N_1/N'_f + I + T)$ (none used = 0)

V' = variable cost of the fixture = \$0.08 (none used = 0)

R'_m = cost of machine used per hour = \$2.50

R'_f = labor cost per hour = \$2.00 (omitted when none used)

R' = labor cost per hour when no fixture is used = \$2.25

K' = cost per set-up = \$100.00 (none used = 0)

N'_s = number of pieces made per set-up = 3,000 (omitted when none used)

t' = processing time per piece .09 hr. (none used = 0.012)

C'_p = cost per piece

Q' = material cost per piece = \$0.80 (none used = \$0.85).

It will be noted that straight-line depreciation plus interest on the original investment is used for computing the factors D and I. This obviously introduces some error, but since the time is short, in most cases this error is not significant. If a more precise determination is desired, the method of straight-line depreciation plus *average* interest can be used. This would give for depreciation and interest, in terms of N_1 and N_f,

$$C_f \left[\frac{N_1}{N_f} + I \frac{N_f + N_1}{2N_f} \right].$$

In terms of L, the life of the fixture in years, the expression for depreciation and interest would be

$$C_f \left[\frac{1}{L} + I \left(\frac{L+1}{2L} \right) \right].$$

Obviously exact depreciation and interest can be determined by using the capital recovery factor, CRF.

The cost per piece, using a fixture, is

$$C_p = Q + R_f t + R_m t + \frac{K}{N_s} + \frac{C_f}{N_1} \left(\frac{N_1}{N_f} + I + T \right) + Vt. \quad (14.1)$$

From the previous paragraphs, it is apparent that when no fixture is used most of the cost factors may be omitted from this expression. Thus if no fixture is used the cost per piece is

$$C'_p = Q' + R't' + R'_m t'. \quad (14.2)$$

For a given fixture to be justified, C_p must be equal to C'_p. The number of pieces per year, N, for break-even for fixture A versus no fixture, may be determined as follows, substituting N for N_1 in the equations:

$$C_p = \$0.80 + \$2.00 \times 0.08 + \$2.50 \times 0.08 + \frac{\$120.00}{3,000} +$$
$$\frac{\$3,000.00}{N} \left(\frac{N}{36,000} + 0.10 + 0.02 \right) + \$0.10 \times 0.08$$

$$= \$1.29 + \frac{\$360.00}{N} \qquad (14.3)$$

$$C'_p = \$0.85 + \$2.25 \times 0.12 + \$2.50 \times 0.12 = \$1.42$$

$$\$1.29 + \frac{\$360.00}{N} = \$1.42$$

$$N = 2,770 \text{ pieces}$$

It is thus apparent that if 12,000 pieces per year are to be made, the fixture should be used.

Two fixtures, A and B, can be compared using these formulas by determining the number of pieces, N, per year at which a break-even cost per piece would be obtained. For fixture A the cost per piece, from Equation (14.3), would be

$$\$1.29 + \$360/N_1.$$

For fixture B,

$$C'_p = \$0.80 + \$2.00 \times 0.09 + \$2.50 \times 0.09 + \frac{\$90.00}{3,000} + \frac{\$1,600.00}{N_1}$$
$$\left(\frac{N_1}{24,000} + 0.10 + 0.02 \right) + \$0.08 \times 0.09 = \$1.309 + \frac{\$192.00}{N_1}. \quad (14.4)$$

Equating C_p and C'_p and solving for N, it is found that the break-even point would occur at $N_1 = 8,840$ pieces per year. Below this number fixture B would be cheaper, while above it fixture A should be used.

Several other jig and fixture cost problems, such as determining the amount of money that can economically be invested in tooling, can be solved by the use of such formulas.

LIMITATIONS IN THE USE OF FORMULAS

Considerable caution should be observed in the use of formulas as a method of making economy studies. It will readily be recognized that Equation (14.1), for example, is simply an expression in symbols of the usual cost factors, such as depreciation, labor, materials, taxes, overhead, etc., that ordinarily are expressed in figures in economy studies. As a result, most economy study formulas are complex because of the necessity of making provision for all of the possible cost factors which may be encountered. Some have been derived that are so complex that electronic computers must be used to obtain a solution in a reasonable time.

Proponents of formulas usually justify them on the basis of

(a) the claim that they save time,

(b) the fact that they can be used by persons who do not understand the principles on which they are based and who could not otherwise solve economy study problems,

(c) the argument that they provide some assurance that pertinent factors will not be omitted from consideration.

While all of these claims *can* be true, they are not always so, and the following precautions should be kept in mind.

1. Formulas do not always save time.

2. The use of formulas by those who do not completely understand them can often be dangerous. (For example, how can they know whether a factor should be included or omitted?) Decisions seldom should be made by those who don't fully understand their implications.

3. There is no assurance that a given formula will make provision for all of the factors which exist in a particular situation.

4. An important precaution is that a solution derived by a formula may be mathematically correct but economically unsound. For example, on page 353 it was shown that fixture A should be used in preference to no fixture if annual production exceeded 2,770 pieces. Yet for an annual production of 3,000 pieces the fixture would have a life of twelve years! Very few fixtures would ever be useful over such a life. Yet the blind use of Equation (14.1), which is theoretically correct, would not bring out this vital fact. Undoubtedly one who thoroughly understood the theoretical basis for the formula would immediately be aware of this difficulty. However, there is considerable evidence that the less sophisticated who attempt to use such formulas become involved in such difficulties.

5. Formulas reveal the cost relationships only at the break-even point. There are many cases where the effect of not operating at the theoretically correct point is of prime importance in making a decision. Graphical solutions, as will be discussed in following paragraphs, frequently are of great help in such problems.

6. Formulas give no consideration to intangibles. Where there are non-monetary factors, formulas should be used with great caution.

Thus formulas are of value, but should be used only, and with due precautions, by those who thoroughly understand their implications. In most cases those who do understand basic economy study procedures prefer to make regular economy studies of specific alternatives so that all factors may be given proper consideration.

BREAK-EVEN-POINT CHARTS FOR BUSINESS ENTERPRISES

One of the most satisfactory uses of break-even charts is to show the relationship between income and costs of a business. The balance sheet and income statement give information about a business for one particular time or period. However, they do not show what would happen to the profits if the rate of production changed. From the standpoint of analysis and control, it is of considerable advantage to be able to depict the effect of a change in production rate.

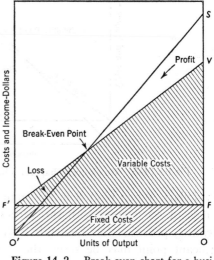

A number of people have done excellent work in adapting break-even charts to this use. Outstanding among these have been C. E. Knoeppel, Professor Walter Rautenstrauch, and Raymond Villers. Such charts may be very simple or quite complex. Figure 14–2 shows a simple break-even chart for a typical business. Fixed costs, variable costs, and income are plotted against units of output. Thus, the line $F'F$ represents the fixed costs of

Figure 14–2. Break-even chart for a business enterprise.

production. The line $F'V$ shows the variation in total variable cost with production; since its starting point is at F', it actually represents the sum of all production costs. The gross income from sales is represented by the line $O'S$. Since $F'V$ represents the total costs of production and $O'S$ the total income from sales, the intersection of these two lines is the point at which income is exactly equal to costs and is often called the *break-even point*. With the rate of production at that point, the business will make no profit and have no loss. If the production rate is greater than that at the break-even point, a profit will result. When the rate is less than that at the break-even point a loss will be sustained. By representing the income and costs of a business in this manner, the possibility of profit for any rate of production can be determined easily. Since these break-even charts show the relationship between income and costs for all possible volumes of activity, they are, in effect, continuous profit-and-loss sheets.

A more elaborate break-even chart for a business is shown in Figure 14–3. Here the income and costs are plotted as functions of the amount of sales

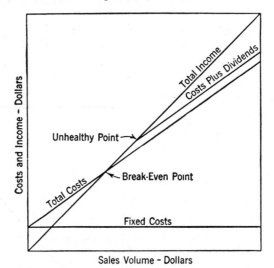

Figure 14–3.   Break-even chart for a business, showing provision for dividends.

in dollars. When plotted in this manner, the income line always makes an angle of 45 degrees with the vertical and horizontal axes. As an added feature, provision for dividends is shown on this chart. Thus, another significant point may be seen—the "unhealthy point," which indicates the sales volume at which the business will be able to pay exactly the desired rate of dividends. The location of the unhealthy point is, of course, dependent upon an arbitrary setting of the desired rate of dividends. Break-even charts drawn in this manner make the effect of production rate on profits very apparent and afford an excellent method of representing this relationship.

EFFECT OF CHANGES IN FIXED AND VARIABLE COSTS

One of the most satisfactory uses of break-even charts is to show the relative effects of changes in fixed and variable costs of a business. This is illustrated in Figure 14–4. Figure 14–4*a* shows the break-even chart for a certain business which has a sales capacity of $300,000 per year. For the values of income and cost shown, the break-even point occurs at 50 per cent of sales capacity. For any volume of sales over $150,000, the business will make a profit.

The chart in Figure 14–4*b* is drawn to determine what the effect will be if the variable costs are decreased 10 per cent, with all other factors remaining constant. It is apparent, of course, that the profits are increased by $20,000 when the business is operated at 100 per cent of sales capacity.

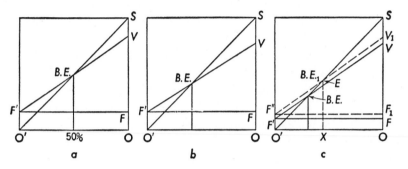

Figure 14–4. The effect of changes in fixed and variable costs on the location of the break-even point.

However, a more significant effect is the change in the break-even point. The 10 per cent decrease in variable costs lowers the break-even point to approximately 41 per cent of sales capacity. This means that not only will the company make greater profits if the plant is operated at capacity, but, more importantly, some profit will be earned if operations are greater than 41 per cent of capacity; before the saving was effected the business had to operate at greater than 50 per cent of capacity in order to make a profit. In times of depression it is usually more important that a business be able to earn some profit, or not go in the red, when operating at partial capacity than it is for it to be able to earn a very large profit if operated at a capacity which is entirely beyond the realm of possibility.

The third break-even chart, Figure 14–4*c*, was drawn to determine to what extent the break-even point will be shifted if the same saving of $20,000 is effected out of the fixed costs. The solid lines in Figure 14–4*c*, give the solution to this question. It is shown that this change in fixed costs will lower the break-even point from 50 per cent to approximately 29 per cent of sales capacity. This makes the importance of controlling fixed costs very apparent. The saving of $20,000 in fixed costs lowers the break-even point nearly 12 per cent more than would be the case if the same saving were made in variable costs.

Unfortunately, it is usually easier to effect savings in variable costs than in fixed costs. One might wish to know what saving in fixed costs would give the same result as a greater economy in variable costs, and the dotted lines in Figure 14–4c provide this information. A vertical line XE is drawn upward from a point corresponding to 41 per cent of sales capacity until it intersects the income line $O'S$ at point E. Through point E a line $F''V_1$ is drawn parallel to $F'V$. $F''V_1$ is the fixed-cost line which will give the required break-even point of 41 per cent of sales capacity. The fixed costs are determined by the ordinate $O'F''$, corresponding to \$42,000. This means that a saving of only \$8,000 in fixed costs will lower the break-even point as much as a saving of \$20,000 in variable costs. Thus the effect of fixed costs upon the break-even point is evident.

It should be noted that in each case illustrated in Figure 14–4b and c the profit at 100 per cent of capacity is the same. However, the percentage of capacity at which *some* profit can be earned differs. It should also be remembered that the changes in percentages apply only to the conditions of the example given, although other cases will show a similar change.

BREAK-EVEN CHART REPRESENTATION OF ECONOMIC CHARACTERISTICS OF BUSINESSES

An interesting use of break-even charts has been developed by Professor Walter Rautenstrauch. It was thought that for many business enterprises the total costs over a period of years would tend to be equal to a fixed amount plus a certain percentage of sales income. Thus the total cost line of a business would be approximated by a line having the equation

$$\text{Total cost} = a + bx,$$

where

$a =$ the constant portion of the total costs,

$x =$ the annual output in dollars,

$b =$ ratio of variable total cost to output.

Using the data given in the annual reports of businesses, the total sales volume and total costs for various years may be determined. If these are plotted and straight lines drawn through the plotted points, break-even charts result. Two such charts, compiled by Professor Rautenstrauch, are shown in Figures 14–5 and 14–6. These two charts show how closely the

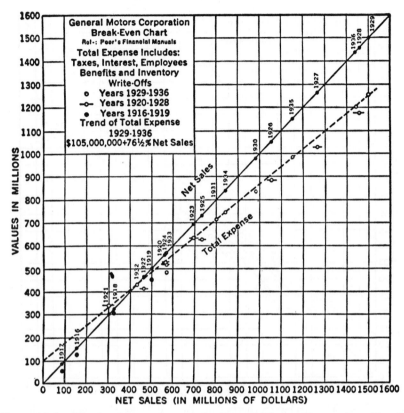

Figure 14–5. The break-even chart of the General Motors Corporation. (Reprinted by permission from *Economics of Business Enterprise* by Walter Rautenstrauch, published by John Wiley & Sons, Inc.)

actual total costs agree with the theoretical relationship. That such a relationship does exist is not as surprising as it might seem at first when one remembers that large businesses operate on a budget procedure and that the items in a budget tend to remain within rather close limits in terms of percentage.

It frequently is found that the total expenses for a particular business follow a certain trend for a period of years and then a change in management policy brings about a new expense trend. Such major changes in operating policy are readily revealed by break-even charts, such as that shown in Figure 14–6.

Break-even charts of this type for a given business may be determined by obtaining income and total cost data from a series of annual reports. When these data are plotted and straight income and cost lines drawn, their intersection gives the approximate break-even point for the business, and the

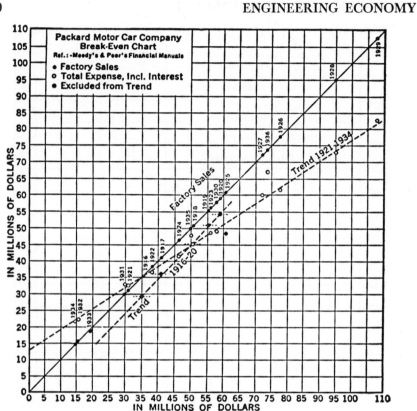

Figure 14–6. The break-even chart of the Packard Motor Car Company. (Reprinted by permission from *Economics of Business Enterprise* by Walter Rautenstrauch, published by John Wiley & Sons, Inc.)

intersection of the cost line with the zero vertical axis gives an approximation of the fixed costs. From such a chart the economic characteristics of a given business may be determined. Similar charts for several companies provide a convenient method for comparing their profit possibilities. It must be remembered that both the location of the break-even point and the angle of divergence between the income and cost lines (profit potentiality) are important.

MINIMUM-COST POINT

In many business operations total costs, as a function of one variable, decrease up to a certain point and then increase beyond that value of the variable. Under such conditions, it obviously is important to determine at what value of the variable the costs will be a minimum. Such cases are known as minimum-cost-point problems. Obviously, such a total cost variation exists because some of the cost elements increase as a function of the variable while others decrease.

It will be recognized that several of the problems discussed in Chapter 3 were of this general type; for example, the problem of the number of men in a work crew, on page 45. However, most problems involving minimum-cost points are more complex than those presented in Chapter 3.

GRAPHICAL REPRESENTATION OF KELVIN'S LAW

The problem from which Kelvin's law originated furnishes a good illustration of the use of break-even or minimum-cost-point charts. The energy lost in an electrical transmission line is I^2RH, where I is the current in amperes, R is the resistance of the line in ohms, and H is the number of hours during which the line is used. This lost energy represents a loss in dollars and may be considered one of the expenses of operating the line. Additional expenses are the fixed charges of depreciation, taxes, insurance, and interest. These are proportional to the amount of money invested in the transmission line.

If the size of the conductors is increased, the resistance of the line is decreased, and less energy is lost as a result. Thus the amount of this expense is lessened. However, since larger conductors cost more money, the fixed-expense items become greater. Therefore, by increasing the size of the conductors one expense is decreased, but another is increased. If these two expenses do not change by the same amounts, there will be some size of conductor for which the sum of the two types of expenses will be less than

TABLE 14–1   Annual Cost of Lost Power and Investment Charges for Various Sizes of Copper Wire (per 1,000 Feet)

	Wire Size	000	00	0	1	2
A						
B	Resistance, ohms (20°C)	0.0618	0.0779	0.0983	0.124	0.156
C	Weight, lbs.	508	403	320	253	201
D	Kw.-hr. at 50 amp. and 4,500 hour per year	695	876	1,107	1,397	1,757
E	Cost of lost energy at $0.015 per kw.-hr.	$10.43	$13.14	$16.60	$20.95	$26.35
F	Investment at $0.45 per lb.	$177.80	$141.05	$112.00	$88.55	$70.35
G	Investment costs (Depreciation, taxes, interest, and insurance) 16%	$28.45	$22.57	$17.92	$14.17	$11.26
H	Total annual cost	$38.88	$35.71	$34.52	$35.12	$37.61

for any other. A minimum-cost-point chart offers a convenient method of determining the most economical size.

Table 14–1 shows the computed values of the two types of expenses for five sizes of copper conductor. The values in lines *E, G,* and *H* are plotted on the minimum-cost-point chart shown in Figure 14–7, being shown in relation to wire size. The two expense

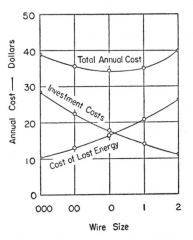

curves, *Cost of Lost Energy* and *Investment Costs,* intersect at a point corresponding approximately to size-0 wire. Thus it is noted that a minimum total expense is obtained when the cost of lost energy is equal to the investment charges upon the conductor. This corresponds to the statement of Kelvin's law given on page 28.

Figure 14–7. Break-even chart for determining the most economical size of copper conductor (data from Table 14–1).

ECONOMIC LOT SIZE

In many plants parts or products can be produced at a higher rate than they are used. This means that, although the parts may be used at a uniform rate throughout the year (or some other period), they may be produced in lots of varying sizes. Some of the costs of producing a lot are independent of the number of pieces in the lot. The costs of set-up and tear-down and the costs of paper and clerical work required to initiate a production order are examples of the fixed costs of a lot. Other costs vary as a function of lot size. Examples are direct labor and material costs and, often, depreciation. In addition, because the size of the lot will determine the number of units tied up in inventory, interest on the inventory funds, taxes, insurance, and storage costs will also be affected by it. As a result, the total and unit costs of a year's output will be affected by lot size. It is therefore desirable to determine the lot size that will result in minimum costs. Such problems commonly are called *economic lot-size* determinations.[1]

In developing the economic lot-size equation the following notation will be used:

---

[1] It should be pointed out that many economic lot-size formulas have been derived and published. Most are substantially equivalent but may vary slightly because of simplifying assumptions. Some which appear to be quite different are actually identical in meaning, differing only in the manner in which the various factors are defined. It is therefore most important that the user of any formula study carefully the notation that is used.

$Y =$ total cost of one year's requirements

$N =$ total quantity to be produced and used in one year

$\quad =$ demand rate per year (assuming a uniform rate)

$n =$ lot-size quantity

$C_f =$ fixed costs per lot, including set-up, tear-down, and order-origination costs

$C_v =$ variable production cost *per unit*, including direct labor and materials, and overhead

$I' =$ interest on investment in *average* inventory, taxes, insurance, expressed as a percentage of variable production cost

$W =$ storage cost per unit per year

$I = I' + W$, with W converted into an equivalent percentage of production cost. (This will be explained later.)

$P =$ production rate per year (after set-up)

One may state that

Total cost = (number of lots) $\times$ (preparation and set-up costs)
$\qquad + $ (production quantity) $\times$ (sum of all variable costs per unit)
$\qquad + $ [(average inventory quantity) $\times$ (production cost per unit) $\times$ (percentage rate for interest, taxes, insurance)]
$\qquad + $ (maximum inventory) $\times$ (storage cost per unit for one year). (14.5)

Using the above notation, the average inventory quantity, assuming a constant demand rate, will be [2]

$$\frac{n}{2}\left(1 - \frac{N}{P}\right).$$

Similarly, if it is assumed that storage space must be provided throughout the year for the maximum inventory, the maximum inventory will be

$$n\left(1 - \frac{N}{P}\right),$$

and storage costs must be based on this amount.

The total cost for one year's supply may be written, following Equation (14.5),[3] as

[2] If no production took place during use, and replacement of the inventory were instantaneous, the average inventory would be $n/2$. However, since the production rate is greater than the demand rate, the average inventory is reduced by the amount $(N/P) \times (n/2)$.

[3] Theoretically, the taxes and insurance which are included in the factor I in this equation should be based upon total unit costs, including overhead, rather than only production cost. However, this slight difference usually is not sufficient to justify the added complexity.

$$Y = \frac{N}{n} C_f + NC_v + \frac{n}{2} \left(1 - \frac{N}{P}\right) I'C_v + n \left(1 - \frac{N}{P}\right) W. \quad (14.6)$$

If the storage cost per unit, W, may be assumed to be expressed as an equivalent percentage, I'', of the production cost per unit, then the storage cost may be expressed as a percentage of the value of the average inventory:

$$n \left(1 - \frac{N}{P}\right) W = \frac{n}{2} \left(1 - \frac{N}{P}\right) I''C_v$$

From this it follows that $I'' = 2W/C_v$. By combining I' and I'' into a single percentage factor, I, Equation (14.6) may be written

$$Y = \frac{N}{n} C_f + NC_v + \frac{n}{2} \left(1 - \frac{N}{P}\right) IC_v. \quad (14.7)$$

Equation (14.7) may also be written in the form

$$Y = N \left[\left(\frac{I}{2}\right) \left(\frac{1}{N} - \frac{1}{P}\right) C_v n^1 + C_v n^0 + C_f n^{-1} \right]. \quad (14.8)$$

The most economical lot size may be determined by setting the first derivative of Equation (14.8), with respect to lot size, equal to zero and solving for n. Thus

$$\frac{dY}{dn} = 0 = N \left[\frac{I}{2} \left(\frac{1}{N} - \frac{1}{P}\right) C_v - \frac{C_f}{n^2} \right] \quad (14.9)$$

$$n = \sqrt{\frac{2C_f}{I \left(\frac{1}{N} - \frac{1}{P}\right) C_v}}. \quad (14.10)$$

If it is assumed that the storage space can be used for other purposes as the inventory decreases, the same expression for n, the economic lot size, will be obtained but the value of I'', which must be included in the value I, will be W/C_v.

The minimum cost obtainable by producing in the most economical lot size may be determined by substituting the value of n, obtained in Equation (14.10), in Equation (14.8). This gives

$$Y_{min} = N \sqrt{2I \left(\frac{1}{N} - \frac{1}{P}\right) C_v C_f} + NC_v. \quad (14.11)$$

By using Equations (14.10) and (14.11), the most economical lot size and the minimum total cost for a given set of conditions and a *given* method may be determined. For example, consider the following case in which a part is to be produced on a turret lathe. The cost, production, and demand factors are as follows:

Fixed costs per lot $= C_f = \$30.00$
Variable costs per unit $= C_v = \$0.10$
Percentage charge for interest, taxes, insurance and storage $= I = 50\%$
Production rate $= P = 100,000$ pieces per year
Demand rate $= N = 10,000$ pieces per year

Substituting these values in Equation (14.10),

$$n = \sqrt{\frac{2 \times \$30}{0.5(1/10,000 - 1/100,000)\$0.10}} = 3,650 \text{ pieces.}$$

Substituting in Equation (14.11),

$$Y_{min} = 10,000\sqrt{2 \times 0.5(0.0001 - 0.00001)\$0.10 \times \$30} + 10,000 \times$$
$$\$0.10 = \$1,164.$$

Figure 14–8 shows the effect of lot size on unit costs for the above example. This illustration shows clearly an advantage of having a graphical solu-

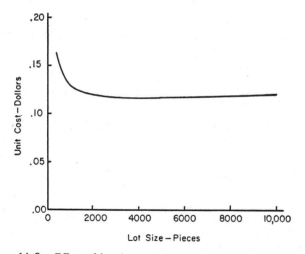

Figure 14–8. Effect of lot size on unit costs for a specific example.

tion for this type of problem. The curve shows that the lot size could be increased considerably above 3,650 without causing much increase in the unit cost. On the other hand, only a moderate decrease below that level would cause considerable increase in the cost. In many cases there may be reasons for producing some amount below or above the theoretically correct lot size. The graphical solution readily shows that a larger lot size would be preferred, while the mathematical equation for either lot size or total cost does not reveal this information.

ECONOMIC PURCHASE-ORDER QUANTITIES

From the nature of the economic production-order and the economic lot-size problems it might be expected that virtually the same equations would apply. Regardless of order size, certain costs—of requisitioning, ordering, paying the vendor, making entries on the stores records, etc.—are fixed. Other costs vary with the lot size—namely the product of unit cost and quantity. There are also costs which are a function of inventory size, such as interest, taxes, insurance, and depreciation (if any). In addition, there are storage costs which are a function of average or maximum inventory size, depending on whether the storage space can or can not be used for other purposes as the inventory is depleted.

If in Equation (14.6) C_f represents the fixed costs for each purchased lot and $C_v =$ the unit delivered purchase price, only the factor $(-N/P)$ does not apply to the purchase-order case, since no replacement is taking place simultaneously with demand (use). Thus by omitting the factor $(-N/P)$, the equation for cost of a year's supply when supplied by purchase may be written directly from Equation (14.6) as

$$Y = \frac{N}{n} C_f + NC_v + \frac{n}{2} I'C_v + nW. \qquad (14.12)$$

By combining I' and W into a single term, I, as was done in Equation (14.7),

$$Y = \frac{N}{n} C_f + NC_v + \frac{n}{2} IC_v. \qquad (14.13)$$

By differentiating and equating Equation (14.13) to zero, the economic purchase order size is

$$n = \sqrt{\frac{2NC_f}{IC_v}}. \qquad (14.14)$$

It should be remembered that I is a percentage factor which includes interest, taxes, insurance, depreciation (if any), and storage costs for one piece per year in terms of a percentage of the variable cost per piece, C_v.

Consider a case where

$$N = 8,000 \text{ units per year}$$
$$C_v = \$2.00$$
$$I = 0.30$$
$$C_f = \$5.00.$$

In this case,

$$n = \sqrt{\frac{2 \times 8,000 \times \$5.00}{0.3 \times \$2.00}}$$

$$= 365 \text{ units.}$$

Almost 22 lots of this size are necessary to provide the year's requirements.

ECONOMIC PURCHASE-ORDER SIZE FOR VARIABLE PRICE SCHEDULES

Price schedules which vary with lot size also may have a pronounced effect upon the economic size for lots which are purchased. For example, assume that the item mentioned in the previous section can be purchased under the following price schedule:

Lot size	Unit price
1–200	$2.10
201–500	2.00
501 and over	1.85

Figure 14–9 shows the cost of obtaining the year's requirement of 8,000 units under this price schedule. It will be noted that a real minimum-cost point exists only in the case of lot sizes of from 201 to 500 units. Further, this does not provide the minimum cost that can be obtained. Minimum cost would be obtained by purchasing in lots of 501 pieces, requiring sixteen lots.

Since there is never any assurance that the theoretical economic purchase-lot size in any price range will fall within the lot-size range for the particular price, or that this lot size will give the minimum total cost, problems of this type must be solved by a multiple-step procedure. (Of course, if curves such as are shown in Figure 14–9 are drawn, the correct solution is at once apparent.) The economic lot size for one or more of the prices in the price-quantity schedule is computed until a result is obtained which falls within the corresponding range of the schedule. The annual cost resulting from the use of the corresponding number of lots is then computed. Next the annual cost which would result from using the smallest lot size at the next lower price is determined. If this cost is less, the theoretical lot size for this price range should be computed and the annual cost at this theoretical lot size determined, in order to determine whether the total cost curve is increasing

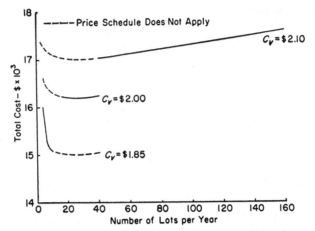

Figure 14–9. Cost of obtaining a year's requirement of 8,000 units under a lot-size pricing schedule.

or decreasing. If the cost increases as the lot size increases, the entire procedure—determining the cost for the most economical lot size and comparing it with the cost for the minimum lot size of the next lower price—must be repeated until the lowest annual cost is obtained.

PROBLEMS

14–1   A privately-owned interoffice telephone system costs $400 + $40N, where N is the number of connected phones. Such a system will last for ten years with maintenance costs not exceeding $4.00 per phone per year. Annual taxes and insurance on such a system would cost 2% of the first cost. The telephone company will furnish a comparable system for a monthly charge of $3.00 plus $1.25 for each phone. If capital is worth 8%, how many phones will be required to justify the installation of a privately-owned system?

14–2   An untreated telephone pole costs $60.00 and will last ten years under certain soil conditions. A treated pole costs $70.00. How long must the treated pole last to justify the added investment if 12% return before taxes is required? Assume annual taxes and insurance amount to 1% of first cost.

14–3   Draw a break-even chart for the following company:

Capital stock	$4,000,000.00
Labor costs	$0.41 per $ of sales
Materials costs	$0.31 per $ of sales
Fixed costs (interest, depreciation, etc.)	$800,000.00 per year
Dividend policy	10% per year on capital stock

a. Determine the sales volume to break even

b. Determine the sales volume to pay usual dividends

c. Determine amount of surplus if practical sales limit is $6,500,000 per year.

14-4 Solve Problem 14–3 with provision for income taxes equal to 50% of profits, the dividend policy being 10% paid to stockholders after taxes.

14-5 In a certain chemical process either of two materials may be used. Material A can be purchased under the following price schedule:

Up to 1,000 lb. per month.	$0.40 per lb.
1,001 to 2,000	$0.38
2,001 to 5,000	$0.34
5,001 to 10,000	$0.32

Material B can be obtained according to the following price schedule:

Basic price for amounts up to 3,000 lb. per month = $0.37 per lb. Decrease price by $0.01 per lb. for each 2,000 lb. increment above the base 3,000 lb., up to and including 13,000 lb. per month.

Show by graphical methods which material should be used if the monthly requirements of the company are 5,000 lb., and determine the quantity at which the two materials would be equal in cost. Assume that the material is ordered once each month to meet the needs of the month.

14-6 Determine the most economical size of copper conductor to carry forty amperes continuously throughout the year, with copper costing $0.40 per pound. Assume interest at 10%, and taxes and insurance at $1\frac{1}{2}\%$ of first cost. Assume a fifteen year life with $0.10 per pound scrap value. Electric energy is worth $0.01 per kw.-hr. (Consult electrical engineering handbooks for values of weights and resistances.)

14-7 A company which manufactures electric motors has a capacity of 200 motors per month. The variable costs are $150 per motor. The average selling price of the motors is $275. Fixed costs of the company amount to $20,000 per month, which includes all taxes. Present policy is to pay an annual dividend of $2 per share on each of the 15,000 shares of common stock.

a. By graphical methods, determine the number of motors that must be sold each month to break even, and the sales volume corresponding to the unhealthy point.

b. If the company can bring about a 20 per cent reduction in both fixed and variable costs, what will be the new break-even point and how much profit will be achieved if operations are at 90 per cent of capacity?

14-8 The fixed costs of a company are $100,000 per year. When operating at 80 per cent of capacity, its variable costs are $350,000 per year and its income is $700,000. By means of a break-even chart, show the effect of decreasing its selling prices by 10 per cent if this results in increasing its output to 100 per cent of capacity.

14–9   When operating at full capacity a company makes 200 pumps per week at a total cost of $200 each. Records show that when it operates at 75 per cent, 50 per cent, and 25 per cent of capacity the costs are $220, $260, and $380 per pump respectively. Assuming constant unit variable costs, determine the probable fixed costs of this company.

14–10 The *XYZ* Company had sales of $120,000 in 1959. Fixed costs, including insurance, utilities, depreciation, etc., were $15,000. Variable costs were $3 per unit. Plant capacity was 40,000 units, and the selling price was $4 per unit. Total investment in plant and equipment was $110,000.

    a. Draw a break-even chart for the company.

    b. Determine and show the break-even point.

    c. Find and show the profit before taxes, if any, and compute the rate of return on the investment.

14–11 Two types of tooling are being considered for making 25,000 pieces of a given part. The cost of type *A* tooling is $4,000.00; the variable cost of this tooling will be $0.05 per hour. The hourly cost of the machine on which the tooling is to be used is $3.00 and the labor cost will be $2.10 per hour. Set-up cost for this type of tooling is $80.00. Processing time will be 0.12 hour per piece.

Type *B* tooling would cost $1,200.00, and the variable cost would be $0.02 per hour. Set-up cost would be $120.00, and processing time 0.15 hour per piece.

The part is made in lots of 3,000 pieces and three lots are produced each year. It is believed that either type of tooling would be adequate for producing 30,000 pieces before renewal. Material costs are $1.10 per piece. Taxes and insurance would amount to 1% of first cost per year in either case, and capital is worth 15%.

Which type of tooling would be more economical?

14–12 If no special tooling is used in making the part in Problem 14–11, machinists who would be paid $2.75 per hour would be employed, working on the same machines, and would require 0.25 hour per piece. Determine the number of pieces required to justify the use of the more economical type of tooling found in Problem 14–11, assuming all other applicable data to remain the same.

14–13 Determine the most economical lot size for the following conditions:

Fixed costs per lot	$75.00
Variable costs per unit	$0.25
Percentage charge for interest, taxes, insurance, storage	40%
Production rate	80,000 pieces per year
Demand rate	15,000 pieces per year

14–14 Two alternative improvements, requiring the same investment, are being considered in connection with Problem 14–13. One would increase the fixed costs per lot by $25.00 but would decrease the variable costs per unit by $0.05 and increase the production rate by 20,000 pieces per year. The second would decrease the charge for interest, taxes, insurance, and storage to 30%. Which would have the greater effect in reducing the cost?

14–15 The annual requirements for a certain material are 80,000 lbs. Present price trends indicate that the average price of the material during the coming year will be $0.42 per pound and that only a slight increase appears likely. The fixed costs of initiating an order are $10.00, and the percentage factor to cover interest, taxes, insurance, and storage costs is 0.20. In what quantity should the material be ordered?

14–16 An improved procedure is available for initiating the orders and for inspecting and handling the material in Problem 14–15. This will reduce the ordering cost by $5.00 per order and reduce the percentage factor by 25%. This will require an investment of $2,000, which will have to be written off in two years. If capital is worth 12% to the company, would this be a desirable investment?

14–17 Assume that the material referred to in Problem 14–15 can be purchased at the following prices:

1– 500 lbs.	$0.50 per lb.
501–1,000 lbs.	$0.48
1,001–2,500 lbs.	$0.45
2,501–5,000 lbs.	$0.40
Over 5,000 lbs.	$0.35

What would be the most economic purchase-lot size?

CHAPTER 15

Capacity, Load,
and Utilization
Effects

Capacity, or size, may affect the economy of projects in several ways. The effect of size on the first cost of a product is encountered so often that people seldom stop to consider it. For example, a tube of shaving cream may sell for $0.43. One may also be able to purchase the same shaving cream in a jar containing three times the amount in the tube for only $0.85. One thus obtains three times as much shaving cream for less than twice as much money. While this situation is very common, it creates diverse problems. The producer must consider what size of product may be produced most economically. At the same time, he must take into account the needs of the consumer as to size. Too frequently it is forgotten that if the producer can not produce economically, there is little possibility of economy for the consumer.

Another effect of capacity is also experienced by everyone. For an example of this, consider a man and wife who own a two-passenger automobile. When only one of them is riding in the car, the gasoline consumption may be one gallon for every twenty miles traveled. If both of them ride in the car, the gasoline consumption will not be doubled. Instead, they will probably obtain at least nineteen miles to the gallon. In the first case the gasoline consumption is 0.05 gallon per passenger mile. In the second case the consumption is only 0.0263 gallon per passenger mile. Thus the fuel consumption per passenger mile varies greatly with the load that is placed on the car. This same effect is experienced in engineering work and has a very appreciable effect upon economy.

IMPORTANCE OF FIXED COSTS AND FIXED CHARGES

A little study of the problems involving capacity, load, and utilization reveals that their effect is due to the existence of fixed-expense items which must be met regardless of capacity, load, or demand. If all the expenses of an enterprise or business could be kept exactly proportional to the capacity, load, or demand, these factors would have no appreciable effect upon economy. The fact that they are not proportional makes a careful consideration of the fixed expenses of an enterprise all the more important. Since the investment per worker in fixed plant and equipment is increasing at a rapid rate, it is becoming increasingly important to give full consideration to all the effects of such investment.

Because automation involves high fixed costs, the extent to which automated plants can be fully utilized will be a most important factor in the increase in the use of automation. For economy, high fixed costs require a high level of utilization. Therefore it may be expected that economy studies concerning the effect of the utilization of capacity will be made with increasing frequency in the future.

EFFECT OF CAPACITY ON FIRST COST

Probably the simplest and most apparent effect of capacity on engineering projects is in initial cost. This is illustrated in Table 15–1, which shows the

TABLE 15–1 Cost of General Motors Corporation Diesel Engines of Various Sizes Delivered in San Francisco

Horsepower	Cost	Cost per horsepower
85	$2,450	$28.80
120	2,965	24.70
180	4,225	23.45

cost of various sizes of General Motors Diesel engines delivered in San Francisco. It is at once apparent that as the capacity of the engine is increased, the cost per unit of capacity decreases. One may also observe that the decrease in cost per horsepower is not proportional. By increasing the capacity from 85 to 120 horsepower, an increase of 35 horsepower, the cost per horsepower decreases $4.10. A further increase of 60 horsepower decreases the cost per horsepower only $1.25. Both of these effects are quite typical and are matters of common experience.

Figure 15–1 shows the effect of capacity on the price of turbine-generator units. This effect will be found in the majority of all products and projects. The reason for such an effect is readily ascertained. Consider some of the costs of producing 5,000- and 30,000-kw. turbines. The cost of originally designing a 30,000-kw. turbine would be little more than that for the smaller one, and far from six times as great. The machining costs would have a somewhat similar ratio. Likewise, the labor and supervision costs would not be in proportion to the size. Even if the larger turbine required six times as much material, the total cost for materials should not be six times as great, because they would be purchased in larger amounts and would therefore cost less per pound. Similarly, the various overhead charges of the plant making the turbines would not be six times as great for the 30,000-kw. machine. It is thus very easy to see why the 30,000-kw. turbine-generator unit should cost only half as much per kilowatt of capacity as the 5,000-kw. unit. Similar conditions will be found to exist for other products and structures. One may therefore say that a general effect of increasing capacity is to bring about decreased costs of production.

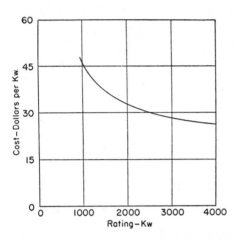

Figure 15–1. The effect of size on the cost of 3,600-r.p.m. condensing turbine-generator units.

The effect of increased capacity in making it possible to use more efficient equipment and production methods should not be overlooked. While this is usually the direct result of larger-scale production, the reduction in production costs is not due to only the element of capacity. It is also due to this intermediate factor of more efficient equipment which the larger capacity makes possible. Therefore, savings brought about through the use of more efficient equipment and methods used to produce larger amounts of products are really an indirect effect of capacity. However, the result on the cost of production is the same, and the possibility of such savings should not be neglected when capacity is being considered. Very often the savings from this source are greater than from the direct factor.

It has been stated previously that the usual effect of capacity is to decrease first cost and production costs. The examples in Chapter 2, in the discussion of the law of diminishing returns, show that this effect is not experienced in all cases. The possibility that the opposite effect may occur should never be neglected. When the effect of capacity is being considered, one should always examine the circumstances and determine whether the law of diminishing returns will reverse the more general effect. One should also consider the effects of size in relationship to increasing or decreasing business activity. A single large unit may be more economical in times of high activity but be very uneconomical when activity decreases. If the equipment is to be used over a wide range of conditions, it may be more desirable to have several smaller units than one large one.

Another consideration is the fact that all capacities of a given article may not be made or available in comparable qualities. As a result, an increase in size at certain stages may mean an actual increase in cost. For example, smaller gasoline engines may be purchased in nearly any quality desired. The cheapest ones will operate, but not over long periods at full load. One may obtain such an engine of given size for about whatever he wishes to pay. On the other hand, when one wishes to purchase a gasoline engine of 100 horsepower, he will find that there are few, if any, low-quality engines available. He may therefore find that he has to pay more per horsepower than he would for certain of the small engines. Obviously, quality must be considered when comparing the unit costs of small- and larger-sized products.

CAPACITY FACTOR

The usual effect of increased capacity has been stated to be a decrease in initial cost or cost of production. Accompanying this usually good effect is another which must be watched closely. This involves the extent to which the available capacity is utilized. The extent of the utilization of capacity is measured by *capacity factor*. This is defined as the ratio of the average actual use to the available capacity. Most of the early studies of the effect of capacity factor were made in the utilities industries, where the investment costs are high relative to total production costs. However, since the effects are the result of fixed investment, they are just as important to nonutility companies and are receiving more attention. This effect was mentioned in Chapter 2, where economic laws were discused. Whenever any capacity for production or service exists, the capacity factor at which the equipment is utilized has a vital effect upon the economy of the enterprise.

As a simple example of the effect of capacity factor, consider the case of a six-passenger station wagon. If it is used by only two persons, it is operated at a capacity of only $33\frac{1}{3}\%$. For such conditions a two-passenger Volkswagen, operated at 100 per cent of capacity, would be a much more economical means of transportation. On the other hand, if six persons were to be transported, it would be considerably more economical to use one six-passenger station wagon than three Volkswagens. In this simple example the effects of capacity upon first cost and its utilization upon operating costs are apparent.

EFFECT OF UTILIZATION ON ECONOMY
OF ALTERNATIVES

An example of the effect of the degree of utilization on the relative economy of alternatives is found in the case of a city which obtained bids on two pumps to be used in connection with a storm-sewer project. The "Handy" pump and motor cost $7,500.00 and would require 100 kw. of power for operation. The "Dandy" pump and motor cost $9,000.00 but would require only 90 kw. of power. Each pump was estimated to have at least a twenty-year life, and all maintenance and other costs were estimated to be equal. Power cost $0.02 per kw.-hr., and the project was being financed by a twenty-year, 6% bond issue.

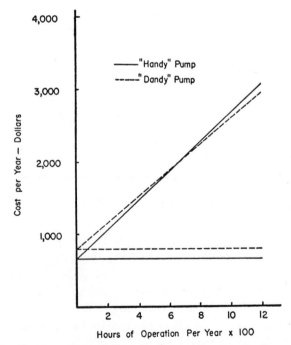

Figure 15–2. Fixed, variable, and total annual costs of two pumps as functions of hours of use per year.

Figure 15–2 shows the fixed, variable, and total annual costs for each pump as functions of the number of hours of use per year. It will be noted that for less than 655 hours of use per year the "Handy" pump would be more economical, while for utilization above that level the "Dandy" pump would be more economical.

This example points out the way in which the degree of utilization of capacity may affect the economy of alternatives, and also demonstrates that where a low capacity factor is expected low first cost may be of much greater importance than low variable costs of operation.

LOAD FACTOR

The second factor which must be considered in connection with available capacity is *load factor*. This is defined as the ratio of the average demand to the maximum demand. Obviously, if the maximum capacity were equal to the maximum demand, capacity factor and load factor would be identical. However, this is seldom the case, so load factor has special significance in measuring the effect of variations in demand.

In any attempt to measure the load factor it is necessary to decide which maximum demand shall be used. Should it be an instantaneous maximum demand or the maximum demand that lasts over several minutes? Thus, in stating a load factor the period of the maximum demand should be given. Electric power companies commonly use the fifteen-minute maximum demand as the basis of determining the load factor of their individual customers.

Load factors are commonly used in measuring the utilization of a system for which the capacity is difficult to determine, while capacity factors are applied to individual units for which the absolute capacity can be determined without difficulty. It should also be kept in mind that load and capacity factors may refer to a daily or to a seasonal variation in utilization.

Public utility companies pay particular attention to load factor. The reason for this is easily seen by looking at the power curve shown in Figure 12–2. As a result, most of the studies concerning load factors have been made by the utility companies. However, it can be shown that other industries are affected just as seriously by this factor. The majority of the customers of a public utility are limited as to the load they may throw on the system only by the maximum capacity of their equipment; the utility must make provision to supply whatever demand is placed upon its lines. Theoretically, the maximum total load would be the summation of the maximum demands of all the customers. For the modern utility company this would be a very great and serious load. In actual practice this condition never occurs.

DIVERSITY FACTOR

Since a condition where the maximum load of a utility would be the sum of all the individual customers' maximum possible demands would be very serious, it is advisable to consider the circumstance that prevents this from occurring. This may be explained by a very simple example. Assume that a utility company has only two customers. One is a residence which uses the power for lighting. The other is a small factory which uses power for the operation of machinery between the hours of 8 A.M. and 5 P.M. Since the residence uses power only for lighting, it is unlikely that all of the lights would ever be turned on between the hours of 8 and 5 during the daytime. Similarly, the factory would not use any appreciable amount of power during the evening, when the lights in the residence would be turned on. If the total connected load in the residence is 3 kw. and that of the factory 8 kw., the total possible load that can be thrown on the line is the sum of the two loads, or 11 kw. However, because of the diversity of the load, the maximum demand is actually 9 kw. It is thus seen that the maximum actual demand may be considerably less than the maximum possible demand because the two or more customers have different demand characteristics.

Ordinarily a utility has many customers of various types, providing power for residences, stores, factories, street lights, street railways, etc. No two of these have the same load characteristics. The utility is able to supply all of such a diversity of customers satisfactorily with generating capacity considerably less than the sum of all the maximum demands of each consumer. Great effort is made to obtain customers who will use power during periods when others are using very little. Attractive rates are usually offered to those who will buy power during off-peak periods and not consume any during the peak hours.

Since the diversity of load is of such importance, a standard method of measurement has been adopted. This is the *diversity factor* which is defined as the following ratio:

$$\frac{\text{Sum of the individual users' maximum demands}}{\text{Maximum demand actually experienced}}$$

Thus a diversity factor of four would indicate that the utility would need to have generating equipment of only one-fourth the capacity of the sum of the individual customers' demands.

The discussion of diversity factor has been in terms of an electric utility. Of course, diversity is just as important to other utilities. Water and gas companies must pay attention to the diversity of demand by their consumers. These utilities do have one advantage in that they can provide some storage of their product during off-peak hours to meet the peak loads. Electric companies are able to do this only in rare cases.

A system with a high load factor may have a high diversity factor—but not necessarily. The effect may be just the opposite. High load factor comes from continuous use of connected equipment. If all the customers on a utility system used all of their connected equipment all of the time, the company would have a load factor of 100 per cent. However, the diversity factor would be unity—a most undesirable situation. Thus it is desirable to obtain a high diversity factor by having many customers of different types.

Until recent years the nonutility industries have given relatively little attention to diversity. At present, however, considerable effort is being expended in this direction, as will be discussed in later paragraphs.

EFFECTS OF CAPACITY UTILIZATION IN PUBLIC UTILITY INDUSTRIES

There are three characteristics of public utility industries that make utilization of plant capacity of very great importance. First, the investment in fixed plant and equipment is very high, often being as much as $70,000 per worker, with the result that the fixed costs are the major portion of the unit production cost. Second, in the case of privately-owned companies, the rates which can be charged for the services are regulated by a public regulatory body so as to permit the company to earn only a reasonable return on invested capital. Third, once rates have been established, the utility must accept all customers who apply for service under the approved rate schedule. Because of these conditions, the utility companies were among the first to recognize the importance of plant utilization and to take steps to improve their load factors through special rate schedules.

From the load curve shown in Figure 12-2 it can be seen that an electric utility company must provide and maintain a vast amount of generating and distributing equipment that is not utilized during a large portion of the day. Expensive generating stations and distribution lines capable of carrying much more than the average load must be built and maintained in good condition. Administration and customers' expenses are nearly constant, regardless of the load which is placed upon the system. In many cases the fixed expenses are more than 70 per cent of the total cost of delivering power to the consumer. With such conditions, the expense of generating sufficient power to increase the plant load factor from 60 to 70 per cent would be relatively little. The cost of such power is really only the differential expense of production, and the utility can afford to sell such power for any amount greater than the increment cost. Many consumers will adjust their production processes to take advantage of such low-cost power.

Where a utility has a load curve such as is shown in Figure 12–2, it is apparent that there are two desirable objectives. The first, and usually the more profitable, is to increase the customer demand during off-peak hours, thus increasing income without increasing investment in generating capacity and with relatively little or no increase in distribution equipment; this tends to flatten out the load curve. Such a result may be achieved by encouraging customers to purchase power during only the off-peak hours, or by encouraging them to reduce the demands during the peak hours. The second objective is to increase total sales. This raises the entire load curve but requires additional capacity. The rate schedules used by utilities are designed to accomplish both of these objectives.

The total cost of providing a utility service is composed of three portions:

(a) Costs proportional to plant capacity, determined by the *demands* of the customers;

(b) Costs proportional to service consumed by the customers;

(c) Costs proportional to the number of customers.

On this basis, the cost of the service to a customer for a given period should theoretically be made up of three parts, as follows:

$$\text{Cost of service} = Ax + By + C,$$

where

$Ax =$ demand charge for demand of x during the period,

$By =$ energy charge for y units of service during the period,

$C =$ customer cost for the period.

Such a three-part rate schedule is too complicated for convenient use and for customers to understand and so is almost never used. Further, the principle of charging "what the traffic will bear" makes it inadvisable to adhere strictly to the theoretically correct procedure. This is simply recognition of the fact that some types of customers can afford to pay and will pay more than others for the service received; in other words, a given service is more valuable to some types of customers than to others. A two-part rate, commonly known as a Hopkinson type of rate, is sometimes used. An example of this type of rate is

$1.50 per month per kw. of measured maximum demand, plus
$0.015 per kw.-hr. of energy consumed.

CAPACITY, LOAD, AND UTILIZATION 381

More commonly used, however, is the Wright type of rate structure in which the amount of power a customer must purchase at a given rate, before being able to buy at a lower rate, is determined by his maximum demand. The following is an example of the rate schedule used by one company.

Service charge per month	$1.60
Energy charge (to be added to the service charge)	
First 1,000 kw.-hr. per month	$0.027 per kw.-hr.
Next 2,000 kw.-hr. per month	0.023 per kw.-hr.
Next 5,000 kw.-hr. per month	0.019 per kw.-hr.
For all excess over 8,000 kw.-hr. per month	
First 50 kw.-hr. per kw. of maximum demand	0.017 per kw.-hr.
Next 150 kw.-hr. per kw. of maximum demand but not more than 85,000 kw.-hr.	0.012 per kw.-hr.
All excess	0.007 per kw.-hr.

Utility companies attempt to obtain higher diversity factors by obtaining customers who have different load characteristics. Customers may be influenced to alter their load demands by the possibility of securing energy at very low rates during the utility's off-peak hours. One utility company includes the following clause in the rate schedule for general power consumers:

Any customer whose billing demand has exceeded 400 kw. for 3 consecutive months and thereafter until it has fallen below 300 kw. for 12 consecutive months, may, upon request, have his maximum demand measured by a type of meter which records the demand at all hours, in which case demands occurring between 10:30 P.M. and 6:30 A.M. of the following day and on Sundays and legal holidays will be ignored in determining the billing demand.

Another company uses the following clause to allow discounts for off-peak power:

For current used for industrial power purposes, . . . the rate for peak hours shall be the same as for commercial purposes and for off-peak hours the rate shall be twenty-five per cent (25%) less on all loads of 21 horsepower and over. The peak hours shall be between 4:30 P.M. and 9:30 P.M.

Gas companies have an additional complicating factor in connection with the load factor of their pipelines. This is the effect of weather. Electric transmission lines are affected very little by changes of temperature, but the temperature has a great effect upon the amount of gas or oil that can be transmitted in pipelines. In some cases the transmission capacity may be maintained only at greatly increased pumping expense. In order to transmit oil or gas during cold weather, increased pumping costs must be met. Yet this is the time of year when the demands are heaviest. Thus these companies are faced with the problem of providing equipment which is adequate to meet their peak cold-weather demands. During the summer months this equipment will be operated at a very low capacity factor. In most localities it is very difficult to find customers who can use large quantities of gas or oil during only the summer months, no matter how low the price.

While gas companies can provide for the storage of certain amounts of their product during the off-peak periods, the amount of storage that must be provided is determined by the load factor and diversity factor of the system. Therefore, these factors are of great importance to these companies.

It can be seen that load, capacity, and diversity factors are related to fixed costs which must be met regardless of output. These fixed costs are due to the necessity for large investments in generation or production capacity. It has been shown that the fixed costs are often the largest portion of production expense. In such cases it may be desirable to employ a production unit which is less efficient but has a much lower initial cost than some other unit. The decrease in fixed costs will more than offset the increased variable expenses. It has been said, truly, that the possession of the capacity for production is accompanied by the obligation to use that capacity to its fullest extent.

COST OF SERVICE WITH BLOCK-DEMAND RATE SCHEDULES

Where electric power or other utility service is purchased under block-demand rate schedules, the effect of demand must be taken into account in computing the cost of the power used not only by the proposed equipment, but also possibly that used by existing equipment. For example, a company which used an average of 20,000 kw.-hr. of power per month, purchased under the rate schedule shown on page 381, was going to purchase a spot welder which would consume 2,000 kw.-hr. per month. The existing maximum demand was 55 kw. The ABC machine, which cost $4,500.00, would increase the maximum demand by 15 kw., while the XYZ machine, costing $6,000.00, would increase the demand by only 5 kw. The welder selected would have to be written off over a five-year period, using a profit rate of 8%. Taxes and insurance on either machine would be 2 per cent of first cost per year, and other costs were estimated to be the same for either welder.

It is evident that the difference in maximum demand for the two welders would not only affect the cost of the power actually used by the welders, but also the cost of the power used by other equipment. Therefore the actual cost of power due to the use of the welders can be determined only by computing the total power bill before and after each welder is used. The existing monthly power bill was:

Service charge	$ 1.60
First 1,000 kw.-hr.	27.00
Next 2,000 kw.-hr.	46.00
Next 5,000 kw.-hr.	95.00
Service charge plus 8,000 kw.-hr.	$169.60
Next 50 × 55 kw.-hr.	46.75
Next 150 × 55 kw.-hr.	99.00
Next 1,000 kw.-hr.	7.00
Total	$322.35

If the ABC welder were used, the charges would be as follows:

Service charge plus 8,000 kw.-hr.	$169.60
Next 50 × 70 kw.-hr.	59.50
Next 150 × 70 kw.-hr.	126.00
Total	$355.10

For the XYZ welder:

Service charge plus 8,000 kw.-hr.	$169.60
Next 50 × 60 kw.-hr.	51.00
Next 150 × 60 kw.-hr.	108.00
Next 2,000 kw.-hr.	14.00
Total	$342.60

It is thus apparent that the actual cost of the increased power due to the ABC welder would be $32.50 per month, and due to the XYZ welder would be $20.25 per month. The comparison between the two machines would then be:

	ABC		XYZ	
Depreciation	$4,500/5.87 =	$ 767	$6,000/5.87 =	$1,023
Power	$32.75 × 12 =	393	$20.25 × 12 =	243
Taxes and Insurance	=	90	=	120
Totals		$1,250		$1,386

It is thus apparent that the ABC welder should be purchased.

Since power and other utility services often can be purchased under more than one rate schedule, sometimes considerable economies can be effected by a careful analysis of the actual costs when changes are contemplated from existing loads. Likewise, when utility services are purchased under block schedules, with or without maximum demand clauses, a proper analysis is required to determine the true cost of the service due to an additional piece of equipment.

POWER FACTOR

An additional factor, which accompanies the use of alternating-current electric power, should be considered. A detailed explanation of the cause of the *power factor* is outside the purpose of this book. It is sufficient for this discussion to say that the measured power consumed per phase by an alternating current device is equal to $E \times I \times \cos \theta$, where E is the voltage, I the current, and θ the phase angle between the voltage and current maxima. Power factor is equal to the value of the cosine of θ. It may also be defined as the ratio of the kilowatts per phase to the kilovolt-amperes per phase. The effect upon the utility company is to make it necessary to provide excess capacity in generating and distributing equipment, since the company does not receive payment for some of the current generated. Increased costs result, owing primarily to this necessity for increased capacity of all current-carrying apparatus, the increased losses which occur in this equipment and the poor voltage regulation in the system. Thus the power company incurs additional expense due to heavy inductive loads placed on the system which cause low power factor.

Low power factor may be corrected in several ways. One is to eliminate improperly loaded induction motors from the system. Another is to substitute synchronous or unity-power-factor motors for induction motors. Improvement may also be achieved by placing static condensers or synchronous condensers on the lines. All of these methods are used, but the use of the first two methods is limited to the extent to which the users of the power may wish to cooperate with the power company. In other words, the power factor of the system would be improved, at no expense to the power company, if the consumers would substitute synchronous motors for induction motors in their plants.[1] Since synchronous motors are more expensive than induction motors, it is natural that few consumers are willing to make this substitution unless given some monetary consideration.

---

[1] The power factor could be improved by the installation of synchronous or static condensers, but this would necessitate investment by the utility.

In order to influence consumers to help the power company improve its power factor, most utility companies grant certain rate reductions to consumers who maintain a high power factor. For example, the rate schedule of one company includes the following clause:

When the billing demand has exceeded 300 kw. for 3 consecutive months and thereafter until it has fallen below 200 kw. for 12 consecutive months, charges for energy will be adjusted for weighted monthly power factor, as follows.

If the power factor exceeds 80%, bills should be reduced by 0.3% for each 1% of such excess up to and including 90% power factor and by 0.2% for each 1% of such excess over 90% power factor. If the power factor is less than 65%, bills shall be increased by 0.5% for each 1% of such deficiency in power factor, provided that the maximum increase shall not exceed 5%. In no case, however, shall the total charge, after adjustment for power factor, be less than the minimum charge.

For determining the weighted monthly average power factor for the purpose of this schedule a meter to measure the reactive kilovolt-ampere-hours of the load shall be installed in conjunction with the kilowatt-hour meter. The power factor computed from the ratio of the monthly reactive kva.-hr. to the kw.-hr. shall be computed to the nearest whole per cent. In any case, where the power factor is likely to be leading at any time, the reactive component meter may be ratcheted to prevent reversal.

With such bonus and penalty clauses applying to the power consumed by manufacturing establishments, it is often necessary to consider the economy of installing equipment which will improve the power factor and thereby enable lower power costs to be obtained. For example, assume that a company is considering the installation of a 100-horsepower motor which will operate at 85 per cent of capacity during eight hours per day and an average of 22 days per month. An induction motor may be purchased for $800 which would have an efficiency of 91 per cent and operate at 79 per cent power factor. A synchronous motor would cost $1,100, have an efficiency of 90 per cent and operate at unity power factor. The power output of each motor would be 11,260 kw.-hr. per month. The cost of the power consumed would be at the rate of $0.007 per kw.-hr. before any adjustment for power factor penalty or bonus. If the power were purchased under the power factor clause cited previously, the two motors would be compared as follows:

> Induction motor
> Power consumed = 11,260/0.91 = 12,380 kw.-hr. per month
> Cost of power = 12,380 × $0.007 = $86.60 per month

```
Synchronous motor
  Power consumed = 11,260/0.90 = 12,500 kw.-hr. per month
  Cost of power
    Base cost                12,500 × $0.007 = $87.50
    Bonus for power factor
      From 80 to 90%,  10 × 0.3% = 3%
      From 90 to 100%, 10 × 0.2% = 2%
          Total bonus             5% =    4.37
      Net Bill                             $83.13
```

Saving per year by use of synchronous motor = ($86.60 − $83.13) 12 = $41.64. This saving should be related to the added cost of the synchronous motor, in the usual manner, to determine the advisability of purchasing this motor.

CAPACITY AND LOAD EFFECTS IN NONUTILITY INDUSTRIES

Because of the very high ratio of fixed costs to variable costs and the necessity for meeting whatever load demands are made by the customers, public utilities early recognized the importance of capacity utilization. As a result, careful cost studies were made in order to establish rate structures which would help to improve the utilization of such facilities. Until recent years nonutility industries have, in general, not given as much attention to capacity utilization. In fact, many people appeared not to realize that the same problems exist and that corrective steps could be taken. However, because of the great increase in the cost of plants and facilities, and their experiences during the forced conditions of World War II, manufacturing and retail industries have been giving much more attention to capacity and load factor problems. With the ratio of fixed to variable costs tending to increase in virtually all industries, it is certain that even more attention will be given to such problems in the future.

The problem is illustrated by a large automobile company that could produce about 1,750,000 cars per year if its plants were operated at full capacity throughout the year. Yet in 1957 the actual production was a little over 1,000,000 cars. Thus the capacity factor was about 57 per cent. One can not help but speculate on what reduction in selling price of this company's cars could be made if the operations could be carried out in plants which were about 60 per cent of the size of the existing plants and were operated at capacity.

Some companies have made excellent progress in moving their capacity factors toward 100 per cent. Notable among these is a manufacturer of specialized textiles. Through careful study he has determined the "least, economical" size of plant for his business. By this term, "least, economical," is meant the smallest size of plant that can be operated with a good degree of efficiency. These plants are built in various localities. No new plant is built until sales have reached a sufficient amount beyond existing capacity to assure that the new unit can be operated with a satisfactory capacity factor. Orders beyond the existing capacity are sublet to other manufacturers if necessary.

Another notable example of maintaining an approximately uniform capacity factor is that of the Nunn-Bush Company.[2] In this case the primary purpose of the attempt to obtain a uniform rate of production was to provide uniform employment for the workers. The variations in retail sales are absorbed largely by the stocks maintained in the stores.

An interesting result occurred in some of the canneries of Wisconsin, where manufacturers were practically forced to better their capacity factors. When this state put unemployment insurance laws into effect, it was apparent that the canneries were going to have to pay heavy unemployment-insurance assessments unless they were able to stabilize their employment. A great many changes were made in order to spread out the canning season and provide more uniform employment. Without realizing it, the canneries were increasing their capacity factors. Many of them found that the savings which resulted from better utilization of their production facilities more than offset the cost of the unemployment-insurance payments.

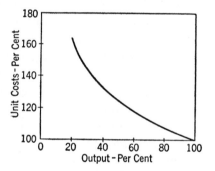

Figure 15–3. Variation in unit costs with percentage of operation for a company manufacturing heavy equipment.

Figure 15–3 shows the variation in unit cost with percentage of operation for one company in the field of heavy manufactures. The figure assumed no change in wage rates or other direct costs of operation. The company had no bonded indebtedness, so the variation in unit costs is less than would be experienced by many companies. The advantage of high capacity factor is apparent.

The methods used by nonutility industries to increase their capacity and load factors are many and varied and usually not as direct as those used by the utilities. A utility, for example, may offer a direct reduction in rates if power is purchased during off-peak hours. In the automobile industry a

[2] See the article, "Fifty-two Pay Checks a Year," *Fortune,* November, 1938, for a complete discussion of this.

comparable procedure would be to vary the established price schedule for cars throughout the year so that direct price decreases would be in effect during the weeks when low sales volume normally is experienced. Obviously such a practice would require very careful study and experimentation to avoid reversing the peak and off-peak seasons. Instead of using such a direct method of inducing customers to purchase automobiles during off-peak seasons, indirect methods are used, such as offering higher trade-in allowances on used cars. In other industries reduced price "sales," increased advertising, or special quantity discounts may be utilized to increase the load factor.

Multiple-shift operation of plants and stores is another effective means of increasing capacity and load factors. It is interesting to note that in certain industries two- or three-shift operation has been in effect for many years, while in others such operation is the exception. Only in the last few years have major retail stores, and even banks, started to remain open a few evenings a week—a form of multi-shift operation and a means of increasing the utilization of existing capacity. In multi-shift operation, as in most other methods of increasing capacity factor, it usually is necessary to balance increased costs (as for example, extra payment for nightwork) against the increased income or savings which will result. Thus economy studies, based upon accurate cost analysis, are necessary.

Whereas utilities usually can not store their products during off-peak periods in order to meet peak demands, manufacturing and retail industries frequently can do so. For example, a large manufacturer of vegetable oil shortening has built several plants to operate on virtually a uniform production schedule for fifty weeks of each year. Larger than normal warehouses were built to provide storage during the off-peak periods. This arrangement has proved to be very economical, since the manufacturing facilities were built considerably smaller than otherwise would have been done, at a considerable saving in investment. However, there are limitations to the use of this procedure. Where the product is compact, relatively inexpensive, and does not involve changes in model or style, storage to meet peak demands is usually feasible. For such products as automobiles, for example, such a procedure would not be economical. Therefore it is necessary in each case to explore the various possibilties and to make the necessary economy studies to determine the best solution for obtaining the most economical use of facilities.

The problem of diversity also differs somewhat in a manufacturing or retail industry as compared with a utility. In most cases utilities achieve increased diversity factors by providing service to different types of customers. Manufacturers and retailers usually must obtain diversity through the production and sale of different products. The major difficulty is to find products which will have different seasonal demand characteristics but which can, to a major extent, be produced with the same facilities. It often is essential that the various products be sold and distributed through the same distribution channels. A few years ago, for example, an automobile manufacturer merged with a producer of refrigerators and found that virtually no economies resulted because the two products had almost no common factors in manufacturing, sales, or distribution.

CAPACITY UTILIZATION IN CONNECTION WITH RISK REDUCTION

When capital is invested to reduce the probability of damage from a natural catastrophe, such as fire or flood, it is usually expected that the assets involved will have a very low use factor. For example, a sprinkler system to reduce the damage that might result from a fire would be installed with the hope that the system will never have to be used. If a dam is built to control flooding, it is expected that most of the time the dam will be empty, or nearly so, in order that its storage capacity may be a maximum if flood conditions should arise. Economy studies of such projects must attempt to balance costs against savings, where the utilization is expressed in terms of the probable frequency of the emergency. The frequency must be expressed in a statistical manner.

This type of problem may be illustrated by a simple example. Assume that a man agrees that once each year, for the next twenty years, he will cut a deck of 52 playing cards and that if he cuts an ace he will pay $500.00 to a second individual. How much could he afford to pay, in one immediate sum, to avoid this obligation and risk, assuming that capital is worth 6% to him?

With four aces in a deck of 52 cards it is apparent that, on the average, an ace will be cut four times out of 52 attempts. In other words, it is probable than an ace will be cut in $\frac{1}{13}$ of the attempts. Therefore the cost to him over the twenty years should be

$$20 \times \frac{1}{13} \times \$500.00 = \$769.20.$$

The average cost per year would be $\frac{1}{20}$ of this amount, or $38.46.[3] With

[3] These calculations assume that average frequency would apply to an individual. Obviously the actual frequency might vary considerably from this for a single individual with such a limited number of attempts. If a large number of persons made the same agreement, the amount of $38.46 would be the true probable annual cost. This calculation also does not consider the probability of the player's death during the twenty-year period.

money worth 6%, the present worth of the twenty annual payments of $38.46, would be

$$\$38.46 \times a_{\overline{20|}} = \$38.46 \times 11.47 = \$441.14.$$

Thus with the probable frequency of an event known, as well as the cost of that event and the value of capital, the single or annual amount which one can afford to pay to avoid the liability resulting from its occurring can be calculated.

Similar calculations form the basis for all insurance, once the probability of an event's occurring is known. In the case of insurance, of course, extra charges must be added to the basic cost to cover overhead costs of the company. Thus annual insurance premiums may be assumed to represent the average annual reduction in risk to the buyer which the company has found will result if insurance is purchased to cover a given event. For example, if the annual fire insurance premium on a given building is $100 per year, it means that the insurance company has found that on this type of structure the average annual fire loss, plus the necessary overhead and profit (if any) of the company, is $100.

INVESTMENT TO REDUCE FIRE RISK

A company has a warehouse which has no automatic sprinkler system. Annual fire-insurance premiums have been $1,200. If a sprinkler system costing $8,000 is installed, the insurance premium will be reduced by 50 per cent. The system is estimated to have a life of thirty years with the annual costs for taxes and maintenance amounting to $75. Capital is worth 8%.

The company engineer estimates that the actual loss resulting from any fire, including such factors as lost orders, personnel required to arrange for repairs, etc., would be at least 50 per cent greater than the physical loss covered by insurance. It is assumed that the reduction in insurance premium is a good measure of the difference in the probable annual physical loss without and with a sprinkler system. Therefore, with the premium reduction being equal to $600 per year, the probable saving in actual loss due to fire is estimated to be $900. The costs would be

Capital recovery and profit = $8,000 × 0.0888 = $710
Taxes and maintenance   =   75
   Total annual cost $785

It thus appears that the sprinkler system would be a good investment.

INVESTMENT TO REDUCE FLOOD-DAMAGE RISK

Sewers and flood-control projects are good examples of structures which may be subjected to unusual loads at infrequent intervals. To provide for all possible contingencies may be very costly. Yet if such structures are not large enough, overloading may occur so frequently that repeated property damage also becomes very costly. As a result, one might expect that the most economical size would provide for most of the expected loads while anticipating that some overloading and damage may occur at infrequent periods.

An example of this kind involved the enlarging of a drainage ditch in a mountain community in the West where "flash" floods were experienced. The existing ditch had capacity sufficient to carry 700 cubic feet per second. Engineering studies showed the following data regarding the probability of water flow in any one year and the cost of enlarging the sewer:

Water flow (cu. ft. per sec.)	Probability of a greater flow occurring in any one year	Cost to enlarge ditch to carry this flow
700	0.20	
1,000	0.10	$20,000
1,300	0.05	30,000
1,600	0.02	44,000
1,900	0.01	60,000

Records indicated that the average damage when serious overflow occurred amounted to $20,000. It was believed that this would be the average damage whenever the storm flow was greater than the capacity of the ditch. Reconstruction of the ditch would be financed by forty-year bonds bearing 5% interest. It was thus computed that the annual cost, for repayment of the bonds plus interest, would be approximately 6 per cent of the initial cost (CRF for 5% and 40 years = 0.058). On this basis the total annual cost for the structure plus probable property damage would be as follows:

Ditch capacity (cu. ft. per sec.)	Annual investment cost	Probable annual property damage [4]	Total annual cost
700		$4,000	$4,000
1,000	1,200	2,000	3,200
1,300	1,800	1,000	2,800
1,600	2,640	400	3,040
1,900	3,600	200	3,800

[4] Obtained by multiplying $20,000 by the probability of greater water flow occurring, as shown in the previous tabulation.

From these calculations it may be seen that greatest economy would be achieved by enlarging the ditch so that it would carry 1,300 cubic feet per second, with the expectation that a greater flood might occur and cause property damage. It will be noted that the probability of such flooding is five out of one hundred storms.

It should be noted that when loss of life might result from the disaster, there usually is considerable pressure to disregard pure economy and build such projects larger than economically necessary in order to avoid public criticism.

PROBLEMS

15-1 Give examples of two manufactured products and two services where selling price is affected, more than proportionally, by size, and indicate some of the specific factors which cause this effect.

15-2 Explain the difference between the way in which an electric utility company obtains diversity and the method used by a manufacturer of consumer goods.

15-3 A company which has been buying power under the rate schedule shown on page 381 has had an average monthly power bill of $176.40 and a maximum demand of 20 kw. It is installing some electric drying ovens which will consume 6,000 kw.-hrs. per month and increase the maximum demand by 40 kw. What will be the cost of the power consumed by the ovens?

15-4 A company which produces a single product selling for $10.00 per unit is operating at 80 per cent of capacity. Its overhead costs are equal to $24,000.00 + $5,000.00 × C.F., where C.F. is the capacity factor expressed in decimal form. The capacity of the plant is 10,000 units per year. Material and labor costs are $3.20 and $2.10 per unit, respectively.

A market study indicates that if the selling price were decreased $0.50 per unit, sales would increase so that the plant would operate at 90 per cent of capacity. It also is found that this increased volume would permit a saving of 5 per cent in material costs. If other costs are unaffected, would the decrease in selling price be advisable?

15-5 A factory has a large number of induction motors. The resulting power factor for the plant is 81 per cent. A large piece of equipment is being installed. If this equipment is driven by an induction motor, the power factor for the entire plant will be reduced to 78 per cent. On the other hand, if a synchronous motor is installed, the resulting power factor will be 91 per cent. A synchronous motor will cost $1,400 more than an induction motor. The average monthly power bill has been $430 per month, and it is estimated that if the induction motor is installed, the bill will increase to $540 per month. Either motor would be written off over a ten-year period and capital is worth 10%. Annual taxes and insurance would be 2% of first cost. If the company buys power under the rate schedule shown on page 385, which type of motor should be installed?

15–6   The load on an oil pipeline varies as follows during the year:

Load	Hours
4,000 gallons per minute	1,400
3,000 gallons per minute	3,600
2,000 gallons per minute	3,760

Two alternative pump-and-electric-motor installations are being considered. The first is to use a single pump, A, having a capacity of 4,000 gallons per minute. The other is to use two pumps of type B, each having a capacity of 2,000 gallons per minute. The power required for these pumps is as follows:

Load	Pump A	Pump B
1,000 g.p.m.	6.3 kw.	3.6 kw.
2,000 g.p.m.	7.0 kw.	5.6 kw.
4,000 g.p.m.	10.5 kw.	

A type A pump and motor will cost $4,000 installed while each type B pump will cost $2,500. Each would have a useful life of ten years with a 10 per cent salvage value. Annual taxes and insurance would be 2% of first cost in either case. It is believed that the maintenance costs would be about the same with either alternative. If capital is worth 15% and power costs $0.025 per kw.-hr., which alternative should be selected? (Draw curves to obtain intermediate power-consumption values needed.)

15–7   The company involved in Problem 15–3 can obtain a reduction of 25 per cent in the cost of the power required for the drying ovens by not using them during peak hours. Such a procedure would, however, cause an increase of 5 per cent in the amount of power used because the ovens would have to be reheated. It would also necessitate paying a total of $40 a month in nightshift premium pay to two workmen. Should the ovens be shut down during the peak hours?

15–8   The industrial power rate of a certain public utility is as follows:

Monthly service and standby charge	$5.00
1st 500 kw.-hr. per month	$0.03 per kw.-hr.
Next 1,000 kw.-hr. per month	$0.02 per kw.-hr.
All above 1,500 kw.-hr. per month	$0.015 per kw.-hr.

All consumption above 1,000 kw.-hr. per month is subject to a penalty of 3 per cent for each per cent the customer's power factor falls below 90 per cent.

The ABC Company has a heavy inductive load and a power factor of 74 per cent. Its average monthly power bill during the past year has been $120. By purchasing suitable condenser equipment for $1,250, the power factor can be raised to 90 per cent. Such equipment would have an economic life of ten years and would involve no other expense except annual taxes and insurance, which would amount to 1½% of the first cost. If capital is worth 8% to the company, should the condenser equipment be installed?

15-9   A pumphouse is to be built in a remote area where there is considerable hazard from grass fires. A concrete house will cost $6,000, have an estimated life of thirty years, and involve an annual insurance premium of $40. A house built of wood will cost $2,000 and have an estimated life of fifteen years. Insurance on this type of structure would be $175 per year. If a fire should occur, it is unlikely that it would cause any damage to the pumping equipment if a concrete house were used, but it is estimated that there would probably be $1,000 in damage if a wooden structure should burn. Available records indicate that such a fire might occur each fifteen years. Taxes on either type of structure would be 1% of first cost per year. If capital is worth 8%, which type of pumphouse should be built?

15-10   In building a rural power line four designs are being considered, costing $30,000, $32,000, $35,000, and $38,000 respectively. It is estimated that the probability of a major failure because of ice, wind, and snow would be once in eight, fifteen, twenty-five, and thirty years respectively. Any such failure would cause a loss equal to 20 per cent of the first cost of the line, due to the difficulty of repair under the conditions. Taxes and insurance would amount to 2% of the first cost of the line each year. If capital is worth 8%, which design should be used? Assume a thirty-year life for all types and zero salvage value.

15-11   To install a fire sprinkler system in warehouse will cost $18,000 and effect a reduction in the fire insurance premium from 1.23% to 0.47% of the $250,000 base value of the building and contents. The sprinkler system would have an annual maintenance cost of $100 and an estimated life of twenty years. It is estimated that the actual loss in event of fire would be at least double the amount recovered from insurance. If capital is worth 10%, should the sprinkler system be installed?

CHAPTER 16

Studies Involving

Increasing

Future Demand

In many engineering and business projects there are clear indications that the future demands for products or services will considerably exceed those of the present. Such cases present the problem of determining whether it is more economical to provide immediately for all of the foreseeable future demand or to provide only for the immediate demands and then make additional provisions at a later date. The situation may be illustrated by considering the installation of domestic gas mains for a new real-estate subdivision. Two extreme possibilities exist. The first would be to provide a completely separate main from outside the subdivision to each house as it is completed and occupied. This would require repeated tearing up of streets and the digging of many parallel ditches. The other extreme would be to at one time install mains of sufficient size to provide service to all of the houses that might ever be built in the subdivision, even though many of them might not be built for several years. Obviously many alternatives could be provided intermediate to these two extremes.

In this case it is apparent that the first alternative would require less immediate expenditure of capital. However, it is quite possible that in the long run it might not be as economical as the second extreme. One would at once suspect that some intermediate alternative might be more economical than either of the two extremes. Thus, where provisions for meeting increased future demand in more than one way exist, it is necessary to make economy studies of two or more alternative methods in order to determine which will be the more economical.

Such studies ordinarily involve relatively long-range demands, usually from ten to fifty or more years. They therefore are encountered most fre-

395

quently in connection with public works—such as roads, bridges, water reservoirs, sewers—or in connection with public utilities—such as power plants, gas and water mains, or telephone central offices and cable installations. It will be noted that all such projects involve relatively stable services for which the demand is likely to continue, and the necessity for meeting the future demands, whatever they may be. In some cases there is a limitation of site location. For example, in locating the central office of a telephone company a difference of a block or two may mean thousands of dollars in cable costs. Unless the correct site is determined and acquired well in advance, it may not be available when the actual demand occurs.

DETERMINING FUTURE DEMANDS

It is apparent that the accuracy of the estimated future demands is a prime factor in such economy studies. The procedures whereby future demands are estimated are beyond the scope of this text. The subject is a fascinating one, and much interesting work has been done in developing the various techniques that are used. Satisfactory results usually require many years to develop in a given company. In general, the factors which cause demand must be determined and projections made of the probable future increases and decreases in those factors and their net effect on the demand. Usually the projections are made for several years beyond the actual time which is to be considered in economy studies, frequently twice as far into the future. The projections are corrected each year, or more frequently, in the light of current information. While such estimates, involving five, ten, or twenty years, can not be expected to be completely accurate, a number of companies are able to predict demands ten to twenty years in advance with accuracy of 80 to 90 per cent. Such information obviously is of great value in economy studies involving future demand. At the same time, however, it should always be remembered that future demand data are not absolutely accurate, and due consideration must be given to this fact both in the methods employed for such studies and in the interpretation of the results.

DIFFICULTIES ENCOUNTERED IN ATTEMPTING TO USE CUSTOMARY PATTERNS IN FUTURE-DEMAND STUDIES

Unfortunately it usually is not feasible to use the usual rate-of-return or the minimum-annual-cost procedures in making economy studies involving provision for increasing future demand. There are several reasons for this, as illustrated in the following simple example. A small highway bridge must be built. It is believed that a six-lane bridge, built at a cost of $200,000, will provide for all possible future needs. The annual maintenance costs on such a bridge are estimated to be $2,000 per year. An alternative is to build a three-lane bridge, at a cost of $125,000, which will take care of the needs for the next ten years, and then build a second three-lane bridge, at the same cost, to meet the increased needs of the future. Annual maintenance costs for each three-lane bridge are estimated to be $1,500. Thus one may provide for all future demands by an immediate investment of $200,000 and annual expenditures of $2,000. An alternative is to make an immediate investment of only $125,000 and annual expenditures of $1,500 for ten years, followed by an additional investment of $125,000 at the end of ten years and annual expenditures of $3,000 thereafter.

It is apparent that investments of capital are different and made at different times for the two alternatives. In addition, with the second alternative the annual maintenance costs would be one amount during the first ten years and a different amount thereafter. It is therefore very difficult to use either the rate-of-return or annual-cost procedures. Likewise, the revenues and disbursements frequently can not be equated to determine a rate of return, since in many problems of this type there is no revenue. This is usually true in cases involving public works. Therefore such studies customarily are made either by the capitalized-cost or the present-worth-cost procedures.

Cases involving increasing future demand are of two types. In the first a perpetual future need is assumed. In such cases the capitalized-cost method —present cost plus the present cost of perpetual service—may be used. This procedure is often used for such structures as tunnels, dams, bridges, etc. However, the concept of perpetual need is unrealistic for most projects; even such structures as bridges and dams frequently have been found to be unused after 75 to 100 years. Therefore for most studies the present-worth-cost procedure, with a limited life or study period, is used. However, as will be pointed out, this method also frequently involves some difficulties, primarily because the lives of the alternatives may not be the same, since some of the structures in one may be built at a later date. It thus is essential that the results of deferred investment studies be carefully interpreted.

PERPETUAL FUTURE DEMAND

A certain water reservoir of sufficient capacity to supply all future loads will cost $40,000. An alternative would be to construct a smaller reservoir having sufficient capacity to meet all of the demands of the next ten years and adequate to supply one-half of the demand after ten years; this reservoir would cost $27,000. At the end of the ten-year period it would be necessary to build a second reservoir to meet the other half of the demand; this reservoir would cost $23,000. Annual maintenance costs for the larger reservoir are estimated to be $1,500 and for each of the smaller reservoirs to be $850. It is assumed that the need for the reservoirs will be perpetual and that, properly maintained, they will last indefinitely. Capital is worth 5%.

For the first alternative the capitalized cost would be

Cost to build reservoir	$40,000
Present cost to provide perpet- ual annual $1,500 maintenance $= \dfrac{\$1,500}{0.05}$	$= \underline{30,000}$
Capitalized cost	$70,000

For the second alternative the capitalized cost would be

Cost to build first reservoir	$27,000
Present cost to build second reservoir 10 years hence $= \$23,000 \times 0.614$	$= 14,130$
Present cost to provide maintenance on first reservoir $= \dfrac{\$850}{0.05}$	$= 17,000$
Present cost to provide main- tenance on second reservoir $= \dfrac{\$850}{0.05} \times 0.614$	$= \underline{10,440}$
Capitalized cost	$68,570

It thus is found to be less expensive to use the second alternative. It should be kept in mind that the difference of $1,430 in capitalized costs represents the present value of the annual differences throughout the lives of the alternatives. Also, it should be remembered that the interest rate is extremely important. For example, if an interest rate of 4% had been used in the above study, the capitalized cost of the second alternative would have been $640 greater than that of the first alternative.

INTERPRETING FUTURE-DEMAND ECONOMY STUDIES

In interpreting the results of an economy study of this type, it is at once apparent that an alternative which permits a portion of the investment to be deferred has certain advantages, other factors being equal. Such a plan reduces the amount of capital required during the early years, and before additional capital is invested more time will have elapsed, so the demand will be more certain, with respect to both type and quantity. By waiting one may be able to take advantage of new technological developments.

On the other hand, there may be some disadvantages in deferring investment. The major disadvantage is the possibility of price increases. Such increases are difficult to anticipate, but the long-term trend has been one of increasing price levels and there are strong indications that it will continue. Another disadvantage in certain cases is the matter of public nuisance. For example, repeated tearing up of a given street to install a succession of small gas mains might have serious repercussions for the utility involved, even if such a procedure were economic.

A third disadvantage sometimes arises where financing is by means of a bond issue. It often is easier and cheaper to sell one large bond issue than two smaller ones. It also may be more difficult to get voter approval, in the case of public projects, for two separate bond issues than it would be for a single larger issue. Occasionally, as in the case of a bridge, there may be only one site available, so two or more projects can not be built to meet the expected demands of the future.

But, in general, one usually will favor an alternative which permits deferring a portion of the total investment. Methods for giving due consideration to such alternatives must be considered.

When the capitalized cost (or present-worth cost) of the alternative permitting deferred investment is less than that of the alternative requiring immediate provision for all future needs, a decision usually is very easy. Unless a factor of public nuisance is involved, the alternative with deferred investment will be selected, since it is more economical and also has all the inherent advantages of such a proposal. The same decision probably would be made without difficulty if the costs turned out to be the same. The question then arises as to just how much more one should be willing to pay in total costs in order to be able to defer some of the investment and thereby have the privilege of making a final decision at a later date. This obviously is a question to which a numerical answer can not be given. Each person must decide such matters for himself in the light of all of the factors involved.

It should be recognized that selection of the interest rate used in such economy studies can create a bias in favor of or against deferring investment. Whenever the interest rate used in such a study is less than the rate required to justify the investment, the study automatically is biased in favor of the alternative having the higher immediate investment. For this reason, one should avoid using as the interest rate the average cost of capital if this rate does not truly measure the risks involved in the particular project being considered. It should also be remembered, as was shown previously that a higher interest rate, because of the discount effect, produces a bias in favor of the alternative permitting deferred investment.

PERPETUAL DEMAND WITH LIMITED LIFE

In the previous example it was assumed that the reservoirs would last indefinitely. What would be the effect if the life were only fifty years? Such a situation means that, in addition to paying for the first installation, an additional sum of capital would theoretically have to be invested, and that the interest on that sum would have to accumulate each fifty years to the amount required for replacement. Thus for the first alternative, under these conditions, the capitalized cost would be:

Cost to build initial reservoir $40,000

Present cost of all replacements =

$$\frac{\$40,000}{0.05 \times s\overline{_{50|}}} = \frac{\$40,000}{(0.05)(209.3)} \qquad = \quad 3,830$$

Present cost of $1,500 annual maintenance   30,000

Capitalized cost $73,830

Similar provision would have to be made in computing the capitalized cost for the other alternative.

INDEFINITE OR LIMITED DEMAND PERIOD WITH LIMITED ASSET LIFE

In many economy studies involving provision for increasing future demand one can not realistically assume unlimited duration of demand. For most goods or services technological progress assures that the demand will not always exist. Also, such situations usually involve assets which have limited lives. This makes it necessary to take into account the fact that an alternative which permits deferring a portion of the investment ordinarily has a longer life than one in which provision is made immediately for all of the needs throughout the expected demand period. The following example will illustrate the problems involved and methods for handling them.

In 1950 a company decided to build a new power plant. It was believed that the plant would be needed for a number of years, but no absolute need was seen after ten years. Two plans were being considered. Plan *A* was to build immediately a plant of sufficient size to meet all of the needs of the next ten years—1951 through 1960. Such a plant would be of 5,000-kw. capacity and cost $400,000. The life of this plant was estimated to be at least ten years. Plan *B* would be to construct a plant of 3,000-kw. capacity immediately to meet the demands of the first six years—1951 through 1956—and at the end of six years to enlarge this plant by an additional 2,000 kw. in order to meet the needs of the last four years—1957 through 1960. The 3,000-kw. plant would cost $310,000, and the additional 2,000 kw. would cost $180,000. Annual taxes and insurance would amount to 2% of the first cost in each case. Annual operating and maintenance expenses for the two plans were estimated to be:

	Plan A	Plan B
First and second years	$48,000	$45,000
Third and fourth years	54,000	52,000
Fifth and sixth years	61,000	60,000
Seventh and eighth years	78,500	80,000
Ninth and tenth years	96,000	97,000

Capital was considered to be worth 7%.

If the 2,000-kw. addition was of the same type and quality as the 3,000-kw. portion of plan B, it would be expected to have the same physical life. Under these conditions the two plans would be able to provide service as follows:

Plan A		Plan B	
5,000 kw.	1951 through 1960	3,000 kw.	1951 through 1960
		2,000 kw.	1957 through 1966

Thus with plan B, permitting deferred investment, a portion of the assets would be available for service, if needed, after all of the assets of plan A had become useless. This is a factor that must be taken into account in many studies of this type. There are several procedures that may be used.

If there is considerable certainty that demand will continue beyond the life of the alternative of immediate total provision—plan A in this case—a comparison may be made by determining the present worth of the costs over the period provided for by the shorter-lived alternative. Thus, for the two power plant proposals the period considered would be ten years, the life for plan A. For plan A the present worth of the costs would be:

Present cost to possess	$400,000
Present worth of taxes and insurance $= \$400,000 \times$	
$0.02 \times a_{\overline{10}\rceil}$	$= \qquad 56,200$

Present-worth cost of operation and maintenance expense

First and second years	$= \$48,000 \times a_{\overline{2}\rceil}$	$= \$ \ 86,900$
Third and fourth years	$= \ 54,000 \times a_{\overline{2}\rceil} \times v^2 =$	$85,300$
Fifth and sixth years	$= \ 61,000 \times a_{\overline{2}\rceil} \times v^4 =$	$84,200$
Seventh and eighth years	$= \ 78,500 \times a_{\overline{2}\rceil} \times v^6 =$	$94,600$
Ninth and tenth years	$= \ 96,000 \times a_{\overline{2}\rceil} \times v^8 =$	$101,100$
Total		$\$452,100$
Total present-worth cost to possess and operate		$\$908,300$

For plan B the present worth of the 3,000-kw. unit would, of course, be $310,000. For the 2,000-kw. unit the *annual* cost throughout its ten-year life would be $180,000 \times 1/a_{\overline{n}|} = \$25,630$. For the four-year period 1957 through 1960 the present worth of the annual costs would be $25,630 \times a_{\overline{4}|} \times v^6 = \$57,900$. Thus the present worth of the costs for plan B for the years 1951 through 1960 would be:

Present cost of 3,000-kw. plant $310,000
Present-worth cost of 2,000-kw. plant built 6 years hence   57,900
Present-worth cost of taxes and insurance
 First 6 years = $310,000 \times 0.02 \times a_{\overline{6}|}$ $= \$29,600$
 Last 4 years = $490,000 \times 0.02 \times a_{\overline{4}|} \times v^6 =$ 22,150
  Total $ 51,750

Present-worth cost of operation and maintenance expenses

 First and second years $= \$45,000 \times a_{\overline{2}|}$ $= \$ 81,400$
 Third and fourth years $= \$52,000 \times a_{\overline{2}|} \times v^2 =$ 82,100
 Fifth and sixth years $= \$60,000 \times a_{\overline{2}|} \times v^4 =$ 82,800
 Seventh and eighth years $= \$80,000 \times a_{\overline{2}|} \times v^6 =$ 96,500
 Ninth and tenth years $= \$97,000 \times a_{\overline{2}|} \times v^8 =$ 102,100
  Total   444,900
Total present-worth cost to possess and operate $864,550

On this basis plan B would be cheaper than plan A during the ten-year period, and the 2,000-kw. unit would be available for service during the following six years.

Obviously a study on this basis is justified only if there is assurance that the additional life involved will be needed. Another fact that must be taken into consideration is that if plan B is selected and demand does continue after the ten-year period, provision will have to be made to replace the 3,000-kw. unit at the end of 1960, when it presumably must go out of service. Thus selection of an alternative providing deferred investment may set up a pattern of partial replacements which could continue for some time. While this conceivably might not be most economical in the long run, it nevertheless provides a certain degree of flexibility with respect to meeting changes in demand and taking advantage of possible technological advances. Therefore the primary factor in determining whether this method of selecting the study period should be used is the certainty of continued need for the service beyond the study period.

RECOGNITION OF ADDITIONAL LIFE OF DEFERRED INVESTMENTS THROUGH SALVAGE VALUE

Several methods for handling the matter of probable longer life of deferred-investment alternatives may be used under certain circumstances. The first is where the assets in such an alternative will have a fairly definite salvage or scrap value at the end of the study period if their use is not required beyond that time. For example, assume that the 2,000-kw. unit in plan B could be sold for $30,000 if it were not needed at the end of 1960. The present value in 1950 of this salvage value would be $30,000 \times v^{10} = $30,000 \times 0.508 = $15,240. The present-worth cost for plan B would then be:

Present cost of 3,000-kw. plant	$310,000
Present cost of 2,000-kw. plant 6 years	
hence $= $180,000 \times v^6$ $= 120,000$	
Less: present value of salvage $\underline{15,240}$	
Net present worth cost	104,760
Present-worth cost of taxes and insurance	51,750
Present-worth cost of operation and maintenance	$\underline{444,900}$
Total present-worth cost	$911,410

PROVIDING FOR FUTURE DEMAND WITH "INFERIOR" ASSETS

Another method sometimes can be used to deal with the matter of additional life of deferred investments. Actually, this method eliminates the additional life, thus avoiding the problem. It can be used when the asset required to meet the future demand can be obtained in different qualities which would have different lives; quite frequently this is possible. For example, physical structures, such as buildings, bridges, or pipelines, can be constructed of different materials which will have quite different lives. If one wishes to construct a building to meet the increasing needs over a fifty year period, an initial building might be built of concrete, and at the end of twenty years a wooden structure could be constructed to have a life of thirty years. In this way both structures could reasonably be considered to serve only to the end of the desired fifty year period.

While the opportunity for using this method is not always present when equipment is involved, even in this case different types are frequently available which will provide the required service over different useful lives.

Assume that in the previous example of the power plant a 2,000-kw. unit which would provide satisfactory service for four years could be obtained for $100,000. The present worth cost of plan B for the years 1951 through 1960 would then be as follows:

Present cost of 3,000-kw. plant	$310,000
Present cost of 2,000-kw. plant 6 years hence = $100,000 $\times v^6$ =	50,830

Present-worth cost of taxes and insurance
First 6 years = $310,000 $\times$ 0.02 $\times a_{\overline{6}|}$ = $29,600
Last 4 years = $410,000 $\times$ 0.02 $\times a_{\overline{4}|} \times v^6$ =   18,540

Total	$ 48,140
Present-worth cost of operation and maintenance	444,900
Total present-worth cost	$853,870

Plan B under these conditions would be considerably cheaper than plan A.

It should be kept in mind that although an "inferior" asset is assumed as a part of the deferred-investment alternative, this does not rule out the possibility of deciding at a later date to use a better asset should the conditions at the time the deferred-investment is to be made warrant such action.

RECOGNITION OF ADDITIONAL LIFE
AS AN INTANGIBLE FACTOR

Where there is no reasonable assurance that the additional life available from a deferred-investment alternative will be needed or that there will be any definite salvage or scrap value, and where the possibility of an "inferior" asset does not exist, no assignable value can be given to such added life, and it must be considered as only an intangible value. The total life provided by the alternative permitting deferred investment must be considered to be the same as that available from the alternative requiring immediate provision for the future needs. Thus, if these were the conditions for the power plants in plans A and B, the present annual cost of plan B would be:

Present cost of 3,000-kw. plant	$310,000
Present cost of 2,000-kw. plant 6 years hence = $180,000 $\times v^6$ =	120,000
Present-worth cost of taxes and insurance	51,750
Present-worth cost of operation and maintenance	444,900
Total present-worth cost	$926,650

Using this method, imposed by the life conditions, plan B is considerably more costly than the $908,300 present-worth cost of plan A. The fact that 2,000 kw. of the capacity of plan B would be available for six years longer than the life of plan A, *if needed*, would be an intangible tending to offset the greater cost of plan B.

Obviously, the fact that a definite value can not be assigned to the additional life provided by a deferred-investment alternative imposes a rather serious penalty upon such an alternative, and there thus is a bias in favor of immediate investment.

DETERMINING THE BREAK-EVEN DEFERMENT PERIOD

As was pointed out previously, there is always some uncertainty as to what future requirements will be and when they will occur. Provision of a certain amount of capacity will establish a limit to the amount of service that can be provided in the future. It often is helpful to know at what future date a deferred investment will be needed in order for an alternative permitting deferred investment to break even with one which provides immediately for all future demands. Where only the costs of acquiring the assets by the two alternatives need to be considered, or where the annual costs through the entire life are not affected by the date of acquisition of the deferred asset, the break-even point may be determined very easily and may be helpful in arriving at a decision between alternatives.

Using as an example the case of the reservoirs discussed on page 397, for the costs of the two alternatives to break even

$$\$70,000 = \$27,000 + \$17,000 + \left[\$23,000 + \frac{\$850}{0.05} \right] v^n,$$

where v^n is the present value factor at 5% for some number of years of deferment n. Solving this equation, it is found that $v^n = 0.65$. This corresponds to a value of n equal to a little less than nine years. Thus, if the additional reservoir is not needed for nine years, it will be cheaper to use the second alternative, permitting deferred investment.

Obviously this break-even method of analysis is based upon a possible variation in the future-demand schedule. In cases where a fixed future-demand schedule is assumed, as in the power-plant problem on page 400, the break-even method of analysis is not practicable.

OTHER FACTORS AFFECTING
DEFERRED-INVESTMENT STUDIES

Since studies of the type discussed in this chapter involve future demand, often over a considerable period of time, it is obvious that considerable attention must be given to possible effects which the future may have.

The type of project being considered should be kept in mind in evaluating the probable accuracy of the future-demand estimates. For some types of industries such estimates can be made with considerable accuracy. For other types the inaccuracy is notorious.

It has been pointed out that the fact that some of the assets are not needed immediately tends to favor deferring a portion of the investment. Another factor having the same effect is that such an alternative requires less immediate financing. Even though alternatives are compared on the basis of the present worth of the costs, ordinarily no capital will be set aside immediately to pay for a deferred asset. Most businesses are always short of capital and therefore usually favor an alternative which will reduce current capital requirements.

On the other hand, alternatives requiring immediate investment sometimes are justified on the basis that increasing demand will soon make them economical. If there is a good chance of demand increasing rapidly, this is an important factor to be considered. Delay in providing an asset might make it impossible to meet rapidly increasing demand.

There are some cases where demand depends upon a service or product being available. For example, the demand for gasoline stations on a superhighway which does not exist is zero. On the other hand, if a long superhighway without intermediate entry and exit roads were built without service stations, travel on it would not be great. The proper combination of highway and service stations would have a great effect on the services from each. Thus it sometimes is necessary to provide a service before any realistic evaluation of the demand can be made. When the service is available, the demand often can be developed.

Occasionally the possibility of material or equipment shortages in the future may be an important factor in favoring immediate investment. Over short periods, particularly in times of national crisis, material shortages may sometimes be anticipated. In such cases one might wish to favor immediate provision over deferred provision. If study periods are more than a few years, however, the probability of foreseeing material shortages is rather low.

PROBLEMS

16–1   In extending the services of an irrigation district, two plans are being considered. The first is to construct a canal of sufficient capacity to take care of the requirements for the next ten years. Such a canal would cost $28,000 to construct and would have an annual maintenance cost of $1,500. If this plan is followed, the canal would have to be enlarged at the end of ten years, at a cost of $36,000. It would then have an additional life of ten years and would be adequate for the needs of that period. Maintenance costs during the second ten-year period are estimated to be $2,500 per year.

The second alternative calls for constructing a canal which would be adequate for all of the foreseeable needs of the next twenty years, at a cost of $58,000. Annual maintenance costs on this canal are estimated to be $2,000.

Taxes and insurance in either case would amount to $1\frac{1}{2}\%$ of first cost per year. If capital is worth 6%, which alternative should be used?

16–2   A department store is constructing the first unit of a new building. Adjacent ground is owned for a second unit which it expects to build within ten years. If the foundation and basement for the second unit are built to ground level at the same time the first unit is built, they will cost $82,000, a saving of $20,000 over the anticipated cost if they were built at a later date. Until the second unit is completed there will be no use for the extra basement space. Annual taxes and insurance amount to 2% of first cost and capital is worth 12%. What would you recommend?

16–3   A power company is designing a new steam-electric plant to supply a growing community. The initial load when the plant is completed will be 10,000 kw. This load is expected to increase 1,000 kw. each year for twenty years. Two alternatives are being considered. Plan A is to build a 30,000-kw. plant at a cost of $3,000,000.00. This plant would consume coal as follows:

Load	Coal consumption
10,000 kw.	1.28 lb. per kw.-hr.
10,000 kw.–20,000 kw.	1.15
20,000 kw.–30,000 kw.	1.05

Plan B is to build a 15,000-kw. plant at a cost of $2,000,000.00 and then to add a second 15,000-kw. plant when required at a cost of $1,600,000.00. Each of these plants could be operated to consume coal at the rate of 1.1 lbs. of coal per kw.-hr.

Assume the plants would have no value after thirty years. Annual taxes and insurance would amount to 2% of first cost per year. Coal costs $6.50 per ton and has a heat value of 13,000 B.T.U. per pound.

If capital is worth 10%, and all other costs for the two alternatives are assumed to be equal, which alternative should be used?

16–4   In the planning of a two-story municipal office building the architect has submitted two designs. The first provides foundation and structural details so that two additional stories can be added at a later date, without modifications to the original structure. This building would cost $140,000. The second design, without such provisions, would cost only $125,000.

If the first plan is adopted, it is estimated that an additional two stories could be added at a later date at a cost of $85,000. If the second plan is adopted, however, considerable strengthening and reconstruction would be required, which would add $30,000 to the cost of a two-story addition.

Assuming that the building is expected to be needed for 75 years, at what time would the additional two stories have to be built to make the adoption of the second design justified? Assume interest at 6%.

16–5   A Diesel power plant is to be installed at a new mine. Two installations are being considered to meet the requirements of the next fifteen years:

(a) A single heavy-duty engine and generator of sufficient capacity to meet all of the needs of the fifteen-year period. This installation will cost $34,000 and have a life of fifteen years. Average operation and maintenance costs during the first six years are estimated to be $6,000 per year; during the last nine years they would be $9,000 per year.

(b) A smaller heavy-duty engine and generator which could supply all of the requirements of the first six years and one half of the load during the last nine years. It would cost $22,000 and have a life of fifteen years. Operation and maintenance costs during the first six years are estimated to be $4,500 per year, and during the last nine years $5,100 per year. At the end of six years a lighter-duty engine and generator would be added to carry one half of the total load. This unit would cost $18,000 and have an estimated life of twelve years. It is probable that the salvage value of this unit would follow a straight-line relationship. Operation and maintenance costs on this smaller engine and generator are estimated at $5,700 per year.

Taxes and insurance on all equipment will amount to 2% of first cost per year. If capital is worth 10%, before taxes, which installation would you advise?

16–6   A municipally-owned water company must extend its mains into a new residential area which is being opened. One possibility is to install mains of sufficient size to meet all of the requirements of the next forty years, which is taken to be the life of such mains. Such an installation would cost $35,000.

A second alternative is to provide at present mains of sufficient size to meet the expected needs of the next ten years, at a cost of $22,000. At the end of ten years additional mains would be installed at a cost of $25,000 to provide for the additional requirements of the following thirty years.

Since it is a municipally-owned company, no taxes are paid. If the second alternative is used, it is expected that annual repairs during the last thirty years probably will be about $200 per year less than if the first alternative is used, because a portion of the system would be newer.

If capital costs 5%, which alternative should be used?

16–7   An oil company must install a pipeline to carry crude oil from an oil field to a refinery. Two plans are being considered. The first is to construct a pipeline now of sufficient capacity to handle all of the requirements of the next thirty years, the period corresponding to the estimated life of such pipelines. This line, A, would cost $560,000 to build, $40,000 per year to maintain and operate during the first ten years, and $60,000 per year thereafter.

The second plan is to build line B_1 now, at a cost of $310,000, with sufficient capacity for the requirements of the next ten years. The operation and maintenance costs on this line would be $42,000 per year. At the end of ten years a second line, B_2, would be put into operation, paralleling the line B_1, at a cost of $375,000, in order to meet the increased requirements of the following twenty years. Annual operation and maintenance costs of this line would be $20,000.

Annual taxes and insurance will be $1\frac{1}{2}\%$ of the first cost. It is probable that the lines will not be needed beyond thirty years.

If capital is worth 12%, which plan should be adopted?

16–8   A factory is planning to build a new warehouse. It must decide whether to build one large enough to take care of the foreseeable needs of only the next few years or to construct a building with considerable excess capacity in order to provide for all of the probable needs of the next forty years. Two plans are being studied:

(a)   A six-story building which it is believed will be adequate for all of the projected needs for at least forty years. During the first twenty years it appears certain that only the first three stories will be needed. However, it is believed that the remaining stories can be rented to other companies in the area for warehouse purposes if the rental rate is rather low; considerable investigation leads to the conclusion that an annual rental of $12,000 could be realized. Such a building would cost $500,000. Annual maintenance costs would be $5,000 per year.

(b)   A three-story building, with provision for adding three additional stories when needed, probably in twenty years. The first unit of this building would cost $310,000, and the second unit $275,000. Maintenance on the first unit would be $3,500 per year, and $5,000 on the completed building.

Taxes and insurance on each structure would amount to 2% of the first cost per year. If capital is worth 10%, and a forty-year study period is used, which alternative should be adopted?

16–9   A telegraph company must install three miles of cable in a section of a city which is fully built and in which there is high density of street traffic. To provide for the foreseeable needs of the next thirty years would require a four-cable conduit and four cables, each costing $1.10 per foot, installed in available conduits. Such a conduit, including installation, costs $0.95 per foot. To dig a ditch for a conduit costs $1.05 per foot, including backfilling and repaving costs.

The requirements could also be met by installing a two-cable conduit and two cables at the present time and then adding a second two-cable conduit and two cables ten years hence. A two-cable conduit now costs $0.75 per foot installed. A ditch of the same size is required for either the two- or the four-cable conduit.

It is expected that all construction and material costs will have increased by 10 per cent in ten years. Additional cables can be pulled in available conduits at any time without any proportionate increase in cable cost. All cable is estimated to have an ultimate scrap value of 20 per cent of first cost.

Taxes and insurance on all installations will amount to 1½% of the total first cost annually. If capital is worth 10%, which size conduit should be installed?

16–10   A public utility is going to build a new power plant. A plant of sufficient capacity to meet all of the demands for the next forty years will cost $15,000,000.00 and have a capacity of 50,000 kw. It is estimated that the average demand during the first ten years will be 35,000,000 kw.-hr. per year. During the second ten-year period it will be 80,000,000 kw.-hr. per year, and thereafter will be 190,000,000 per year.

An alternative is to build a 25,000-kw. plant, at a cost of $9,000,000.00, to provide the required service during the first twenty years, and a second plant of the same size, at an estimated cost of $8,000,000, at the end of that time. It is estimated that the cost of generating the power would be $0.003 greater per kw.-hr. during the first twenty years if the first alternative were built due to the lower load factor during that time, but that the costs would be $0.001 per kw.-hr. less during the last twenty years.

Annual taxes and insurance will amount to 2% of first cost in either case. If capital is worth 10%, before income taxes, which alternative should be adopted? Assume a forty-year study period.

16–11   What effect would an assumption that all plants have a life of forty years have on Problem 16–10 if the salvage value follows an SYD curve?

CHAPTER 17

Personnel
Factor
Studies

More and more engineering economy studies are being made in which personnel factors are of considerable importance. Such studies differ basically from others only in that a larger portion of the cost or income items can not be evaluated as accurately, and, as a result, intangible or irreducible factors may play an unusually large part in final decisions. Indeed, in some cases it is difficult to place monetary values on any of the factors involved. Frequently the result of this situation is that engineers and others conclude that, since many cost and income factors are unknown, it is useless to attempt to make economy studies of such cases. Instead, they choose to base investment decisions on hunches or other indefensible bases.

In reality, the conditions that exist today regarding unknown costs and incomes in studies involving personnel factors existed in many other fields in earlier years. It is only because of experience that costs in most areas of industrial and engineering activity are known today. The necessity and desire for cost information resulted in studies and records to supply the desired values. Only in relatively recent years has the need for economy studies in fields where personnel factors are prominent been apparent. As a result of the limited demand and experience, relatively few cost data have been developed. In addition, of course, human nature being as variable as it is, it is impossible to completely evaluate all of the factors which are present in a situation where the human element exists to a high degree. Where economy studies have been attempted for quite a few years, as in the case of accident prevention, a considerable body of cost information has been developed. In other situations, such as the prevention of industrial strikes, where studies have been attempted only in recent years, few cost data are available. The growing realization of the importance of the effect of personnel factors upon the economy of projects makes it certain that the number of economy studies involving these factors will increase greatly. As more and more such studies are made, more and more cost data will become available.

In most cases involving personnel factors one will find that some of the factors can be evaluated very satisfactorily. Others can only be estimated with fair accuracy. Still others can not be evaluated to any degree of satisfaction. Obviously, in many cases the factors could be evaluated quite completely if one could afford the necessary time and expense. In most cases this is not possible. Instead, one must adopt the procedure of evaluating all of the factors as completely as is practicable and then carefully considering the intangibles. Because it may not be possible to evaluate as many of the factors as would be done in other types of economy studies, it is to be expected that more weight must be assigned to the intangibles. It sometimes is desirable to list the intangibles under two headings—those that favor the investment and those that do not. One then must weigh the relative merits of each and attempt to arrive at a proper decision.

In dealing with economy studies involving personnel factors, the items that can be evaluated frequently result in complete justification of an investment or course of action, or reduce the problem to a borderline case. Proper consideration of the intangibles then makes the final decision quite clear. If, for example, there are some important intangibles which will produce favorable results, even though they can not be evaluated in terms of dollars, a borderline case clearly becomes one where investment is justified. On the other hand, if all of the intangibles point to unfavorable results, one probably would not go ahead with such a project. Thus a proper consideration of both those factors which can be evaluated and those which can not is necessary in order to determine the degree of uncertainty which exists and to learn whether these uncertainties are overbalanced by other factors.

It should also be kept in mind that each study of this type which is made usually contributes to a body of knowledge that enables subsequent studies to be evaluated more fully. In addition, in the process of making such a study one usually finds ways of evaluating some factors which he had thought could not be done.

STUDIES OF ACCIDENT PREVENTION

As was mentioned previously, some of the earliest economy studies involving personnel factors were made in connection with accident-prevention work. This field also provides historical case studies showing how factors which were quite irreducible in the earlier years can now be evaluated because of the development of cost data as time passed and the importance of such data became apparent.

At first thought, it seems strange that it should be necessary to make an economy study of accident-reduction programs. Accident-reduction work should be carried on by all companies in the most intensive manner without regard to cost. Undoubtedly, at the present time most of such work is done in this manner. However, this was not always the case. It is a shameful fact that in the beginning accident-reduction work had to be forced upon certain companies by indignant social workers, employees, and legislatures. On the other hand, many companies entered upon such work from a purely humanitarian interest in the welfare of their workers and were very surprised to find that actual profits were obtained from their money and efforts. In spite of the progress which has been made, it is still probably true that many companies would make less effort along the lines of accident prevention if they did not realize that such programs produce real economy.

From another viewpoint, studies of the economy of accident-reduction programs are advisable. When a company is interested in reducing accidents, without regard to profit, economy studies of the work may give an indication of how efficient its efforts have been and indicate where additional expenditure is needed.

It is impossible to place a monetary value on the loss of a life or injury to human beings; thus the actual cost of accidents can never be determined. However, some of the direct costs to the companies involved can readily be determined. The direct cost in compensation, medical, and hospital bills can usually be found with little effort. The indirect costs, represented by lost time of workers who were not directly involved in the accident, damage to machinery, spoiled work, training new employees, preparation of reports or attending hearings of industrial accident commissions, etc., are usually much greater than the direct costs. One investigator states that the indirect costs are four times as great as the direct costs. The Travelers Life Insurance Company, which has made exensive studies of this matter, states that the indirect costs are at least four times as great as those of the insurance company which was affected by the accident. The National Bureau of Casualty and Surety Underwriters has stated that the direct cost of claims, medical service, and hospitalization arising out of industrial accidents in this country is in excess of 600 million dollars per year. The Bureau also estimates the indirect costs to be at least four times the direct costs. This would make the total bill for industrial accidents in this country amount to over three billion dollars per year.

When economy studies of accidents were first started, they had to be based almost entirely on the direct costs which were easily determinable. As more and more studies were attempted, more was learned about the indirect costs, until at present a considerable body of information is available. This information concerns not only industrial accidents, but accidents of other types as well.

The highway department of the state of Pennsylvania found that the average cost of compensation for serious eye accidents was over $2,000. Addition of the indirect costs would make the total cost of each such accident amount to $10,000. A study in the state of New York showed that the average cost of compensation in 23,000 cases of handling [1] accidents was $211. Again adding indirect costs, the total cost of each such accident would be $1,055. These are among the most common accidents occurring in industry.

That accidents can be reduced by continued and intensive accident-prevention work is proved by the experience of numerous companies. Typical of these is that of the United States Rubber Company. In ten years this company reduced the number of lost-time accidents from 1,100 to 158 per year. It operated its factories for 34 consecutive months without a fatality. One of its subsidiary plants, employing 2,000 workers, operated for fifteen consecutive months without a lost-time accident. The cost of accidents was reduced from $0.60 to $0.36 per $100.00 of payroll. This represented a saving of over $50,000.00 per year to this company.[2]

Another outstanding record is that of the Western Clock Company, where 2,300 employees worked for 10,000,000 hours without a lost-time accident. This record was the result of 25 years of safety work. Every operation in the factories was studied carefully, and safety appliances and guards were installed wherever possible.

Another excellent example is that of the United Parcel Service in Los Angeles, whose eighteen truck drivers drove over 310,000 miles in one year without a single accident. Equally impressive records have been attained by other companies which have made determined efforts to eliminate needless injury and loss of life.

The United States Steel Corporation has spent large sums for accident-prevention work with excellent results. During a ten-year period it spent over $9,700,000 and obtained an actual saving of over $14,600,000.[3] This

---

[1] Handling is defined as lifting, carrying or manipulating an object or material by human strength.

[2] E. W. Beck, *Safety Engineering*, vol. 66.

[3] W. H. Cameron, *Factory and Industrial Management*, vol. 77, No. 1.

is just one more indication of the economic aspect of accident-prevention work.

An example of the success of a somewhat spectacular safety appliance was the use of a rope safety net under the entire span of the Golden Gate bridge during construction. This net was responsible for the saving of nineteen lives. The chief engineer stated that the saving that resulted from the workers' increased output, owing to lack of fear of falling, paid for the net many times over. This was a typical example where it was rather easy to show definite direct savings and also very obvious intangibles favorable to investing enough to provide the safety net. The success of this device was so outstanding, from the viewpoint of both dollars and morale, that it has become almost standard practice in bridge construction.

In connection with industrial accidents, it is well to point out that accidents are more prevalent among very new workers and those who have been on the job for many years. Inexperienced workers are not acquainted with possible sources of danger, while long-experienced workers tend to become careless.

At the present time there is probably no place where the cost of accidents needs to be considered more than in our streets and highways. The loss of human life should be enough to cause all concerned to adopt radical measures to eliminate this evil. However, it appears probable that vast expenditures could be made to make the highways and streets safer on the basis of the monetary savings which would result. Many studies are now in progress attempting to evaluate more accurately the true total costs of highway accidents.

LIGHTING

Lighting has two primary effects upon economy of production. First is its relationship to accidents. The second effect is upon quality and quantity of production. The United States Department of Labor has stated that 15 per cent of all industrial accidents are due to faulty lighting. This department has estimated the cost of industrial accidents caused by poor lighting to be in excess of $150,000,000 annually. It is interesting to note that this amount would pay for the power for one 100-watt light for each of thirty million workers for fifty forty-hour weeks if such power were worth $0.025 per kw.-hr. The actual cost of providing adequate lighting to eliminate this cause of accidents is usually very little. In most cases it does not exceed 1 per cent of the payroll. In industrial work any such increase in lighting usually produces large dividends in increased production, as will be mentioned later.

Lighting has a very vital connection with the accident rates on public streets and highways. The effect is probably more pronounced than in industrial work. Here, again, is an example of where some pioneering had to be done to obtain relevant cost data. In 1931, 1932, and 1933 the city of Detroit obtained data which gave vivid testimony to the effect of street lighting upon automobile accidents. Table 17–1 gives the results of a decrease in the

TABLE 17–1   Effect of Variations in Street Lighting upon Traffic Fatalities in the City of Detroit; 1931, Taken as 100%

(Courtesy of *Safety Engineering*)

	Fatalities	
	Night	Day
Street lighting at 100% in 1931 (10 months)	124	119
Street lighting at 65% in 1932 (10 months)	151	75
Street lighting at 85% in 1933 (10 months)	138	90

amount of street lighting as an "economy" measure and the effect of again utilizing more adequate lighting. Figure 17–1 shows the data of Table 17–1 in graphical form. This gives eloquent testimony as to the effect of lighting upon night-time accidents. It is interesting to project the curve beyond the 100 per cent lighting value and note how little extra lighting would have to be added to eliminate entirely (theoretically) accidents caused by darkness.

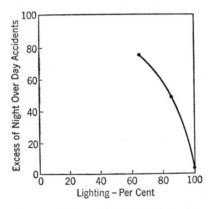

Figure 17–1. Effect of variations in street lighting on the excess of night accidents over day accidents in the city of Detroit (1931 lighting taken as 100%).

Another example was found on Wilshire Boulevard in Los Angeles. On one five-mile section of this street (this section being much better lighted than other portions) there were no traffic fatalities during the year 1938, in spite of the very heavy traffic volumes and somewhat notorious high speeds which existed. Other streets, where traffic was relatively light but lighting inadequate, were the scenes of many accidents. Considerable education is needed to convince taxpayers that additional taxes for improved lighting are just as necessary as those used to provide fire and police protection. In fact, the return often would be greater.

The relationship of lighting to industrial accidents is well illustrated in an example given by Mr. R. E. Simpson of the Travelers Insurance Company in an address before the Illuminating Engineering Society.[4]

The company . . . employed an average of 1,000 workers, had an annual payroll of one and three-quarters million dollars, and paid a yearly compensation premium of approximately $22,000. For some time the annual number of accidents (many of them minor, none of them fatal) was approximately 425. The compensation payments and medical fees averaged nearly $15,000 per year, or about $35 per accident.

The entire lighting system of the plant was revamped by substituting large lamps with approved reflectors in place of the original lighting equipment, and locating the units in a proper manner with respect to the work. The electric current consumption was increased from an average of 40 watts per employee to 100 watts per employee. The contract for the electrical work was $5,000, and the annual lighting bill increased from $1,900 to $4,700. The accidents, however, dropped from an average of 425 to 170 per year, and the compensation payments were reduced to approximately $6,000.

If we apply the four-to-one principle referred to earlier in this discussion, we find that with the original lighting system the company paid $1,900 a year for electric current and $59,500 to meet the hidden or uninsurable costs resulting from 425 accidents. With the new system the company paid $4,700 for lighting and only $23,800 for the hidden costs of 170 accidents. The direct and immediate saving amounted to $35,700, and in addition to this the favorable accident experience would have a weighty influence when the proper time came to adjust the compensation premium.

While improved lighting can nearly always be justified on the grounds of its effect on accidents, such improvements are usually accompanied by additional savings through increased production or improved quality. It is estimated that 25 per cent of all human energy is consumed in seeing. It is also well established that the amount of energy required for seeing is a function of the amount and quality of the light available. It is therefore reasonable to expect that the output of workers will be affected by lighting. Many cases are available to prove this effect. A number have been summarized by Munroe and Cook[5] and are shown in Table 17–2. It is important to note that from an average increase of only 2 per cent of the payroll an average of 15 per cent increase in production was obtained. It is doubtful if such results could be obtained by the expenditure of the same amount of money in any other way.

The effect of lighting upon quality is probably recognized to a greater

[4] R. E. Simpson, "Accidental Lighting Costs," *Trans. I. E. S.*, vol. XXIII, No. 6.
[5] C. C. Munroe and H. A. Cook, *Trans. A. S. M. E. Man.*, 51–8, 1929.

TABLE 17-2   Comparative Production with Old and New Systems of Factory Lighting

Work and shop	Average foot-candles with old system	Average foot-candles with new system	Increase in production with new system, per cent	Additional lighting costs, per cent of payroll
Pulley finishing (Pyott Foundry Co.)	0.2	4.8	35.0	5.0
Soft-metal bearing (Foote Bros.)	4.6	12.7	15.0	1.2
Heavy steel machine (Lee Loader & Body Co.)	3.0	11.5	10.0	1.2
Carburetor assembly (Stromberg Carburetor Co.)	2.1	12.3	12.0	0.9
Plant manufacturing electric and gas irons (Dover Mfg. Co.)	4.0 at tool point	13.5	12.2	2.5
Semi-automatic buffing of brass shell sockets (General Electric Co.)	3.8	11.4	8.5	1.8
Manufacturing piston rings (Detroit Piston Ring Co.)	1.2	18.0	25.8	2.0
Letter separating (U. S. Post Office Dept.)	3.6	8.0	4.4	0.6
Inspection in roller bearing-plant (Timken Roller Bearing Co.)	2.0	20.0	12.5	2.5
Average	2.72	12.5	15.0	1.97

extent than the effect upon production. Most companies are providing quite good lighting at the points where inspection of quality takes place. However, in many cases they fail to provide adequate illumination at the points where the work is originally done in order that quality might be improved at the source. The extent to which lighting may affect quality is illustrated by a situation in a tire factory. A worker was building 6.50–16 white sidewall tires which required great care to assure perfect appearance. Suddenly defects started appearing in the tires which he built, averaging two tires per six-hour shift. These tires, being defective in appearance only, had to be classed and sold as "seconds," resulting in a loss of over $1.00 for each tire. An investigation disclosed that someone had substituted 50-watt bulbs for the two 100-watt bulbs which furnished light for this worker. The correct lamps were replaced, and nothing was said to the worker about the defects. The defects immediately ceased, and no further trouble was experienced. Computation revealed that the saving in electric current through the use of the smaller bulbs amounted to less than $0.01 per shift, and the resulting defects caused a loss of over $2.00. Many other similar cases could be cited to emphasize the effect of lighting upon quality.

AIR CONDITIONING

Air conditioning is similar to lighting in that many of the first industrial installations were made to improve or control quality. After the installations were in use, it was found that output had also been improved.

The first important installations of air conditioning where economy of production was greatly affected were in the textile and perishable food industries. In some of these plants unsuitable weather conditions made production impossible during certain seasons. For example, the dipping of chocolates was extremely difficult in summer months. Air conditioning eliminated all of this trouble. Similar experiences were encountered in the textile, chewing gum, and baking industries. Since these earlier experiences, the use of air conditioning has become widespread, being commonplace in almost every type of industry from entertainment to heavy manufacturing.

A number of cases have shown that proper air conditioning may produce increases in productivity of workers as great as 20 to 25 per cent; increases of 10 per cent are very common. The experiences with the so-called black-out plants built during World War II have provided considerable factual data regarding the results obtained with air conditioning and artificial lighting.

As the use of air conditioning has become common, more and more income and cost data have become available, with the result that, as in the case of accident prevention, economy studies can be based more on numerical data and less on intangibles. However, in most cases there are obvious intangibles which can be rated as favorable or not favorable to the proposal being considered and thus be given due weight in the investment decision.

DRINKING WATER

Drinking water is another factor which has often been neglected but which may have a considerable effect upon output and contentment of workers. This is especially true where work must be done during very hot weather or in high temperatures. Not only should good, cool water be available, but it should be located at places where the workers can obtain it readily without having to take too much time from their work. Considerable progress has been made recently in this respect. Much of this is due to the efforts of companies manufacturing water-dispensing and -cooling equipment. Water-coolers of various types are available in compact units which are reasonable in first cost and will operate for as little as $0.02 per day.

A recent practice is to provide salt for workers who are working in hot places, either in the form of convenient salt tablets or by the addition of salt to the drinking water. This replaces the salt which is lost from the body in perspiration. Replacing this salt gives much greater worker comfort and increases efficiency to a considerable extent. This particular practice has been found to yield very great dividends, both in output and increased morale.

Unlike air conditioning, very few factual, numerical data are available regarding the effect of drinking water upon productivity. Thus in this case one might expect that major reliance would have to be placed on intangible factors.

WASHROOMS

The economy resulting from the provision of clean and attractive washrooms is usually rather difficult to determine. However, a sufficient number of cases have been studied closely to leave no doubt that money invested in such facilities pays adequate dividends. It is unreasonable to expect workers to be neat and efficient in their work if they are forced to use filthy toilet facilities. Even where dirty tasks must be performed, they will usually be done more readily and better if the workers know that adequate washrooms are available where they may remove the evidences of their labor before going to their homes. One can not expect workers to take any pride in their appearance if they are forced to wash in dirty, germ-laden washrooms.

One of the direct results of good washrooms is a decrease in minor disease among the workers, resulting in less lost time due to illness. This alone should repay any investment made for such facilities.

One foundry which installed very elaborate and beautifully tiled shower rooms for its workers stated that the result in increased efficiency and morale among the workers was far beyond any expectation. It was also noticed that the workers began to wear rather good street clothes to work, changing to their work clothes after arriving at the plant. Some foundry workers presented a better appearance when coming to the plant than some of the office workers. This example merely shows that most workers do wish to be clean and want to appear neat and respectable. An effort to help the worker achieve this is bound to be reflected in his work. In addition, it is a long step toward better employee relations.

NOISE REDUCTION

Until rather recently little attention was given to noise reduction. Obviously, determining the costs attributable to noise is not easy. Yet the problem is often a serious one. The extent to which noise may affect economy is illustrated by a judgment of $2,000 which was rendered against a company in Minneapolis in 1938.[6] A woman who lived across the street from the plant brought suit for damages, alleging that the noise from the plant caused her to lose sleep, made her nervous, and inflicted mental anguish. While this is an extreme case, it illustrates what may result from uncontrolled noise.

While it is difficult to obtain a measure of the direct effect of noise on productivity, indirect effects, such as errors and absenteeism, can and have been determined in numerous experiments. In one of these the Aetna Life Insurance Company of Hartford, Connecticut, reduced the noise level in certain offices by 14.5 per cent. The efficiency of the workers increased 8.8 per cent. Errors of the typists decreased 29 per cent, errors of machine operators decreased 52 per cent, employee turnover dropped 47 per cent, and absences decreased 37.5 per cent.

When noise was reduced in the telephone receiving room of a telegraph station, the result was a decrease of 42 per cent in the number of errors and a decrease of 5 per cent in the cost per message. Other tests have been conducted by comparing the number of errors made by typists using regular and noiseless typewriters. The results showed a large reduction in errors when noise was reduced.

If noise is shown to have such pronounced effects upon errors and absenteeism, it seems inescapable that it must also have a direct effect upon productivity. The data available regarding the effect of noise on errors and absenteeism usually are adequate for economy studies concerning investment in noise-control materials.

The effect traffic and street noises have upon the economy of the nation is difficult to determine. Certainly it is not less than has been found to exist in factories and offices. One has only to try to sleep in many expensive hotel rooms while listening to the yelling of newsboys and the honking of automobile horns to become convinced that much remains to be done along the line of noise control.

LABOR TURNOVER

The number of separations from service to an employer during a given period is referred to as *labor turnover*. Its measurement is not entirely standardized, although two methods are generally employed. One is that specified by the Bureau of Labor Statistics of the United States Department of Labor. This bureau's formula is

---

[6] *Business Week*, November 19, 1938, has an account of this case.

$$\text{Labor turnover ratio} = \frac{\text{Number of separations}}{\text{Average number in the working force}}.$$

Another formula which is used by a number of industries is

$$\text{Labor turnover per 100 employees} = \frac{\text{Separations} \times 100}{\text{Average number on the payroll}}.$$

The greatest weakness of both of these formulas is that they give no indication of what percentage of those who were employed at the beginning of any period were employed continuously throughout the period. For example, assume that an average of 1,000 persons were employed during a given period and that the number of separations from employment during that period was 200. The labor turnover would be 20%. This does not mean that only 800 of the 1,000 people who were employed at the beginning of the period were on the payroll at the end of the period. If the period were 200 days, the 20% labor turnover might have been caused by hiring one man at the beginning of each day and discharging him at the end of the day. Thus, although 999 of the 1,000 original employees had been employed continuously, labor turnover, as computed by the formula, would be 20%.

Only a little thought is required to realize that there is considerable expense involved in hiring a new worker and training him to do his work efficiently. The exact cost of this procedure is sometimes difficult to determine, but it is certain that it is becoming more costly all the time as industry becomes more complex. Numerous surveys have been made in order to determine the cost of labor turnover for various companies. These estimates have ranged from $2 to $250 per man. Obviously, the cost will vary with the type of labor involved and the task which is to be performed. A number of estimates place the average cost of labor turnover at $50. As more extensive pre-employment tests and physical examinations are used, the cost of an individual labor turnover increases rapidly. The total cost is made up of employment and personnel office expense, cost of training the worker, medical examination expense, and the costs of unemployment insurance, decreased production during the learning period, possible breakage of equipment because of inexperience, increased supervision, inferior production, and many other items.

By using the measure of labor turnover and the average cost of each change in personnel, it is possible to obtain some idea of how much could be spent profitably in order to reduce labor turnover. For example, if a company normally employing 600 workers experienced a labor turnover of 50%, the yearly cost of this turnover would be

$$600 \times 50\% \times \$50 = \$15,000.$$

If the turnover in labor could be reduced to 25%, the annual saving would be $7,500. Thus the company could well afford to spend $5,000 or $6,000 to obtain such a reduction in labor turnover. In fact, it could afford to spend the entire $7,500, since there are always other profits to be obtained from reduced labor turnover above those which can be measured directly in money. Practically all companies that have spent considerable sums of money to obtain low labor turnover have found that such expenditures have turned out to be very good investments.

EXECUTIVE TURNOVER

Less attention has probably been given to the cost of executive turnover than to that for ordinary labor turnover. This has undoubtedly been due to the fact that the number of executives who leave companies is rather insignificant in comparison with the actual number of ordinary workers. However, if the average cost of labor turnover is $50 per case, the cost of executive turnover is probably from ten to fifty times this amount. It is not at all uncommon for the cost of changing one executive to be several thousand dollars. This is due to the fact that the entire organization of the business may have to be changed and disrupted. If one executive leaves a company, he may take several minor executives with him. When a new executive is brought in from outside the business, he may bring several new men with him. He will also, in most cases, wish to introduce new ideas and procedures which will necessitate considerable expense. The entire cost of such changes is difficult to determine, but it is no small amount. While the turnover of executives may result in gain in the long run, it is apparent that considerable immediate costs do attend such turnover.

Expenditure of money to assure executive loyalty and low turnover usually results in many indirect returns. For example, satisfied and loyal executives will usually be interested in the welfare and loyalty of those who work under them. This will be reflected in the turnover of the ordinary workmen.

TRAINEE TURNOVER

Another phase of labor turnover is worth considering. This is the turnover of young college graduates who are just entering the industrial world, particularly of young engineers and technically trained graduates. It is usually a considerable time before these workers really earn a profit for their employers. Many companies use the first six months or more of their employment as a training period. As a result, the expense of turnover of this class of workers is rather high. Therefore a number of companies have taken rather extensive steps to reduce the turnover rate. Most of the effort has been to improve the initial selection procedure. As a result of economy studies of this problem, some companies have found it economical to spend money to bring prospective engineers to the plant for inspection trips and careful interviews, thus avoiding a high percentage of resignations later. Another procedure which has been very successful, when properly conducted, is summer employment between the junior and senior years of college. Some of the companies use as careful selection procedures for such summer employment as they use for employment after graduation.

WAGES

The matter of wage payment is an entire subject in itself. It has a very real connection with economy. The most obvious problem is the manner in which labor is compensated for its efforts. All of the various methods of wage payment fall into three essential types: *time wages, piece work,* and *bonus systems.* The extent of the use of these types is the same as the order in which they are given.

The basis of *time wages* is that the worker is paid for the amount of time he works, regardless of the amount that he produces during this time. All salaried workers and those who work by the day, week, or month are paid upon this basis. From the viewpoint of determining the payroll its advantages are obvious. Similarly, the worker always knows how much he is to receive for his work during a given period. Its great weakness lies in the fact that it is very difficult to predict or determine production costs when this method of payment is used, since there is no assurance of the amount of goods which will be produced during any given period. Since the worker receives the same amount, regardless of what he produces, there is not much incentive for him to always do an equal amount of work for the same amount of wages. The effect of variations in production upon the worker's earnings is shown in Figure 17–2. With this method of wage payment there is, of course, no effect. The effect of variations in production upon labor costs for each unit produced is shown in Figure 17–3. It is apparent that any attempt to predict unit labor costs would be very difficult with this method of wage payment.

Time wages are usually advantageous where work of very high quality is to be done. This is especially true when inspection of the completed product is difficult. When a worker is being paid according to the time consumed, he is more likely to do good work. This method of wage payment is also needed where workers are constantly performing different tasks and have no chance to standardize their methods, or where the amount of time required for the task is difficult to predict.

Piece-work payment is used where workers are performing the same operations repeatedly, so that a standardized method of work may be established and the amount of time which should be required may be determined with considerable accuracy. In this method the worker is paid a

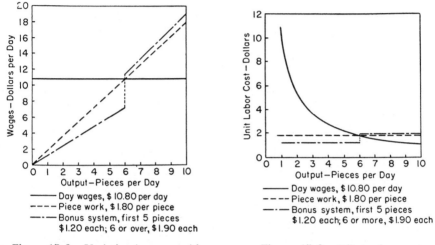

Figure 17–2. Variation in wages with output for three wage payment systems.

Figure 17–3. Effect of wage systems upon unit labor cost.

definite sum for each unit which he produces. His wages are therefore in direct proportion to his output. The results of this method of wage payment are also shown in Figures 17–2 and 17–3. Since the worker's wages vary with his production, payroll accounting is considerably more complicated than for time wages. However, this is offset by the facts that unit labor costs are constant and the employer always receives the same amount of work for a given amount of money. Similarly, the worker who attains great skill and produces more than the average receives extra compensation for his efforts.

There are two serious objections offered by workers to this method of wage-payment. First is the fact that the worker does not know in advance what his earnings will be. This is usually met by the employer's guaranteeing a certain minimum wage, regardless of output, as long as the worker makes a reasonable amount of effort. This guaranteed wage, in many cases, is about 75 per cent of what would be earned by producing a normal day's output. There should always be assurance that the worker will not be penalized for delays that are beyond his control.

The second objection is that piece rates are set too "tight." This is usually due to insufficient or incorrect time studies, or to unfairness on the part of the management. The remedy in both cases is apparent. The fault does not lie in the method of wage-payment.

Several recent surveys have shown that the piece-work method of payment is becoming more widely used. Its simplicity, both to the management and the worker, is one of its great advantages. The worker understands it readily and realizes that he is being paid in proportion to what he produces. It is probably the most satisfactory method of wage-payment when all viewpoints are considered.

Bonus or *incentive wage systems* attempt to obtain greater productive effort from the worker by giving him some type of bonus when his output exceeds a certain arbitrary amount. The systems vary widely, each having been originated by some person with an idea as to what the bonus should be and how it should be paid. Among these are the Taylor Differential Piece-Rate Plan, the Halsey Premium Plan, the Gantt Task and Bonus Plan, and the Emerson Efficiency Bonus Plan. It is characteristic of these plans that the worker's wage is not directly proportional to the amount of his output, nor is the unit labor cost constant. One disadvantage of such systems is that they are so complicated that workers do not understand them and are often not able to compute what they have earned. They are also subject to the disadvantages of incorrect base rates.

From Figures 17–2 and 17–3 it can be seen that both the worker's earnings and the unit labor cost are dependent upon the output. When such a wage payment system is used, the accounting becomes quite complicated. It is apparent that the output per worker would have considerable effect upon the economy of production. For example, if each worker, under the plan illustrated by Figure 17–3, produced five units per six-hour day, the unit labor cost would be only $1.20. However, if each worker produced six units per day the unit labor cost would be increased to $1.90, an increase in labor cost of over 58 per cent. Of course, this would be offset to some extent by a decrease in overhead, but this decrease would be small in comparison to the increase in labor cost.

The bonus plan illustrated in Figures 17–2 and 17–3 is probably the simplest of those which exist, and, as a result, the effect upon the economy of production is not as great as if one of the more elaborate plans were used. A number of them are so complicated that their application is often not understood by the workers, and sometimes it appears that even the management is not fully aware of their effects. Labor unions have been quite universally opposed to the bonus methods of wage payment.

STRIKES

The economic effect of strikes is one which is extremely difficult to determine accurately. This is due, to a great extent, to the fact that both parties to such arguments are usually extravagant in their claims, and truth usually goes out the window. Nearly everyone realizes, however, that such industrial conflict has a tremendous effect upon the companies involved. The effect upon the economy of the workers is usually overlooked.

A number of estimates of the total cost of various strikes have been made. Unfortunately, such figures have not been considered very seriously by those who could profit most from their study. An idea of how much anyone usually profits from a strike may be gained by considering one fairly recent instance. Approximately 1,500 workers of a certain company were on strike for four weeks. The average earnings of the workers of this company were nearly $2.00 per hour for a forty-hour week. Being off the job for four weeks meant a loss of $320.00 for each worker. When the strike was finally settled, the workers had won a wage increase of $0.07 per hour more than the company had originally offered. This meant that 114 weeks would have to pass before the workers would get back the wages they had lost during the strike.[7] From the viewpoint of the company the strike was said to have caused an actual loss of $3,000.00 per day. This was a total loss of $60,000.00 during the duration of the strike. Simple division will show that the company could have paid the wage increase for fourteen weeks for the amount of the strike cost in actual dollars.

It does not take much study to become convinced that the statement "nobody wins in a strike" is no idle platitude. While this is not the correct basis for lasting industrial peace, it is quite possible that considerable progress may be made toward that goal when adequate figures regarding the cost of industrial strikes are available and understood by all parties concerned. There are several groups in this country that are endeavoring to gather cost data on strikes, and undoubtedly much of this data will be available within a few years.

PROBLEMS

17–1 A company is attempting to evaluate the results of increasing the size of its personnel department and expanding its activities. The costs of operating the department were $18,000 per year prior to the expansion and now are $28,000 per year. In addition, some new offices were added

---

[7] Although the workers were receiving strike benefits from the union, this money had come out of their previous earnings.

at a cost of $12,000, which is being written off over a five-year period. Employment and training costs which can be accounted for directly are $30 per employee hired. It has been estimated that the actual total costs, due to decreased production, equipment damage, etc., are probably at least double the direct costs. Since the expansion in the personnel department, the turnover rate has decreased from 40% to 25%. The company has 1,800 employees. If capital is worth 12%, has the expansion of the personnel department paid off?

17–2 A large company, employing 20,000 workers, proposes to give comprehensive aptitude and interest tests to new employees, in order to better fit them to the job openings and thus reduce labor turnover. The present labor turnover rate is 42%, and, in addition, the company expects to be increasing the number of employees by about 300 each year for the next few years. The present cost of hiring and training a new employee is about $45.

The proposed plan of tests would cost $8,000 per year to administer, plus $8 per test. What reduction in labor turnover would have to be obtained to justify the tests solely on the basis of this factor?

17–3 In a certain western state there are 1,300,000 passenger cars and 140,000 trucks in operation. Ninety per cent of the passenger cars and all of the trucks carry public liability and property damage insurance at an average annual premium of $70 per passenger vehicle and $175 on each truck. The premiums of this type of insurance have been increasing at the rate of about 5% per year, and it does not appear that this rate of increase will stop unless some drastic measures are taken.

A $500,000,000 bond issue is proposed to speed the building of a network of freeways. It is estimated that these highways would reduce the existing insurance premiums by 10% and prevent further increases in premiums such as are now occurring. The bonds would have a twenty-year maturity date and bear interest at the rate of $3\frac{1}{2}$%. The state gasoline tax rate would be increased $0.01 per gallon to meet the increased cost of the bonds. One half of the cost of the bond issue can be met out of existing gasoline taxes. Since the new highways would eliminate some old roads and thus avoid their maintenance, it is estimated that the total bill for highway maintenance would not be greater than if the highway program were not accelerated through the bond issue. If the bonds are not issued, highway improvements will take place at a much slower rate on a pay-as-you-go basis out of existing gasoline taxes.

Make an economy study, and recommend what should be done. Include a list and evaluation of the intangible factors.

17–4 A foundry having 700 employees had an annual turnover rate of 105% among its workers. The personnel department was reorganized and one new staff member added at an annual cost of $7,000. New washroom

facilities were added at a capital cost of $35,000 and annual main-
tenance and operating costs of $4,000. At the end of one year the
turnover rate had dropped to 50%, and there was some increase in
productivity. However, the direct cost per hire had increased by $10
per person hired. If the improvements were written off on a ten-year
basis, and capital was worth 10%, was the program economically sound?

17–5 Because of a shortage of funds a high school is unable to provide a
driver-training program. A group of parents has proposed that such
training be provided on a cost-fee basis for the students who take the
training. Local automobile dealers have agreed to furnish the necessary
cars without charge, but the school will have to provide insurance and
pay for the gasoline and oil used. The insurance would cost $275 per
year for each car, and the gasoline and oil $550 per car per year. An
instructor would be required for each car at an annual salary of $7,000.
Each car and instructor could train 200 students per year. Insurance
companies have agreed to give a reduction of 15 per cent in the annual
penalty premiums applying to drivers between the ages of sixteen and
twenty-five if they have completed such driver training courses. The
penalty premiums average $85 per year.

a. What fee would have to be charged to each student?

b. Would the program be financially justified, assuming that most of
the students involved would start driving at the minimum legal age of
sixteen?

17–6 The average production per worker on a certain operation has been
24 units per day. The present unit costs for this part are

Labor	$0.70
Material	0.62
Variable overhead	0.10
Fixed overhead	0.40
Total	$1.82

It is estimated that each worker could produce several extra units
each day if given the proper incentive. The company proposes to pay a
bonus of $0.10 for the first unit over 24 produced each day, $0.20 for
the second unit, $0.30 for the third, etc.

a. At what output per day for each worker would the company just
break even on this plan?

b. Assuming that 24 units per day was a fair standard, resulting from
proper motion and time studies, would you expect the output to reach
the break-even point? (Consult standard references on motion and time
study for information regarding probable increases in output.)

17–7 In a certain steel mill operation, because of the severe heat and high
degree of attention required if the equipment is operated at maximum

speed, the work crew must have frequent rest periods. To meet anticipated output requirements under these conditions would require three
units of equipment, each costing $1,500,000.

An alternative method of operation is to provide two work crews for
each unit so that each group works for alternate thirty-minute periods.
With this method of operation, only two units of equipment would be
required.

Each work crew would be paid $80 per day and would work 250 days
per year. The plant operates three shifts per day. Operation and maintenance costs on each unit would be $12,000 per year. Taxes and insur-
ance amount to 2% of first cost per year. Payroll taxes and fringe benefits are 10% of payroll. If capital is worth 15%, and the equipment
would be written off over a twenty-year period, which method of operation should be used?

17-8   In harvesting field crops in the Imperial Valley very high temperatures
are encountered during about 100 working days per year. A large ranch
employs many field workers, each receiving $1.40 per hour and working
eight hours per day. The workers customarily have carried canvas water
bags in which the water becomes very warm. It is proposed that a re-
frigerated water tank on a trailer be provided for each group of thirty
workers, together with salt tablets. Each tank would cost $475.00 to
build and about $1.25 per day to operate and maintain. Salt tablets
would cost about $0.05 per worker per day. The equipment would have
to be written off in five years, and capital is worth 10%. What increase
in productivity would be required to justify the use of the water tanks
and salt tablets?

17-9   A large trucking company pays an average of $200 per year for insurance
on its trucks. Its insurance company offers to give a reduction of 10 per
cent in annual insurance premiums if all of the company's drivers complete a safety-training course which is given by a local trade school. The
course would cost the trucking company $30 for tuition and $50 for salary for each driver sent to take the course.

Assuming that the average driver stays with the company for eight
years, that capital is worth 12%, and that the company operates 100
trucks, would the program be a profitable one for the company to
follow?

CHAPTER 18

Effects of

Income Taxes in

Economy Studies

The effects of income taxes have been omitted from the various discussions of economy studies which have been presented in the previous chapters. As was pointed out in Chapter 9, income taxes need not be considered in most economy studies because of the fact that all of the alternatives involve the same types of deductible costs and will produce taxable income. However, as was pointed out, there are at least seven situations wherein income taxes must be included for an economy study to be reliable.[1] These are:

1. Economy studies using the payout method.
2. Economy studies in regulated public utilities.
3. Situations where one alternative involves tax-free income.
4. Situations where one alternative involves investment to provide income through the use of depreciable property while another utilizes capital to pay for nondeductible expenses which produce income.
5. Economy studies to enable the true cost of capital to be determined where a portion is borrowed.
6. Situations where income is derived from foreign subsidiaries.
7. Situations where short-term financing may be done with accumulated tax money which is not yet due for payment.

All but one of these (situation 6) will be discussed in this chapter.

Since income tax rates in recent years have become quite high, resulting in a large proportion of income going to pay taxes, some people prefer to include income taxes in all economy studies. It is therefore essential that

[1] See page 224 for a more complete statement of these situations.

those making economy studies have a reasonably thorough understanding of the basic principles involved in income tax calculations and their relationship to economy studies. It must be remembered, however, that income tax regulations are complex; if the situation involved appears to be at all complicated, competent tax counsel should be consulted.

BASIC PRINCIPLES RELATING TO INCOME TAXES

Income taxes are levied by the federal government on both personal and corporation incomes. They also are collected by many states. While the income tax regulations of most of the states have the same basic features as those of the federal regulations, there is a great variation in the tax rates. In addition, state income taxes are in most cases much less than the federal taxes. Therefore, no attempt will be made to discuss state income taxes. An understanding of the federal income tax regulations will enable one to apply the proper procedures if state taxes must be considered.

Income taxes are disbursements, as are any other costs, and thus reduce the profits available to owners and stockholders. However, there is an important difference in that income taxes are computed as a percentage of "taxable income," which is equal to gross revenue minus all out-of-pocket costs and depreciation and certain specified, permitted deductions. Thus, while income taxes are disbursements, they are dependent upon profits, whereas profits are dependent upon the normal disbursements. Therefore, income taxes can not be included in the usual profit determination, but must be included in computing the amount of profit available to owners.

It must also be remembered that income taxes are determined by man-made tax rates which are changed from time to time and which are subject to social, economic, and political pressures. In general, they are based upon "ability to pay." However, other factors frequently are taken into consideration. One such example will be discussed later in connection with corporation income tax rates. It is therefore difficult, and usually not sound practice, to attempt to predict what future changes may occur in income tax rates when considering income taxes in economy studies.

Another basic principle involved in income taxes is the assumption that profit in any given year can be determined precisely. As was pointed out in Chapter 5, depreciation cost can not be determined exactly until the depreciable asset has been retired from service. Therefore, the annual amounts which are charged as depreciation cost are no more than estimates and thus are seldom correct. It is apparent that, in order for annual profit to be computed and for income taxes to be determined, the depreciation estimate must be assumed to be correct.

A final principle, which considerably complicates income tax consideration in economy studies, is that income tax rates usually are set up on a block
pattern, so that the rates increase on added increments of profits. For example, the 1957 federal income tax rates on personal income vary from 20% on
taxable income not over $2,000 to 91% on all taxable income over
$200,000 per year. Similarly, for corporations the rates vary from 30% for
the first $25,000 of taxable income to 52% of taxable income above $25,000
per year. While the rates usually increase with increased taxable income, this
is not always true. For instance, the 1950 federal income tax rates for
corporations started at 21% on taxable income up to $5,000, increased to a
maximum of 53% on taxable income from $25,000 to $50,000, and then
decreased to 38% on taxable income above $50,000. This was an obvious
exception to the general "ability-to-pay" principle.

PERSONAL FEDERAL INCOME TAX

Every citizen or resident of the United States having an annual gross
income of $600 or more must file an income tax return if he or she is less
than 65 years of age. Those 65 or older must file a return if their gross

TABLE 18–1   Federal Income Tax Rates for Single Taxpayers, Except Those Qualifying
as Head of a Household, and Married Persons Filing Separate Returns

If taxable income is		Income tax is	
Not over $2,000..........		20% of taxable income.	
Over—	But not over—		of excess over—
$2,000	— $4,000.........	$400, plus 22%	— $2,000
$4,000	— $6,000.........	$840, plus 26%	— $4,000
$6,000	— $8,000.........	$1,360, plus 30%	— $6,000
$8,000	— $10,000.........	$1,960, plus 34%	— $8,000
$10,000	— $12,000........	$2,640, plus 38%	— $10,000
$12,000	— $14,000........	$3,400, plus 43%	— $12,000
$14,000	— $16,000........	$4,260, plus 47%	— $14,000
$16,000	— $18,000........	$5,200, plus 50%	— $16,000
$18,000	— $20,000........	$6,200, plus 53%	— $18,000
$20,000	— $22,000........	$7,260, plus 56%	— $20,000
$22,000	— $26,000........	$8,380, plus 59%	— $22,000
$26,000	— $32,000........	$10,740, plus 62%	— $26,000
$32,000	— $38,000........	$14,460, plus 65%	— $32,000
$38,000	— $44,000........	$18,360, plus 69%	— $38,000
$44,000	— $50,000........	$22,500, plus 72%	— $44,000
$50,000	— $60,000........	$26,820, plus 75%	— $50,000
$60,000	— $70,000........	$34,320, plus 78%	— $60,000
$70,000	— $80,000........	$42,120, plus 81%	— $70,000
$80,000	— $90,000........	$50,220, plus 84%	— $80,000
$90,000	— $100,000.......	$58,620, plus 87%	— $90,000
$100,000	— $150,000.......	$67,320, plus 89%	— $100,000
$150,000	— $200,000.......	$111,820, plus 90%	— $150,000
$200,000	....	$156,820, plus 91%	— $200,000

annual income is $1,200 or more. Husbands and wives may file joint returns so that their total tax will be twice the tax on one-half of their total taxable income, thus resulting in a lower tax than if both filed separate returns.

The 1957 federal income tax rates on individual incomes are shown in Tables 18–1 and 18–2. Since the tax is based on "taxable income" it is

TABLE 18–2   Federal Income Tax Rates for Married Taxpayers Filing Joint Returns

If taxable income is		Income tax is	
Not over $4,000..........		20% of taxable income.	
Over—	But not over—		of excess over—
$4,000	— $8,000.........	$800, plus 22%	— $4,000
$8,000	— $12,000........	$1,680, plus 26%	— $8,000
$12,000	— $16,000........	$2,720, plus 30%	— $12,000
$16,000	— $20,000........	$3,920, plus 34%	— $16,000
$20,000	— $24,000........	$5,280, plus 38%	— $20,000
$24,000	— $28,000........	$6,800, plus 43%	— $24,000
$28,000	— $32,000........	$8,520, plus 47%	— $28,000
$32,000	— $36,000........	$10,400, plus 50%	— $32,000
$36,000	— $40,000........	$12,400, plus 53%	— $36,000
$40,000	— $44,000........	$14,520, plus 56%	— $40,000
$44,000	— $52,000........	$16,760, plus 59%	— $44,000
$52,000	— $64,000........	$21,480, plus 62%	— $52,000
$64,000	— $76,000........	$28,920, plus 65%	— $64,000
$76,000	— $88,000........	$36,720, plus 69%	— $76,000
$88,000	— $100,000.......	$45,000, plus 72%	— $88,000
$100,000	— $120,000.......	$53,640, plus 75%	— $100,000
$120,000	— $140,000.......	$68,640, plus 78%	— $120,000
$140,000	— $160,000.......	$84,240, plus 81%	— $140,000
$160,000	— $180,000.......	$100,440, plus 84%	— $160,000
$180,000	— $200,000.......	$117,240, plus 87%	— $180,000
$200,000	— $300,000.......	$134,640, plus 89%	— $200,000
$300,000	— $400,000.......	$223,640, plus 90%	— $300,000
$400,000	....	$313,640, plus 91%	— $400,000

essential to have an understanding of how this is determined. Basically the method of computing taxable income for individuals is as follows:

1. Income from all wages, salaries, bonuses, commissions and other compensation $.....
2. Income from interest, dividends, rents or royalties   .....
3. Net income from business or profession   .....
4. Income from capital gains   .....
5. Total adjusted gross income $.....

6. Less deductions:
   a. Contributions to religious, educational and
       charitable organizations $.....
   b. Interest paid   .....
   c. Taxes paid   .....
   d. Medical expenses in excess of 3 per cent of ad-
       justed gross income   .....
   e. Loss from fire, storms or other casualties not
       covered by insurance   .....
   f. Exemptions for self and dependents   .....
   Total deductions and exemptions $..... $.....
7. Taxable income $.....

CAPITAL GAINS AND LOSSES

The nature of the income in situations 1, 2, and 3 in the previous listing is quite obvious. Income from capital gains, however, requires some explanation. Capital gains are net income received from the sale of an asset, provided the person (or corporation) is not a dealer in such assets. This provisions thus excludes the sale of stock in trade. The assets most commonly involved in capital gains are stocks and bonds, real estate, and equipment.

Capital gains are divided into two categories, which are taxed differently. *Short-term* capital gains arise from the sale of assets which have been held for not more than six months. Such gains, or losses, are treated in the same manner as other income. *Long-term* capital gains, or losses, arise from the sale of assets which have been held more than six months. The tax on this type of gains may be computed by two methods, either of which assures that the tax on the net long-term gains will not exceed 25%.

Using the first method, one-half of the excess of net long-term capital gains over short-term capital losses is added to the regular income, and the income tax is then figured in the usual way. If, in using this procedure, the highest tax bracket does not exceed 50%, no part of the capital gains is taxed at more than 25%; that is, 50% of one-half of the net capital gains. Thus for individuals whose incomes do not place them in a tax bracket higher than 50% when one-half the capital gains are included, this method can be used.

The alternative procedure should be used by those with large incomes. The tax on ordinary income, exclusive of capital gains, is computed. The tax on the capital gains is then taken as 25% of these gains, and added to the tax on the regular income. Thus, using this procedure, regardless of what the tax rate is on regular income, the tax on capital gains is a constant 25%. This method of computation has obvious advantages for those with large incomes.

If net short-term capital gains exceed net long-term capital losses in a given year, the excess is taxed as ordinary income. If, however, the net long-term gains exceed the net short-term losses for a given year, the excess may be reduced by 50 per cent and entered as income.

CARRY-OVER OF GAINS AND LOSSES

Special provisions are made for balancing gains and losses for individuals and corporations. For individuals, if the summation of short-term and long-term gains and losses in a given year results in a net loss for the year, a tax-payer may deduct such a loss from his taxable income for the year, provided the deduction does not exceed the amount of his taxable income computed without consideration of capital gains or loses or $1,000, whichever sum is smaller. If the loss exceeds the permissible deduction for the current year, the remainder may be used to reduce taxes, on a similar basis, during the five following years.

The carry-over provisions for corporations are somewhat different and will be discussed later.

PERMISSIBLE DEDUCTIONS FOR INDIVIDUALS

Since the rules governing deductions change from times to time, when one must deal with income taxes he should consult the latest rules of the Bureau of Internal Revenue. For 1957 they were essentially as follows.

The contributions may not exceed 20 per cent of the adjusted gross income, except that they may be increased to 30 per cent of adjusted gross income if all of the additional 10 per cent is contributed to churches, tax-exempt educational institutions or hospitals, or certain medical research organizations.

Virtually all taxes can be deducted, including retail sales taxes and state income taxes, except those levied by the federal government.

Each individual taxpayer under 65 years of age is entitled to a deduction of $600 for himself and for each dependent. A dependent is defined as a person who receives 50 per cent or more of his or her support from the tax-payer and whose annual earnings are less than $600. The $600 limitation does not apply to a dependent child of the taxpayer who is less than nineteen years of age or who is a full-time student in a recognized educational institution taking predominantly day-time classes. For example, a taxpayer having a wife and two children may claim four exemptions of $600 each, a total of $2,400.

Persons 65 years old or older are entitled to a personal deduction of $1,200 and a $1,200 deduction for a wife or husband 65 years old or older. Blindness entitles a taxpayer or dependent to an additional deduction of $600.

CORPORATION INCOME TAXES

The computation of federal income taxes for corporations is basically similar to the procedure for individual income taxes. Here, again, the tax is imposed on net earnings, the difference between the income derived from the sale of goods or services and the cost of providing them. Obviously, since the operations of a corporation are usually much more complex than those of an individual, the forms for reporting corporation income taxes are considerably more complicated than those used for individual income taxes, and somewhat different deductions are permitted. Corporations can not deduct items of a personal nature, such as dependents, medical care, etc., but are entitled to deductions for income received as dividends, or from certain governmental obligations, and for some organizational expenses which would not be applicable to an individual. There also is a major difference in the manner in which capital gains and losses may be handled.

Since the regulations regarding corporation income taxes may be changed from year to year, it is important that anyone who must deal with economy studies in which income taxes play a significant part should be familiar with the current provisions. However, the basic considerations seldom are affected. Corporation incomes are subject to two taxes—the normal tax and the surtax. For 1957 the normal tax rate was 30% of the taxable income, and the surtax rate was 22% of taxable income in excess of $25,000. It is thus apparent that for a small corporation having a taxable income of $25,000 or less the tax rate is 30%, while for a large corporation with a larger taxable income the tax rate approaches 52%. The intent of the surtax is to give a tax advantage to smaller corporations. Supposedly the lower income tax rate would help new, small corporations during their early years. However, it adds a complicating factor when income taxes are included in economy studies. The basic procedure for computing corporation income tax is as follows:

1. Gross income from sales   . . . . .
2. Less cost of producing goods or services
    a. Out-of-pocket costs   . . . . .
        (Material, labor, supervision, etc.)
    b. Deductions   . . . . .
        (Compensation of officers, repairs, interest,
        taxes, contributions, losses due to fire or storm,
        amortization, depreciation, depletion)
    c. Special deductions   . . . . .
        (Partially tax-exempt interest, dividends-
        received deductions)
    Total costs   . . . . .
3. Taxable income   . . . . .
4. Normal tax
    Taxable income × normal tax rate (0.30)   . . . . .
5. Surtax
    (Taxable income − $25,000) × surtax rate (0.22)   . . . . .
6. Total normal tax plus surtax (Items 4 plus 5)   . . . . .

Because a number of the deductions, such as depreciation, amortization, and depletion, involve long-range, continuing activity, it is apparent that the annual income tax is a computed amount, based upon the long-range assumptions. Thus there is in all income tax computations a certain amount of possible error. It is important to keep this fact in mind when including income taxes in economy studies.

CAPITAL GAINS AND LOSSES FOR CORPORATIONS

In the case of a corporation, both short- and long-term capital gains are included as income for the current year and are subject to the regular normal and surtax rates. However, an alternative method of computing the tax may be used, in which the tax on the excess net long-term capital gain less short-term capital loss is computed separately from the tax on the remainder of the income at a rate of 25%. Thus, as in the case of individual incomes, the tax on long-term capital gains never exceeds 25%.

CARRY-BACK AND CARRY-FORWARD PROVISIONS

In recognition of the fact that businesses frequently experience considerable variations in profitability, often resulting in losses in some years and profits in others, the federal income tax laws make certain provisions for balancing poor years against good years and thus reducing income taxes. These commonly are known as "carry-back" and "carry-forward" provisions. Operating losses for years after 1953 may be carried back for three preceding years and/or forward to each of five subsequent years until the loss is exhausted. Thus a loss sustained in 1959 may be carried backward to 1956, 1957, and 1958 and forward to 1960, 1961, 1962, 1963, and 1964. Using this procedure, the loss of one year may be used to reduce the taxable income of a previous or succeeding year. Obviously, if a loss is carried backward, the final income tax for the year to which the loss was assigned will be different than had previously been computed. This would have some effect on previously made economy studies for the assigned year.

TAX ON RETAINED CORPORATION INCOME

Income earned by a corporation is taxed twice—first as corporation income, through the corporation income tax, and secondly as individual income when dividends have been paid to the stockholders. As a result, the total tax on corporation income usually is greater than it would have been if the business had not been incorporated. If the income is retained by a corporation, and not paid as dividends, the individual income tax is avoided. This sometimes is attempted by corporations, particularly those whose stock is held by a small number of persons, as a means of reducing the total income taxes. At the same time, corporations usually need to retain some income to provide for legitimate expansion.

To prevent the retention of income for tax-dodging purposes and yet permit such retention for "reasonable anticipated" needs, the Internal Revenue Code imposes an additional tax on improperly retained earnings. The rulings in this respect have been modified several times; the 1954 code, for example, permitted $60,000 to be retained with no tax but imposed a tax of $27\frac{1}{2}\%$ on the first $100,000 of improperly retained surplus and $38\frac{1}{2}\%$ on all improperly retained amounts above $100,000. The burden of proof is on the corporation as to whether the amount retained is proper. The Bureau of Internal Revenue appears to be very reasonable in this matter, provided the corporation can show lawful, specific, and planned needs for the money, no intent to avoid surtax on the shareholders, and payment of about 70 per cent of the income to the stockholders.

CONSIDERATION OF INDIVIDUAL INCOME TAXES BY CORPORATIONS

The fact that the stockholders must pay individual income tax upon corporation income raises the question as to whether this fact should be taken into account in economy studies of corporations. Ordinarily this is not done. In most cases the ownership of a corporation is spread over a large number of individuals, and there is no practicable way of knowing what the appropriate tax rate would be for the various stockholders. Where a corporation is owned by a few persons this difficulty does not exist. In such cases the effect of the individual income tax sometimes is included in an economy study of a corporation.

WHAT INCOME TAX RATE SHOULD BE USED IN ECONOMY STUDIES?

Since federal income tax rates, on both individual and corporate incomes, and also many state income tax rates, are graduated or set up in blocks, one must consider what rate would apply in a given situation. There is disagreement on this matter. A few persons hold that a computed average rate of tax for a given business should be used for all economy studies. Their theory is that the total income tax paid is based upon the total profits of the enterprise, and that this total profit is a composite of the profits of the various operations of the business. Thus it is held that one can not separate the profits from the individual activities and compute the corresponding income taxes, since the sum of the taxes on the components will not add up to the taxes on the profits of the total enterprise.

While this line of reasoning is valid if an entire enterprise is being considered, it overlooks two important facts. Most economy studies deal only with proposed changes in a portion of the enterprise, and all economy studies deal with alternatives. Economy studies are concerned with what the results will be if one alternative is adopted, as compared with what they will be if a different alternative is followed. Since in most cases it is *differences* which are significant, it therefore follows that the income tax which must be considered is the income tax on the difference in profits from the alternatives. This is clearly an incremental viewpoint. It therefore seems clear that if an economy study involves an entire venture, the income taxes on the entire resulting profits must be considered, and use of an average rate would be justified. On the other hand, if the study involves a change from existing profits, the income tax rate should be the rate which applies to the increment change in profits.

EFFECTS OF TAX-FREE INCOME

Interest received on bonds or other obligations of states, United States' territories, or the District of Columbia, or political subdivisions thereof (such as cities and counties), is exempt from federal income tax. Obviously, where one alternative in an economy study involves income upon which no tax is paid while the income from another alternative is taxable, these facts must be given proper consideration. Ordinarily the interest rate of such tax-exempt securities is from $2\frac{1}{2}\%$ to 4%. An individual who derives his entire income from such securities would thus pay no income tax. In some instances the net income so derived, despite the relatively low interest rates received, may be greater than that which would be obtained from investments yielding larger interest rates but subject to income tax.

As an example of the above situation, consider the case of a single individual who already has a net taxable income of $20,000 and is planning to invest $5,000 of capital. Opportunity A offers a prospective return of 7% per year. Opportunity B is to buy tax-exempt bonds which pay interest at the rate of 4%. From Table 18–1 it is seen that this individual will have to pay income taxes at the rate of 56% on any additional income. His net income, after taxes, from opportunity A would be as follows:

$$\text{Gross income} = \$5,000 \times 0.07 \qquad = \$350$$
$$\text{Additional income tax} = \$350 \times 0.56 = \underline{196}$$
$$\text{Net income} \qquad\qquad\qquad\qquad = \$154$$

This net income of $154 is a return of only 3.08%, so the 4% offered by opportunity B is quite a bit higher.

Obviously the higher the income one has, the more attractive do tax-exempt security provisions become. In most business investment problems, however, the alternative of investing capital in tax-exempt securities is not of sufficient attractiveness to merit much consideration. The probable rate of return from most business investments is high enough so that the net return after taxes is still considerably greater than can be obtained from tax-exempt securities. However, investment in tax-exempt securities is a possibility that should not be overlooked.

DEPRECIABLE VERSUS NONDEPRECIABLE INVESTMENT

Economy studies sometimes involve alternatives where one requires investment in depreciable assets while another does not. For example, capital may be used to purchase income-producing land or to maintain an inventory of goods in a new sales territory. In such studies two factors—income taxes and cash generation—are of considerable importance, although they need not be given much consideration in other economy studies. The following example will illustrate this situation.

	Alternative A (Fixed, depreciable assets)	Alternative B (Inventory, land, etc.)
Investment	$ 50,000	$ 50,000
Income and costs, per year		
Gross income	100,000	100,000
Costs requiring cash outlay (excluding depreciation)	80,000	80,000
Depreciation (5 year straight-line)	10,000	
Total costs for tax purposes	90,000	80,000
Before taxes		
Net income	$ 10,000	$ 20,000
Cash generation	20,000	20,000
After taxes (52% tax rate)		
Net profit	4,800	9,600
Cash generation	14,800	9,600

If an economy study were made of these alternatives, using the usual before-taxes procedure, the results would be as follows:

	Alternative A	Alternative B
Income before depreciation	$20,000	$20,000
Depreciation (25% S.F.)	6,090	
Profit before taxes	$13,910	$20,000
% return	$\frac{\$13,910}{\$50,000} = 28\%$	$\frac{\$20,000}{\$50,000} = 40\%$

According to this study, alternative B, involving no depreciable investment, is much superior to alternative A. If a 52% income tax rate is assumed, the after-tax profits and rates of return would be as follows:

	Alternative A	Alternative B
Profit before taxes	$13,910	$20,000
Income taxes	7,230	10,400
Profit after taxes	$ 6,680	$ 9,600
% return	$\frac{\$6,680}{\$50,000} = 13.4\%$	$\frac{\$9,600}{\$50,000} = 19\%$

Thus, while Alternative B still appears to be more attractive, the difference between the two has decreased from 12 to about $5\frac{1}{2}\%$. This could be anticipated from the fact that income taxes at 52% would take slightly over half of any difference in before-tax profits.

The use of sinking fund depreciation theory, either through the use of the factor $1/s_{\overline{n}|}$ or the proper use of the capital recovery factor, will give correct results when income taxes are included in an economy study, even though straight-line depreciation will be used in actual accounting practice. Table 18-3 shows what would result by using straight-line depreciation for

TABLE 18-3   Total After-Tax Profits Resulting from Investment in Alternative A, Using Straight-Line Depreciation

Year	Profits before taxes plus depreciation	Depreciation	Profits before taxes	Amount in depreciation fund during year	Profits from depreciation fund	Total profits	Income taxes, 52%	Profits after taxes
(1)	(2)	(3)	(4)	(5)	(6)	(7)	(8)	(9)
1	$20,000	$10,000	$10,000	—	—	$10,000	$ 5,200	$ 4,800
2	20,000	10,000	10,000	$10,000	$ 2,500	12,500	6,500	6,000
3	20,000	10,000	10,000	20,000	5,000	15,000	7,800	7,200
4	20,000	10,000	10,000	30,000	7,500	17,500	9,100	8,400
5	20,000	10,000	10,000	40,000	10,000	20,000	10,400	9,600
					Totals		$39,000	$36,000

alternative A. In this table a before-tax profit rate of 25% was assumed (and was used in computing sinking fund depreciation) so that the retained depreciation funds would earn this rate of profit. The actual rate of return on the investment may be determined by equating the receipts and disbursements. Thus

$$\$50,000 = \$4,800\ v^1 + \$6,000\ v^2 + \$7,200\ v^3 + \$8,400\ v^4$$
$$+ \$9,600\ v^5 + \$50,000\ v^5.$$

Solving this equation for i gives a rate of return of approximately $13\frac{1}{2}\%$, virtually the same as was obtained by the sinking fund calculation.

The same type of calculation applied to alternative B, which would provide a uniform after-tax annual profit of $9,600 for five years and the recovery of the $50,000 investment at the end of that time, results in an annual rate of profit of 19%.

While the effect of income taxes upon the relative profitabilities of alternatives A and B is significant, the matter of cash generation is also important. The amount of cash which becomes available each year during the life of an investment is of great concern to most businesses. It was noted that *before taxes* the cash generation was the same for both alternatives—$20,000. However, when income taxes were considered, there was a cash generation of $14,800 for alternative A but of only $9,600 for alternative B.

This obviously is due to the fact that since alternative A involved depreciable assets, the tax-free amount set aside each year for depreciation is available for reinvestment. In the case of alternative B the original investment is not recovered until the end of the assumed five-year period. Therefore, if cash generation is an important factor, alternative A would have a distinct advantage in this respect, tending to offset the slightly greater rate of return obtainable by investment in alternative B.

Thus this example illustrates the fact that if one is interested in the cash generation of alternatives, income taxes should be included in the study. It should be pointed out that some persons appear to attach too much importance to cash generation, sometimes neglecting the over-all rate of return.

EFFECT OF DEPRECIATION METHOD ON INCOME TAXES

Considerable confusion exists as to the effect of the various depreciation methods on the amount of income taxes that must be paid. This appears to be due to the obvious fact that if the sum-of-the-years'-digits or the declining-balance methods are used in accounting, rather than the straight-line procedure, a greater depreciation cost is deducted during the first few years, resulting in lower net income and income taxes during these years. The fact that the depreciation funds usually are kept in the business and thus produce additional taxable income is overlooked.

The results of this situation may be seen by comparing the data in Table 18–4 with those in Table 18–3. Table 18–4 applies to the same invest-

TABLE 18–4 Total After-Tax Profits Resulting from Investment in Alternative A when SYD Depreciation Is Used

Year	Profits before taxes plus depreciation	SYD Depreciation	Profits before taxes	Amount in depreciation fund during year	Profits from depreciation fund	Total profits	Income taxes, 52%	Profits after taxes
(1)	(2)	(3)	(4)	(5)	(6)	(7)	(8)	(9)
1	$20,000	$16,660	$ 3,340	—	—	$ 3,340	$ 1,738	$ 1,602
2	20,000	13,340	6,660	$16,660	$ 4,160	10,820	5,640	5,180
3	20,000	10,000	10,000	30,000	7,500	17,500	9,100	8,400
4	20,000	6,660	13,340	40,000	10,000	23,340	12,130	11,210
5	20,000	3,340	16,660	46,660	11,665	28,325	14,720	13,605
						Totals	$43,328	$39,997

ment situation as in Table 18–3—a $50,000 investment depreciated over a five-year period and average before-tax earnings of 25% on the accumulated depreciation funds. It will be noted that in this particular case the total income taxes and profits after taxes are somewhat greater when the SYD depreciation method is used. However, when the actual rate of profit is computed by equating the present worth of the receipts and disbursements, it is found to be approximately 14%, virtually the same as when the straight-line method was used. The use of SYD depreciation produces higher *total* computed profits, while straight-line depreciation gives higher *immediate* computed profits. When the effect of time is properly considered, the results are virtually identical. Obviously the results in any particular case will depend upon the relative profitability of the major investment and the reinvested depreciation funds, and the tax rate involved. However, there is seldom any significant long-range difference. Although there may be an immediate advantage in changing from straight-line to SYD depreciation, this advantage usually involves some rather dubious guessing as to what future profits and tax rates will be.

EFFECT OF DEPRECIATION METHOD ON AFTER-TAX ECONOMY STUDIES

While it is possible to use other depreciation methods than the sinking fund procedure, if properly modified, in economy studies which do not consider income taxes, it is difficult to do so when income taxes are included. Therefore, if after-tax studies are made on an annual basis it is easiest to use sinking fund depreciation. However, it should be remembered that the interest or profit rate used in the sinking fund calculation should be the before-tax rate. As was shown in Table 5–2, the profits earned by the accumulated depreciation funds (Column 6) belong to the depreciation fund. Since these profits are tax-deductible, the profit rate of these earnings obviously is the before-tax rate. If this procedure of using sinking fund depreciation, based on the before-tax profit rate, is followed, the before-tax profits can be found in the usual manner and the income tax can then be computed by applying the tax rate to these profits. Deduction of the income tax will then give the after-tax profits.

Straight-line or SYD depreciation can be used in economy studies by utilizing the receipts vs. disbursements method. Income taxes are disbursements. However, it must be remembered that depreciation is not a disbursement, but is used in computing the proper amount of income tax.

EFFECT OF INCOME TAXES ON COST
OF BORROWED CAPITAL

Since interest paid for the use of borrowed capital is deductible when computing taxable income, while the cost of owned capital is not, income taxes may have a considerable effect on the cost of capital. If 6%, for example, is paid for the use of borrowed capital which will produce income that is subject to the 52% corporation income tax rate, it follows that the income will be reduced by the amount of the interest paid and that the income tax will, in turn, be reduced by 52% of the interest. Therefore, the net cost of the borrowed capital is only $6\% \times (1 - 0.52) = 2.88\%$. Since the cost of equity capital usually is not less than the ratio of earnings to price (the measure of the return to the stockholder), and this cost is seldom less than 6 to 8%, it is apparent that it usually is desirable, from a cost viewpoint, for a business to use some borrowed capital.

When both equity and borrowed capital are used, it frequently is desirable to determine the average cost of the capital used. To do so, income taxes must be considered. The resulting effect when various percentages of borrowed capital are used is shown in Table 18–5. Many companies use such

TABLE 18–5   Effect of Income Taxes on the Cost of Capital
(52% tax rate; cost of equity capital = 10%; cost of borrowed
capital = 6%)

Equity/borrowed capital relationship	Cost before taxes	Cost after taxes
100% equity	10%	10%
90% equity	10%	10%
10% borrowed	6%	2.9%
Average	9.6%	9.29%
80% equity	10%	10%
20% borrowed	6%	2.9%
Average	9.2%	8.58%
50% equity	10%	10%
50% borrowed	6%	2.9%
Average	8.0%	6.44%

an average capital cost rate for measuring the required profit, after taxes, to justify investments.

EFFECT OF INCOME TAXES ON REPAYMENT
OF BORROWED CAPITAL FROM PROFITS

While the data in Table 18–5 show that income taxes reduce the cost of using borrowed capital, income taxes also make it difficult to repay borrowed capital out of profits. Frequently capital is borrowed for a relatively short time to aid in financing a project which will have a considerably longer economic life and which must be depreciated over a longer life for tax purposes. Under such conditions, it may be necessary to use profits, in addition to depreciation funds, to repay the borrowed capital. If a corporation is operating in the 52% tax bracket, it is apparent that over twice as much profit must be earned, before taxes, as is required for debt repayment. This situation is one reason for the use of the SYD depreciation procedure when borrowed capital is used, since that method provides more tax-free money during the early years of a project for debt repayment.

SHORT ECONOMY STUDY LIFE VERSUS LONG
TAX WRITE-OFF PERIOD

Occasions sometimes arise where, although a piece of equipment, or a property, is expected to have a relatively short life during which it will be used for regular purposes, it may be retained during a longer period for stand-by or emergency use. If the write-off period for income tax purposes must be based upon the extended-use period, the effect of income taxes should be considered.

As an example, consider the following case:

Required investment	$20,000
Active-use life	5 years
Additional stand-by life	5 years
Write-off period for tax purposes	10 years
Net income before depreciation and income taxes	$5,200

If this situation were to be considered *before taxes* on a five-year basis, dividing the income of $5,200 by the $20,000 investment gives a capital recovery factor of 0.26. By referring to Table XXV in the Appendix, it may be seen that this corresponds to an annual interest rate of 10%. However, when income taxes are considered, the situation is found to be considerably less attractive. If the asset could be depreciated by the straight-line procedure over the five-year period of active life, the net taxable income would be $5,200 − $4,000 = $1,200; at a tax rate of 52% the income tax on this amount would be $624. This would leave $4,576 per year for capital recovery and profit, which would be a profit rate of approximately 4.7%.

Since it is stipulated, however, that the asset must be written off over a ten-year period for tax purposes, the actual deduction each year for depreciation would be only $2,000. As a result, this would leave a net taxable income of $3,200 during each of the first five years. Income taxes on this amount would be $1,664, leaving an after-tax recovery of $3,536 per year. However, during each of the following five years there would be a deduction of $2,000 for depreciation to offset taxable income from other sources. Thus a tax saving of $2,000 × 0.52 = $1,040 would result during the sixth through the tenth years. The total income and disbursement relationship is

$$\$3.536 \ a_{\overline{5}|} + \$1,040 \ a_{\overline{5}|}v^5 = \$20,000.$$

Solving this equation for i gives a return of approximately 2½% as the rate of profit after taxes. It may thus be seen that where an asset must for tax purposes be written off over a substantially longer period than the active, income-producing life, the effect of income taxes should be considered. If such property is disposed of at the end of the active-use period, it may be possible to establish immediately the capital gain or loss and thus escape the necessity for an extended write-off period.

EFFECT OF DEPLETION ALLOWANCES

As was discussed in Chapter 5, income from investment in certain natural resources is subject to depletion allowances before income taxes are computed. Under certain conditions, notably where the taxpayer is in a relatively high tax bracket, depletion provisions in the tax law can provide considerable savings.

As an example, consider the case of a married individual who has a present net taxable income of $100,000.00. He spends $100,000.00 to drill and develop a new oil well which has an estimated reserve of 200,000 barrels. Oil is produced and sold in accordance with the schedule shown in Coluumn (2) of Table 18–6 to produce the gross income shown in Column (3).

The depletion allowance which may be deducted in a given year may be based on a fixed percentage of the gross income (27½% for oil), provided the deduction does not exceed 50% of the net income before such deduction. Depletion, computed in this manner, is shown in Column (7) of Table 18–6. Another method is to base depletion on the estimated investment cost of the product. In this case the estimated 200,000 barrels of oil in

Table 18-6 Capital Recovery Provided by an Oil Well Using Cost and Percentage Depletion Allowances when Computing Income Taxes

Year (1)	Barrels of oil sold (2)	Gross income (3)	Net income before depletion and income taxes (4)	50% of net income (5)	Cost depletion at $0.50 per barrel (6)	Depletion allowance at 27½% of gross income (7)	Net taxable income (8)	Income tax at 75%, 78% and 81% rates (9)	Capital recovery (net income after taxes plus depletion) (10)
1	70,000	$140,000	$80,000	$40,000	$35,000	$38,500 [a]	$41,500	$31,815	$48,185
2	60,000	120,000	70,000	35,000	30,000	33,000 [a]	37,000	20,460	49,540
3	45,000	90,000	48,000	24,000 [b]	22,500	24,750	24,000	18,120	29,880
4	20,000	40,000	24,000	12,000	10,000	11,000 [a]	13,000	9,750	14,250
5	5,000	8,500	2,500	1,250	2,500 [c]	2,340	0	0	2,500

[a] Percentage depletion shown deducted.
[b] Only amount shown can be deducted due to percentage depletion exceeding 50% of net income.
[c] Cost depletion deducted since it exceeds percentage depletion.

the well cost $100,000.00. Depletion may therefore, if desired, be charged at the rate of $0.50 per barrel, as shown in Column (6).

The net taxable income resulting from the most favorable application of these depletion allowances is shown in Column (8). Since the taxpayer already has a net taxable income of $100,000.00, the first $20,000.00 of additional income will be taxed at a 75% rate, the second $20,000.00 at a 78% rate, and any portion of the next $20,000.00 at 81%, thus giving the income tax shown in Column (9). Column (10) shows the capital recovery (net after-tax income plus depletion allowance) provided to the investor. By equating the sum of the present values of the capital recoveries shown to the $100,000.00 of investment, it is found that the rate of profit after taxes is approximately 20%. Similarly the before-tax rate of profit—using the data in Column (4)—is approximately 40%.

If the same individual were to invest his $100,000.00 in an ordinary business venture which would produce a before-tax rate of return of 40% (a net taxable income of $40,000.00), the annual income tax would be $30,600.00, leaving an after-tax profit of $9,400.00, or 9.4%. When this is compared with the 20% after-tax rate of profit resulting from the oil well, the advantages of depletion allowances become quite obvious. Likewise, it is evident that if any alternative involving depletion is compared with one where ordinary depreciation must be used, it is essential that income taxes be considered.

EFFECT OF INCOME TAXES ON PAYOUT PERIOD

In computing the payout period for any project it is essential that income taxes be included in the calculations. Since the payout period is the length of time required for recovery of the invested capital, it is obvious that only the income remaining after all taxes are paid can be applied to the desired end.

As is pointed out in Chapter 8, the payout period may be computed either with or without the inclusion of a specified rate of return on the invested capital. This is purely a matter of preference.

For an example of the effect of income taxes on the payout period, consider the case of a corporation, already in the 52% income tax bracket, which is considering investment of $50,000 in a project which will produce an annual gross income of $15,000. Operation, maintenance, and overhead costs, exclusive of depreciation, are estimated to be $5,000 per year. Straight-line depreciation will be used on a ten-year basis. The payout period, excluding any profit, would be:

Gross income		$15,000
O + M + OH	$5,000	
Depreciation	5,000	
		10,000
Net taxable income		$ 5,000
Income taxes		2,600
Net income		$ 2,400

Available for payout = $2,400 + $5,000 = $7,400
Payout period = $50,000/$7,400 = 6.75 years.

If income taxes were omitted from this determination, the payout period would be only five years.

LEASING VERSUS PURCHASING OF ASSETS

In recent years there has been a considerable increase in the practice of leasing rather than purchasing certain assets. Most frequently automobiles, trucks, or buildings are involved, but the practice is being applied increasingly to various other types of equipment, ranging from electronic computers to lift trucks. In most cases it is essential to consider the income tax implications in order to compare accurately the two alternatives of leasing and purchasing.

The reasons companies decide to lease rather than purchase are not as simple and clear as might be expected. One quite naturally would think that a decision in favor of leasing would be based on the fact that it was more economical, yet this very often is not the basis for the decision. A recent study [2] of 35 companies which had leased fleets of automobiles and trucks revealed that in the majority of cases no detailed comparison of the costs of leasing versus purchasing had been made. The major reasons given by these companies were in order of frequency:

1. Leasing freed needed working capital, or enabled needed equipment to be acquired without going into debt.
2. Leasing was thought to have some income tax advantages.
3. Leasing reduced maintenance and administrative problems; for example, it eliminated the necessity for a company to be a fleet operator, leaving this to the specialist.
4. Leasing was cheaper.

Since leasing is only one of several ways of obtaining working capital, a decision to lease should consider the cost of obtaining capital by all possible

[2] J. F. Rodgers, *An Investigation of the Reasons Used to Justify the Leasing of Trucks and Automobiles by Corporations,* M.S. thesis, University of California, 1958.

methods. In the study cited, it was found that very few of the companies had made such a comparison. It is true that borrowing capital establishes some fixed obligations, but most leases can not be cancelled, or can be only with costly penalties. A lease is essentially a 100 per cent mortgage on property.

A number of studies have shown that there is no real income tax advantage in leasing. This is particularly true since the declining-balance and sum-of-the-years'-digits methods have been permitted for depreciation. The lessor can charge no more for depreciation than can the owner of assets. If assets are leased, the annual lease payments are deducted in computing income taxes, while if the assets are purchased, annual depreciation is deducted. Most companies have now come to realize that leasing does not offer tax advantages, but the myth still persists in some quarters.

There may or may not be savings in maintenance costs through leasing. This will depend on the actual circumstances, which should be carefully evaluated in each case. There is no doubt that leasing usually does simplify maintenance problems, and this may be an important factor. Also, many indirect costs, which frequently are difficult to determine, will usually be associated with ownership.

In many instances leasing can be shown to be cheaper than owning, but the actual comparative costs and all other factors should be considered before a decision to lease is made.

LEASING VERSUS PURCHASING AN AUTOMOBILE

There are different lease plans available to both individuals and corporations for various types of assets. However, the significant facts in economy studies of leasing versus purchasing may be illustrated by an example of the leasing of automobiles.

Three types of lease plans are commonly used for automobiles and trucks. *Maintenance leases* usually provide that the lessor will pay nearly all maintenance costs, such as motor repair, brake relining, tire replacement, and the cost of license fees and insurance. *Net lease* plans do not cover maintenance costs, providing only the automobile for a specified period of time. *Finance leases* supply only the asset for a specified period of time, after which the automobile is returned to the lessor, or the lessee may have an option to purchase it at a stipulated price or receive any amount above a fixed price when it is sold second-hand. Unless this type of lease is very carefully worded, it may be held by the Bureau of Internal Revenue not to be a lease but a purchase agreement.

Table 18–7 shows the comparative cost data for owning and leasing an automobile. These data were compiled for a 1958 model Chevrolet to be

TABLE 18–7 Comparative Costs of Owning and Leasing a 1958 Chevrolet by a Corporation (12,000 miles per year; 2-year trade-in; 52% income tax)

	Item	Purchase	Lease
A	Depreciation or lease cost	$ 750.00	$1,206.00
B	Operation and maintenance	555.30 [a]	391.40 [b]
C	Sales tax	50.00	48.24
D	License fees	48.00	
E	Insurance	193.17 [c]	121.67 [d]
F	Total cost	$1,596.47	$1,767.31
G	Less added income	150.00 [e]	500.00 [f]
H	Net total cost	1,446.47	1,267.31
I	Less reduction in income tax [g]	752.16	659.00
J	Net annual cost after income taxes	$ 694.31	$ 608.31
K	Monthly cost	$ 57.86	$ 50.69

[a] Includes gasoline, lubrication, oil filter, oil changes, washing and polishing, and such maintenance as tune-up, carburetor cleaning, repacking front wheel bearings, brake adjustments, wheel aligning, tires, brake relining, and nonroutine maintenance. All actual costs converted to equivalent uniform annual costs by use of proper annuity factors using 20% nominal rate.

[b] Includes gasoline, oil, washing and polishing, and second replacement of tires.

[c] Comprehensive and $100 deductible collision, personal liability, property damage, and medical payments.

[d] Personal liability, property damage, and medical payments.

[e] Average amount in depreciation reserve $750 at 20% before-tax profit rate.

[f] $2,500 available for investment in business at 20% before-tax profit rate.

[g] 52% income tax rate assumed.

used as one of a fleet by a corporation in the 52% income tax bracket. The lease terms were those offered by a national leasing company. It was determined that this car could have been purchased at fleet prices for $2,500.00, and it was estimated that the trade-in value at the end of two years would be $1,000.00, assuming 12,000 annual mileage. All operating and maintenance costs were estimated very carefully, making use of actual records obtained from several sources. The corporation had a before-tax earnings rate of 20%, so this was used in all the calculations.

Because of the short time involved and since income taxes were to be computed on the basis of actual accounting data, straight-line depreciation was used in the computations in Table 18–7. The average profits that would be earned by the accumulated depreciation funds in the case of a purchased car, or by the capital not tied up in the automobile in the case of leasing, were deducted (Line *G*) in order to determine the net cost of each plan (Line *H*) before income taxes were considered. Since the net cost of operating the automobile can be deducted from income before computing income taxes, in both cases 52% of the net cost is deducted from income taxes, as shown in Line *I*. Thus, as shown in Line *J*, the net annual cost after income taxes if the automobile were purchased would be $694.31, while the corresponding cost through leasing would be $608.31.[3]

Since the operation and maintenance costs for the car would be nearly the same for either the lessor or an owner, it is apparent that the lower net cost through leasing is due to the fact that the leasing company is able to acquire the car from the manufacturer at a lower cost and to sell it second hand at a higher price. This fact also enables the leasing company to make a satisfactory profit on its operations. This example also brings out the basic fact that whether it will be cheaper to lease or purchase depends primarily on the cost of capital, the income tax rates, and the depreciable cost of the asset for the lessor and lessee. Leasing often is a desirable method of obtaining the use of assets, but there is no inherent or magic cost-saving element in leasing.

AN EXAMPLE OF LEASING VERSUS PURCHASING OF BUILDINGS

Table 18–8 shows a method for making a comparative cost analysis of leasing versus purchasing a factory site and building. In this case the land would cost $20,000 and the building $100,000. The corporation has a 50% income tax rate and would borrow the entire amount required to purchase the facility at an interest rate of 6%, making repayment at the rate of $2,000 per year plus an additional payment of $20,000 at the end of fifty years when the land could be sold. The before-tax profit rate is 20%. Although the entire cost of the building could be written off in fifty years for tax purposes, it was estimated that the assets could be sold for a total of $40,000 at the end of fifty years, giving a return of the $20,000 invested in the land and a capital gain of $20,000 on the building. The same site and building could be leased for fifty years at a monthly rental of $1,375.

The method of analysis used in Table 18–8 is essentially the same as was used in Table 18–7. It will be noted that, because of the long time and high interest rate involved, the annual value of the future salvage value of the

[3] For an annual mileage of 30,000 miles this same study showed a cost of $95.56 per month if purchased and $73.15 if leased. For a personal car, not used for business purposes, and assuming a 3% interest rate, and 12,000 miles per year, monthly cost was $140.73 if purchased and $136.22 if leased. If used by an individual for business purposes, and assuming a 38% income tax rate, the monthly cost by leasing was $80.29 and by purchasing was $84.85. These data were compiled by Mr. Charles H. Falkner while a graduate student at the University of California.

TABLE 18–8   Comparative Annual Costs of Leasing and Purchasing a Factory Building
Using Borrowed Capital for Purchasing

	Purchase	Lease
Cost of land	$ 20,000	
Cost of building (to be fully depreciated)	100,000	
Write-off and lease period	50 years	50 years
Estimated resale value at end of 50 years	$ 40,000	
Average outstanding loan $\dfrac{\$100,000 + \$2,000}{2} + \$20,000$	$ 71,000	
Interest rate on borrowed capital	6%	
Annual Costs		
Depreciation (amortization)	$ 2,000	
Lease payments		$16,500
Maintenance	2,500	
Insurance	750	
Taxes	2,000	
Interest ($71,000 × 0.06)	4,260	
Total cost before income tax	$ 11,510	$16,500
Less reduction in income tax at 50%	5,755	8,250
Annual cost after income tax	$ 5,755	$ 8,250
Less equivalent annual income from sale of property at end of 50 years	30	
Net annual cost	$ 5,725	$ 8,250

property is very small, and the possible future value of the property therefore has very little effect on the economy of the situation.

In this particular case it would be cheaper to purchase the property than
to lease it. Obviously where money can be borrowed at an interest rate considerably less than the profit rate of the company, and one half of the interest
cost is chargeable to income taxes, this will have a very considerable effect
in a decision concerning leasing or purchasing.

INCOME TAXES BASED ON INVESTED CAPITAL OR COST OF MONEY

Income taxes, while actually computed on the basis of taxable income,
may be computed on the basis of invested capital for economy study purposes under certain conditions. Using this procedure, the cost of income
taxes may be included as a percentage of each dollar of required investment;
it is essential that the applicable tax rate be known with considerable certainty. This means that best results are obtained when the prospective
income from all investments is quite uniform and predictable and a large
portion of the profits are taxed at a single rate. These conditions are encountered only by large corporations, primarily by public utilities. The general

procedure for determining income taxes on this basis will be discussed here, and special problems relating to public utilities will be considered in Chapter 19.

From the normal method of determining income taxes, assuming there is no retained surplus *and assuming there is only equity capital invested,*

$$\text{Taxable Income} = (\text{Dividends}) + (\text{Income Tax}), \quad (18.1)$$

and

$$\text{Income Tax} = (\text{Taxable Income}) \times (\text{Income Tax Rate}). \quad (18.2)$$

Substituting Equation (18.1) in Equation (18.2),

$$\text{Income Tax} = (\text{Dividends} + \text{Income Tax}) \times (\text{Income Tax Rate}). \quad (18.3)$$

Rewriting Equation (18.3),

$$\begin{aligned}(\text{Income Tax}) = {}&(\text{Income Tax}) \times (\text{Income Tax Rate}) \\ &+ (\text{Dividends}) \times (\text{Income Tax Rate}). \quad (18.4)\end{aligned}$$

This equation may be written in the form

$$\begin{aligned}(\text{Income Tax}) \times [1 - (\text{Income Tax Rate})] \\ = (\text{Dividends}) \times (\text{Income Tax Rate}), \quad (18.5)\end{aligned}$$

and

$$\text{Income Tax} = (\text{Dividends}) \times \left[\frac{(\text{Income Tax Rate})}{1 - (\text{Income Tax Rate})}\right]. \quad (18.6)$$

Dividing by (Investment), Equation (18.6) becomes

$$\frac{(\text{Income Tax})}{(\text{Investment})} = \frac{(\text{Dividends})}{(\text{Investment})} \times \left[\frac{(\text{Income Tax Rate})}{1 - (\text{Income Tax Rate})}\right]. \quad (18.7)$$

Since

$$\text{Dividends} = (\text{Profit Rate After Taxes}) \times (\text{Investment}), \quad (18.8)$$

$$\frac{(\text{Dividends})}{(\text{Investment})} = \text{Profit Rate After Taxes}. \quad (18.9)$$

$$\text{Income Tax} = (\text{Income Tax Rate on Investment}) \times (\text{Investment}), \quad (18.10)$$

or

$$\frac{(\text{Income Tax})}{(\text{Investment})} = (\text{Income Tax Rate on Investment}). \quad (18.11)$$

Then by substituting Equations (18.9) and (18.11) in Equation (18.7)

Income Tax Rate on Investment = (Profit Rate After Taxes) $\times$

$$\left[\frac{(\text{Income Tax Rate})}{1 - (\text{Income Tax Rate})}\right]. \quad (18.12)$$

Equation (18.12) may be written in a simpler manner by letting

t = income tax rate,
t' = income tax rate on investment,
r_{at} = profit rate of return after taxes.

Then,

$$t' = r_{at} \times \frac{t}{1 - t}. \quad (18.13)$$

If all capital is owned, the after-tax cost of money, C/M, is equal to the sum of dividends and retained earned surplus. For this condition income tax can be expressed as a function of the cost of money by rewriting Equation (18.6) as

$$\text{Income Tax} = \text{C/M} \times \frac{(\text{Income Tax Rate})}{(1 - \text{Income Tax Rate})} \quad (18.14)$$

If the cost of money, C/M, is expressed in dollars the income tax is also expressed in dollars. On the other hand, if C/M is expressed as a percentage figure, the income tax is a percentage *rate* which can be applied to the invested capital, corresponding to t' in Equation (18.13).

EQUATED COST OF MONEY

When making economy studies where both the cost of money and income taxes, based on invested capital, are included as costs, it frequently is convenient to be able to use straight-line instead of sinking fund depreciation. This can be done by computing an *equated cost of money*. In Chapter 5 it was shown that

Present Worth (Straight-Line Depreciation + Interest on Remaining Investment) = Present Worth (Sinking Fund Depreciation + Interest on Gross Investment)

and that each side of this equality could be substituted for the other. This expression can also be stated as

PW (St.-Line Depr. + C/M on Net) = PW (S. F. Depr. + C/M on Gross).

$$(18.15)$$

The problem is to determine an equivalent rate X for the cost of money which will fulfill the relationship

$$(X \text{ on Gross}) + (\text{St.-Line Depr.}) = (\text{C/M on Gross}) + (\text{S. F. Depr.})$$
$$(18.16)$$

If the equivalent rate X is called the equated cost of money, or Eq. C/M,

$$\text{Eq. C/M} = (\text{C/M}) + (\text{S. F. Depr.}) - (\text{St.-Line Depr.}).$$
$$(18.17)$$

It is apparent that the last term in Equation (18.17) deducts the straight-line depreciation that has been included and the remaining portion of the equation substitutes sinking fund depreciation plus interest on the gross investment. Thus this equation bears out previous statements that whenever profit or interest return figures are to be based on the amount of original investment sinking fund depreciation, or its equivalent, must be used. The interest or profit rate used in computing the Eq. C/M should be the same as would be used in computing sinking fund depreciation—normally the before-tax rate. At the same time, the C/M, where income tax is to be included, is the after-tax rate.

When one considers that a sinking fund factor must be used in computing the Eq. C/M, it might appear that there is no advantage gained by its use. For most cases this is true. However, when repeatedly making comparisons on an after-tax basis between alternatives being considered by a given company, where the cost of money is considered to be the same for all alternatives, the Eq. C/M can be computed once for each write-off period that is commonly used. It is then possible to make valid comparisons by using straight-line depreciation and including the equated cost of money and income tax, both as fixed percentages of the invested capital.

PROVISION FOR BORROWED CAPITAL IN INCOME TAX FACTOR

Most companies borrow a portion of their capital. Interest paid on such capital is tax free. In such cases the

total cost of money = (dividends + earned surplus + interest).

If income tax is to be computed on the basis of invested capital, it is necessary to modify the tax factor to take the borrowed capital into account. The modification is determined by the cost rate for total capital, the interest rate on borrowed capital, and the per cent of borrowed capital in terms of the total capital utilized. Basically, one must determine the proportion of the total capital—owned plus borrowed—upon which income tax must be computed. To do this, it is necessary to subtract from the total capital the amount which would produce before-tax profits sufficient to pay the interest on the borrowed capital. This tax-exempt capital is equal to

$$\% \text{ Tax-Exempt Capital} = \frac{(\text{Interest Rate}) \times (\% \text{ Debt})}{\% \text{ C/M}}.$$

$$(18.18)$$

For example, if a company has

$$
\begin{aligned}
\text{Cost of money} &= 6\%, \\
\text{Interest rate on borrowed capital} &= 3\%, \\
\text{Per cent of total capital that is borrowed} &= 30\%,
\end{aligned}
$$

then

$$\% \text{ Tax-Exempt Capital} = \frac{3\% \times 30\%}{6\%} = 15\%.$$

Thus no income tax would be paid on 15% of the total capital. Therefore for cases where some borrowed capital is used the income tax factor, based on Equation (18.14), becomes

$$\text{Income Tax Factor} = \% \text{ C/M} \times \left[\frac{(\text{Income Tax Rate})}{1 - (\text{Income Tax Rate})} \right] \times$$
$$\left[\frac{100\% - (\% \text{ Tax Exempt Capital})}{100\%} \right]. \quad (18.19)$$

The income tax factor may then be multiplied by the total invested capital to obtain the income tax.

INCOME TAXES IN PUBLIC UTILITY ECONOMY STUDIES

As will be discussed in Chapter 19, privately owned public utilities are regulated by public regulatory agencies. This regulation consists, basically, of controlling the rates which a utility may charge for its services. The general concept is that the utility should be permitted to charge only as much as will be required to cover the cost of the capital used, thus being assured of an adequate supply of required capital. Since the profits which a utility can pay to its stockholders for the use of their capital must come from the net income which remains after income taxes have been paid, it is essential that income taxes be given proper consideration in economy studies of such companies. Therefore most public utilities include income taxes in their economy studies, either directly or by using a before-tax required profit rate which includes an equivalent provision for income taxes.

Since the income which will result from an investment by a regulated public utility can be estimated with greater certainty than can that of a non-utility, income tax effects can be predicted with considerable accuracy.

FINANCING WITH ACCUMULATED TAX MONEY

Under the income tax laws applying to corporations, effective in 1959, only 25% of the estimated tax liability for the current year is due for payment on September 15 and an additional 25% on December 15. On March 15 of the succeeding year a return must be filed, and a payment of one half of the balance due must be paid. The remainder of the balance must be paid on the following June 15. This results in the situation illustrated in Figure 18–1. Assuming that income taxes are set aside out of

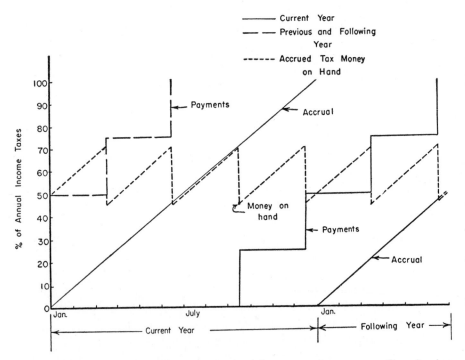

Figure 18–1. Annual income tax accruals and payments for a corporation, showing amount available for use as working capital.

income at a uniform rate, at all times there is a minimum of 45.8% of the annual income taxes on hand and available as working capital. If the average tax rate for the corporation is 50%, this cost-free capital amounts to 27.9% of the annual net income before taxes.

While the amount of capital made available by this situation usually is not great as compared with the total capital used in a business, it is not insignificant. For example, assume that a corporation earns 15% on capital, before taxes, and has an average tax rate of 50%, but is currently in the 52% tax bracket; planned and average effective use of the accrued tax money will produce an increase of 4% in the after-tax income.

Since the estimated tax liability may be based on either an actual estimate of the current year's income or on the tax for the previous year, corporations that are growing may obtain larger tax accruals by basing the estimate on the previous year's tax, thereby lowering the current payments.

PROBLEMS

(Use the 1957 income tax rates given in Tables 18–1 and 18–2 and on pages 433 and 434 in working the following problems)

18–1   A single individual now has a net taxable income of $18,000. He is going to invest $3,000 of additional capital. One possibility is to buy some tax-exempt municipal bonds which pay interest at the rate of $3\frac{3}{4}\%$.

a. What rate of profit would he have to obtain from a taxable investment to obtain the same after-tax return?

b. Assume this individual got married at the beginning of the year in which he invested the $3,000. What would be the net effect upon the rate of profit required to make the taxable investment equal to the tax-free bonds?

18–2   A small corporation, having a taxable income of $15,000 per year, is considering an expansion program which would involve investing $25,000 in depreciable property having an economic life of ten years. The necessary capital can be obtained by a five-year bank loan at 7% interest. Careful studies indicate that an annual profit, excluding financing and depreciation costs, of $10,000 per year can be obtained from this new program. Determine the after-tax rate of profit and state the advisability of the proposed program.

18–3   A married taxpayer owns some income property which he purchased ten years ago for $30,000, with $5,000 of this amount being the cost of land. Straight-line depreciation has been charged on the remainder of the property on a twenty-year write-off basis. The owner has been paying taxes on a net taxable income of $29,000, filing joint returns.

He now has an opportunity to sell the property for $40,000. Disposal of the property will, of course, eliminate the $3,800 before-tax annual income which the property has produced for him. He estimates that if he holds the property for another ten years he will be able to

sell it at that time for $25,000. If he sells the property, he will invest
the money in tax-exempt bonds paying 3½%.

Would you advise selling now, or should he wait ten years?

18–4   John Doe is married and owns a business which is his sole source of
income. He started the business thirty years ago and has built it to the
point where it now produces an annual net taxable income of $30,000.
He has been thinking of retiring and also wishes to realize a capital
gain on his business, into which he has put back a large portion of his
profits over the years. He has received an offer from a large corporation
to purchase his company for $400,000. The present depreciated value
of his company on the books is $175,000. He has already made up his
mind that he will retire in another ten years, at which time the depreciated book value would be $100,000, and he estimates that he could
easily sell the company at that time for at least twice its book value.
If he sells the business now he would invest the proceeds in tax-exempt
bonds which would earn an average yield of 3½%. What would you
advise him to do?

18–5   The net taxable income of a corporation in 1958 was $80,000.

a. Determine the corporation's income tax for 1958.

b. It is expected that the 1959 tax rates will be the same as those for
1958 and that the profits from existing operations will also be the same.
A new undertaking is being considered which is known to be somewhat risky. This venture will require the investment of $100,000, in
non-depreciable activities, but, if successful, should produce additional
net income of $25,000 per year. What after-tax rate of return would be
obtained from this investment?

c. Assume that the venture is unsuccessful and actually produces a
net loss of $20,000 per year. What will be the annual net loss to the
corporation after taxes?

18–6   A married taxpayer who files joint returns expects to have a net taxable
income for the year of $30,000. He plans to make an additional busi-
ness expenditure of $2,000 per year to maintain a membership in an
exclusive golf club for the purpose of promoting his business and thus
increasing his income. He thus believes the entire expense will be
deductible.

a. What increase in taxable income must he obtain to offset the cost
of the membership?

b. If the membership produces no increase in income, what will be
the net annual cost to the taxpayer?

18–7   Ten years ago John Doe, who is unmarried, invested $10,000.00 for
1,000 shares of common stock of a new corporation. The stock now has
a market price of $25,000, and the price has been increasing at the rate
of about 5% each year. Because of the earnings and dividend policy, it

is probable that this rate will continue for at least the next five years. The dividend policy of the corporation has been stabilized so that each share pays $1.50 per year. Mr. Doe's current taxable income is $15,000. He can sell the stock now and invest the proceeds in tax-exempt bonds which pay 4%, or hold the stock for another five years before selling. Compare the results of these two alternatives over the next five years. Assume he pays no state income tax.

18–8   An engineer who is unmarried has a net taxable income of $14,000. He has an opportunity to invest $2,000 in the common stock of the corporation for which he works; the stock is currently paying dividends amounting to 6% of the present market price. He can also invest his money in tax-exempt bonds paying 4% interest.

a. Compare the after-tax results obtainable from these two alternatives.

b. Make the same comparison assuming the engineer is married.

18–9   A construction company, operating as a corporation, has a contract for building a section of highway which will be completed within the current year and on which it expects to make a taxable profit of $40,000 if conventional methods are used. Its current total taxable income averages about $200,000 per year. On this particular job it is considering using a new procedure which, if successful, would reduce the total cost of the job by $20,000. If not successful, it would add $10,000 to the cost of the job. Examine the proposed use of the new procedure and determine the net after-tax results if it is successful and if it is not.

18–10   Three months ago a corporation, having a 50% income tax rate, purchased some property for $12,000. It now finds it does not need the property and has received an offer of $18,000 for it. If it should keep the property until four years after the purchase date, and in the meantime have to pay annual property taxes at the rate of 2% of the original cost each of the four years, what selling price would it have to obtain for the property to produce an after-tax result equivalent to that which would be provided by the present offer? After-tax earnings of the company are approximately 10%.

18–11   Richard Roe is married and has a net taxable income of $20,000. He has two opportunities for investing $20,000. The first is to purchase some land which can be rented to a rancher for $3,000 per year. The only expense Mr. Roe would have to pay would be annual taxes of $500.

The second opportunity is to purchase a store building which can be leased to a tenant for $400 per month on a twenty-year lease. Depreciation could be charged on a straight-line basis, and the entire cost of the property written off over the twenty-year period. Annual maintenance costs are estimated to be $300 per year, and taxes and insurance 2% of the first cost.

Assuming the property to be worthless at the end of the twenty-year period, compare the after-tax results obtainable from the two alternatives.

18–12 Assume that the land in Problem 18–11 could be sold at the end of twenty years for $25,000, and that the store building, although fully depreciated, could be sold for $10,000, of which $5,000 would represent the original cost of the land on which it was built. Determine the after-tax rate of profit resulting for each investment.

18–13 The after-tax net income of a corporation is 8% on total capital. The ratio of borrowed to equity capital is 0.25, and an average interest rate of 6% is paid for the borrowed capital. If the corporation is in the 52% tax bracket, what is the before-tax rate of earnings on equity capital?

18–14 A married taxpayer having a net taxable income of $42,000 invests $100,000 to purchase land and drill an oil well. The venture is successful, and for ten years the well, estimated to contain 200,000 barrels of oil, produces oil in the following amounts, which is sold for $2 per barrel.

Year	Barrels	Cost of production
1	34,000	$15,000
2	34,000	15,000
3	34,000	15,000
4	34,000	15,000
5	33,000	14,000
6	23,700	10,000
7	13,200	8,000
8	8,000	7,500
9	5,400	6,000
10	1,800	5,000

Determine the total saving in income taxes if depletion is based on income rather than on investment cost.

18–15 Determine the total federal income tax saving involved in an investment of $25,000 made by a married taxpayer having an existing net taxable income of $20,000 if it produces an income of $4,500 per year for ten years subject to a 27½% depletion allowance on income, as compared with the same investment producing the same income from which straight-line depreciation over a ten-year life can be deducted.

18–16 A corporation in the 52% income tax bracket is considering investing $50,000 in a building on land which is already owned. This investment will eliminate annual rentals of $8,000 now being paid. Maintenance on the building is estimated at $1,200 per year, and taxes and insurance at 2% of first cost. There will be an estimated additional saving in trucking expense of $2,000 per year. The company normally makes economy studies of such projects on the basis of a twenty-year write-off period, and it is unwilling to assume any savings beyond that period. However, it is most likely that a thirty-year write-off period will have to be used for tax purposes. The corporation has an after-tax profit rate of about 10%. Make an after-tax analysis of the prospective return and a recommendation regarding this project.

18–17   Obtain from a local leasing company the terms for leasing a Ford, Plymouth, or Chevrolet. Then obtain the retail selling price for a car of the model selected and estimate the trade-in value at the end of two years, assuming 12,000 miles per year operation. Make a comparison of the relative costs of leasing and purchasing the car, assuming a 52% corporation tax rate. Use the operating and maintenance cost data in Table 18–8 where applicable. (Use license and tax data applicable in your state.)

18–18   A corporation operating retail grocery stores, and in the 52% federal income tax bracket, must open a new store. It can acquire land for $30,000 and construct the building for $80,000. Annual maintenance on the building would be $3,000, and taxes and insurance would amount to $2,800 per year. The building would have to be written off over a forty-year period but would probably have a salvage value of at least $5,000 at the end of that time.

A real estate firm is willing to provide the building on a forty-year lease for a rental of $1,000 per month. If the corporation purchases the property, it will borrow the required capital at 6% interest. Should the property be leased or purchased?

18–19   A corporation in the 52% income tax bracket has for several years had a net taxable income of not less than $40,000,000. By making use of the provision permitting the payment of 25% of the annual tax liability on September 15 of the current year, an additional 25% on December 15 of the current year, and payments of 25% on March 15 and June 15 of the following year, what minimum amount of capital will be available at all times from this source?

18–20   Make an after-tax study of Problem 10–19, assuming a corporation will be formed and the usual corporation income tax rates apply.

CHAPTER 19

Economy Studies
in Public Utilities

Public utilities differ from ordinary business organizations in certain respects which usually must be taken into account in economy studies. While the economy studies are made in essentially the same manner as for non-utility businesses, an understanding of these basic differences and characteristics is very helpful in order that the information and data may be handled properly and correct decisions reached.

Utilities may be either publicly or privately owned. While many of the characteristics are the same in both cases, publicly-owned utilities usually are not regulated and do not have to make profits and pay income taxes. As a result, their economy studies are essentially the same as those of any other public project, such as will be discussed in Chapter 20. Therefore, this chapter will be devoted to privately owned utilities.

THE NATURE OF PUBLIC UTILITIES

Public utilities provide services, such as gas, electric power, water, telephone and radio communication, and transportation, including air, rail, bus, and pipeline. In order to provide these services public property, such as streets, highways, or air space, must be utilized, or the utility must be given the right of eminent domain in order to acquire property where and when needed.

Because a utility must have large amounts of capital invested in fixed plant and equipment, economy of operation for the company and lower rates to the public can be brought about only by high use factors for such assets. This means that unnecessary duplication of such facilities would not be economical or in the public interest. For example, two competing electric power companies in the same area would not provide the most economical service. If each had customers on the same street, power-line poles, transformers, distribution lines, and many clerical functions would have to be duplicated. One of the companies could serve all of the customers with very little increase in its investment in fixed assets. Similarly, many of the customer costs, such as those for meter-reading, would be increased very little. The same general conditions apply to virtually all utilities.

In some types of utility services it is virtually impossible for satisfactory service to be obtained by the public except through a single utility, or at least a group of closely coordinated and noncompeting companies. For example, if two competing telephone companies served the same area and one company would not accept calls from the customers of the other, a completely unsatisfactory situation would result.

Recognizing the advantages of avoiding wasteful duplication and competition, the public usually grants a utility an exclusive franchise in a given geographical area. Thus most utilities have, in effect, monopolies with respect to the particular service which they render. They are in many instances, however, subject to competition from other utilities rendering different services. For example, a gas company may compete with an electric company in respect to domestic water-heating and cooking.

Since the public, acting as cities, states, or the federal government, must grant the use of streets, highways, etc., frequently through a franchise, and also grant a monopolistic position to a single utility, it retains the right to regulate the utility so that no undue profit is made as a result of the privileges which have been granted. It is obvious that without competition the price to be charged for the services can not be established through the usual competitive forces. Therefore a public regulatory body is established by the people to exercise the desired control through various types of measures. Such regulation is a very important factor that greatly affects the operations of a public utility and which is not present in the case of nonutility businesses.

HOW UTILITIES ARE REGULATED

Intrastate public utilities usually are regulated by a state agency, commonly known as a public utilities commission. The members of the commission may be appointed or elected, depending upon the laws of the individual state. Utilities that operate interstate, such as railroads, bus lines, telephone companies, and pipeline companies, are regulated by federal agencies. These include primarily the Interstate Commerce Commission, the Federal Communications Commission, and the Federal Power Commission.

Governmental regulation was established originally to prevent public utility companies from discriminating between customers as to service provided and prices charged. The functions of regulatory agencies have been expanded so that at present they are concerned with the setting of rates and the establishing and maintaining of standards of service.

Basic to the setting of rates for public utility services is the concept that the utility company must be able to earn profits and to pay dividends sufficient to assure the obtaining of the capital necessary to provide the assets and working capital that are required for rendering the service. If an adequate rate of profit is not obtained, the necessary capital will not be forthcoming from investors, and, as a result, the public will not be able to have the desired utility service. On the other hand, the utility operates at the permission of the public, through necessary franchises or other grants of permission, and thus is granted a monopolistic position by its customers. The public, therefore, has a right to expect that it should pay no more for the services than will permit an efficiently operated utility to earn the minimum required rate of profit that will assure the continuity of service at the level of quality desired. Thus the regulatory commissions have a delicate task of sensing the desires of the public as to the level of service desired and its willingness to pay for it, the price which must be paid for capital in the current money market, and the efficiency of the plans and operations of the utility.

Utility commission control is exercised primarily through the setting or approving of rates that may be charged for utility services. These are set so as to permit the utility to earn the required rate of profit on the capital utilized in rendering the service. This amount of capital is sometimes called the rate-base value. The rates approved or set by the commission are subject to appeal to the courts through usual legal procedures. Relatively few cases are taken to the courts. As discussed in Chapter 5, such cases usually involve the value of assets acquired some years previous to the time involved. At present utilities are permitted to earn from 5 to 7% on their investment.

In order to carry on their functions properly, the regulatory commissions usually prescribe certain accounting procedures that must be followed by the utilities under their jurisdiction. This assures that the same accounting procedures are followed from year to year and enables some comparisons to be made among utilities. As might be expected, the task of such a regulatory body is no bed of roses. Ordinarily the public is not in favor of an increase in service rates, even though the regulatory commission knows that they are necessary and in the long-range interest of the public. Likewise, a utility is seldom pleased when a commission orders a decrease in rates, though it may be evident that its profits are above the rate required to obtain necessary capital.

While the matter of public utility regulation is complex and sometimes seems to be quite ponderous, it has worked rather well. Some of the best managed companies in this country can be found among public utilities in states where there are very strong, but fair, regulatory bodies. Services of excellent quality are consistently provided by these companies at low cost. The greatest difficulties are experienced where regulatory bodies are weak, are not farsighted or aware of current developments, or tend to impose managerial restrictions rather than merely regulation.

CHARACTERISTICS OF PUBLIC UTILITIES

Because of the inherent nature of the services they render, their monopolistic position, and the regulation to which they are subject, public utilities have a number of economic characteristics differentiating them from other businesses which must be taken into account in making economy studies. The major ones are discussed in the following paragraphs.

1. The investment per worker and the ratio of fixed costs to variable costs are very high. As shown in Table 19–1, the investment per dollar of

TABLE 19–1 Comparison of Certain Investment and Cost Characteristics of Utilities and Nonutilities

	Electric utilities	Ten steel companies	General manufacturing companies
Annual gross revenue	$100.00	$100.00	$100.00
Plant cost	$400.00	$125.00	$ 75.00
Federal Income Tax	$ 12.25	$ 8.25	$ 6.50

gross revenue for typical electric utilities is about 3.2 times that of steel companies and about 5.3 times that of general manufacturing companies. This results in high fixed costs. It is not uncommon for the fixed costs to be 70 per cent of the total unit cost. This means that careful attention must be given to investment problems and to assuring an adequate flow of capital for expansion.

2. Utilities must render whatever service is demanded by customers, within established rate schedules. Subject to regulatory safeguards, a utility must expand to meet the growth of the community it serves.

3. A utility is *required* to keep abreast of technical developments in its

field which would permit reduction in the cost to the customer for its services or would improve the quality of the service if such improvement is demanded by the customers. A utility should be prepared to improve the quality of the service, even though not demanded immediately by the customers, in order to maintain public good will and to protect its monopolistic position.

4. The rates charged for a utility's services are based on total costs, including a fair return, after income taxes, on the rate-base value of its property.

5. The earnings of a public utility are virtually limited by the rate base. As a result, profit on sales is of very little significance. If sales income is increased as the result of increased operating costs—for example by increased and more effective advertising—it may not produce any long-term profit increase. Profits for the current year might be realized, but if the increase were to result in a return which was judged by the regulatory commission to be greater than necessary, a rate reduction would be ordered. Thus the benefits of the improved operation in terms of financial gain to the company would be eliminated. The same situation exists with respect to increased earnings due to improved efficiency of operation.

This situation might appear to, and possibly does, reduce the incentive of a public utility to improve the efficiency of its operations. However, it is a condition which a utility accepts in return for the preferred position granted to it by the public. The public, in turn, has the right to expect the best possible efforts on the part of a utility, and a utility must take a long-range view and recognize that it can progress only through the good will of the public. Income increases for a given year are retained by the utility, and lowered rates almost always assure an expansion of service demands and greater *total* profits in the future. This does not, however, alter the fact that the rate of earnings per dollar of investment probably will not change to any great extent.

6. Utilities have much greater stability of income than other companies. The upper limit of earnings, after income taxes, usually is not permitted to exceed about 7%. While there is no guarantee of a minimum return, if the utility can show that it is operating efficiently, it usually can obtain permission to increase its rates sufficiently to maintain its earnings at a level high enough to assure an adequate flow of capital. This stability of earnings, of course, has considerable effect in lowering the rate the utility must pay for capital.

7. Income taxes are a larger part of gross income for utilities than for other companies, as is shown in Table 19–1. This, of course, is due to the

fact that the revenue of a utility is controlled to yield a profit equal to the cost of capital plus income taxes. Thus income taxes are a very significant factor in economy studies of public utilities. Further, since the after-tax profit can be estimated with considerable accuracy, the income taxes can also be readily determined. This makes it easier to include income taxes in all economy studies for utilities than in those for other companies.

8. The assets of a utility, on the average, involve longer write-off periods than those of nonutilities. This is due both to the physical nature of the assets and to the fact that the monopolistic situation results in less functional depreciation.

9. Utilities must rely on a larger proportion of new capital for expansion than do other companies. This follows from the fact that earnings are so regulated that they are sufficient to pay only for the cost of capital. Therefore, if the earnings are just high enough to meet the payment of dividends demanded by investors, it follows that very few profits can be retained as surplus to provide for expansion. For example, one utility having equity capital of over $1,375,000,000 has only $104,000,000 in earned surplus, accumulated in over forty years.

COMPUTING INCOME TAXES FOR PUBLIC UTILITIES

As was pointed out in Chapter 18, where the prospective income from investments is quite uniform and can be predicted with some reliability, it is possible to compute income taxes on the basis of invested capital with sufficient accuracy for economy study purposes. It is apparent that these conditions are exactly those that exist in a public utility. Therefore many public utilities use this method of estimating income tax costs. There are, however, some special problems which often have to be taken into account, usually because of accounting practices required by regulatory commissions.

Most regulatory commissions require utilities to use straight-line depreciation for accounting purposes. In order to avoid misunderstandings, many public utilities prefer also to use straight-line depreciation and profit return on the initial investment in economy studies. This makes it necessary to use the equated cost of money, given in Equation (18.17).

Another complication arises from the fact that depreciation accruals are frequently required to be made monthly. The effect of this procedure is illustrated in Figure 19–1, where the effects of once-per-year and six-times-per-year depreciation accruals on net investment in the plant are shown. It is apparent that more frequent depreciation accrual reduces the remaining net

investment as compared with that which results from annual accruals. It
follows, then, that an adjustment must be made if *annual* income tax costs
are to be included with monthly
straight-line depreciation accruals
and profit or cost of money based on
the gross investment.

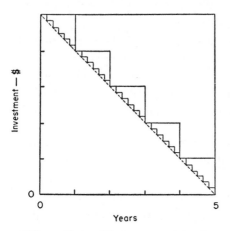

The necessary adjustment usually
is made by modifying the equated
cost of money. If the same total
annual straight-line depreciation is
deducted, but in twelve equal
monthly amounts, this means that
for every dollar of annual depreciation cost $\frac{1}{12}$ dollar is accrued each
month. This situation obviously involves a partial-payment annuity,
discussed in Chapter 4. With money
worth 6% per annum, from Table
XXVI, of the Appendix, $\$\frac{1}{12}$ depos-
ited at the end of each month for twelve months would amount to
$1.0272. Thus for 6% interest the equated cost of money in Equation
(18.17) would be adjusted as follows:

Figure 19–1. Effect on remaining investment in an asset of six times per year
accrual of depreciation versus annual
accrual.

Adjusted Eq. C/M = C/M + (S. F. Depr.) − 1.0272 × (St.-Line Depr.)

It should be noted, however, that the C/M rate is the after-tax rate while
the interest rate used in the remainder of the calculation is the rate used in
the sinking fund depreciation calculation. In general terms the Adjusted
Equated Cost of Money for monthly depreciation accruals would be

$$\text{Adjusted Eq. C/M} = \text{C/M} + (\text{S. F. Depr.}) - s_{\overline{1}|}^{(p)} \times (\text{St.-Line Depr.}).$$
$$(19.1)$$

SOME GENERAL CONCEPTS OF PUBLIC UTILITY
ECONOMY STUDIES

Because of the nature of public utilities, there are some general features
which usually are reflected in economy studies of such companies.

1. They usually involve alternative ways of, or alternative programs for,
doing something. Since a utility is obligated to provide the service demanded
by its customers, studies are seldom made of the economy of doing versus

not doing. Instead, it is usually a matter of how to do it most economically.

2. Administrative and general supervision costs often are not included. Since these expenses will be about the same for each alternative, they may be omitted.

3. Revenue data seldom are included. Here, again, the revenue ordinarily will be the same, regardless of the method of providing the service.

4. The cost of money, depreciation, income taxes, and property taxes are usually expressed in terms of the capital invested, except in replacement studies. In replacement studies present salvage value is used for determining cost of money, depreciation, and income taxes for existing assets. Property taxes are based on actual assessed value, if known, otherwise on original cost.

In other respects economy studies of public utilities are essentially the same as those for other industries.

AN EXAMPLE OF ALTERNATIVE NEW INSTALLATIONS

A public utility must extend electric power service to a new shopping center. A decision must be made as to whether a pole-line or an underground system should be used. The pole-line system would cost only $4,860 to install, but, because of numerous changes which are anticipated in the development and use of the shopping center, it is estimated that annual maintenance costs would be $2,300. An underground system would cost $31,500 to install, but the annual maintenance costs would not exceed $550. Annual property taxes are $1\frac{1}{2}\%$ of first cost. The company operates with 35% borrowed capital, on which it pays an interest rate of 4%. Capital costs about 7%. The utility is in the 52% income tax bracket. A twenty-year study period is to be used.

The adjusted income tax factor for the utility is

$$7\% \times \frac{0.52}{1-0.52} \times \frac{100\% - (4\% \times 35\%)/7\%}{100\%} = 6.07\%.$$

The comparison between alternatives then is as follows:

Depreciation		Pole-Line			Underground	
(15% S. F.)	$4,860 × 0.0098 =	$	48	$31,500 × 0.0098	= $	309
Maintenance			2,300			550
Property taxes	$4,860 × 0.015 =		73	$31,500 × 0.015	=	473
Cost of money	$4,860 × 0.07 =		340	$31,500 × 0.07	=	2,205
Income taxes	$4,860 × 0.0607 =		295	$31,500 × 0.0607	=	1,912
Total annual cost			$3,056			$5,449

There would thus be a very substantial saving in favor of the pole-line system.

EXAMPLE OF A UTILITY REPLACEMENT PROBLEM

Because of earth slippage, a flume operated by a privately-owned water company requires annual maintenance costing $10,000. It is estimated that this flume will not be needed beyond five years because of changes that are contemplated in the system. A question has arisen as to whether it would be advisable to replace the flume immediately with a new steel pipe, costing $40,000, which would require no maintenance expense during the next five years, or to continue the high maintenance costs of the old flume. The old flume has been fully depreciated and has no scrap value but is assessed for property tax purposes at $10,000. The new pipeline would have to be written off in five years and probably would have no salvage or scrap value because of the high cost of removal. Property taxes are 1% of new or assessed value. The company uses 30% borrowed capital for which it pays an interest rate of 4%. Cost of money is 6%. This company has a 50% income tax rate.

For these conditions the comparison between the alternatives is as follows:

	Retain old flume	Replace now
Depreciation (12% S. F.)	$ 0	$40,000 × 0.1574 = $ 6,250
Maintenance	10,000	0
Property taxes	100	400
C/M	0	$40,000 × 0.06 = 2,400
Income tax [1]	0	$40,000 × 0.048 = 1,920
Total annual cost	$10,100	$10,970

These figures show a definite advantage in keeping the old flume.

This problem raises a matter which frequently causes confusion. Because there is no investment remaining in the old flume, no income tax is included for this alternative. Since each alternative will render the same service, the revenue from each will be the same. However, since the costs with the new flume will be less, the taxable income will be increased by an amount proportional to the earnings of the new investment. Therefore the economy study is concerned only with the added income taxes accompanying the proposed investment.

[1] Tax-free capital $= \dfrac{4\% \times 30\%}{6\%} = 20\%$

Income tax rate with 30% borrowed capital $= 0.06 \times \dfrac{0.50}{1 - 0.50} \times \dfrac{100 - 20}{100} = 0.048$

EXAMPLE OF IMMEDIATE VERSUS DEFERRED INVESTMENT

Public utilities frequently must make economy studies involving immediate versus deferred investment. Future demands must be met and can be estimated with somewhat greater accuracy than in the case of ordinary companies. The typical problems encountered in such studies are illustrated in the following example.

A telephone company wishes to determine whether a manually operated toll exchange should be changed over to dial equipment January 1, 1960, or whether the change should be delayed until January 1, 1965, by which time increasing operation and maintenance costs and capacity limitations would make it imperative. Cost and life data are as follows:

Cost of dial installation and change-over	$375,000
Annual operation and maintenance	38,000
Property taxes	7,500
Income tax factor	4%
Cost of money	7%

Annual operating and maintenance costs on the manual equipment are $78,000 and are increasing about 10 per cent each year. Annual property taxes are $1,000. Scrap value at the time of removal is estimated at 5 per cent of first cost for all equipment.

Two viewpoints can be taken regarding the life of the dial equipment. The first is to assume that at the end of twenty years (January 1, 1980) the equipment will be replaced, regardless of whether it is installed at the beginning of 1960 or 1965. Such a replacement situation would be due to functional obsolescence and inadequacy. The second possibility is that the equipment will have a life of twenty years from the installation date, with a 5 per cent scrap value. It is decided to investigate both possibilities.

If the first condition is assumed—identical terminal dates for both alternatives—the same *total* amount of depreciation will be involved in each case, so the problem may be solved on the basis of the annual saving resulting during each of the first five years if the investment is deferred. This saving will be:

Cost of money	$375,000 × 0.07 =	$26,250
Income taxes	$375,000 × 0.04 =	15,000
Property taxes		7,500
Operation and maintenance		38,000
Annual saving each of first 5 years		$86,750

Since the annual saving obtained by deferring the investment also is the added cost if the investment is made immediately, and since it is considerably in excess of the annual cost of operating and maintaining the manual equipment, it is apparent that the change should not be made immediately.

Another method of making this study would be to determine the present worth of the annual costs of both alternatives. By this procedure the annual costs would be:

	Install now			Defer five years
Depreciation [2]	$\frac{\$375,000}{41.0} \times 0.95$	= \$ 8,690	$\frac{\$375,000}{25.1} \times 0.95$	= \$ 14,200
Operation and maintenance		38,000		38,000
Property taxes		7,500		7,500
C/M $375,000 \times 0.07$		= 26,250	$375,000 \times 0.07$	= 26,250
Income tax $375,000 \times 0.04$		= 15,000	$375,000 \times 0.04$	= 15,000
Annual cost during life		$95,440		$100,950

Present worth of 20-year annual costs [2] $95,440 \times 10.59 \times $1,010,000
Present worth of 15-year annual costs deferred
  5 years [2] $100,950 \times 9.11 \times 0.713 = $655,000
Difference in favor of deferring 5 years $355,000
Equivalent annual savings [2] $355,000 \times 1/a_{\overline{5}|} = \$355,000 \times 0.244 = \$86,600

The difference between the result obtained by this method and that obtained by the simpler computation of the annual savings during the deferral period is due to the rounding of values and the use of a slide rule. Thus, for problems of this type the method of determining the annual savings during the deferral period is considerably easier to use and produces identical results.

For the second condition to be investigated, assuming that the service life would be twenty years from the date of installation of the equipment, it may readily be seen that the alternative permitting deferment would be even more attractive, since less would be charged for depreciation each year, because a twenty-year rather than a fifteen-year write-off period would be used. Thus during each year of assumed life the annual costs would be the same as for the alternative providing for immediate installation—namely, $95,440. The present worth of the annual costs for the years 1965–1980, deferred five years, would be

$$\$95,440 \times a_{\overline{15}|} \times v^5 = \$95,440 \times 9.11 \times 0.713 = \$620,000.$$

---

[2] Theoretically the before-tax profit rate of 11% (corresponding to an after-tax rate of 7% and an income tax factor of 4%) should be used in the depreciation and present-worth calculations. However, it can be shown that due to determining the present worth of the annual costs the results would be exactly the same as are obtained by using the after-tax rate of 7% throughout.

The difference in favor of deferring 5 years would be

$$\$1,010,000 - \$620,000 = \$390,000.$$

The equivalent annual savings for the 5-year deferral period would be

$$\$390,000 \times 1/a_{\overline{5}|} = \$390,000 \times 0.244 = \$95,200.$$

It is apparent that an assumption of equal service life after the date of installation might make deferment appear preferable when an assumption of identical retirement dates would not. Therefore, as pointed out in Chapter 16, the matter of probable use of the deferred asset beyond the date of retirement for the immediate asset is of prime importance in deciding which assumption to use.

THEORETICAL BASIS FOR UTILITY RATES

The costs of providing utility services usually are grouped into three classifications: capacity costs, commodity or energy costs, and customer costs. These are applicable to virtually any type of utility. Capacity costs are those resulting from the provision of the assets required to produce the commodity or energy sold and to bring it to a point from which it can be diverted to the individual customers. For a power company, for example, this would include the costs for generators, dams, power plants, substations, transformers, a part of the labor at power plants and substations, transmission lines, and usually most of the distribution lines up to the point of step-down transformers to customers' voltage. For a gas company these costs would include major pipelines, pumping stations, storage tanks, and a considerable portion of the major gas mains to customer areas. Capacity costs constitute a very large part of the total costs of providing most utility services, frequently as much as one-half.

Commodity or energy costs include fuel, most of the labor at power plants and substations, the price paid for gas at the source, operating costs of pumping plants, and most maintenance costs. In a telephone company these costs are primarily those of labor.

Customer costs include investment charges on meters and customer service lines or pipes, a portion of the investment costs of distribution lines or pipe mains in the immediate customer area, and the cost of reading meters, billing, collecting, and the maintenance of business offices.

Of these three categories, the capacity costs tend to be a function of the maximum capacity which must be provided, the commodity or energy costs tend to be a function of the amount of commodity or energy produced and sold, and the customer costs tend to be proportional to the number of customers served (although there usually is a certain amount of relatively fixed customer cost). Therefore, in setting its rate schedules a utility theoretically should charge each class of customers for its share of each of these three categories of costs. An attempt is made to do this in actual practice, but the theoretical cost allocation usually must be modified in order to construct a simpler and more workable rate structure and to take into account the practical reality that some types of customers will pay more for a given service than others. However, the actual rates are based upon an analysis of the actual costs.

The following tabulation shows the various annual costs of a gas company distributed according to the three classes.

	Capacity	Commodity	Customer
Investment costs (C/M, property taxes, income taxes, depreciation)	$23,500,000.00		$ 8,500,000.00
Production costs	1,500,000.00	$24,600,000.00	
Transmission and distribution	3,500,000.00	750,000.00	8,130,000.00
Other costs	500,000.00	150,000.00	1,150,000.00
	$29,000,000.00	$25,500,000.00	$17,780,000.00
Basis for distribution	per MCF per day	per MCF	per customer
Base units for distribution	1,000,000 MCF per day	123,000,000 MCF	550,000 customers
Unit cost	$29.00 per year per MCF per day	$0.2075 per MCF	$32.30 per customer

It next is necessary to allocate the costs according to the two classes of customers. For this utility the customers were divided into two groups, "General" and "Industrial." The "General" classification included all residential customers, and the "Industrial" customers used gas for any purpose except cooking of meals. The allocation of costs to these two groups was made as follows:

	Industrial	General
Estimated capacity requirements, MCF per day	350,000	650,000
Annual consumption, MCF	48,000,000	75,000,000
Number of customers	50,000	500,000
Capacity cost	$10,150,000.00	$18,850,000.00
Commodity cost	9,950,000.00	15,550,000.00
Customer cost	1,615,000.00	16,165,000.00
Total cost	$21,715,000.00	$50,565,000.00
Cost per MCF	$0.462	$0.674

Theoretically, a three-part rate would be required to properly assess each customer with his share of the capacity, commodity, and customer costs. As mentioned previously, this is seldom done because of the complexity of rate schedules which would result. Different types of utilities customarily use different types of schedules. Gas companies usually use quite simple block-type schedules. This company, for instance, utilized the following rate schedules:

	Per Customer per Month
For "General" gas service	
First 200 cu. ft. or less	$0.91
Next 2,300 cu. ft., per 100 cu. ft.	0.06
Next 17,500 cu. ft., per 100 cu. ft.	0.0575
Next 80,000 cu. ft., per 100 cu. ft.	0.055
Over 100,000 cu. ft., per 100 cu. ft.	0.053
For "Industrial" gas service	
First 100 MCF, per MCF	$0.51
Next 900 MCF, per MCF	0.499
Next 2,000 MCF, per MCF	0.488
Over 3,000 MCF, per MCF	0.476
Minimum Billing Charge	
800,000 cu. ft. or less	$40.00
Over 800,000 cu. ft.	$80.00

It may be seen from these rate schedules that the "Industrial" service is probably somewhat more profitable per cu. ft. sold than the "General" service. Further, the only direct attempt to recover the fixed customer costs is through the minimum charge of $0.91 for the first 200 cu. ft. or less in the "General" service schedule and the $40.00 or $80.00 minimum billing in the "Industrial" schedule. This practice is quite generally followed by gas companies.

Electric companies quite generally use a fixed service charge, as shown in the rate schedule on page 381. Water companies frequently employ rate schedules which are tied to the size of the installed meter connection. Either the constant monthly meter charge or the initial rate block in a schedule for a larger meter connection is higher than the charge when a smaller meter is used. This helps to meet the higher capacity costs caused by customers with potentially high demands.

The major purpose of cost allocation analysis in regard to rate schedules is to attempt to have the amounts paid for service by each class of customers cover the total costs caused by that class, so that one group does not carry a portion of the costs of another. This usually is required by the regulatory commissions. In some cases there is room for doubt as to whether the accounting and cost allocation procedures required by a commission permit this objective to be achieved.

Cost allocation studies are, of course, very helpful in determining increment costs for purposes of setting up the rates to be charged for the various blocks of service and for special categories of service, such as off-peak power.

PROBLEMS

19–1   What are eight ways in which privately owned public utilities typically differ from manufacturing enterprises?

19–2   The cost of money for a privately owned public utility is 5%, and its income-tax rate is 50%. Depreciation is charged monthly on all depreciable assets on a straight-line basis. Determine the adjusted equated cost of money when a twenty-year write-off period is involved.

19–3   A privately owned public utility has invested capital amounting to $320,000,000, of which 30 per cent is borrowed at an average cost of 4%. The average cost of equity capital is 5%. Depreciable assets are written off, on the average, on a twenty-year straight-line basis, with depreciation charged monthly. Determine the annual income tax for this company if it is in the 50% tax bracket.

19–4   What would be the net effect on the income taxes of the utility in Problem 19–3 if all capital were owned and depreciation charged annually instead of monthly?

19–5   A gas company must install mains to a new residence area. One alternative will cost $32,000 and involve estimated annual maintenance costs of $4,000 per year over the estimated thirty-year life. A second alternative would cost $50,000 but annual maintenance costs probably would not exceed $1,500 per year. Taxes on either installation would be 1% of first cost per year. This utility has a ratio of borrowed capital to total capital of 0.30 and pays 5% for its borrowed funds. The average cost of equity capital is 7½%, and the company has an average income tax rate of 50%. Make an after-tax comparison and a recommendation as to which alternative should be used.

19–6   Plan A for providing certain telephone service would cost $25,000 for equipment and installation and $1,250 per year for maintenance. Plan B would cost $17,500 for equipment and installation and $1,875 annually for maintenance. Both plants would have a service life of ten years and 20 per cent salvage value at the end of that time. Capital costs the utility 6%, and 25 per cent of total capital is borrowed at an interest rate of 5%. Depreciation accruals are made annually. Taxes and insurance total 2% of first cost per year. The company has a 50% income-tax rate. Which of the two plans would be more desirable?

19–7   Capacity, commodity, and customer costs for an electric utility are as follows:

	Capacity Cost	Commodity Cost	Customer Cost
Investment charges	$475,000		$100,000
Production costs	80,000	$375,000	
Transmission and			
distribution costs	40,000	7,000	68,000
Other costs	30,000	60,000	70,000
Total	$625,000	$442,000	$238,000
Basis for distribution	per kw.	per kw.-hr.	per customer
Base units	15,000 kw.	35,000,000 kw.-hr.	20,000 customers

The utility has 300 "Industrial" customers whose maximum demand is 4,000 kw. and who use 13,000,000 kw.-hr. of power annually, 1,700 "Commercial" customers whose peak demand is 6,000 kw. and who use 6,000,000 kw.-hrs. annually, and 18,000 "Residential" customers whose peak demand is 5,000 kw. and who use 16,000,000 kw.-hrs. annually. Make a suitable allocation of the costs, and determine an appropriate cost per kw.-hr. for each type of customer.

19-8 A gas company, having only equity capital which costs an average of 8%, must install a gas main in a new real estate subdivision. A study of probable demands during the next thirty years leads to consideration of two alternatives with costs as follows:

	Cost of pipe and installation	Paving costs
Alternative A		
One 3-in. main now	$10,000	
One 3-in. main in five years	11,000	$1,500
One 3-in. main in ten years	12,000	1,750
Alternative B		
One 6-in. main now	18,000	

All mains are assumed to have a life of thirty years, and the company has a 50% income tax rate. While there does not appear to be any limit as to the length of time the gas service will be needed, a thirty-year study period is used for all such studies. Annual taxes will amount to 2% of the cost of the installed cost of the mains, not including paving costs.

Which alternative should be installed?

19-9 A forecast of the requirements for a telephone cable installation to provide service for the next forty years indicates that within twenty years a 1,100-pair cable will be needed. The requirements could be met by installing a 1,100-pair cable immediately, at a cost of $14,000, or by installing a 700-pair cable now, at a cost of $10,000, and a 400-pair cable in twenty years, at a cost of $7,000. In either case an underground conduit of sufficient size to accommodate either installation will be installed now at a cost of $4,000. Obsolescence and inadequacy are likely to limit the life of all cable to the terminal date of forty years from now, but all cable would probably have at least a 15 per cent salvage value upon removal. Property taxes will amount to $1\frac{1}{2}\%$ of the installed cost annually. Money costs the utility 8%, and it utilizes 30 per cent borrowed capital on which it pays an interest rate of 5%. Assume annual depreciation accruals on a straight-line basis, and a 50% income tax rate. Which installation should be used?

19–10   An electric utility company is studying the advisability of a hydro-electric plant which would be operated by the tide waters from a coastal inlet where very high tides are experienced. A minimum tidal drop of twenty feet can be counted on to operate the turbines. The plant would have a capacity of 20,000 kw. but, because of the inter-rupted nature of the service, could produce only 50,000,000 kw.-hr. of power per year. The initial cost of the project would be $2,000,000. Annual operation and maintenance costs are estimated at $30,000. It would also be necessary to build a seventy-mile transmission line, at a cost of $800,000, to transmit the power, and this line would involve a 10 per cent power loss and annual maintenance costs of $4,000. The line would probably have a 10 per cent value at the end of forty years.

   If the project is built, it will be part of a general program of expansion involving several steam-electric plants. If the project is not built, one of these plants will be built larger than otherwise at an increment cost of $1,000,000. The added cost of operation and maintenance for this steam plant would be $80,000 per year.

   Annual taxes and insurance on all types of installations would be 2% of first cost. The company analyzes all such investments on a forty-year basis. The cost of money for the company is $7\frac{1}{2}\%$. The ratio of borrowed to total capital is 0.25, with an interest rate of 5% being paid on borrowed funds. The income tax rate is 50%. Which project should be built?

19–11   A telephone company must expand the capacity of a central office which now is manually operated. The present office building is being leased at an annual rental of $3,000 per year. The lessor will construct an addition to this building, adequate to house additional manual equipment, at an increased annual rental of $1,000 per year for the three years the lease has to run.

   It has already been decided that at the end of three years the existing office will be converted to dial operation in a new building to be built. If the existing office is enlarged and continued, the new equipment required will cost $30,000 and have a salvage value of 40 per cent at the end of three years. The existing equipment has a value of $5,000, and is to be completely written off during the next three years. Annual operating and maintenance costs for the manual office would be $175,000.

Land for the new office would cost $20,000, and the building $160,000. The dial equipment would involve an investment of $750,000. Cut-over costs would be $42,000. Annual operation and maintenance costs would be $97,000. The building would be written off over 40 years and the equipment over 20 years.

Annual property taxes and insurance would be 2% of present value of all property. The cost of money to the company is 7½%. Borrowed capital is 30 per cent of total capital, with interest at 5%. The income tax rate is 50%. Assume annual depreciation accruals.

Should the change to dial equipment be made now, or would it be more economical to wait three years?

19–12 A utility company finds that with modern, steam-electric equipment the cost of generating electric power is 7 mills per kw.-hr. if a 60 per cent load factor is obtained; this cost includes income taxes and profit on capital. As the result of the construction of a governmentally owned multiple-purpose project, wholesale power will soon be available at a point seventy miles distant from its main transformer station. It will cost $60.00 per kw. of capacity to build the necessary transmission line, and annual maintenance costs will be $0.25 per kw. of capacity. Assume a 60 per cent load factor on the transmission line, and that the line is 93 per cent efficient. The cost of money for the company is 7½%, with 30 per cent borrowed capital at an interest rate of 5%. Depreciation accruals are made annually on a 40-year basis, and the company has a 50% income tax rate. At what price must it be able to purchase the power in order for it to be as cheap as generation with a local steam-electric plant?

CHAPTER **20**

Economy Studies
of Public Projects

Many engineering projects are financed and carried out by governmental agencies—federal, state, and local. The number, magnitude, and total cost of such projects have increased considerably in the past thirty years, particu-

TABLE 20-1   Percentage Distribution of Gross National Product, 1929–50 [1]

Year	Gross private domestic investment (Per cent)	Government purchases of goods and services	
		Federal (Per cent)	State and local (Per cent)
1929	15.2	1.3	6.9
1930	11.2	1.6	8.5
1931	7.1	2.0	10.1
1932	1.5	2.5	11.3
1933	2.3	3.6	10.7
1934	4.3	4.6	10.4
1935	8.5	4.1	9.6
1936	10.1	5.8	8.4
1937	12.7	5.0	7.8
1938	7.5	6.2	8.8
1939	10.9	5.6	8.7
1940	13.8	6.1	7.7
1941	14.5	13.4	6.2
1942	6.7	32.2	4.8
1943	2.9	41.8	3.8
1944	3.6	41.7	3.5
1945	5.0	34.8	3.7
1946	13.6	9.9	4.7
1947	12.9	6.8	5.5
1948	16.5	8.1	6.0
1949	12.8	9.9	7.0
1950	17.3	8.1	7.0

[1] From *National Income Supplement, Survey of Current Business*, 1951.

484

larly at the federal level, as is shown in Table 20–1. Such projects and expenditures have economy aspects just as if they were carried out by private organizations. However, because they are public projects, a number of important and special problems arise which affect the economy studies of such activities. These problems are complex, and, to a considerable extent, they are based on personal philosophies and desires which are subject to change. In order to make and interpret economy studies of public projects, it is essential to have some understanding of these problems.

During peace time public works tend to be of a durable nature, involving structures that have a long life. It appears likely that the number and magnitude of such projects will increase rather than decrease. This is explained by the public's increasing demand for governmental services and by the fact that, in order to take advantage of many of the remaining undeveloped natural resources of the country, very large expenditures of capital will be required, two or more states will be concerned, and multiple purposes will be involved.

RELATIONSHIP OF GOVERNMENT TO PUBLIC PROJECTS

In the United States there is a generally held concept that government exists in order to permit the people to accomplish collectively those things which are believed by the majority to be essential and which can not be accomplished by individuals acting alone. This applies to all levels of government. In the constitution the federal government is given the responsibility to provide for the national defense and the "general welfare" of the people; under these two authorizations virtually all federal projects are undertaken. State and local governments have similar responsibilities in the form of protection from domestic lawbreakers and the initiation, development, and operation of projects at the state and local level for the general welfare.

Since the term "general welfare" is both broad and indefinite, there is great diversity in the activities and projects that are carried on by public agencies. However, regardless of type, it is important that each be done in as economical a manner as conditions will permit.

RELATIONSHIP OF ENGINEERS TO PUBLIC WORKS

Engineers as a group have a greater interest in and more responsibility for public projects than most other people. Since a large proportion of public works involve engineering structures or equipment and their subsequent operation, many engineers are employed by governmental agencies to design, construct, operate, or manage various projects. These engineers have a direct responsibility to see that the projects are accomplished as economically as possible. Other engineers may be employed by private companies with which some governmental projects compete. To these engineers the economic basis of such governmental activities obviously is important.

All engineers, regardless of by whom they are employed, are taxpayers and thus have a very real stake in many governmental projects; they should take an active interest in the economy of such activities. But, as citizens, engineers also have a responsibility to the community in helping interpret the economic facts regarding public works to those who are not as well trained to understand the problems and issues involved. Many of the issues and problems regarding public works are not black or white. As will be pointed out later, many involve highly technical matters and basic principles of engineering economy. It therefore is to be expected that those without the engineer's specialized knowledge may not understand all of the factors and thus may arrive at erroneous conclusions, particularly if misled by an interested group or a politician with an axe to grind. As professional men, engineers have a special responsibility to aid in interpreting the problems and issues with respect to public projects for the general public.

BASIC CLASSES OF PUBLIC PROJECTS

Governmental projects may be classified into three broad categories: Protection (defense), Cultural Development, and Economic Services. At the federal level these categories would include the following:[2]

Protection
    Armed forces
    Federal Bureau of Investigation
    Justice Department
    Coast Guard
    Flood control
    Lighthouses and aids to navigation
    Air-beacon and emergency-landing-field system
    Old age and social security system
    Public health services

Cultural development
    Armed forces academies
    Library of Congress
    Postal service
    Recreational facilities

[2] This is not an all-inclusive list.

Economic services
   Postal service
   Emergency air landing fields
   Harbor improvements
   Irrigation projects
   Research services: Bureau of Standards, Department of Agriculture, Bureau of Mines, etc.
   Regulatory agencies: Federal Communications Commission, Interstate Commerce Commission, etc.

In examining this list of federal activities, it may be noted that some are of such a nature that only the federal government could conduct them, either because of the broad authority required or their relationship to other nations. The defense establishment, Coast Guard, public health services, and the regulatory agencies are of this character. As a result, there is virtually unanimous agreement that the federal government should operate such agencies.

There are other activities which now are held quite unanimously to be proper for only the government to operate, but which have reached this status only because of custom. For example, the postal service did not always handle parcels, and many opposed the parcel post service when it was inaugurated. Yet today it would be difficult to find anybody who would advocate abandoning this governmental activity. Thus after a governmental agency has carried on a particular function for a number of years the public comes to accept it as the sole and proper angency for performing the activity. Yet before, at, and shortly after the time the activity is started, there may be much dissension regarding the appropriateness of the government's engaging in it.

Still other activities are listed in which it is difficult to set an exact boundary between the area that is almost completely acceptable as proper for governmental conduct and the area about which there is much doubt. Further, the concept of the dividing line will vary among different people, depending upon their social, cultural, and economic backgrounds and their occupations. Public health service is an example. Few, if any, would question that there must be such an agency to set and maintain certain health standards and to prevent the importation and spread of communicable diseases. But it is extremely difficult to set a clear boundary between public health and socialized medicine, and individual views on the subject vary greatly.

The situation is illustrated by the views expressed by a dentist at a dinner party. He was declaiming rather loudly on the subject of private ownership of utilities, finally making the statement that "no one should be forced to pay a profit to a privately owned company for a service that is essential." Another guest remarked that this was exactly the view some people hold regarding medical and dental care. Immediately the dentist insisted that this was an entirely different matter. Thus it must be expected that there will not be, in certain areas, complete agreement about what are and are not activities in which the government should engage. Since people are involved, there are bound to be honest differences of opinion. But a clear understanding of this fact, and the reasons for it, will help one to analyze each particular situation and arrive at a reasonable decision.

It may also be noted in the foregoing tabulation of governmental activities that some can fall in two or more categories. For example, the postal service is listed as both a cultural and an economic-service activity. To the ordinary citizen, who may send and receive personal letters and receive books and magazines through the mail, the service clearly is of a cultural nature. To a mail-order house, which uses the postal service as a means of receiving and delivering orders, it is a distinct economic service. This dual nature of many public activities also serves to complicate their economic status.

Other public projects have a dual nature in the relationship to their benefits to the public. As an example, an irrigation project may be of benefit to all of the public by increasing the food supply and possibly reducing prices. At the same time, it is of very direct benefit to the owners of the land which is irrigated. As a result, it is difficult to assign the benefits derived from the project. Some are directly measurable in dollars, while others are difficult to quantify, and the proportion of each type of benefit can often be established only through arbitrary decisions.

While the previous discussion has been related to federal governmental activities, state and local projects can be similarly classified. In general, the same problems exist, although ordinarily to a somewhat lesser degree, since public projects at these levels tend to be smaller and more limited in scope and diversity.

FINANCING OF PUBLIC PROJECTS

Public projects, like private projects, require money, frequently in very large amounts, for acquiring assets and for working capital. The problems and methods of acquiring the necessary capital, however, are somewhat different. Except in the case of self-liquidating projects, which will be discussed later, the ultimate source of capital required for public projects is taxes. Even many self-liquidating projects use tax monies to acquire the initial assets, with provision for repayment over an extended period during the life of the project.

All federal projects are financed out of tax money and federal borrowing. No attempt is made to relate the tax money to a particular project. The only limit to the amount of capital that can be obtained, after expenditures are authorized by the Congress, is the legal limitation on the national debt. With financing coming primarily from current taxes, there technically is no interest cost. However, since the federal government is in debt, it is realistic to assume that all federal projects are of an incremental nature and are thus financed out of borrowed funds, and that the cost of money is not less than the average interest rate currently being paid on federal borrowing.

Unlike federal projects, state and local public works may be financed out of tax monies or by bond issues. Bond issues may be general or issued against a specific project. As a rule, local governments tend to issue bonds for financing specific projects to a greater extent than do the states. However, practices vary greatly, and the facts must be determined in each case.

When bonds are issued by state or local governments for financing public projects, or when the cost of money to the federal government must be considered, the interest rate is almost always less than that which would have to be paid by a private business. This is due to a number of factors that reduce the risk, such as the taxing power of a governmental unit, control to avoid competition, and the tax-exempt status of many state and local bond issues. Because of the lower cost of money, public projects are correspondingly easier to justify economically than private projects, not because of their inherent characteristics but due to the preferred credit status of the borrower.

When bonds are issued, the usual procedure is to retire uniform amounts each year during the bond life. Interest, of course, must be paid each year on the outstanding bonds. The average annual cost of the financing under this procedure is the same as straight-line depreciation plus average interest.

A relatively recent development is the formation of special public "Authorities" to finance, build, and operate public works where two or more governmental units, such as states, counties, or cities, are involved. Outstanding examples of this kind are the Port of New York Authority—established by the states of New York and New Jersey to construct and operate harbor facilities, airports, and tunnels—and the San Francisco-Oakland Bay Bridge Authority—set up within the state of California to finance, build, and operate bridges between San Francisco and cities on the east side of San Francisco Bay.

Financing of state and local projects by bond issues sometimes presents special problems. Often approval of the voters is required before bonds may be issued. Frequently an affirmative approval of two-thirds of the voters is required. Revenue bonds, dependent upon the revenues from specific projects for their interest and repayment, may be exceptions. Laws frequently require repayment of all bonds within a specified period, thus limiting the life of bond issues. All such factors must be taken into account in economy studies of public projects which are to be financed by bond issues.

There are, of course, some broader implications of financing public works, particularly through bond issues, such as possible inflationary effects and reduction of unemployment. Such matters will not be considered further here.

When financing is done out of general tax monies, a difficulty arises in respect to the economy of a project, since there usually is no direct connection between the costs and the benefits received. In a privately financed business the products or services must be sold, and the buyer evaluates their worth by the price he is willing to pay for them. On the other hand, if a flood-control project is financed out of income taxes or some other tax monies, the taxes also pay for a multitude of other services, and the taxpayer has no direct knowledge as to what portion of his taxes was used to pay for a particular project. Further, he may live a thousand miles from the project and thus be an indirect beneficiary in only the most remote sense. Thus, where this method of financing is used, as it is for most public works, there frequently is an inherent difficulty in attempting to relate the benefits to the costs and considerable indifference on the part of those who actually pay the costs and are, in reality, the owners.

TYPES OF FEDERAL FINANCIAL AID

Federal financing and financial aid may take several forms. The first and most common is direct payment, which is used to finance most federal activities. In most cases the government does not expect direct financial return, and the projects are of an essential nature and of general benefit to all or a considerable segment of the people. This last provision often is interpreted very loosely, particularly with respect to the improvement of local rivers and harbors, commonly and fittingly called "pork-barrel" legislation. The more necessary a project is considered to be, and the more general the benefits, the less are the requirements for justification in terms of accurately measured monetary benefits. Such activities frequently are important factors in determining cost allocations in multiple-purpose projects, as will be discussed later.

A second form of financial aid provided by the federal government is a loan without interest. Grants of this type are made, for example, to public irrigation districts. Such loans are made for an extended period of years, frequently up to forty, with provision that no payments need be made toward repayment of the principal for ten years. While at first glance it might appear that such financing is without cost to the government, this obviously is not the case, since the federal government must either borrow the funds or pay interest on the existing debt. The amount of the interest thus paid becomes a *grant-in-aid* to the project. The grant-in-aid, plus the longer amortization period than that which could be obtained from private lenders, makes projects possible which would not be economic if they had to be financed by usual means.

Financial aid of this type is justified on the basis that such subjects provide long-range development of the nation's resources and contribute to the general welfare of the entire nation.

A third type of financial aid provided by the federal government is in the form of loans at low rates of interest made to other public agencies and certain nonprofit institutions for special purposes. Such loans, in effect, are made to finance large self-liquidating projects, such as T.V.A., where the project is expected to repay the cost and interest. Another use of such loans is to finance dormitories at state colleges and universities and, more recently, at private nonprofit colleges. The interest rate on such loans usually is around $3\frac{1}{2}\%$, and the loan period is longer than could economically be obtained from usual sources of money.

A fourth type of financial aid is an indirect grant. This type of aid is used to encourage the development or continuance of services which are held to be vital to the national defense or general welfare. In less polite, but more realistic, terms such aid is known as a *subsidy,* and it has been used for many purposes for many years. The early transcontinental railroads were given alternate sections of land along certain stretches of their rights of way to encourage them to build their tracks into newly opened territories; some of these railroads at present are obtaining a considerable portion of their incomes from the sale of petroleum and uranium obtained from these lands. Contracts for carrying air mail were granted to airlines in earlier years at prices considerably in excess of the actual cost in order to encourage the development of commercial aviation. A considerable portion of the cost of certain types of ocean-going ships is paid by the government, provided they have certain features which make them readily convertible to wartime usage, in order to help maintain an adequate merchant marine. Lighthouses, radio compass stations, and weather-forecasting services are maintained for the benefit of shipping companies without cost. Similar services are provided for the airlines.

Such services constitute an indirect but very definite form of financial aid. In many cases they are so disguised that the general public is not aware of the amount of aid or by whom it is received. In recent years there has been considerable agitation to have such aid take the form of direct subsidies, in order that better control can be exercised over it. Many subsidies are felt to be necessary, but it is argued that the taxpayers should know where, and how much of, their money is spent. Such information would undoubtedly lead to greater economy.

The fifth type of financial aid differs from the others in that no government money is granted or loaned. Instead, a governmental agency insures private loans for private housing. This type of aid originated in the Federal Housing Administration, FHA, as a means of making the financing of private homes easier. If a person wishes to build or buy a home under this plan, he applies to a regular private lending agency, such as a bank, for a loan. If the plans and specifications of the house and lot and the terms of the loan as to length and interest rate meet the requirements established by the FHA, the lending agency may then apply to the FHA to have the loan insured up to the maximum percentage permitted by law. Under the provisions of the 1958 revision of the act, persons may borrow up to a maximum of $20,000 on the basis of 97% of the appraised value of the property up to $13,500, 85% of the excess over $13,500 up to $16,000, and 70% of the excess over $16,000, at a maximum interest rate of $5\frac{1}{4}\%$ and with repayment in up to 25 years. The borrower pays a small application fee and a charge of $\frac{1}{2}\%$ per annum on the remaining balance of the loan as the cost of the insurance. Since the lending agencies are insured against possible loss, they will grant loans at lower interest rates and for longer periods than they would otherwise.

The costs to the government for this plan are only those of a portion of the overhead involved. The plan has been outstandingly successful, the record of repayment of these home loans being very high. A number of loans are grouped together for risk purposes, and in nearly all cases the $\frac{1}{2}\%$ insurance premium has more than covered the losses in the group; excess premiums are returned to the borrower when the loan is paid. Thus, with this plan, although the borrower does not receive any government funds, he does receive aid in the form of lower interest and more favorable terms.

It appears that this same type of aid might well be used for some other projects which now are financed directly out of government funds.

FEDERAL FINANCING DURING EMERGENCIES

During times of national emergency many deviations are made from the usual forms of governmental financial aid. For example, during World War II various types of manufacturing plants were financed by the federal government and leased to private companies in order to obtain production of needed products. During and after the war companies which built needed defense plants with private funds were permitted to write off these assets in five years, the accelerated depreciation rate thus assuring recovery of capital and permitting the depreciation costs to be charged against operating income of the first few years. During the depression years of the 1930's many projects were financed by federal funds to help relieve unemployment. For a number of years federal funds have been available to help finance slum-clearance housing projects.

Traditionally the federal government paid 50 per cent of the cost of constructing interstate national highways. This was later raised to 60 per cent and in 1956 legislation was passed to increase the government's contribution to 90 per cent on certain types of interstate highways in order to help relieve the critical highway shortage.

Thus the policies of the federal government are varied as the needs change in the interest of the "general welfare." It must be expected that such financing often is not based on the usual type of economy studies. The criteria for the financing of state and local projects also vary in times of emergency but usually not as widely as in the case of federal works.

SELF-LIQUIDATING PROJECTS

The term "self-liquidating project" is often applied to a governmental project which is expected to earn direct revenue sufficient to repay the cost in a specified period of time. Such projects usually provide utility services, such as water, electric power, sewage disposal, or irrigation water. In addition, toll bridges, tunnels, and highways are built and operated in this manner. Projects of this type come under the classification of economic service.

Self-liquidating projects are not expected to earn profits or pay income taxes. Neither do they pay property taxes, although in some cases they do make *in-lieu* payments in place of the property or franchise taxes which would have been paid to the cities, counties, or states involved had the project been built and operated by private ownership. For example, the U.S. Government agreed to pay each of the states of Arizona and Nevada

$300,000 annually for fifty years in lieu of taxes which might have accrued if Hoover Dam had been privately constructed and operated. In most cases the "in-lieu" payments are considerably less than the actual property or franchise taxes would be. Further, once the "in-lieu" payments are agreed upon, usually at the time the project is originated, they virtually never are changed thereafter. Such is not the situation in the case of property taxes.

Whether self-liquidating projects should or should not pay the same taxes as privately owned projects is not within the scope of this text. Such payments undoubtedly would make it much easier to compare the economy of similar publicly and privately operated activities. However, that public projects do not have to earn profits or pay certain taxes is a fact which must be given proper consideration in making economy studies of such projects and in making decisions regarding them.

MULTIPLE-PURPOSE PROJECTS

Many governmental and private projects have more than one purpose or function. A governmental project, for example, may be intended for flood control, irrigation, and generation of electric power. A private project may utilize waste gases in a petroleum refinery to generate steam and electricity for refinery use and electricity for public sale.[3] Such projects commonly are called "multiple-purpose projects." By designing and building them to serve more than one purpose, greater over-all economy can be achieved. This is very important in projects involving very large sums of capital and utilization of natural resources, such as rivers. It is not uncommon for a public project to have four or five purposes. This usually is desirable, but, at the same time, it creates economy and managerial problems because of overlapping utilization of facilities and, sometimes, conflict of interest between the several purposes and agencies involved. An understanding of the problems involved in such situations is essential to anyone who wishes to make economy studies of such projects or to understand the cost data and political issues arising from them.

A number of basic problems may arise in connection with multiple-purpose public works. These may be illustrated by the simple example of a dam, such as is portrayed in Figure 20–1, which is to be built in a semiarid portion of the United States, primarily to provide control against serious floods. It is at once apparent that if the flow of the water impounded behind the dam could be regulated and diverted onto the adjoining land, in order to provide irrigation water, the value of the land would be increased tre-

---

[3] The Pacific Gas and Electric Company, a large and efficient operating utility, has several generating plants of this type.

mendously. This would result in an increase in the nation's resources, and it thus appears desirable to expand the project into one having two purposes—flood control and irrigation.

The existence of a dam with a high water level on one side and a much lower level on the other side, at least during a good portion of the year,

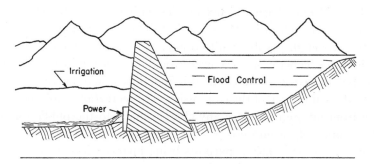

Figure 20–1. Schematic representation of a multiple-purpose project involving flood control, irrigation, and power.

immediately suggests that some of the nation's resources will be wasted unless some of the water is permitted to run through turbines to generate electric power which can be sold to customers in the adjacent territory. Thus the project is expanded to have a third purpose—the generating of power.

In the semiarid surroundings the creation of a large lake, such as would exist behind the dam, would provide valuable recreation facilities for hunting, fishing, boating, camping, etc. This gives a fourth purpose to the project. All of these have desirable economic and social worth, and what started as a single-purpose project has ended by having four purposes. Not to develop the project to fill all four functions probably would mean that valuable national resources would be wasted.

If the project is built for four purposes, the important fact that one dam will serve all of them will result in at least three basic problems. The first is the allocation of the cost of the dam to the four purposes it will serve. Assume, for example, that the dam will cost $10,000,000. What portion of this amount should be assigned to flood control? What amounts to irrigation, power generation, and recreation? If the identical dam will serve all four purposes, deciding how much of its cost should be assigned to any one of the purposes obviously might present considerable difficulties. One extreme would be to decide that since the dam was required for flood-control its entire cost should be assigned to this purpose. If this were done, the cost of the electric power and the irrigation water would obviously be far less than if a considerable part or all of the $10,000,000 had been assigned to these functions.

The cost allocation problem is complicated considerably by the different ways in which the allocated costs would be financed by the federal government. The costs for flood control in the project which has been described would be paid out of general tax monies without any attempt to recover them from the beneficiaries of the project. The costs assigned to irrigation might be recovered, possibly with no interest or with interest at a very low rate. Since the generation of power would be self-liquidating in nature, presumably the costs allocated to this function would be recovered with interest. Most, if not all, of the costs assigned to recreation would be financed directly from tax monies, since any charges made to the public for recreational use probably would not pay for the current upkeep of the facilities. With the costs of the various purposes being financed in the different manners indicated, it is obvious that the amounts allocated to flood control and recreational facilities would have a considerable effect upon the resulting unit costs and selling prices for power and irrigation water. It is only to be expected that those who would be direct beneficiaries of these two purposes would exercise their influence to have as large a proportion as possible of the dam cost allocated to flood control and recreation.

Another extreme would be to assign each purpose with an amount equal to the total cost of the dam. Such a procedure would have two effects. First, it would undoubtedly make some of the purposes—for example, recreation and irrigation—so costly that they could not be undertaken. Secondly, using this procedure, the cost of the dam might be returned to the government several times. While many taxpayers would appreciate such a profitable occurrence it would probably be so upsetting to government procedures that it would cause a minor national emergency.

The second basic problem in multiple-purpose projects is the matter of conflict of interest between the several purposes. This may be illustrated by the matter of the water level maintained behind the dam. For flood control it would be best to have the reservoir empty most of the year in order to provide maximum storage capacity during the season when floods might occur. Such a condition would be most unsatisfactory for power generation. For this purpose it would be desirable to maintain as high a level as possible behind the dam during most of the year. For recreational purposes a fairly constant level also would be desirable. The requirements for irrigation probably would be somewhere between those for flood control and power generation. Thus some very definite conflict of interest usually arises in connection with multiple-purpose works. As a result, compromise decisions must be made. These decisions have arbitrary effects on the economy of the various portions of a multiple-purpose project. This is a fact that never should be overlooked in evaluating the economy of such projects and the costs of the services produced.

A third problem connected with multiple-purpose public works is the matter of politics. Since the various purposes are likely to be desired or opposed by various segments of the public and by various interest groups that will be affected, it is inevitable that such projects frequently become political issues. This often has an effect upon cost allocations and thus on the over-all economy of these projects.

A basic motive of every political candidate or officeholder is to get elected or re-elected. Though he may honestly claim that his basic objective is to "serve the people," he cannot serve them unless he is in office. One primary way of obtaining votes is to demonstrate that the candidate is able to obtain direct benefits for the electorate. Such benefits as cheap irrigation water or electric power are easily recognized. As a result, there is a rather natural tendency for some politicians to exert influence in the allocation of costs of multiple-purpose public projects so that undue portions are assigned to such purposes as flood control and recreation; thus the services provided by the self-liquidating purposes, such as power-generation, may be sold to the public at very low rates.

The net result of these three factors is that the cost allocations made in multiple-purpose public projects are arbitrary. As a consequence, production and selling costs of the services provided also are arbitrary. Because of this, they can not be used as valid "yardsticks" with which similar private projects can be compared to determine the relative efficiencies of public and private ownership. A recognition of this fact will do much to eliminate meaningless claims and arguments and to encourage the development and use of sound procedures which will assure that only economical and essential multiple-purpose public works are authorized and that they are operated with maximum efficiency.

AUTHORIZATION OF FEDERAL PROJECTS

The authorizations under which federal projects are undertaken frequently are confusing. For example, the Bonneville Dam on the Columbia River was approved as a navigation project, although its contribution as a power project is probably of more importance. Hoover Dam on the Colorado River also was approved as a navigation project but is used primarily for irrigation, water supply, flood control, and power. Such situations result from legislation which permits more flexibility in projects authorized for certain purposes than in those for others. These procedures are illogical but must be recognized and accepted as conditions which frequently exist in connection with public works.

WHY ECONOMY STUDIES OF PUBLIC WORKS?

In view of the various problems that have been cited, engineers and other individuals sometimes raise the question as to whether economy studies of governmental projects should be attempted. It must be admitted that such economy studies frequently can not be made in as complete and satisfactory a manner as in the case of studies of privately financed projects. However, one must remember that decisions regarding investment must be made in connection with public works. The alternative to basing such decisions on the best possible economy studies is to base them on hunch and expediency. It is therefore essential that economy studies be made in the best possible manner, but with a sound understanding of the nature of such activities and of all of the background, conditions, and limitations connected with them.

It must be recognized that economy studies of public works can be made from several viewpoints, each applicable for certain conditions. Many studies are made from the point of view of the governmental body involved. In comparing alternative structures or methods for accomplishing the same objective, such a point of view is satisfactory. The point of view of the citizens in a restricted area is used in other studies, such as local self-liquidating or service projects where those who must pay the costs are the direct beneficiaries of the project. In other cases the entire nation may be affected, so the economy study should reflect a very broad point of view. Such studies are apt to involve many intangibles and benefits which can not be assigned to specific persons or groups. In each case as many factors as possible should be evaluated in monetary terms, since this usually will be most helpful in making decisions regarding the expenditure of public funds. However, it must also be recognized that nonmonetary factors often exist and are frequently of great importance in final decisions.

DIFFICULTIES INHERENT IN ECONOMY STUDIES
OF PUBLIC WORKS

There are a number of difficulties which are inherent in public works and which must be considered in making economy studies and economic decisions regarding them. Some of these are:

1. There is no profit standard to be used as a measure of financial effectiveness. Most public works are intended to be non-profit.
2. There is no monetary measure of many of the benefits provided by a public project.
3. There frequently is little or no direct connection between the project and the public, who are the owners.
4. Politics: Whenever public funds are used, there is apt to be political influence. This can have very serious effects on the economy of projects, from conception through operation, and knowledge of its actual or possible existence is an important factor which must be considered.
5. Indefinite motivation of personnel: The usual profit motive as a stimulus to effective operation is absent. This may have a marked effect on the effectiveness of a project, from conception through operation. In some cases the major motivation may be toward inefficient operation and the creation of unnecessary services because an individual's advancement depends upon having more people under his supervision. This does not mean that all public works are inefficient or that many managers and employees of them are not trying to do, and are actually doing, an effective job. But the fact remains that the direct stimuli present in privately owned companies are lacking and that this lack may have a considerable effect.
6. Legal restrictions: Public works usually are much more circumscribed by legal restrictions than are private companies. Their ability to obtain capital usually is restricted. Frequently their area of operations is restricted, as, for example, where a municipally owned power company can not sell power outside the city limits. There often are severe restrictions with respect to hiring, firing, and paying employees.
7. In many cases decisions concerning public works, particularly their conception and authorization, are made by elected officials whose tenure of office is very uncertain. As a result, immediate costs and benefits may be stressed, to the detriment of long-range economy.

PATTERNS SUITABLE FOR ECONOMY STUDIES OF PUBLIC WORKS

Of the basic patterns discussed in Chapter 8, three are suitable and commonly used for economy studies of public works. These are the annual-cost, present-worth-cost, and the capitalized-cost methods. The use of the capitalized-cost method has decreased considerably in recent years because of its unrealistic assumption that the structures involved will be needed in perpetuity.

In most economy studies of proposed public works the primary objective is to determine whether the benefits will exceed the costs during the life of the project. Where financing is by means of a bond issue, the major concern is that the benefits or revenues shall at least meet the costs during the life of the bond issue, when the costs of amortization and interest must be met. It usually can safely be assumed that if the project is economically satisfactory during this period, the service and benefits derived thereafter will further enhance its attractiveness. Thus either the reasonable project life or the bond life may be used as a study period, depending primarily upon the conditions regarding financing. When no bonds are involved, the study period adopted usually is somewhat arbitrary. Forty- or fifty-year study periods are common for projects involving major structures having very long physical lives, and in recent years some studies have involved sixty- and even seventy-five-year periods. Usually various governmental agencies have relatively fixed policies regarding the study periods to be used for various types of projects, but there is some evidence that the period is stretched when necessary in order to economically justify a desired project. Sometimes the study period is set directly or indirectly by legislative policy in connection with obtaining financing.

For studies of this type either the present-worth-cost or the annual-cost patterns may be used. If revenues, or benefits, and costs vary over the bond-life or study period the present-worth-cost pattern normally is used. For cases where the revenues and costs are uniform the annual-cost method is suitable.

Aside from the matters of original cost allocation on multiple-purpose projects and the evaluation of benefits in monetary terms, the only major items which must be considered somewhat differently than in ordinary economy studies are those of depreciation, bond amortization, and interest rate. In most instances they are one and the same problem. Where financing is completely out of tax monies, either of two procedures may be used. One is to consider first cost, and there is no need to include depreciation. Frequently such projects involve long-lived structures. Maintenance costs of sufficient magnitude to provide indefinite life are included. The second procedure is to show the cost of sinking-fund amortization over the study period, even though no bonds will be issued, plus interest on the original investment. This is obviously the usual procedure followed in ordinary economy studies.

Where bonds are used for financing, the usual practice is to include the costs of amortization and bond interest and omit depreciation. Obviously, both amortization and depreciation should not be included, since this would provide for both the original project and its replacement. If the life of the physical assets is considerably in excess of the bond life, it is more realistic to include depreciation—based on the actual expected economic life—and interest cost, omitting bond amortization. This procedure should be followed in comparing alternatives which have different lives but which might be financed by bond issues having the same lives.

INTEREST RATE IN PUBLIC WORKS STUDIES

The interest rate that should be used in depreciation, amortization, and present-worth calculations in economy studies of public works is a matter of some controversy, or at least what is done in practice is often contrary to what is believed to be proper by most authorities in the engineering economy field. It is fundamental that the interest rate used in all calculations of capital recovery and present worth should reflect the cost of capital and thus be a measure of the risk involved. There obviously are uncertainties and risks involved in most public projects. In many cases it is true that the risk is somewhat less than that for similar private projects, because of the control which a public agency may have over competition. The difficulty is that the cost of money for a public project may not be a measure of the risks involved in the particular project. For example, suppose that a project is financed by bonds which have first claim upon the revenues of the project but which also are general obligations of the governmental unit involved and are thus backed by its taxing powers. A case of this kind existed in the financing of the Golden Gate bridge where any deficit was to be paid by San Francisco County. A similar situation exists when financing is to be done from general tax monies; the interest rate used is the average rate paid on general bonds issued by the governmental unit. It is obvious that in these cases there is virtually no connection between the cost of money and the risks inherent in the project. It follows that three rules should be observed in selecting the interest rate which should be used in economy studies of public works:

1. The interest rate should measure the risk. (If the bond rate does measure this factor, it may be used.)
2. If there are no bonds, or if the bonds do not reflect the risk, an interest rate should be selected which does measure the risk.
3. If the public project is being compared with a private project, the same interest rate should be used for both. (Any lower monetary cost that might be obtained by public ownership is not due to the merits of the project but to other factors related to public credit.)

ECONOMY STUDIES USING BENEFITS-TO-COST RATIOS

A very common procedure in making economy studies of public works is to compute benefits-to-cost ratios (or costs-to-benefits). This practice is used to a great extent for federal projects and to a somewhat lesser extent for state and local works. It is particularly useful for projects having multiple purposes. Using this procedure, all benefits are evaluated in monetary terms, and if the ratio of benefits to costs is in excess of 1, the project is assumed to be justified.

It is obvious that some difficulty may be encountered in assigning monetary values to some benefits—for example, recreation benefits or some flood-control benefits. Therefore, it should be recognized that the computed monetary benefits may contain some more or less arbitrarily assigned values.

Some progress has been achieved at the federal level in standardizing the procedures for determining the benefits. A subcommittee representing the major construction departments of the government has prepared a report entitled *Proposed Practices for Economic Analysis of River Basin Projects,* dated May, 1950. It is assumed in every project that the social usefulness of the project must be established to the satisfaction of the Congress before it may be undertaken. It is extremely difficult to devise a method of measuring, in monetary terms, the amount of social usefulness of one project as compared or contrasted with another. Some of the methods of reducing costs or increasing benefits are probably affected by these difficulties of measurement and may represent progress in the direction of such measurement. From the point of view of customary appraisal for industrial works, they are quite unorthodox. The difficulty seems not to be that the amounts listed as measures of social benefits are incorrect but that social benefits should probably not be measured economically. In a few cases, perhaps in some classes of cases, the economic elements of social benefits can be measured. In other cases such measurement is out of the question. A further difficulty is that the amount required to satisfy Congress as to the social usefulness too frequently is affected by the "back-scratching" connected with "pork-barrel" legislation or by other political ramifications.

The annual benefit-to-cost ratio may be a curve, depending upon the cost in dollars of the project. This means that if a portion of a development is undertaken, the benefit-to-cost ratio may be low; at a somewhat larger investment it may be quite high; and for still larger investments it may again become low. This is illustrated in Figure 20–2. It will be noted in the curves in the upper figure that the maximum ratio of benefits to costs occurs at a

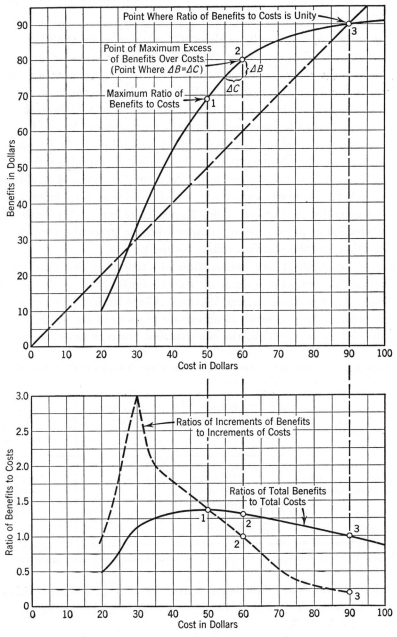

Figure 20–2. Benefit-cost relationships.

503

cost of $50. The maximum excess of benefits over cost occurs at $60. The ratio of benefits to cost is unity at about $27 cost and again at $90 cost.

The lower drawing in Figure 20–2 illustrates the measurement of the ratio of benefits to cost when the project is an increment to an existing project. It should in this case be studied as an incremental cost, discussed in earlier chapters of this book. It will be noted that at $30 the ratio of the increment of benefit to increment of cost is a maximum. At $50 the incremental ratio equals the ratio of total benefits to total costs. At $60 the ratio of benefits to cost has dropped to unity, but the ratio of total benefits to total costs of the project remains above unity. At point 3 the ratio of total benefits to total costs has dropped to unity and that of increments is far below unity— about four-tenths. A drawing of this kind is extremely useful, since it permits a selection of answers in accordance with the particular project under consideration and the situation calling for the project.

A typical example of an economy study of a federal project using costs-to-benefits ratios is found in a study of a flood-control and power project on the White River in Missouri and Arkansas.[4] Considerable flooding and consequent damage had occurred along certain portions of this river, as shown in Table 20–2. In addition, the uncontrolled water flow increased flood

TABLE 20–2   Annual Loss Due to Floods on Three Stretches of the White River

	Annual value of loss	Annual loss per acre improved land in flood plain	Annual loss per acre for total area in flood plain
Crops	$1,951,714.00	$6.04	$1.55
Farm (other than crops)	215,561.00	0.67	0.17
Railroads and highways	119,800.00	0.37	0.09
Levees [a]	87,234.00	0.27	0.07
Other losses	168,326.00	0.52	0.13
Total	2,542,635.00	$7.87	$2.01

[a] Expenditures by the United States for levee repairs and high-water maintenance.

conditions on the lower Mississippi River. The cost-and-benefits summary for the Table Rock and Bull Shoals reservoirs involved in the project is shown in Table 20–3.

Several interesting facts may be noted concerning this study. First, there was no attempt to allocate the cost of the dams between flood control and power production. Second, a very large portion of the flood benefits were

[4] See House Document 917/76/3 for the complete report on this project.

TABLE 20–3 Estimated Costs, Annual Charges, and Annual Benefits for Table Rock and Bull Shoals Reservoirs, Flood Control and Water Power Combined

Item	Table Rock	Bull Shoals	Total for the two reservoirs
Cost of dam and appurtenances, and reservoir			
Dam, including reservoir-clearing, camp, access railroads and highways, and foundation exploration and treatment	$20,447,000	$25,240,000	$45,687,000
Powerhouse and equipment	6,700,000	6,650,000	13,350,000
Power transmission facilities to existing load-distribution centers	3,400,000	4,387,000	7,787,000
Lands	1,200,000	1,470,000	2,670,000
Highway relocations	2,700,000	140,000	2,840,000
Cemetery relocations	40,000	18,000	58,000
Damage to villages	6,000	94,500	100,500
Damage to miscellaneous structures	7,000	500	7,500
Total construction cost (estimated appropriation of public funds necessary for the execution of the project)	$34,500,000	$38,000,000	$72,500,000
Federal investment			
Total construction cost	$34,500,000	$38,000,000	$72,500,000
Interest during construction	1,811,300	1,995,000	3,806,300
Total	36,311,300	39,995,000	76,306,300
Present value of federal properties	1,200	300	1,500
Total federal investment	$36,312,500	$39,995,300	$76,307,800
Annual charges: Interest, amortization, maintenance, and operation	$ 1,642,200	$ 1,815,100	$ 3,457,300
Annual benefits			
Prevented direct flood losses in White River Basin			
Present conditions	60,100	266,900	327,000
Future developments	19,000	84,200	103,200
Prevented indirect flood losses owing to floods in White River Basin	19,800	87,800	107,600
Enhancement in property values in White River Valley	7,700	34,000	41,700
Mississippi River	220,000	980,000	1,200,000
Annual flood benefits	326,600	1,452,900	1,779,500
Power value	1,415,600	1,403,400	2,819,000
Total annual benefits	$ 1,742,200	$ 2,856,300	$ 4,598,500
Ratio of annual charges to annual benefits	1:1.06	1:1.57	1:1.33

shown to be in connection with the Mississippi River and are not indicated in Table 20–2; these were not detailed in the main body of the report, but shown in an appendix. Only a moderate decrease in the value of these benefits would have changed the costs-to-benefits ratio considerably. Third, without the combination of flood-control and power objectives the project undoubtedly would not have been economical for either purpose. These facts point to the advantages of multiple purposes for making desirable projects economical which otherwise would not be feasible, and to the necessity for very careful evaluation of the several benefits.

A STUDY OF ALTERNATIVE PUBLIC WORKS

An example of an economy study of alternative public works is found in the case of proposed improvements in the harbor channels at Ashland, Wisconsin, where ships grounded occasionally when attempting to enter a coal company dock to discharge cargo. During a one-year period ships had lost a total of 75 hours due to groundings, which constituted an annual loss of $3,750.[5] This loss did not include damage which frequently resulted to the vessels. Proposal A was to add an extensive area to the channel, involving the removal of 648,000 cubic yards of material by dredging, at an estimated cost of $200,000. Proposal B was to add a smaller area at the turning point. This alternative involved the removal of only 67,000 cubic yards of material, at an estimated cost of only $24,000.

The economic study of these alternatives is shown in Table 20–4. It will be noted that the annual-cost method was used, employing sinking fund

TABLE 20–4 Annual Economic Cost of Proposals for Improvements to Ashland, Wisconsin, Harbor

	Alternative A	Alternative B
Federal first cost & investment	$200,000	$24,000
Non-federal first cost & investment	0	0
Federal annual carrying charges		
Interest (3%)	6,000	720
Amortization (50 years at 3%)	1,773	213
Increased maintenance	0	0
Total federal annual carrying charge	7,773	933
Non-federal annual carrying charge	0	0
Total annual carrying charges	$ 7,773	$ 933

amortization over a fifty-year period plus 3% interest on the original investment. In this particular case proposal B was recommended. Since there were

[5] See House Document 337/76/1 for the complete report on this project.

no direct benefits to the government or the public in general, no benefits-to-cost ratios were computed. The project was justified on the basis that the government-maintained channel was inadequate and that the annual savings to ship owners were considerably in excess of the computed annual cost for alternative *B*.

COST ALLOCATIONS FOR ECONOMY STUDIES OF HIGHWAYS

The problems involved in allocating the costs of highways to the users are quite complex and illustrate the difficulties frequently encountered in studies of public works. In the first place, a decision must be reached as to the proportion of the total cost which should be borne by the direct users. For example, some believe that a part of the cost of all streets and highways should be paid out of general tax money. One proposal has been that the direct users should pay 80 per cent of the cost of state highways, 32 per cent of county and local highways, and 28 per cent of city streets. Where such a policy is followed, it is obvious that the percentages are arbitrary. In recent years many states have tried to charge all of the cost of state highways to the users. Financing is by means of vehicle registration fees, gasoline taxes, and sometimes a load-mile tax on trucks of more than a certain weight.

Regardless of the percentage of total cost that is to be paid by the direct users, there remains the problem of determining the portion of the total cost which should be allocated to and paid by each type of user. For instance, if a highway is built and is used by passenger cars, medium trucks, and heavy trucks, how much of the total cost of construction and maintenance should be paid by each type of vehicle? This is a matter which has been and still is hotly debated. A concrete pavement 5 inches thick and with 7 per cent grades might be entirely satisfactory for passenger cars. For medium trucks a 6½-inch pavement with 5 per cent grades might be satisfactory. However, if heavy trucks are to use the highway a 9-inch pavement and maximum grades of 4 per cent might be required. The costs for each type of highway would be considerably different.

Many studies have been made to determine the costs caused by each type of vehicle, but there is far from general agreement as to the correctness of the results, or as to the method by which these costs should be collected from the users. It is generally agreed that all types of vehicles should share in the costs of a basic highway which would be adequate for ordinary passenger cars, and that any type of heavier vehicles, primarily trucks, should pay the additional costs of constructing and maintaining the roads built to heavier standards required for their use. It is not difficult to determine the added construction costs, but the determination of the maintenance costs is very difficult. Probably the only way this could be done with complete accuracy would be to construct parallel highways, one adequate for and used only by passenger cars, and the other adequate for and used only by trucks. For completely conclusive cost data, there would have to be several parallel highways, one for trucks of each weight group. Such a project would be unreasonably costly and physically difficult, and probably will never be carried out. As a consequence, the cost allocations must be based, to a large extent, on theoretical studies, and the arguments as to their correctness will undoubtedly continue.

Most studies have concluded, first, that the costs are a function of the vehicle-miles of usage, and, second, that the cost per vehicle-mile is the sum of a constant plus a variable which depends on the vehicle weight. For example, one state concluded that the annual cost of providing and maintaining highways for vehicles weighing up to 60,000 pounds was

$$c = 0.78903 \ w + 2.70554,$$

where c was the cost in mills per vehicle-mile, and w the registered gross weight of the vehicle in 1,000 pounds. This study also suggested that the minimum value of c should be 6 mills per vehicle-mile, this being the amount which should be assigned to passenger cars.

If such a formula is assumed to be valid, it then is possible to compute the cost which should be allocated to each class of vehicle. There remains, however, the problem of determining the manner of collecting the allocated costs. Two methods are in general use—gasoline taxes and ton-mile taxes on vehicles above a specified weight. Each is in addition to a flat or somewhat graduated vehicle registration fee, which pays a portion of the basic fixed road cost.

COLLECTION OF HIGHWAY COSTS BY GASOLINE TAXES

The method of determining the amount of gasoline tax required to pay for highway costs may be illustrated by the following example. For simplicity it is assumed that there are only three types of vehicles: passenger cars, medium trucks, and heavy trucks.

Type of vehicle	Number	Miles per year	Miles per gallon
Passenger cars	1,000,000	10×10^9	15
Medium trucks	40,000	1.6×10^9	10
Heavy trucks	10,000	1×10^9	6

The thickness and increment cost of the highways required for these vehicles are:

Type of vehicle	Pavement thickness	Increment cost per year
Passenger cars	5 in.	$32,000,000.00
Medium trucks	6½ in.	4,000,000.00
Heavy trucks	8 in.	5,000,000.00

Using the assumption that the highway costs should be allocated on the basis of the number of vehicles that cause and use each increment of pavement, the annual cost for each type of vehicle would be:

Allocation of Increment Cost per vehicle	Passenger cars	Medium trucks	Heavy trucks
$32,000,000.00/1,050,000	$30.45	$ 30.45	$ 30.45
4,000,000.00/50,000		80.00	80.00
5,000,000.00/10,000			500.00
Total	$30.45	$110.45	$610.45

The number of gallons of gasoline used per year by each vehicle of each type and the corresponding tax per gallon that would be required in each case would be:

Type of vehicle	Number of gallons	Tax per gallon
Passenger cars	667	$0.0472
Medium trucks	4,000	0.0276
Heavy trucks	16,667	0.0367

Obviously it would not be feasible to charge a different gasoline tax for each class of vehicle. A number of solutions could be devised. For example, setting the gasoline tax at $0.025 per gallon and the registration fees at $13.77 for passenger cars, $10.45 for medium trucks, and $193.45 for heavy trucks would theoretically allocate the costs. It may be seen that this solution probably would encounter some objections because the registration fee for medium trucks is lower than that for passenger cars. Thus some arbitrary compromise probably would have to be adopted. Further, it usually is necessary to recognize more than three classes of vehicles in making the cost allocation.

COLLECTION OF HIGHWAY COSTS BY TON-MILE TAXES

While the collection of highway costs by gasoline taxes is a very simple, easy, and economical method, it obviously does not take into account the facts that highway costs probably are determined by the loads imposed and the number of miles traveled and that the amount of gasoline consumed is not necessarily in direct proportion to these factors. Therefore a number of states impose load-mile taxes in addition to vehicle registration fees. For example, one state has the following fees for trucks above 18,000 pounds gross weight:

Gross weight	Tax rate, per mile
18,001 to 20,000 inclusive	$0.006
20,001 to 22,000 inclusive	0.007
22,001 to 24,000 inclusive	0.008
24,001 to 26,000 inclusive	0.009
26,001 to 28,000 inclusive	0.0095
28,001 to 30,000 inclusive	0.010

This method of collection obviously is more difficult and costly, since it requires the vehicle operators keeping extensive records and considerable checking by the state authorities. It has been rather strenuously opposed by trucking associations. Since the method obviously imposes large fees on trucks which carry heavy loads over long distances, and such associations primarily represent trucking companies which engage in such hauling, this opposition is quite natural.

SUMMARY

From the discussion and examples presented in this chapter it is apparent that many public works are essential and desirable. However, because of the methods of financing, the absence of the tax and profit requirements, and political and social factors, the same criteria often can not be applied to such works as are used in evaluating privately financed projects. Neither should public projects be used as "yardsticks" with which to compare private projects. Nevertheless, whenever possible, public works should be justified on an economic basis to assure that the public obtains the maximum return from the tax money that is spent. Whether an engineer is working on such projects, is called upon as a consultant to them, or only fills the role of a taxpayer, he is bound by the ethics of his profession to do his utmost to see that they are carried out in the best possible manner within the limitations of the legislation enacted for their authorization.

Perhaps the most simple view of public works, and as far as that is concerned, of private works, is that the United States is endeavoring to develop its resources to the full. Private resources are the primary base of such construction and have done the major service over the decades past. There has, however, been federal participation from the beginning of the republic, and there is large support for a considerable amount of such public works activity on the part of the government at the present time. If one may judge from past events, the public view will shift from time to time from the conservative to the liberal, or even radical, and back again. The goal, regardless of the means employed for its achievement, is that of a fully developed pattern of natural resources leading to the highest possible type of civilization. The problems are partly those of finance and partly those of planning, design, and construction. Fortunately, the achievements of the past are already great. Many of the finest projects that can be conceived are already in operation, and the prospects for more, through both private and public initiative, are good.[6]

PROBLEMS

20–1   a. Make a list of fifteen public projects which to your knowledge have been undertaken by federal, state, or local agencies, with five being in each of the categories of "protection," "cultural development," and "economic services."

b. In each of the above cases, give your opinion as to whether the projects were justified.

c. Show your list, but not your justification analysis, to another person, preferably not in the same occupational status as yourself. Obtain his opinion as to the justification of the projects. Compare his and your ratings.

20–2   Explain why the cost of capital for a public project that is to be financed by means of a bond issue which is a general financial obligation of the issuing agency may not be a measure of the risk attendant to the project.

20–3   What are public "authorities," and why are they increasingly being used to finance, construct, and operate public works?

20–4   List five types of financial aid provided by the federal government.

20–5   Indicate how each of the following has received indirect public financial support: (*a*) railroads, (*b*) airlines, (*c*) steamship companies, (*d*) trucking companies, (*e*) farmers.

20–6   What is meant by an "in-lieu" payment as made by a self-liquidating public project?

20–7   a. What is a multiple-purpose project?

b. Discuss the difficulty of assigning costs in a multiple-purpose project.

c. Explain why the costs of services rendered by a multiple-purpose public project usually can not be used as a "yardstick" for comparing public and private projects.

20–8   What are seven difficulties inherent in economy studies of public works?

20–9   Using the terms given on page 492 for an FHA loan, determine the

[6] This last paragraph was written by the late Dr. Baldwin M. Woods in the previous edition of this text, of which he was coauthor. It is included here because of its clear statement of the relationship which should exist between private and public works.

down payment and the monthly payment, including taxes and insurance, on a home costing $20,000 covered by a maximum loan, to be repaid in 25 years. Assume annual taxes to be $1\frac{1}{2}\%$ of first cost, and insurance to be $\frac{1}{2}\%$ of first cost, with $\frac{1}{12}$ of each to be included in the monthly payment. (The correct annuity factor will have to be computed.)

20–10   A public transit authority is proposed to replace and operate a private bus company. The present company pays a franchise tax of 2% of gross revenues to the several cities involved and, in addition, pays property taxes and state and federal income taxes. In connection with authorization for a bond issue to finance the project, it has been stated that "the cost of the bonds and all operating costs can be paid out of revenues, without cost to the taxpayers." Discuss the accuracy of this statement.

20–11   It is proposed to finance a forty-mile stretch of limited-access highway by means of a twenty-year 5% bond issue in the amount of $30,000,-000.00. This highway will reduce the distance between two major cities by ten miles and bypass several small communities. Maintenance of the road will amount to $500.00 per mile per year. A traffic check shows that passenger vehicles would make 4,000,000 trips per year over the highway. Average operating costs for these vehicles is estimated to be $0.06 per mile, of which 70% is fixed. It is estimated that trucks will make 1,000,000 trips per year over the highway and that the operating cost for these, exclusive of drivers, is $0.13 per mile, of which 50% is fixed. On the existing highway trucks can average only 25 miles per hour, because of the many stops that must be made, while on the proposed highway an average speed of 40 miles per hour will be practicable. Truck drivers receive an average of $2.25 per hour. Make an economy study of the proposed highway and determine the benefits-to-cost ratio.

20–12   On a particularly sharp corner on a highway an average of forty serious accidents have occurred each year for several years, ten of them involving fatalities. An engineering study has placed the cost of rebuilding this section of the highway to eliminate this curve at $1,500,000. It is estimated that the property damage involved in each nonfatal accident averages $2,000, and the hospitalization and medical charges cost $500. In the case of fatal accidents the property damage is, on the average, $2,700, and the medical and insurance costs $40,000. Using a twenty-year study period and 4% interest rate, determine whether the elimination of the curve can be justified purely from a cost viewpoint.

20–13   In a western city of 14,000 people the water is quite "hard." Approximately one-half of the homes have installed water "softeners" provided on a rental basis by a local company. Such systems cost $15.00 for the installation and $2.00 per month for chemicals and service. It is proposed that the city install a central system to treat all of the water. It is estimated that an investment of $600,000.00 will be required to build the required plant, and that the annual costs will be $12,000.00 for chemicals, $20,000.00 for labor, $1,000.00 for increased pumping costs, and $2,000.00 per year for maintenance. Based on the experience of other communities, it is estimated that the degree of softening of the water obtained will reduce the soap consumption by ten pounds per person per year, and that soap costs an average of $0.30 per pound. The system would be financed by a twenty-year 5% bond issue. It is proposed that the cost be met by an increase of $1.50 per month in the water bill for each of the 3,800 water customers involved. Make an economy study of the project, and give your recommendations.

20-14 In planning for a new state highway two alternate routes are under consideration. The pertinent data are as follows:

	Route A	Route B
Distance	8.2 miles	6.4 miles
Cost of land	$2,300,000	$4,200,000
Cost of construction	$4,270,000	$3,900,000
Annual maintenance	$17,000	$14,000

Construction would be financed out of gasoline taxes. All highways of this class are studied on a twenty-year-life basis, and a 6% interest rate is used.

Traffic surveys indicate the following expected use:

Passenger cars	2,000,000 trips per year
Light trucks	125,000 trips per year
Heavy trucks	80,000 trips per year

The increment costs for operating such vehicles, exclusive of the driver, are $0.025 per mile for passenger cars, $0.03 per mile for light trucks, and $0.045 per mile for heavy trucks. It is estimated that light trucks could maintain an average speed of 45 miles per hour on Route A and 40 miles per hour on Route B, while the corresponding speeds for heavy trucks would be 40 and 30 miles per hour. No consideration is given to driver cost for passenger vehicles, while truck drivers are assumed to receive an estimated $2.25 per hour. Determine the benefits-to-cost ratio and state what should be done.

20-15 A grade crossing of a railroad and a secondary highway near a city has caused considerable difficulty due to the fact that it is adjacent to the railroad yards. Not only have accidents occurred at a frequency of four nonfatal per year and one fatal accident each three years, but freight trains entering the yard hold up traffic, sometimes for several minutes. Detailed studies show that 300 passenger vehicles are held up an average of five minutes per day and 120 trucks the same amount of time. It is estimated that the actual cost of such a delay for passenger vehicles is $0.01 per minute and for trucks $0.05 per minute. Nonfatal accident costs are estimated to be $5,200.00 per incident, and for fatal accidents they are estimated at $35,000.00.

Elimination of this grade crossing will cost $340,000.00. In accordance with a state requirement, half of the initial cost will be paid by the railroad. There will also be an annual cost of $210.00 for pumping drainage water and maintaining the pumping equipment.

Can the elimination of the grade crossing be justified on a benefits-to-cost basis? Assume a twenty-year life and 6% interest.

20–16   A municipal airport must lengthen and strengthen the existing runways to meet the requirements of jet aircraft. Adding to the length would be accomplished at a cost of $80,000 and an annual maintenance cost of $500. Two methods are available for strengthening the existing runway area.

The first is to add two inches of concrete on top of the existing runways at a cost of $30,000. It is expected that upkeep with this plan would cost $4,000 annually.

The second plan is to tear up the old and build new runways at a cost of $150,000. If this is done, it is believed that the annual upkeep on this portion of the runways will not exceed $1,000 per year. If this plan is adopted, the airport will have to be partially closed down for one month, with a loss in revenue of $3,000; traffic will be routed to an adjacent city 22 miles away, a considerable inconvenience for the public.

The adopted plan will be part of a general airport improvement program which is being financed by means of a twenty-year 6% bond issue. What would you recommend?

20–17   Assume that in the highway cost problem discussed on page 508 the number of passenger cars increases by 200,000 and the number of heavy trucks by 5,000, each type driving the same number of miles per vehicle as previously. Show the effect this would have on the allocation cost for each of the three types of vehicles involved.

20–18   Make a brief analysis of some public works project for which data are available. This may be either a federal, state, or local project. Explain the purpose and scope of the project and the justifications used. (The report need not exceed 1,000 words.) The following are typical project reports which may be used:

Saginaw River, Michigan	H.D.*	346/84
Ohio River at Gallipolis, Ohio	H.D.	423/84
Port Aransas-Corpus Christi Waterway, Texas	H.D.	89/82
Duluth Harbor, Minn.	H.D.	374/82
Sakonnet Harbor, R. I.	H.D.	436/82

* H.D. means House Document; 346/84 means Document 346, 84th Congress.

APPENDIX A

MAPI Replacement Formulas

The Machinery and Allied Products Institute has for some years sponsored economic studies relating to investment in capital equipment. The results have been published in various books and pamphlets. Three have resulted in formulas and "systems" dealing with the economic replacement of equipment. These are commonly known as the MAPI formulas. They have received considerable publicity and have been the subject of much discussion. Investigations have shown that they are used rather little by businesses other than the companies—primarily machine tool and related manufacturers—which comprise the institute, despite the publicity and promotional activities in their behalf. However, they are interesting, thought-provoking, and have some merit, and they constitute a definite contribution to the field of engineering economy. It is undeniable that they have caused a great amount of constructive thinking to be done regarding the entire replacement problem. Certainly anyone who makes economy studies should be thoroughly acquainted with the basic features of these formulas.

The MAPI formulas and "systems" were developed by George Terborgh, Director of Research of MAPI. They have gone through several stages of development and presentation. During this process the formulas and the terminology have changed considerably. However, many of the basic concepts have continued. It is not unlikely that further changes will occur in future years.

The original MAPI formulas were presented in basic form in Terborgh's book *Dynamic Equipment Policy*.[1] In 1950 the *MAPI Replacement Manual*[2] was published by the Institute and presented the formulas and certain other data to aid in the determination of economic replacement life for equipment.

In his earlier work Terborgh chose to use several new terms in presenting his formulas. The existing asset, which was being considered for replacement, was called the *defender*. The *challenger* was the asset being considered as a replacement for the defender. The *inferiority gradient* was the annual rate at which the operational cost gap between the defender and the best current challenger widened. The *adverse minimum* was the "lowest combined time-adjusted average of capital cost and operating inferiority obtainable from a machine." It was, in effect, the equivalent equal annual cost which had the same present worth as the actual annual costs for the life which would give the greatest economy. While this terminology was picturesque, it probably hampered the acceptance and use of the formulas.

[1] George Terborgh, *Dynamic Equipment Policy*, McGraw-Hill Book Company, Inc., New York, 1944.
[2] *MAPI Replacement Manual*, Machinery and Allied Products Institute, Chicago, 1950.

The earlier MAPI formulas were based on the following assumptions:

1. Future challengers will have the same adverse minimum as the present one.

2. The present challenger will accumulate operating inferiority at a constant rate over its service life.

3. The need for the service of the asset will be continuous, or at least for a very long time, so that a series of replacements will ensue.

Many questioned the validity of these assumptions, particularly that the history of the depender would be repeated in the challenger and that the pattern would continue indefinitely. Further it is known that in many, if not most, cases technological progress takes place in spurts.

Those who are interested in the older MAPI procedures should consult the references given on page 515.

The New MAPI "System"

In 1958 Terborgh presented a modified MAPI procedure which involves a new formula. This is presented in a book entitled *Business Investment Policy*.[3] The old terminology of *challenger, defender,* and *adverse minimum* has been eliminated and the formula which is used has a completely different significance.[4]

A key concept in the new formula is what Terborgh calls *capital consumption*. The *capital value* of an asset is the present value of its future service or use values. Thus capital value is the present worth of the future capital recovery plus after-tax profits. As an asset is used, its capital value declines through deterioration, obsolescence, increased maintenance costs, and decreased performance and reliability. This decrease in capital value Terborgh calls capital consumption. Thus capital consumption is the annual decrease in the present value of the after-tax capital recovery and profit. One of the costs of utilizing an asset for a year is the cost of capital consumption for that year.

Whereas the old MAPI formulas assumed that the present challenger would accumulate operating inferiority at a constant *rate* over its service life, the new formula assumes that this inferiority will manifest itself through decreased earnings as the asset ages, thus through the pattern of the capital-consumption runoff. The formula is derived for three patterns of capital runoff. The "Standard" pattern provides for the first half of the total runoff occurring during the

[3] George Terborgh, *Business Investment Policy*, Machinery and Allied Products Institute, Washington, D.C., 1958.

[4] Unfortunately, while the old terminology was eliminated, a large portion of the new book is filled with the setting up of "straw men" and knocking them down as justification of the MAPI philosophy and procedure. Those who are at all sophisticated regarding replacement matters will recognize the various "Fables" and "Tales" as being examples of what only the uninitiated would do, and are not likely to be persuaded that the procedure advocated is correct merely because it is not the same as something which obviously is incorrect.

first half of the life of the asset. Variant A shows one-third runoff during the half life, and Variant B provides for two-thirds runoff during the half life.

As in the use of the old formulas, the new system concerns itself only with the next-year costs of the existing and proposed assets, on the assumption that if the replacement is justified on this basis it always will be justified on a longer-term basis. While this assumption is valid in many cases, it is not in many others. Those who use the formula should consider carefully whether the assumption is valid for the particular problem at hand.

Formulas for capital consumption are derived using sum-of-the-years'-digits depreciation and straight-line depreciation. In developing these formulas Terborgh uses the following notation:

$V_0, V_1 \cdots V_n =$ Capital value of the asset at the end of the year indicated

$v^n =$ present value factor

$g =$ decline of earnings during the first year

$n =$ service life of the asset, in years

$p =$ ratio of borrowed to total capital (assumed to remain constant)

$y =$ rate of interest (in decimals) paid on borrowed capital

$(1 - p) =$ ratio of equity capital to total capital

$z =$ rate (in decimals) of after-tax return on equity capital

$b =$ rate (in decimals) of income tax

$i =$ rate (in decimals) of after-tax return on total capital

$w =$ ratio (in decimals) of the salvage value at the end of year $n + 1$ to the salvage value at the end of year n. It is assumed that this ratio is identical with the constant relative decline required to write down the capital cost to the terminal salvage value over n years.

$w^n =$ the ratio (in decimals) of the terminal salvage value to the initial capital cost

For any year

After-tax earnings = earnings − tax rate (earnings − tax-allowable deductions)

$$= (1 - b) \times \text{earnings} + b \times (\text{tax-allowable deductions}). \qquad (A.1)$$

The after-tax earnings may thus be expressed as a series of before-tax earnings and tax-allowable deductions.

The before-tax earnings for any year are made up of two components. The first is a constant amount equal to the earnings at the end of the year n. This is equal to the before-tax interest (profit) on the salvage value,

$$= V_0 \, w^n \left[py + \frac{(1 - p) z}{(1 - b)} \right]$$

plus the salvage value runoff for the $(n + 1)$ year,

$$= V_0\, w^n (1 - w).$$

The sum of these two amounts represents the cost of carrying the asset during the $n + 1$ year, and is

$$= V_0\, w^n \left[1 - w + py + \frac{(1 - p)^z}{1 - b} \right] \tag{A.2}$$

By letting $P = w^n \left[1 - w + py + \dfrac{(1 - p)^z}{1 - b} \right]$, this carrying cost $= PV_0$.

The second component of the earnings depends upon g and the tax-allowable deductions of the year. It can be derived as follows. The before-tax earnings take the following form:

Year	Earnings
1	$ng + PV_0$
2	$(n - 1)g + PV_0$
.	.
.	.
$n - 1$	$2g + PV_0$
n	$g + PV_0$

Since for SYD depreciation the depreciation deduction for tax purposes for any year $A = 2(n - A + 1)/n(n + 1)$, and the interest deduction is py times the capital value at the beginning of the year, the tax-allowable deductions are of the form

Year	Tax-allowable deductions
1	$\dfrac{2V_0(1 - w^n)}{n(n + 1)} \times n + pyV_0$
2	$\dfrac{2V_0(1 - w^n)}{n(n + 1)} \times (n - 1) + pyV_1$
.	.
.	.
$n - 1$	$\dfrac{2V_0(1 - w^n)}{n(n + 1)} \times 2 + pyV_{n-2}$
n	$\dfrac{2V_0(1 - w^n)}{n(n + 1)} + pyV_{n-1}$

The before-tax earnings and tax-allowable deductions can then be combined, according to Equation (A.1), as follows:

Year	After-tax earnings
1	$(ng + PV_0)(1 - b) + \dfrac{2bV_0(1 - w^n)(n)}{n(n + 1)} + bpyV_0$
2	$[(n - 1)g + PV_0](1 - b) + \dfrac{2bV_0(1 - w^n)(n - 1)}{n(n + 1)} + bpyV_1$
.	.
.	.
$n - 1$	$(2g + PV_0)(1 - b) + \dfrac{2bV_0(1 - w^n)(2)}{n(n + 1)} + bpyV_{n-2}$
n	$(g + PV_0)(1 - b) + \dfrac{2bV_0(1 - w^n)}{n(n + 1)} + bpyV_{n-1}$

Terborgh determines the present value (discounted value) of these earnings to obtain a value for g by equating the aggregate present worth to V_0. With this value he then derives an expression for the first year capital consumption C, for the SYD case, as a ratio to V_0, as follows:

$$C = \frac{n(Q^n - w^n)(Q-1)^2 - (1-b)P[(Q^n - 1) - n(Q-1)]}{nQ^n(Q-1) - (Q^n - 1)} - (Q-1)$$

(A.3)

where,

$$Q = 1 + i - bpy.$$

Since $1 + i = s$, and bpy represents the income tax saving due to the deductible interest paid, it may be seen that Q plus the tax saving on the interest paid is equal to the amount which 1 unit of total capital will become in one year.

Terborgh similarly derives the following equation for the first-year capital consumption when straight-line depreciation is used:

$$C = \frac{n(Q^n - w^n)(Q-1)^2 - [(1-b)P + b(1-w^n)/n][Q^n - 1 - n(Q-1)]}{nQ^n(Q-1) - (Q^n - 1)}$$
$$- (Q-1).$$

(A.4)

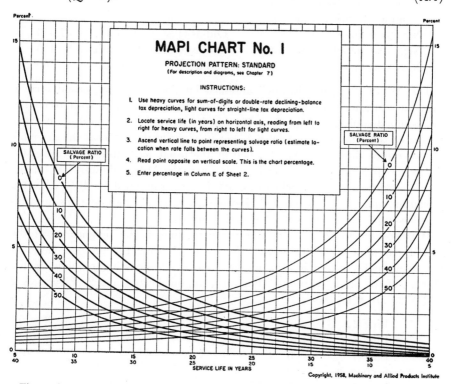

Figure A-1. MAPI chart for determining allowance. (Courtesy Machinery and Allied Products Institute)

Equations also are derived for the two variants, mentioned previously, providing for faster and slower decline in earning value.

Obviously the equations for first-year capital consumption are too complex to be used readily. Therefore, Terborgh has devised three sets of MAPI charts covering the "Standard" and the two variant projections of capital runoff for fixed values of four of the variables: the debt ratio, p, at 25%; the debt interest rate, y, at 3%; the after-tax equity return rate, z, at 10%; and the income tax rate, b, at 50%. The MAPI charts are *not* the first-year capital consumption, however, but are this factor *minus* the tax saving from the first-year deductions for depreciation and interest on borrowed capital. The MAPI chart for the "Standard" projection is reproduced in Figure A–1.

Application of the New MAPI System

The new MAPI system is applied through the use of two special data forms and the MAPI charts. The two forms are shown in Figures A–2 and A–3, with values relating to the following problem:

Cost of the new asset	$8,000
Decrease in salvage value of old asset during next year	$ 300
Next year labor cost:	Old asset $8,250; New asset $7,050
Next year maintenance cost:	Old asset $ 800; New asset $ 450
Next year taxes and insurance	Old asset $ 125; New asset $ 300

The MAPI "Urgency Rating" obtained on line 35 of the second form is the next-year after-tax rate of return available from the project, with, of course, the assumed capital consumption. It must be remembered, however, that this computed after-tax rate of return is not necessarily the same as the after-tax rate of return that would be obtained by the usual accounting procedures for the next year if the replacement is made, since the MAPI allowance is for the frozen conditions of 25% debt ratio, 3% interest rate on debt, 10% after-tax return on equity capital, and 50% income tax rate, and also contains an arbitrary assumption regarding the decline in earnings.

It is possible to obtain a clearer understanding of the significance of the MAPI chart allowance by examining the case where the disposal value of the assets to be retired is zero and no capital additions are required in the absence of the proposed project. For this case, on sheets 1 and 2 (Figures A–2 and A–3) are as follows:

Line 2	= 0
Line 3	= 0
Line 4	= 0
Section B	= 0
Line 31	= Line 29 = next-year operating advantage
Line 32	= next-year after-tax operating advantage

SUMMARY OF ANALYSIS
(SEE ACCOMPANYING WORK SHEETS FOR DETAIL)

I. REQUIRED INVESTMENT

1	INSTALLED COST OF PROJECT	$ 8,000	1
2	DISPOSAL VALUE OF ASSETS TO BE RETIRED BY PROJECT	$ 1,500	2
3	CAPITAL ADDITIONS REQUIRED IN ABSENCE OF PROJECT	$	3
4	INVESTMENT RELEASED OR AVOIDED BY PROJECT (2+3)	$ 1,500	4
5	NET INVESTMENT REQUIRED (1−4)	$ 6,500	5

II. NEXT-YEAR ADVANTAGE FROM PROJECT

A. OPERATING ADVANTAGE
(USE FIRST YEAR OF PROJECT OPERATION)*

6	ASSUMED OPERATING RATE OF PROJECT (HOURS PER YEAR)	2,200	6

EFFECT OF PROJECT ON REVENUE

		Increase	Decrease	
7	FROM CHANGE IN QUALITY OF PRODUCTS	$	$	7
8	FROM CHANGE IN VOLUME OF OUTPUT			8
9	TOTAL	$ 0 A	$ 0 B	9

EFFECT OF PROJECT ON OPERATING COSTS

		Increase	Decrease	
10	DIRECT LABOR	$	$ 1,200	10
11	INDIRECT LABOR			11
12	FRINGE BENEFITS			12
13	MAINTENANCE		350	13
14	TOOLING			14
15	SUPPLIES			15
16	SCRAP AND REWORK			16
17	DOWN TIME			17
18	POWER			18
19	FLOOR SPACE			19
20	PROPERTY TAXES AND INSURANCE	175		20
21	SUBCONTRACTING			21
22	INVENTORY			22
23	SAFETY			23
24	FLEXIBILITY			24
25	OTHER			25
26	TOTAL	$ 175 A	$ 1,550 B	26

27	NET INCREASE IN REVENUE (9A−9B)	$ 0	27
28	NET DECREASE IN OPERATING COST (26B−26A)	$ 1,375	28
29	NEXT-YEAR OPERATING ADVANTAGE (27+28)	$ 1,375	29

B. NON-OPERATING ADVANTAGE
(USE ONLY IF THERE IS AN ENTRY IN LINE 4)

30	NEXT-YEAR CAPITAL CONSUMPTION AVOIDED BY PROJECT:		30
	A DECLINE OF DISPOSAL VALUE DURING THE YEAR	$ 300	A
	B NEXT-YEAR ALLOCATION OF CAPITAL ADDITIONS	$	B
	TOTAL	$ 300	

C. TOTAL ADVANTAGE

31	TOTAL NEXT-YEAR ADVANTAGE FROM PROJECT (29+30)	$ 1,675	31

Figure A–2. Front side of MAPI form for making replacement analysis. (Courtesy Machinery and Allied Products Institute)

III. COMPUTATION OF MAPI URGENCY RATING

32 TOTAL NEXT-YEAR ADVANTAGE AFTER INCOME TAX (31 – TAX) $ 837.50

33 MAPI CHART ALLOWANCE FOR PROJECT (TOTAL OF COLUMN F, BELOW) $ 320.00 *

(ENTER DEPRECIABLE ASSETS ONLY)

Item or Group	Installed Cost of Item or Group A	Estimated Service Life (Years) B	Estimated Terminal Salvage (Percent of Cost) C	MAPI Chart Number D	Chart Percentage E	Chart Percentage × Cost (E × A) F
	$ 8,000	15	10%	1	4%	$ 320
					TOTAL	$ 320

34 AMOUNT AVAILABLE FOR RETURN ON INVESTMENT (32 – 33) $ 517.50

35 MAPI URGENCY RATING (34 ÷ 5) · 100   % 7.97

Figure A–3. Reverse side of MAPI form for making replacement analysis. (Courtesy Machinery and Allied Products Institute)

From these conditions Line 35 becomes

$$\text{MAPI rating } (\%) = \frac{\text{After-tax operating advantage } (\$) \ - \ \text{MAPI allowance } (\$)}{\text{Required investment } (\$)}$$

Since,

$$(\text{MAPI rating}) \times (\text{Required investment}) = \text{After-tax profit}$$

$$\text{MAPI allowance} = (\text{After-tax operating advantage}) - (\text{After-tax profit}).$$

While the new MAPI system has numerous advantages over the old formula, it is, of course, subject to the limitations of all such formula procedures. Those who use it should critically examine the built-in conditions and decide whether the results are reasonable for their situation.

The book, *Business Investment Policy*, contains several modifications to permit using the system for conditions other than those "frozen" into the curves, and to adjust for cases where more than the next-year costs must be considered. Those who wish to use the MAPI system should consult this volume.

APPENDIX B

Selected References for Additional Study

The following is a list of selected books which will be found useful to those who wish additional information regarding the subject matter of this text. The table on pages 525 and 526 indicates those considered to be most helpful for the subjects treated in each chapter of this text.

Title	*Author*	*Publisher*
1. Bulletin "F"	Bureau of Internal Revenue	U.S. Treasury Dept.
2. Business Administration for Engineers	Harding & Canfield	McGraw-Hill Book Co.
3. Business Investment Policy	Terborgh	Machinery and Allied Products Institute
4. Depreciation, 2nd Ed.	Grant & Norton	Ronald Press Company
5. Dynamic Equipment Policy	Terborgh	McGraw-Hill Book Co.
6. Economic Effects of the Federal Public Works Expenditures	National Resources Planning Board	U.S. Government Printing Office
7. Economics, 4th Ed.	Samuelson	McGraw-Hill Book Co.
8. Economics for Engineers, 2nd Ed.	Bowers & Rowntree	McGraw-Hill Book Co.
9. Economics of Bridgework	Waddell	John Wiley & Sons, Inc.
10. Economics of Industrial Management, 2nd Ed.	Rautenstrauch & Villers	Funk & Wagnalls
11. Economy Loading of Power Plants and Electric Systems	Steinberg & Smith	John Wiley & Sons, Inc.
12. Engineering Economy, 2nd Ed.	Thuesen	Prentice-Hall, Inc.
13. Engineering Valuation and Depreciation, 2nd Ed.	Marston, Winfrey & Hempstead	McGraw-Hill Book Co.

Title	Author	Publisher
14. Essentials of Accounting	Paton & Dixon	Macmillan Company
15. Highway Economics	Tucker & Leager	International Textbook Co.
16. MAPI Replacement Manual		Machinery and Allied Products Institute
17. Mathematics of Finance, 2nd Ed.	Hummell & Seebeck	McGraw-Hill Book Co.
18. Principles of Accounting, 2nd Ed.	Bangs & Hanselman	International Textbook Co.
19. Principles of Engineering Economy, 3rd Ed.	Grant	Ronald Press Company
20. Process Engineering Economics	Schweyer	McGraw-Hill Book Co.
21. Production Handbook	Carson	Ronald Press Company
22. Tax Ideas Reports		Prentice-Hall, Inc.

Chapter No.	Subject	References as Listed on Previous Page
1	The Nature and Purpose of Engineering Economy Studies	12, 19
2	Some Economic Relationships	7, 8
3	Selections in Present Economy	9, 12
4	Interest and Annuity Relationships	17
5	Depreciation and Valuation	1, 2, 4, 13
6	Financing Engineering Enterprises	2
7	The Relationship of Accounting to Economy Studies	14, 18, 21
8	Basic Economy Study Patterns	12, 19
9	Handling Income and Cost Data	12, 19
10	Economy Studies of New Projects	19, 20
11	Alternative Investments	12, 19, 20
12	Fixed, Increment, and Sunk Costs	12, 19
13	Replacement Studies	5, 12, 19
14	Break-Even and Minimum-Cost Point Studies	10, 14
15	Capacity, Load, and Utilization Effects	12, 19

Table I.   The Number of Each Day of the Year

Day of Month	Jan.	Feb.	Mar.	April	May	June	July	Aug.	Sept.	Oct.	Nov.	Dec.	Day of Month
1	1	32	60	91	121	152	182	213	244	274	305	335	1
2	2	33	61	92	122	153	183	214	245	275	306	336	2
3	3	34	62	93	123	154	184	215	246	276	307	337	3
4	4	35	63	94	124	155	185	216	247	277	308	338	4
5	5	36	64	95	125	156	186	217	248	278	309	339	5
6	6	37	65	96	126	157	187	218	249	279	310	340	6
7	7	38	66	97	127	158	188	219	250	280	311	341	7
8	8	39	67	98	128	159	189	220	251	281	312	342	8
9	9	40	68	99	129	160	190	221	252	282	313	343	9
10	10	41	69	100	130	161	191	222	253	283	314	344	10
11	11	42	70	101	131	162	192	223	254	284	315	345	11
12	12	43	71	102	132	163	193	224	255	285	316	346	12
13	13	44	72	103	133	164	194	225	256	286	317	347	13
14	14	45	73	104	134	165	195	226	257	287	318	348	14
15	15	46	74	105	135	166	196	227	258	288	319	349	15
16	16	47	75	106	136	167	197	228	259	289	320	350	16
17	17	48	76	107	137	168	198	229	260	290	321	351	17
18	18	49	77	108	138	169	199	230	261	291	322	352	18
19	19	50	78	109	139	170	200	231	262	292	323	353	19
20	20	51	79	110	140	171	201	232	263	293	324	354	20
21	21	52	80	111	141	172	202	233	264	294	325	355	21
22	22	53	81	112	142	173	203	234	265	295	326	356	22
23	23	54	82	113	143	174	204	235	266	296	327	357	23
24	24	55	83	114	144	175	205	236	267	297	328	358	24
25	25	56	84	115	145	176	206	237	268	298	329	359	25
26	26	57	85	116	146	177	207	238	269	299	330	360	26
27	27	58	86	117	147	178	208	239	270	300	331	361	27
28	28	59	87	118	148	179	209	240	271	301	332	362	28
29	29		88	119	149	180	210	241	272	302	333	363	29
30	30		89	120	150	181	211	242	273	303	334	364	30
31	31		90		151		212	243		304		365	31

Note.   For leap years the number of the day is one greater than the number in the table after February 28.

Table II. $\frac{1}{4}\%$

Number of periods n	Amount of 1 at compound interest $s^n = (1+i)^n$	Present value of 1 $v^n = \dfrac{1}{(1+i)^n}$	Present value of an annuity of 1 $a_{\overline{n}\rceil} = \dfrac{1-v^n}{i}$	Amount of an annuity of 1 $s_{\overline{n}\rceil} = \dfrac{(1+i)^n-1}{i}$	Annuity whose present value is 1. (CRF) $\dfrac{1}{a_{\overline{n}\rceil}} = \dfrac{1}{s_{\overline{n}\rceil}}+i$	Number of periods n
1	1.0025 0000	0.9975 0623	0.9975 0623	1.0000 0000	1.0025 0000	1
2	1.0050 0625	0.9950 1869	1.9925 2492	2.0025 0000	0.5018 7578	2
3	1.0075 1877	0.9925 3734	2.9850 6227	3.0075 0625	0.3350 0139	3
4	1.0100 3756	0.9900 6219	3.9751 2446	4.0150 2502	0.2515 6445	4
5	1.0125 6266	0.9875 9321	4.9627 1766	5.0250 6258	0.2015 0250	5
6	1.0150 9406	0.9851 3038	5.9478 4804	6.0376 2523	0.1681 2803	6
7	1.0176 3180	0.9826 7370	6.9305 2174	7.0527 1930	0.1442 8928	7
8	1.0201 7588	0.9802 2314	7.9107 4487	8.0703 5110	0.1264 1035	8
9	1.0227 2632	0.9777 7869	8.8885 2357	9.0905 2697	0.1125 0462	9
10	1.0252 8313	0.9753 4034	9.8638 6391	10.1132 5329	0.1013 8015	10
11	1.0278 4634	0.9729 0807	10.8367 7198	11.1385 3642	0.0922 7840	11
12	1.0304 1596	0.9704 8187	11.8072 5384	12.1663 8277	0.0846 9370	12
13	1.0329 9200	0.9680 6171	12.7753 1555	13.1967 9872	0.0782 7595	13
14	1.0355 7448	0.9656 4759	13.7409 6314	14.2297 9072	0.0727 7510	14
15	1.0381 6341	0.9632 3949	14.7042 0264	15.2653 6520	0.0680 0777	15
16	1.0407 5882	0.9608 3740	15.6650 4004	16.3035 2861	0.0638 3642	16
17	1.0433 6072	0.9584 4130	16.6234 8133	17.3442 8743	0.0601 5587	17
18	1.0459 6912	0.9560 5117	17.5795 3250	18.3876 4815	0.0568 8433	18
19	1.0485 8404	0.9536 6700	18.5331 9950	19.4336 1727	0.0539 5722	19
20	1.0512 0550	0.9512 8878	19.4844 8828	20.4822 0131	0.0513 2288	20
21	1.0538 3352	0.9489 1649	20.4334 0477	21.5334 0682	0.0489 3947	21
22	1.0564 6810	0.9465 5011	21.3799 5488	22.5872 4033	0.0467 7278	22
23	1.0591 0927	0.9441 8964	22.3241 4452	23.6437 0843	0.0447 9455	23
24	1.0617 5704	0.9418 3505	23.2659 7957	24.7028 1770	0.0429 8121	24
25	1.0644 1144	0.9394 8634	24.2054 6591	25.7645 7475	0.0413 1298	25
26	1.0670 7247	0.9371 4348	25.1426 0939	26.8289 8619	0.0397 7312	26
27	1.0697 4015	0.9348 0646	26.0774 1585	27.8960 5865	0.0383 4736	27
28	1.0724 1450	0.9324 7527	27.0098 9112	28.9657 9880	0.0370 2347	28
29	1.0750 9553	0.9301 4990	27.9400 4102	30.0382 1330	0.0357 9093	29
30	1.0777 8327	0.9278 3032	28.8678 7134	31.1133 0883	0.0346 4059	30
31	1.0804 7773	0.9255 1653	29.7933 8787	32.1910 9210	0.0335 6449	31
32	1.0831 7892	0.9232 0851	30.7165 9638	33.2715 6983	0.0325 5569	32
33	1.0858 8687	0.9209 0624	31.6375 0262	34.3547 4876	0.0316 0806	33
34	1.0886 0159	0.9186 0972	32.5561 1234	35.4406 3563	0.0307 1620	34
35	1.0913 2309	0.9163 1892	33.4724 3126	36.5292 3722	0.0298 7533	35
36	1.0940 5140	0.9140 3384	34.3864 6510	37.6205 6031	0.0290 8121	36
37	1.0967 8653	0.9117 5445	· 35.2982 1955	38.7146 1171	0.0283 3004	37
38	1.0995 2850	0.9094 8075	36.2077 0030	39.8113 9824	0.0276 1843	38
39	1.1022 7732	0.9072 1272	37.1149 1302	40.9109 2673	0.0269 4335	39
40	1.1050 3301	0.9049 5034	38.0198 6336	42.0132 0405	0.0263 0204	40
41	1.1077 9559	0.9026 9361	38.9225 5697	43.1182 3706	0.0256 9204	41
42	1.1105 6508	0.9004 4250	39.8229 9947	44.2260 3265	0.0251 1112	42
43	1.1133 4149	0.8981 9701	40.7211 9648	45.3365 9774	0.0245 5724	43
44	1.1161 2485	0.8959 5712	41.6171 5359	46.4499 3923	0.0240 2855	44
45	1.1189 1516	0.8937 2281	42.5108 7640	47.5660 6408	0.0235 2339	45
46	1.1217 1245	0.8914 9407	43.4023 7047	48.6849 7924	0.0230 4022	46
47	1.1245 1673	0.8892 7090	44.2916 4137	49.8066 9169	0.0225 7762	47
48	1.1273 2802	0.8870 5326	45.1786 9463	50.9312 0842	0.0221 3433	48
49	1.1301 4634	0.8848 4116	46.0635 3580	52.0585 3644	0.0217 0915	49
50	1.1329 7171	0.8826 3457	46.9461 7037	53.1886 8278	0.0213 0099	50

Table II (continued). ¼%

Number of periods n	Amount of 1 at compound interest $s^n = (1+i)^n$	Present value of 1 $v^n = \dfrac{1}{(1+i)^n}$	Present value of an annuity of 1 $a_{\overline{n}|} = \dfrac{1-v^n}{i}$	Amount of an annuity of 1 $s_{\overline{n}|} = \dfrac{(1+i)^n-1}{i}$	Annuity whose present value is 1. (CRF) $\dfrac{1}{a_{\overline{n}|}} = \dfrac{1}{s_{\overline{n}|}} + i$	Number of periods n
51	1.1358 0414	0.8804 3349	47.8266 0386	54.3216 5449	0.0209 0886	51
52	1.1386 4365	0.8782 3790	48.7048 4176	55.4574 5862	0.0205 3184	52
53	1.1414 9026	0.8760 4778	49.5808 8953	56.5961 0227	0.0201 6906	53
54	1.1443 4398	0.8738 6312	50.4547 5265	57.7375 9252	0.0198 1974	54
55	1.1472 0484	0.8716 8391	51.3264 3656	58.8819 3650	0.0194 8314	55
56	1.1500 7285	0.8695 1013	52.1959 4669	60.0291 4135	0.0191 5858	56
57	1.1529 4804	0.8673 4178	53.0632 8847	61.1792 1420	0.0188 4542	57
58	1.1558 3041	0.8651 7883	53.9284 6730	62.3321 6223	0.0185 4308	58
59	1.1587 1998	0.8630 2128	54.7914 8858	63.4879 9264	0.0182 5101	59
60	1.1616 1678	0.8608 6911	55.6523 5769	64.6467 1262	0.0179 6869	60
61	1.1645 2082	0.8587 2230	56.5110 7999	65.8083 2940	0.0176 9564	61
62	1.1674 3213	0.8565 8085	57.3676 6083	66.9728 5023	0.0174 3142	62
63	1.1703 5071	0.8544 4474	58.2221 0557	68.1402 8235	0.0171 7561	63
64	1.1732 7658	0.8523 1395	59.0744 1952	69.3106 3306	0.0169 2780	64
65	1.1762 0977	0.8501 8848	59.9246 0800	70.4839 0964	0.0166 8764	65
66	1.1791 5030	0.8480 6831	60.7726 7631	71.6601 1942	0.0164 5476	66
67	1.1820 9817	0.8459 5343	61.6186 2974	72.8392 6971	0.0162 2886	67
68	1.1850 5342	0.8438 4382	62.4624 7355	74.0213 6789	0.0160 0961	68
69	1.1880 1605	0.8417 3947	63.3042 1302	75.2064 2131	0.0157 9674	69
70	1.1909 8609	0.8396 4037	64.1438 5339	76.3944 3736	0.0155 8996	70
71	1.1939 6356	0.8375 4650	64.9813 9989	77.5854 2345	0.0153 8902	71
72	1.1969 4847	0.8354 5786	65.8168 5774	78.7793 8701	0.0151 9368	72
73	1.1999 4084	0.8333 7442	66.6502 3216	79.9763 3548	0.0150 0370	73
74	1.2029 4069	0.8312 9618	67.4815 2834	81.1762 7632	0.0148 1887	74
75	1.2059 4804	0.8292 2312	68.3107 5146	82.3792 1701	0.0146 3898	75
76	1.2089 6291	0.8271 5523	69.1379 0670	83.5851 6505	0.0144 6385	76
77	1.2119 8532	0.8250 9250	69.9629 9920	84.7941 2797	0.0142 9327	77
78	1.2150 1528	0.8230 3491	70.7860 3411	86.0061 1329	0.0141 2708	78
79	1.2180 5282	0.8209 8246	71.6070 1657	87.2211 2857	0.0139 6511	79
80	1.2210 9795	0.8189 3512	72.4259 5169	88.4391 8139	0.0138 0721	80
81	1.2241 5070	0.8168 9289	73.2428 4458	89.6602 7934	0.0136 5321	81
82	1.2272 1108	0.8148 5575	74.0577 0033	90.8844 3004	0.0135 0298	82
83	1.2302 7910	0.8128 2369	74.8705 2402	92.1116 4112	0.0133 5639	83
84	1.2333 5480	0.8107 9670	75.6813 2072	93.3419 2022	0.0132 1330	84
85	1.2364 3819	0.8087 7476	76.4900 9548	94.5752 7502	0.0130 7359	85
86	1.2395 2928	0.8067 5787	77.2968 5335	95.8117 1321	0.0129 3714	86
87	1.2426 2811	0.8047 4600	78.1015 9935	97.0512 4249	0.0128 0384	87
88	1.2457 3468	0.8027 3915	78.9043 3850	98.2938 7060	0.0126 7357	88
89	1.2488 4901	0.8007 3731	79.7050 7581	99.5396 0527	0.0125 4625	89
90	1.2519 7114	0.7987 4046	80 5038 1627	100.7884 5429	0.0124 2177	90
91	1.2551 0106	0.7967 4859	81.3005 6486	102.0404 2542	0.0123 0004	91
92	1.2582 3882	0.7947 6168	82.0953 2654	103.2955 2649	0.0121 8096	92
93	1.2613 8441	0.7927 7973	82.8881 0628	104.5537 6530	0.0120 6446	93
94	1.2645 3787	0.7908 0273	83.6789 0900	105.8151 4972	0.0119 5044	94
95	1.2676 9922	0.7888 3065	84.4677 3966	107.0796 8759	0.0118 3884	95
96	1.2708 6847	0.7868 6349	85.2546 0315	108.3473 8681	0.0117 2957	96
97	1.2740 4564	0.7849 0124	86.0395 0439	109.6182 5528	0.0116 2257	97
98	1.2772 3075	0.7829 4388	86.8224 4827	110.8923 0091	0.0115 1776	98
99	1.2804 2383	0.7809 9140	87.6034 3967	112.1695 3167	0.0114 1508	99
100	1.2836 2489	0.7790 4379	88.3824 8346	113.4499 5550	0.0113 1446	100

Table III. $\frac{1}{3}\%$

Number of periods n	Amount of 1 at compound interest $s^n = (1 + i)^n$	Present value of 1 $v^n = \dfrac{1}{(1+i)^n}$	Present value of an annuity of 1 $a_{\overline{n}|} = \dfrac{1 - v^n}{i}$	Amount of an annuity of 1 $s_{\overline{n}|} = \dfrac{(1+i)^n - 1}{i}$	Annuity whose present value is 1. (CRF) $\dfrac{1}{a_{\overline{n}|}} = \dfrac{1}{s_{\overline{n}|}} + i$	Number of periods n
1	1.0033 3333	0.9966 7774	0.9966 7774	1.0000 0000	1.0033 3333	1
2	1.0066 7778	0.9933 6652	1.9900 4426	2.0033 3333	0.5025 0139	2
3	1.0100 3337	0.9900 6630	2.9801 1056	3.0100 1111	0.3355 5802	3
4	1.0134 0015	0.9867 7704	3.9668 8760	4.0200 4448	0.2520 8680	4
5	1.0167 7815	0.9834 9871	4.9503 8631	5.0334 4463	0.2020 0444	5
6	1.0201 6741	0.9802 3127	5.9306 1759	6.0502 2278	0.1686 1650	6
7	1.0235 6797	0.9769 7469	6.9075 9228	7.0703 9019	0.1447 6824	7
8	1.0269 7986	0.9737 2893	7.8813 2121	8.0939 5816	0.1268 8228	8
9	1.0304 0313	0.9704 9395	8.8518 1516	9.1209 3802	0.1129 7118	9
10	1.0338 3780	0.9672 6972	9.8190 8487	10.1513 4114	0.1018 4248	10
11	1.0372 8393	0.9640 5620	10.7831 4107	11.1851 7895	0.0927 3736	11
12	1.0407 4154	0.9608 5335	11.7439 9442	12.2224 6288	0.0851 4990	12
13	1.0442 1068	0.9576 6115	12.7016 5557	13.2632 0442	0.0787 2989	13
14	1.0476 9138	0.9544 7955	13.6561 3512	14.3074 1510	0.0732 2716	14
15	1.0511 8369	0.9513 0852	14.6074 4364	15.3551 0648	0.0684 5825	15
16	1.0546 8763	0.9481 4803	15.5555 9167	16.4062 9017	0.0642 8557	16
17	1.0582 0326	0.9449 9803	16.5005 8970	17.4609 7781	0.0606 0389	17
18	1.0617 3060	0.9418 5851	17.4424 4821	18.5191 8107	0.0573 3140	18
19	1.0652 6971	0.9387 2941	18.3811 7762	19.5809 1167	0.0544 0348	19
20	1.0688 2060	0.9356 1071	19.3167 8832	20.6461 8137	0.0517 6844	20
21	1.0723 8334	0.9325 0236	20.2492 9069	21.7150 0198	0.0493 8445	21
22	1.0759 5795	0.9294 0435	21.1786 9504	22.7873 8532	0.0472 1726	22
23	1.0795 4448	0.9263 1663	22.1050 1167	23.8633 4327	0.0452 3861	23
24	1.0831 4296	0.9232 3916	23.0282 5083	24.9428 8775	0.0434 2492	24
25	1.0867 5344	0.9201 7192	23.9484 2275	26.0260 3071	0.0417 5640	25
26	1.0903 7595	0.9171 1487	24.8655 3763	27.1127 8414	0.0402 1630	26
27	1.0940 1053	0.9140 6798	25.7796 0561	28.2031 6009	0.0387 9035	27
28	1.0976 5724	0.9110 3121	26.6906 3682	29.2971 7062	0.0374 6632	28
29	1.1013 1609	0.9080 0453	27.5986 4135	30.3948 2786	0.0362 3367	29
30	1.1049 8715	0.9049 8790	28.5036 2925	31.4961 4395	0.0350 8325	30
31	1.1086 7044	0.9019 8130	29.4056 1055	32.6011 3110	0.0340 0712	31
32	1.1123 6601	0.8989 8468	30.3045 9523	33.7098 0154	0.0329 9830	32
33	1.1160 7389	0.8959 9802	31.2005 9325	34.8221 6754	0.0320 5067	33
34	1.1197 9414	0.8930 2128	32.0936 1454	35.9382 4143	0.0311 5885	34
35	1.1235 2679	0.8900 5444	32.9836 6898	37.0580 3557	0.0303 1803	35
36	1.1272 7187	0.8870 9745	33.8707 6642	38.1815 6236	0.0295 2399	36
37	1.1310 2945	0.8841 5028	34.7549 1670	39.3088 3423	0.0287 7291	37
38	1.1347 9955	0.8812 1290	35.6361 2960	40.4398 6368	0.0280 6141	38
39	1.1385 8221	0.8782 8528	36.5144 1488	41.5746 6322	0.0273 8644	39
40	1.1423 7748	0.8753 6739	37.3897 8228	42.7132 4543	0.0267 4527	40
41	1.1461 8541	0.8724 5920	38.2622 4147	43.8556 2292	0.0261 3543	41
42	1.1500 0603	0.8695 6066	39.1318 0213	45.0018 0833	0.0255 5466	42
43	1.1538 3938	0.8666 7175	39.9984 7388	46.1518 1436	0.0250 0095	43
44	1.1576 8551	0.8637 9245	40.8622 6633	47.3056 5374	0.0244 7246	44
45	1.1615 4446	0.8609 2270	41.7231 8903	48.4633 3925	0.0239 6749	45
46	1.1654 1628	0.8580 6249	42.5812 5153	49.5248 8371	0.0234 8451	46
47	1.1693 0100	0.8552 1179	43.4364 6332	50.7902 9999	0.0230 2213	47
48	1.1731 9867	0.8523 7055	44.2888 3387	51.9596 0099	0.0225 7905	48
49	1.1771 0933	0.8495 3876	45.1383 7263	53.1327 9966	0.0221 5410	49
50	1.1810 3303	0.8467 1637	45.9850 8900	54.3099 0899	0.0217 4618	50

Table III (continued). ⅓ %

Number of periods n	Amount of 1 at compound interest $s^n = (1+i)^n$	Present value of 1 $v^n = \dfrac{1}{(1+i)^n}$	Present value of an annuity of 1 $a_{\overline{n}|} = \dfrac{1-v^n}{i}$	Amount of an annuity of 1 $s_{\overline{n}|} = \dfrac{(1+i)^n-1}{i}$	Annuity whose present value is 1. (CRF) $\dfrac{1}{a_{\overline{n}|}} = \dfrac{1}{s_{\overline{n}|}} + i$	Number of periods n
51	1.1849 6981	0.8439 0336	46.8289 9236	55.4909 4202	0.0213 5429	51
52	1.1889 1971	0.8410 9969	47.6700 9205	56.6759 1183	0.0209 7751	52
53	1.1928 8277	0.8383 0534	48.5083 9739	57.8648 3154	0.0206 1499	53
54	1.1968 5905	0.8355 2027	49.3439 1767	59.0577 1431	0.0202 6592	54
55	1.2008 4858	0.8327 4446	50.1766 6213	60.2545 7336	0.0199 2958	55
56	1.2048 5141	0.8299 7787	51.0066 3999	61.4554 2194	0.0196 0529	56
57	1.2088 6758	0.8272 2047	51.8338 6046	62.6602 7334	0.0192 9241	57
58	1.2128 9714	0.8244 7222	52.6583 3268	63.8691 4092	0.0189 9035	58
59	1.2169 4013	0.8217 3311	53.4800 6580	65.0820 3806	0.0186 9856	59
60	1.2209 9659	0.8190 0310	54.2990 6890	66.2989 7818	0.0184 1652	60
61	1.2250 6658	0.8162 8216	55.1153 5106	67.5199 7478	0.0181 4377	61
62	1.2291 5014	0.8135 7026	55.9289 2133	68.7450 4136	0.0178 7984	62
63	1.2332 4730	0.8108 6737	56.7397 8870	69.9741 9150	0.0176 2432	63
64	1.2373 5813	0.8081 7346	57.5479 6216	71.2074 3880	0.0173 7681	64
65	1.2414 8266	0.8054 8850	58.3534 5065	72.4447 9693	0.0171 3695	65
66	1.2456 2093	0.8028 1246	59.1562 6311	73.6862 7959	0.0169 0438	66
67	1.2497 7300	0.8001 4531	59.9564 0842	74.9319 0052	0.0166 7878	67
68	1.2539 3891	0.7974 8702	60.7538 9543	76.1816 7352	0.0164 5985	68
69	1.2581 1871	0.7948 3756	61.5487 3299	77.4356 1243	0.0162 4729	69
70	1.2623 1244	0.7921 9690	62.3409 2989	78.6937 3114	0.0160 4083	70
71	1.2665 2015	0.7895 6502	63.1304 9490	79.9560 4358	0.0158 4021	71
72	1.2707 4188	0.7869 4188	63.9174 3678	81.2225 6372	0.0156 4518	72
73	1.2749 7769	0.7843 2745	64.7017 6423	82.4933 0560	0.0154 5553	73
74	1.2792 2761	0.7817 2171	65.4834 8595	83.7682 8329	0.0152 7103	74
75	1.2834 9170	0.7791 2463	66.2626 1058	85.0475 1090	0.0150 9147	75
76	1.2877 7001	0.7765 3618	67.0391 4676	86.3310 0260	0.0149 1666	76
77	1.2920 6258	0.7739 5632	67.8131 0308	87.6187 7261	0.0147 4641	77
78	1.2963 6945	0.7713 8504	68.5844 8812	88.9108 3519	0.0145 8056	78
79	1.3006 9068	0.7688 2230	69.3533 1042	90.2072 0464	0.0144 1892	79
80	1.3050 2632	0.7662 6807	70.1195 7849	91.5078 9532	0.0142 6135	80
81	1.3093 7641	0.7637 2233	70.8833 0082	92.8129 2164	0.0141 0770	81
82	1.3137 4099	0.7611 8505	71.6444 8587	94.1222 9804	0.0139 5781	82
83	1.3181 2013	0.7586 5619	72.4031 4206	95.4360 3904	0.0138 1156	83
84	1.3225 1386	0.7561 3574	73.1592 7780	96.7541 5917	0.0136 6881	84
85	1.3269 2224	0.7536 2366	73.9129 0146	98.0766 7303	0.0135 2944	85
86	1.3313 4532	0.7511 1993	74.6640 2139	99.4035 9527	0.0133 9333	86
87	1.3357 8314	0.7486 2451	75.4126 4591	100.7349 4059	0.0132 6038	87
88	1.3402 3575	0.7461 3739	76.1587 8329	102.0707 2373	0.0131 3046	88
89	1.3447 0320	0.7436 5853	76.9024 4182	103.4109 5947	0.0130 0349	89
90	1.3491 8554	0.7411 8790	77.6436 2972	104.7556 6267	0.0128 7936	90
91	1.3536 8283	0.7387 2548	78.3823 5520	106.1048 4821	0.0127 5797	91
92	1.3581 9510	0.7362 7125	79.1186 2645	107.4585 3104	0.0126 3925	92
93	1.3627 2242	0.7338 2516	79.8524 5161	108.8167 2614	0.0125 2310	93
94	1.3672 6483	0.7313 8720	80.5838 3882	110.1794 4856	0.0124 0944	94
95	1.3718 2238	0.7289 5735	81.3127 9616	111.5467 1339	0.0122 9819	95
96	1.3763 9512	0.7265 3556	82.0393 3172	112.9185 3577	0.0121 8928	96
97	1.3809 8310	0.7241 2182	82.7634 5354	114.2949 3089	0.0120 8263	97
98	1.3855 8638	0.7217 1610	83.4851 6964	115.6759 1399	0.0119 7818	98
99	1.3902 0500	0.7193 1837	84.2044 8802	117.0615 0037	0.0118 7585	99
100	1.3948 3902	0.7169 2861	84.9214 1663	118.4517 0537	0.0117 7559	100

Table IV. $5/_{12}\%$

Number of periods n	Amount of 1 at compound interest $s^n = (1+i)^n$	Present value of 1 $v^n = \dfrac{1}{(1+i)^n}$	Present value of an annuity of 1 $a_{\overline{n}\rceil} = \dfrac{1-v^n}{i}$	Amount of an annuity of 1 $s_{\overline{n}\rceil} = \dfrac{(1+i)^n-1}{i}$	Annuity whose present value is 1. (CRF) $\dfrac{1}{a_{\overline{n}\rceil}} = \dfrac{1}{s_{\overline{n}\rceil}} + i$	Number of periods n
1	1.0041 6667	0.9958 5062	0.9958 5062	1.0000 0000	1.0041 6667	1
2	1.0083 5069	0.9917 1846	1.9875 6908	2.0041 6667	0.5031 2717	2
3	1.0125 5216	0.9876 0345	2.9751 7253	3.0125 1736	0.3361 1496	3
4	1.0167 7112	0.9835 0551	3.9586 7804	4.0250 6952	0.2526 0958	4
5	1.0210 0767	0.9794 2457	4.9381 0261	5.0418 4064	0.2025 0693	5
6	1.0252 6187	0.9753 6057	5.9134 6318	6.0628 4831	0.1691 0564	6
7	1.0295 3379	0.9713 1343	6.8847 7661	7.0881 1018	0.1452 4800	7
8	1.0338 2352	0.9672 8308	7.8520 5969	8.1176 4397	0.1273 5512	8
9	1.0381 3111	0.9632 6946	8.8153 2915	9.1514 6749	0.1134 3876	9
10	1.0424 5666	0.9592 7249	9.7746 0164	10.1895 9860	0.1023 0596	10
11	1.0468 0023	0.9552 9211	10.7298 9374	11.2320 5526	0.0931 9757	11
12	1.0511 6190	0.9513 2824	11.6812 2198	12.2788 5549	0.0856 0748	12
13	1.0555 4174	0.9473 8082	12.6286 0280	13.3300 1739	0.0791 8532	13
14	1.0599 3983	0.9434 4978	13.5720 5257	14.3855 5913	0.0736 8082	14
15	1.0643 5625	0.9395 3505	14.5115 8762	15.4454 9896	0.0689 1045	15
16	1.0687 9106	0.9356 3656	15.4472 2418	16.5098 5520	0.0647 3655	16
17	1.0732 4436	0.9317 5425	16.3789 7843	17.5786 4627	0.0610 5387	17
18	1.0777 1621	0.9278 8805	17.3068 6648	18.6518 9063	0.0577 8053	18
19	1.0822 0670	0.9240 3789	18.2309 0438	19.7296 0684	0.0548 5191	19
20	1.0867 1589	0.9202 0371	19.1511 0809	20.8118 1353	0.0522 1630	20
21	1.0912 4387	0.9163 8544	20.0674 9352	21.8985 2942	0.0498 3183	21
22	1.0957 9072	0.9125 8301	20.9800 7653	22.9897 7330	0.0476 6427	22
23	1.1003 5652	0.9087 9636	21.8888 7289	24.0855 6402	0.0456 8531	23
24	1.1049 4134	0.9050 2542	22.7938 9831	25.1859 2054	0.0438 7139	24
25	1.1095 4526	0.9012 7012	23.6951 6843	26.2908 6187	0.0422 0270	25
26	1.1141 6836	0.8975 3041	24.5926 9884	27.4004 0713	0.0406 6247	26
27	1.1188 1073	0.8938 0622	25.4865 0506	28.5145 7549	0.0392 3645	27
28	1.1234 7244	0.8900 9748	26.3766 0254	29.6333 8622	0.0379 1239	28
29	1.1281 5358	0.8864 0413	27.2630 0668	30.7568 5867	0.0366 7974	29
30	1.1328 5422	0.8827 2610	28.1457 3278	31.8850 1224	0.0355 2936	30
31	1.1375 7444	0.8790 6334	29.0247 9612	33.0178 6646	0.0344 5330	31
32	1.1423 1434	0.8754 1577	29.9002 1189	34.1554 4090	0.0334 4458	32
33	1.1470 7398	0.8717 8334	30.7719 9524	35.2977 5524	0.0324 9708	33
34	1.1518 5346	0.8681 6599	31.6401 6122	36.4448 2922	0.0316 0540	34
35	1.1566 5284	0.8645 6364	32.5047 2486	37.5966 8268	0.0307 6476	35
36	1.1614 7223	0.8609 7624	33.3657 0109	38.7533 3552	0.0299 7090	36
37	1.1663 1170	0.8574 0372	34.2231 0481	39.9148 0775	0.0292 2003	37
38	1.1711 7133	0.8538 4603	35.0769 5084	41.0811 1945	0.0285 0875	38
39	1.1760 5121	0.8503 0310	35.9272 5394	42.2522 9078	0.0278 3402	39
40	1.1809 5142	0.8467 7487	36.7740 2881	43.4283 4199	0.0271 9310	40
41	1.1858 7206	0.8432 6128	37.6172 9009	44.6092 9342	0.0263 8352	41
42	1.1908 1319	0.8397 6227	38.4570 5236	45.7951 6548	0.0260 0303	42
43	1.1957 7491	0.8362 7778	39.2933 3013	46.9859 7866	0.0254 4961	43
44	1.2007 5731	0.8328 0775	40.1261 3788	48.1817 5358	0.0249 2141	44
45	1.2057 6046	0.8293 5211	40.9554 8999	49.3825 1088	0.0244 1675	45
46	1.2107 8446	0.8259 1082	41.7814 0081	50.5882 7134	0.0239 3409	46
47	1.2158 2940	0.8224 8380	42.6038 8461	51.7990 5581	0.0234 7204	47
48	1.2208 9536	0.8190 7100	43.4229 5562	53.0148 8521	0.0230 2929	48
49	1.2259 8242	0.8156 7237	44.2386 2799	54.2357 8056	0.0226 0468	49
50	1.2310 9068	0.8122 8784	45.0509 1582	55.4617 6298	0.0221 9711	50

Table IV (*continued*). $5\frac{1}{12}\%$

Number of periods n	Amount of 1 at compound interest $s^n = (1+i)^n$	Present value of 1 $v^n = \dfrac{1}{(1+i)^n}$	Present value of an annuity of 1 $a_{\overline{n}|} = \dfrac{1-v^n}{i}$	Amount of an annuity of 1 $s_{\overline{n}|} = \dfrac{(1+i)^n-1}{i}$	Annuity whose present value is 1. (CRF) $\dfrac{1}{a_{\overline{n}|}} = \dfrac{1}{s_{\overline{n}|}} + i$	Number of periods n
51	1.2362 2002	0.8089 1735	45.8598 3317	56.6928 5366	0.0218 0557	51
52	1.2413 7114	0.8055 6084	46.6653 9401	57.9290 7388	0.0214 2916	52
53	1.2465 4352	0.8022 1827	47.4676 1228	59.1704 4503	0.0210 6700	53
54	1.2517 3745	0.7988 8956	48.2665 0184	60.4169 8855	0.0207 1830	54
55	1.2569 5302	0.7955 7467	49.0620 7651	61.6687 2600	0.0203 8234	55
56	1.2621 9033	0.7922 7353	49.8543 5003	62.9256 7902	0.0200 5843	56
57	1.2674 4946	0.7889 8608	50.6433 3612	64.1878 6935	0.0197 4593	57
58	1.2727 3050	0.7857 1228	51.4290 4840	65.4553 1881	0.0194 4426	58
59	1.2780 3354	0.7824 5207	52.2115 0046	66.7280 4930	0.0191 5287	59
60	1.2833 5868	0.7792 0538	52.9907 0584	68.0060 8284	0.0188 7123	60
61	1.2887 0601	0.7759 7216	53.7666 7800	69.2894 4152	0.0185 9888	61
62	1.2940 7561	0.7727 5236	54.5394 3035	70.5781 4753	0.0183 3536	62
63	1.2994 6760	0.7695 4591	55.3089 7627	71.8722 2314	0.0180 8025	63
64	1.3048 8204	0.7663 5278	56.0753 2905	73.1716 9074	0.0178 3315	64
65	1.3103 1905	0.7631 7289	56.8385 0194	74.4765 7278	0.0175 9371	65
66	1.3157 7872	0.7600 0620	57.5985 0814	75.7868 9184	0.0173 6156	66
67	1.3212 6113	0.7568 5265	58.3553 6078	77.1026 7055	0.0171 3639	67
68	1.3267 6638	0.7537 1218	59.1090 7296	78.4239 3168	0.0169 1788	68
69	1.3322 9458	0.7505 8474	59.8596 5770	79.7506 9806	0.0167 0574	69
70	1.3378 4580	0.7474 7028	60.6071 2798	81.0829 9264	0.0164 9971	70
71	1.3434 2016	0.7443 6874	61.3514 9672	82.4208 3844	0.0162 9952	71
72	1.3490 1774	0.7412 8008	62.0927 7680	83.7642 5860	0.0161 0493	72
73	1.3546 3865	0.7382 0423	62.8309 8103	85.1132 7634	0.0159 1572	73
74	1.3602 8298	0.7351 4114	63.5661 2216	86.4679 1500	0.0157 3165	74
75	1.3659 5082	0.7320 9076	64.2982 1292	87.8281 9797	0.0155 5253	75
76	1.3716 4229	0.7290 5304	65.0272 6596	89.1941 4880	0.0153 7816	76
77	1.3773 5746	0.7260 2792	65.7532 9388	90.5657 9109	0.0152 0836	77
78	1.3830 9645	0.7230 1536	66.4763 0924	91.9431 4855	0.0150 4295	78
79	1.3888 5935	0.7200 1529	67.1963 2453	93.3262 4500	0.0148 8177	79
80	1.3946 4627	0.7170 2768	67.9133 5221	94.7151 0436	0.0147 2464	80
81	1.4004 5729	0.7140 5246	68.6274 0467	96.1097 5062	0.0145 7144	81
82	1.4062 9253	0.7110 8959	69.3384 9426	97.5102 0792	0.0144 2200	82
83	1.4121 5209	0.7081 3901	70.0466 3326	98.9165 0045	0.0142 7620	83
84	1.4180 3605	0.7052 0067	70.7518 3393	100.3286 5254	0.0141 3391	84
85	1.4239 4454	0.7022 7453	71.4541 0846	101.7466 8859	0.0139 9500	85
86	1.4298 7764	0.6993 6052	72.1534 6898	103.1706 3312	0.0138 5935	86
87	1.4358 3546	0.6964 5861	72.8499 2759	104.6005 1076	0.0137 2685	87
88	1.4418 1811	0.6935 6874	73.5434 9633	106.0363 4622	0.0135 9740	88
89	1.4478 2568	0.6906 9086	74.2341 8720	107.4781 6433	0.0134 7088	89
90	1.4538 5829	0.6878 2493	74.9220 1212	108.9259 9002	0.0133 4721	90
91	1.4599 1603	0.6849 7088	75.6069 8300	110.3798 4831	0.0132 2629	91
92	1.4659 9902	0.6821 2868	76.2891 1168	111.8397 6434	0.0131 0803	92
93	1.4721 0735	0.6792 9827	76.9684 0995	113.3057 6336	0.0129 9234	93
94	1.4782 4113	0.6764 7960	77.6448 8955	114.7778 7071	0.0128 7915	94
95	1.4844 0047	0.6736 7263	78.3185 6218	116.2561 1184	0.0127 6837	95
96	1.4905 8547	0.6708 7731	78.9894 3950	117.7405 1230	0.0126 5992	96
97	1.4967 9624	0.6680 9359	79.6575 3308	119.2310 9777	0.0125 5374	97
98	1.5030 3289	0.6653 2141	80.3228 5450	120.7278 9401	0.0124 4976	98
99	1.5092 9553	0.6625 6074	80.9854 1524	122.2309 2690	0.0123 4790	99
100	1.5155 8426	0.6598 1153	81.6452 2677	123.7402 2243	0.0122 4811	100

Table V. ½%

Number of periods n	Amount of 1 at compound interest $s^n = (1+i)^n$	Present value of 1 $v^n = \dfrac{1}{(1+i)^n}$	Present value of an annuity of 1 $a_{\overline{n}\rceil} = \dfrac{1-v^n}{i}$	Amount of an annuity of 1 $s_{\overline{n}\rceil} = \dfrac{(1+i)^n-1}{i}$	Annuity whose present value is 1. (CRF) $\dfrac{1}{a_{\overline{n}\rceil}} = \dfrac{1}{s_{\overline{n}\rceil}}+i$	Number of periods n
1	1.0050 0000	0.9950 2488	0.9950 2488	1.0000 0000	1.0050 0000	1
2	1.0100 2500	0.9900 7450	1.9850 9938	2.0050 0000	0.5037 5312	2
3	1.0150 7513	0.9851 4876	2.9702 4814	3.0150 2500	0.3366 7221	3
4	1.0201 5050	0.9802 4752	3.9504 9566	4.0301 0013	0.2531 3279	4
5	1.0252 5125	0.9753 7067	4.9258 6633	5.0502 5063	0.2030 0997	5
6	1.0303 7751	0.9705 1808	5.8963 8441	6.0755 0188	0.1695 9546	6
7	1.0355 2940	0.9656 8963	6.8620 7404	7.1058 7939	0.1457 2854	7
8	1.0407 0704	0.9608 8520	7.8229 5924	8.1414 0879	0.1278 2886	8
9	1.0459 1058	0.9561 0468	8.7790 6392	9.1821 1583	0.1139 0736	9
10	1.0511 4013	0.9513 4794	9.7304 1186	10.2280 2641	0.1027 7057	10
11	1.0563 9583	0.9466 1489	10.6770 2673	11.2791 6654	0.0936 5903	11
12	1.0616 7781	0.9419 0534	11.6189 3207	12.3355 6237	0.0860 6643	12
13	1.0669 8620	0.9372 1924	12.5561 5131	13.3972 4018	0.0796 4224	13
14	1.0723 2113	0.9325 5646	13.4887 0777	14.4642 2639	0.0741 3609	14
15	1.0776 8274	0.9279 1688	14.4166 2465	15.5365 4752	0.0693 6436	15
16	1.0830 7115	0.9233 0037	15.3399 2502	16.6142 3026	0.0651 8937	16
17	1.0884 8651	0.9187 0684	16.2586 3186	17.6973 0141	0.0615 0579	17
18	1.0939 2894	0.9141 3616	17.1727 6802	18.7857 8791	0.0582 3173	18
19	1.0993 9858	0.9095 8822	18.0823 5624	19.8797 1685	0.0553 0253	19
20	1.1048 9558	0.9050 6290	18.9874 1915	20.9791 1544	0.0526 6645	20
21	1.1104 2006	0.9005 6010	19.8879 7925	22.0840 1101	0.0502 8163	21
22	1.1159 7216	0.8960 7971	20.7840 5896	23.1944 3107	0.0481 1380	22
23	1.1215 5202	0.8916 2160	21.6756 8055	24.3104 0322	0.0461 3465	23
24	1.1271 5978	0.8871 8567	22.5628 6622	25.4319 5524	0.0443 2061	24
25	1.1327 9558	0.8827 7181	23.4456 3803	26.5591 1502	0.0426 5186	25
26	1.1384 5955	0.8783 7991	24.3240 1794	27.6919 1059	0.0411 1163	26
27	1.1441 5185	0.8740 0986	25.1980 2780	28.8303 7015	0.0396 8565	27
28	1.1498 7261	0.8696 6155	26.0676 8936	29.9745 2200	0.0383 6167	28
29	1.1556 2197	0.8653 3488	26.9330 2423	31.1243 9461	0.0371 2914	29
30	1.1614 0008	0.8610 2973	27.7940 5397	32.2800 1658	0.0359 7892	30
31	1.1672 0708	0.8567 4600	28.6507 9997	33.4414 1666	0.0349 0304	31
32	1.1730 4312	0.8524 8358	29.5032 8355	34.6086 2375	0.0338 9453	32
33	1.1789 0833	0.8482 4237	30.3515 2592	35.7816 6686	0.0329 4727	33
34	1.1848 0288	0.8440 2226	31.1955 4818	36.9605 7520	0.0320 5586	34
35	1.1907 2689	0.8398 2314	32.0353 7132	38.1453 7807	0.0312 1550	35
36	1.1966 8052	0.8356 4492	32.8710 1624	39.3361 0496	0.0304 2194	36
37	1.2026 6393	0.8314 8748	33.7025 0372	40.5327 8549	0.0296 7139	37
38	1.2086 7725	0.8273 5073	34.5298 5445	41.7354 4942	0.0289 6045	38
39	1.2147 2063	0.8232 3455	35.3530 8900	42.9441 2666	0.0282 8607	39
40	1.2207 9424	0.8191 3886	36.1722 2786	44.1588 4730	0.0276 4552	40
41	1.2268 9821	0.8150 6354	36.9872 9141	45.3796 4153	0.0270 3631	41
42	1.2330 3270	0.8110 0850	37.7982 9991	46.6065 3974	0.0264 5622	42
43	1.2391 9786	0.8069 7363	38.6052 7354	47.8395 7244	0.0259 0320	43
44	1.2453 9385	0.8029 5884	39.4082 3238	49.0787 7030	0.0253 7541	44
45	1.2516 2082	0.7989 6402	40.2071 9640	50.3241 6415	0.0248 7117	45
46	1.2578 7892	0.7949 8907	41.0021 8547	51.5757 8497	0.0243 8894	46
47	1.2641 6832	0.7910 3390	41.7932 1937	52.8336 6390	0.0239 2733	47
48	1.2704 8916	0.7870 9841	42.5803 1778	54.0978 3222	0.0234 8503	48
49	1.2768 4161	0.7831 8250	43.3635 0028	55.3683 2138	0.0230 6087	49
50	1.2832 2581	0.7792 8607	44.1427 8635	56.6451 6299	0.0226 5376	50

Table V (*continued*). ½ %

Number of periods n	Amount of 1 at compound interest $s^n = (1+i)^n$	Present value of 1 $v^n = \dfrac{1}{(1+i)^n}$	Present value of an annuity of 1 $a_{\overline{n}\rvert} = \dfrac{1-v^n}{i}$	Amount of an annuity of 1 $s_{\overline{n}\rvert} = \dfrac{(1+i)^n-1}{i}$	Annuity whose present value is 1. (CRF) $\dfrac{1}{a_{\overline{n}\rvert}} = \dfrac{1}{s_{\overline{n}\rvert}} + i$	Number of periods n
51	1.2896 4194	0.7754 0902	44.9181 9537	57.9283 8880	0.0222 6269	51
52	1.2960 9015	0.7715 5127	45.6897 4664	59.2180 3075	0.0218 8675	52
53	1.3025 7060	0.7677 1270	46.4574 5934	60.5141 2090	0.0215 2507	53
54	1.3090 8346	0.7638 9324	47.2213 5258	61.8166 9150	0.0211 7686	54
55	1.3156 2887	0.7600 9277	47.9814 4535	63.1257 7496	0.0208 4139	55
56	1.3222 0702	0.7563 1122	48.7377 5657	64.4414 0384	0.0205 1797	56
57	1.3288 1805	0.7525 4847	49.4903 0505	65.7636 1086	0.0202 0598	57
58	1.3354 6214	0.7488 0445	50.2391 0950	67.0924 2891	0.0199 0481	58
59	1.3421 3946	0.7450 7906	50.9841 8855	68.4278 9105	0.0196 1392	59
60	1.3488 5015	0.7413 7220	51.7255 6075	69.7700 3051	0.0193 3280	60
61	1.3555 9440	0.7376 8378	52.4632 4453	71.1188 8066	0.0190 6096	61
62	1.3623 7238	0.7340 1371	53.1972 5824	72.4744 7507	0.0187 9796	62
63	1.3691 8424	0.7303 6190	53.9276 2014	73.8368 4744	0.0185 4337	63
64	1.3760 3016	0.7267 2826	54.6543 4839	75.2060 3168	0.0182 9681	64
65	1.3829 1031	0.7231 1269	55.3774 6109	76.5820 6184	0.0180 5789	65
66	1.3898 2486	0.7195 1512	56.0969 7621	77.9649 7215	0.0178 2627	66
67	1.3967 7399	0.7159 3544	56.8129 1165	79.3547 9701	0.0176 0163	67
68	1.4037 5785	0.7123 7357	57.5252 8522	80.7515 7099	0.0173 8366	68
69	1.4107 7664	0.7088 2943	58.2341 1465	82.1553 2885	0.0171 7206	69
70	1.4178 3053	0.7053 0291	58.9394 1756	83.5661 0549	0.0169 6657	70
71	1.4249 1968	0.7017 9394	59.6412 1151	84.9839 3602	0.0167 6693	71
72	1.4320 4428	0.6983 0243	60.3395 1394	86.4088 5570	0.0165 7289	72
73	1.4392 0450	0.6948 2829	61.0343 4222	87.8408 9998	0.0163 8422	73
74	1.4464 0052	0.6913 7143	61.7257 1366	89.2801 0448	0.0162 0070	74
75	1.4536 3252	0.6879 3177	62.4136 4543	90.7265 0500	0.0160 2214	75
76	1.4609 0069	0.6845 0923	63.0981 5466	92.1801 3752	0.0158 4832	76
77	1.4682 0519	0.6811 0371	63.7792 5836	93.6410 3821	0.0156 7908	77
78	1.4755 4622	0.6777 1513	64.4569 7350	95.1092 4340	0.0155 1423	78
79	1.4829 2395	0.6743 4342	65.1313 1691	96.5847 8962	0.0153 5360	79
80	1.4903 3857	0.6709 8847	65.8023 0538	98.0677 1357	0.0151 9704	80
81	1.4977 9026	0.6676 5022	66.4699 5561	99.5580 5214	0.0150 4439	81
82	1.5052 7921	0.6643 2858	67.1342 8419	101.0558 4240	0.0148 9552	82
83	1.5128 0561	0.6610 2346	67.7953 0765	102.5611 2161	0.0147 5028	83
84	1.5203 6964	0.6577 3479	68.4530 4244	104.0739 2722	0.0146 0855	84
85	1.5279 7148	0.6544 6248	69.1075 0491	105.5942 9685	0.0144 7021	85
86	1.5356 1134	0.6512 0644	69.7587 1135	107.1222 6834	0.0143 3513	86
87	1.5432 8940	0.6479 6661	70.4066 7796	108.6578 7968	0.0142 0320	87
88	1.5510 0585	0.6447 4290	71.0514 2086	110.2011 6908	0.0140 7431	88
89	1.5587 6087	0.6415 3522	71.6929 5608	111.7521 7492	0.0139 4837	89
90	1.5665 5468	0.6383 4350	72.3312 9958	113.3109 3580	0.0138 2527	90
91	1.5743 8745	0.6351 6766	72.9664 6725	114.8774 9048	0.0137 0493	91
92	1.5822 5939	0.6320 0763	73.5984 7487	116.4518 7793	0.0135 8724	92
93	1.5901 7069	0.6288 6331	74.2273 3818	118.0341 3732	0.0134 7213	93
94	1.5981 2154	0.6257 3464	74.8530 7282	119.6243 0800	0.0133 5950	94
95	1.6061 1215	0.6226 2153	75.4756 9434	121.2224 2954	0.0132 4930	95
96	1.6141 4271	0.6195 2391	76.0952 1825	122.8285 4169	0.0131 4143	96
97	1.6222 1342	0.6164 4170	76.7116 5995	124.4426 8440	0.0130 3583	97
98	1.6303 2449	0.6133 7483	77.3250 3478	126.0648 9782	0.0129 3242	98
99	1.6384 7611	0.6103 2321	77.9353 5799	127.6952 2231	0.0128 3115	99
100	1.6466 6849	0.6072 8678	78.5426 4477	129.3336 9842	0.0127 3194	100

Table VI. $\frac{7}{12}\%$

Number of periods n	Amount of 1 at compound interest $s^n = (1+i)^n$	Present value of 1 $v^n = \dfrac{1}{(1+i)^n}$	Present value of an annuity of 1 $a_{\overline{n}|} = \dfrac{1-v^n}{i}$	Amount of an annuity of 1 $s_{\overline{n}|} = \dfrac{(1+i)^n-1}{i}$	Annuity whose present value is 1. (CRF) $\dfrac{1}{a_{\overline{n}|}} = \dfrac{1}{s_{\overline{n}|}} + i$	Number of periods n
1	1.0058 3333	0.9942 0050	0.9942 0050	1.0000 0000	1.0058 3333	1
2	1.0117 0069	0.9884 3463	1.9826 3513	2.0058 3333	0.5043 7924	2
3	1.0176 0228	0.9827 0220	2.9653 3733	3.0175 3403	0.3372 2976	3
4	1.0235 3830	0.9770 0302	3.9423 4034	4.0351 3631	0.2536 5644	4
5	1.0295 0894	0.9713 3688	4.9136 7723	5.0586 7460	0.2035 1357	5
6	1.0355 1440	0.9657 0361	5.8793 8084	6.0881 8354	0.1700 8594	6
7	1.0415 5490	0.9601 0301	6.8394 8385	7.1236 9794	0.1462 0986	7
8	1.0476 3064	0.9545 3489	7.7940 1875	8.1652 5284	0.1283 0351	8
9	1.0537 4182	0.9489 9907	8.7430 1781	9.2128 8349	0.1143 7698	9
10	1.0598 8865	0.9434 9534	9.6865 1315	10.2666 2531	0.1032 3632	10
11	1.0660 7133	0.9380 2354	10.6245 3669	11.3265 1396	0.0941 2175	11
12	1.0722 9008	0.9325 8347	11.5571 2016	12.3925 8529	0.0865 2675	12
13	1.0785 4511	0.9271 7495	12.4842 9511	13.4648 7537	0.0801 0064	13
14	1.0848 3662	0.9217 9780	13.4060 9291	14.5434 2048	0.0745 9295	14
15	1.0911 6483	0.9164 5183	14.3225 4473	15.6282 5710	0.0698 1999	15
16	1.0975 2996	0.9111 3686	15.2336 8160	16.7194 2193	0.0656 4401	16
17	1.1039 3222	0.9058 5272	16.1395 3432	17.8169 5189	0.0619 5966	17
18	1.1103 7182	0.9005 9923	17.0401 3354	18.9208 8411	0.0586 8499	18
19	1.1168 4899	0.8953 7620	17.9355 0974	20.0312 5593	0.0557 5532	19
20	1.1233 6395	0.8901 8346	18.8256 9320	21.1481 0493	0.0531 1889	20
21	1.1299 1690	0.8850 2084	19.7107 1404	22.2714 6887	0.0507 3383	21
22	1.1365 0808	0.8798 8816	20.5906 0220	23.4013 8577	0.0485 6585	22
23	1.1431 3771	0.8747 8525	21.4653 8745	24.5378 9386	0.0465 8663	23
24	1.1498 0602	0.8697 1193	22.3350 9939	25.6810 3157	0.0447 7258	24
25	1.1565 1322	0.8646 6803	23.1997 6741	26.8308 3759	0.0431 0388	25
26	1.1632 5955	0.8596 5339	24.0594 2079	27.9873 5081	0.0415 6376	26
27	1.1700 4523	0.8546 6782	24.9140 8862	29.1506 1035	0.0401 3793	27
28	1.1768 7049	0.8497 1118	25.7637 9979	30.3206 5558	0.0388 1415	28
29	1.1837 3557	0.8447 8327	26.6085 8307	31.4975 2607	0.0375 8186	29
30	1.1906 4069	0.8398 8395	27.4484 6702	32.6812 6164	0.0364 3191	30
31	1.1975 8610	0.8350 1304	28.2834 8006	33.8719 0233	0.0353 5633	31
32	1.2045 7202	0.8301 7038	29.1136 5044	35.0694 8843	0.0343 4815	32
33	1.2115 9869	0.8253 5581	29.9390 0625	36.2740 6045	0.0334 0124	33
34	1.2186 6634	0.8205 6915	30.7595 7540	37.4856 5913	0.0325 1020	34
35	1.2257 7523	0.8158 1026	31.5753 8566	38.7043 2548	0.0316 7024	35
36	1.2329 2559	0.8110 7897	32.3864 6463	39.9301 0071	0.0308 7710	36
37	1.2401 1765	0.8063 7511	33.1928 3974	41.1630 2630	0.0301 2698	37
38	1.2473 5167	0.8016 9854	33.9945 3828	42.4031 4395	0.0294 1649	38
39	1.2546 2789	0.7970 4908	34.7915 8736	43.6504 9562	0.0287 4258	39
40	1.2619 4655	0.7924 2660	35.5840 1396	44.9051 2352	0.0281 0251	40
41	1.2693 0791	0.7878 3092	36.3718 4487	46.1670 7007	0.0274 9379	41
42	1.2767 1220	0.7832 6189	37.1551 0676	47.4363 7798	0.0269 1420	42
43	1.2841 5969	0.7787 1936	37.9338 2612	48.7130 9018	0.0263 6170	43
44	1.2916 5062	0.7742 0317	38.7080 2929	49.9972 4988	0.0258 3443	44
45	1.2991 8525	0.7697 1318	39.4777 4248	51.2889 0050	0.0253 3073	45
46	1.3067 6383	0.7652 4923	40.2429 9170	52.5880 8575	0.0248 4905	46
47	1.3143 8662	0.7608 1116	41.0038 0287	53.8948 4959	0.0243 8798	47
48	1.3220 5388	0.7563 9884	41.7602 0170	55.2092 3621	0.0239 4624	48
49	1.3297 6586	0.7520 1210	42.5122 1380	56.5312 9009	0.0235 2265	49
50	1.3375 2283	0.7476 5080	43.2598 6460	57.8610 5595	0.0231 1611	50

Table VI (*continued*). $7/12 \%$

Number of periods n	Amount of 1 at compound interest $s^n = (1+i)^n$	Present value of 1 $v^n = \dfrac{1}{(1+i)^n}$	Present value of an annuity of 1 $a_{\overline{n}|} = \dfrac{1-v^n}{i}$	Amount of an annuity of 1 $s_{\overline{n}|} = \dfrac{(1+i)^n-1}{i}$	Annuity whose present value is 1. (CRF) $\dfrac{1}{a_{\overline{n}|}} = \dfrac{1}{s_{\overline{n}|}} + i$	Number of periods n
51	1.3453 2504	0.7433 1480	44.0031 7940	59.1985 7877	0.0227 2563	51
52	1.3531 7277	0.7390 0394	44.7421 8335	60.5439 0381	0.0223 5027	52
53	1.3610 6628	0.7347 1809	45.4769 0144	61.8970 7659	0.0219 8919	53
54	1.3690 0583	0.7304 5709	46.2073 5853	63.2581 4287	0.0216 4157	54
55	1.3769 9170	0.7262 2080	46.9335 7933	64.6271 4870	0.0213 0671	55
56	1.3850 2415	0.7220 0908	47.6555 8841	66.0041 4040	0.0209 8390	56
57	1.3931 0346	0.7178 2179	48.3734 1020	67.3891 6455	0.0206 7251	57
58	1.4012 2990	0.7136 5878	49.0870 6898	68.7822 6801	0.0203 7196	58
59	1.4094 0374	0.7095 1991	49.7965 8889	70.1834 9791	0.0200 8170	59
60	1.4176 2526	0.7054 0505	50.5019 9394	71.5929 0165	0.0198 0120	60
61	1.4258 9474	0.7013 1405	51.2033 0800	73.0105 2691	0.0195 2999	61
62	1.4342 1246	0.6972 4678	51.9005 5478	74.4364 2165	0.0192 6762	62
63	1.4425 7870	0.6932 0310	52.5937 5787	75.8706 3411	0.0190 1366	63
64	1.4509 9374	0.6891 8286	53.2829 4073	77.3132 1281	0.0187 6773	64
65	1.4594 5787	0.6851 8594	53.9681 2668	78.7642 0655	0.0185 2946	65
66	1.4679 7138	0.6812 1221	54.6493 3888	80.2236 6442	0.0182 9848	66
67	1.4765 3454	0.6772 6151	55.3266 0040	81.6916 3579	0.0180 7449	67
68	1.4851 4766	0.6733 3373	55.9999 3413	83.1681 7034	0.0178 5716	68
69	1.4938 1102	0.6694 2873	56.6693 6287	84.6533 1800	0.0176 4622	69
70	1.5025 2492	0.6655 4638	57.3349 0925	86.1471 2902	0.0174 4138	70
71	1.5112 8965	0.6616 8654	57.9965 9579	87.6496 5394	0.0172 4239	71
72	1.5201 0550	0.6578 4909	58.6544 4488	89.1609 4359	0.0170 4901	72
73	1.5289 7279	0.6540 3389	59.3084 7877	90.6810 4909	0.0168 6100	73
74	1.5378 9179	0.6502 4082	59.9587 1959	92.2100 2188	0.0166 7814	74
75	1.5468 6283	0.6464 6975	60.6051 8934	93.7479 1367	0.0165 0024	75
76	1.5558 8620	0.6427 2054	61.2479 0988	95.2947 7650	0.0163 2709	76
77	1.5649 6220	0.6389 9308	61.8869 0297	96.8506 6270	0.0161 5851	77
78	1.5740 9115	0.6352 8724	62.5221 9021	98.4156 2490	0.0159 9432	78
79	1.5832 7334	0.6316 0289	63.1537 9310	99.9897 1604	0.0158 3436	79
80	1.5925 0910	0.6279 3991	63.7817 3301	101.5729 8938	0.0156 7847	80
81	1.6017 9874	0.6242 9817	64.4060 3118	103.1654 9849	0.0155 2650	81
82	1.6111 4257	0.6206 7755	65.0267 0874	104.7672 9723	0.0153 7830	82
83	1.6205 4090	0.6170 7793	65.6437 8667	106.3784 3980	0.0152 3373	83
84	1.6299 9405	0.6134 9919	66.2572 8585	107.9989 8070	0.0150 9268	84
85	1.6395 0235	0.6099 4120	66.8672 2705	109.6289 7475	0.0149 5501	85
86	1.6490 6612	0.6064 0384	67.4736 3089	111.2684 7710	0.0148 2060	86
87	1.6586 8567	0.6028 8700	68.0765 1789	112.9175 4322	0.0146 8935	87
88	1.6683 6134	0.5993 9056	68.6759 0845	114.5762 2889	0.0145 6115	88
89	1.6780 9344	0.5959 1439	69.2718 2283	116.2445 9022	0.0144 3588	89
90	1.6878 8232	0.5924 5838	69.8642 8121	117.9226 8367	0.0143 1347	90
91	1.6977 2830	0.5890 2242	70.4533 0363	119.6105 6599	0.0141 9380	91
92	1.7076 3172	0.5856 0638	71.0389 1001	121.3082 9429	0.0140 7679	92
93	1.7175 9290	0.5822 1015	71.6211 2017	123.0159 2601	0.0139 6236	93
94	1.7276 1219	0.5788 3363	72.1999 5379	124.7335 1891	0.0138 5042	94
95	1.7376 8993	0.5754 7668	72.7754 3047	126.4611 3110	0.0137 4090	95
96	1.7478 2646	0.5721 3920	73.3475 6967	128.1988 2103	0.0136 3372	96
97	1.7580 2211	0.5688 2108	73.9163 9075	129.9466 4749	0.0135 2880	97
98	1.7682 7724	0.5655 2220	74.4819 1294	131.7046 6960	0.0134 2608	98
99	1.7785 9219	0.5622 4245	75.0441 5539	133.4729 4684	0.0133 2549	99
100	1.7889 6731	0.5589 8172	75.6031 3712	135.2515 3903	0.0132 2696	100

Table VII. $\frac{2}{3}\%$

Number of periods n	Amount of 1 at compound interest $s^n = (1+i)^n$	Present value of 1 $v^n = \dfrac{1}{(1+i)^n}$	Present value of an annuity of 1 $a_{\overline{n}\rceil} = \dfrac{1-v^n}{i}$	Amount of an annuity of 1 $s_{\overline{n}\rceil} = \dfrac{(1+i)^n-1}{i}$	Annuity whose present value is 1. (CRF) $\dfrac{1}{a_{\overline{n}\rceil}} = \dfrac{1}{s_{\overline{n}\rceil}} + i$	Number of periods n
1	1.0066 6667	0.9933 7748	0.9933 7748	1.0000 0000	1.0066 6667	1
2	1.0133 7778	0.9867 9882	1.9801 7631	2.0066 6667	0.5050 0554	2
3	1.0201 3363	0.9802 6373	2.9604 4004	3.0200 4444	0.3377 8762	3
4	1.0269 3452	0.9737 7192	3.9342 1196	4.0401 7807	0.2541 8051	4
5	1.0337 8075	0.9673 2310	4.9015 3506	5.0671 1259	0.2040 1772	5
6	1.0406 7262	0.9609 1699	5.8624 5205	6.1008 9335	0.1705 7709	6
7	1.0476 1044	0.9545 5330	6.8170 0535	7.1415 6597	0.1466 9198	7
8	1.0545 9451	0.9482 3175	7.7652 3710	8.1891 7641	0.1287 7907	8
9	1.0616 2514	0.9419 5207	8.7071 8917	9.2437 7092	0.1148 4763	9
10	1.0687 0264	0.9357 1398	9.6429 0315	10.3053 9606	0.1037 0321	10
11	1.0758 2732	0.9295 1720	10.5724 2035	11.3740 9870	0.0945 8572	11
12	1.0829 9951	0.9233 6145	11.4957 8180	12.4499 2602	0.0869 8843	12
13	1.0902 1950	0.9172 4648	12.4130 2828	13.5329 2553	0.0805 6052	13
14	1.0974 8763	0.9111 7200	13.3242 0028	14.6231 4503	0.0750 5141	14
15	1.1048 0422	0.9051 3775	14.2293 3802	15.7206 3266	0.0702 7734	15
16	1.1121 6958	0.8991 4346	15.1284 8148	16.8254 3688	0.0661 0049	16
17	1.1195 8404	0.8931 8886	16.0216 7035	17.9376 0646	0.0624 1546	17
18	1.1270 4794	0.8872 7371	16.9089 4405	19.0571 9051	0.0591 4030	18
19	1.1345 6159	0.8813 9772	17.7903 4177	20.1842 3844	0.0562 1027	19
20	1.1421 2533	0.8755 6065	18.6659 0242	21.3188 0003	0.0535 7362	20
21	1.1497 3950	0.8697 6224	19.5356 6466	22.4609 2536	0.0511 8843	21
22	1.1574 0443	0.8640 0222	20.3996 6688	23.6106 6487	0.0490 2041	22
23	1.1651 2046	0.8582 8035	21.2579 4723	24.7680 6930	0.0470 4123	23
24	1.1728 8793	0.8525 9638	22.1105 4361	25.9331 8976	0.0452 2729	24
25	1.1807 0718	0.8469 5004	22.9574 9365	27.1060 7769	0.0435 5876	25
26	1.1885 7857	0.8413 4110	23.7988 3475	28.2867 8488	0.0420 1886	26
27	1.1965 0242	0.8357 6931	24.6346 0406	29.4753 6344	0.0405 9331	27
28	1.2044 7911	0.8302 3441	25.4648 3847	30.6718 6586	0.0392 6983	28
29	1.2125 0897	0.8247 3617	26.2895 7464	31.8763 4497	0.0380 3789	29
30	1.2205 9236	0.8192 7434	27.1088 4898	33.0888 5394	0.0368 8832	30
31	1.2287 2964	0.8138 4868	27.9226 9766	34.3094 4630	0.0358 1316	31
32	1.2369 2117	0.8084 5896	28.7311 5662	35.5381 7594	0.0348 0542	32
33	1.2451 6731	0.8031 0492	29.5342 6154	36.7750 9711	0.0338 5898	33
34	1.2534 6843	0.7977 8635	30.3320 4789	38.0202 6443	0.0329 6843	34
35	1.2618 2489	0.7925 0299	31.1245 5088	39.2737 3286	0.0321 2898	35
36	1.2702 3705	0.7872 5463	31.9118 0551	40.5355 5774	0.0313 3637	36
37	1.2787 0530	0.7820 4102	32.6938 4653	41.8057 9479	0.0305 8680	37
38	1.2872 3000	0.7768 6194	33.4707 0848	43.0845 0009	0.0298 7687	38
39	1.2958 1153	0.7717 1716	34.2424 2564	44.3717 3009	0.0292 0354	39
40	1.3044 5028	0.7666 0645	35.0090 3209	45.6675 4163	0.0285 6406	40
41	1.3131 4661	0.7615 2959	35.7705 6168	46.9719 9191	0.0279 5595	41
42	1.3219 0092	0.7564 8635	36.5270 4803	48.2851 3852	0.0273 7697	42
43	1.3307 1360	0.7514 7660	37.2785 2453	49.6070 3944	0.0268 2509	43
44	1.3395 8502	0.7464 9984	38.0250 2437	50.9377 5304	0.0262 9847	44
45	1.3485 1559	0.7415 5613	38.7665 8050	52.2773 3806	0.0257 9541	45
46	1.3575 0569	0.7366 4516	39.5032 2566	53.6258 5365	0.0253 1439	46
47	1.3665 5573	0.7317 6672	40.2349 9238	54.9833 5934	0.0248 5399	47
48	1.3756 6610	0.7269 2058	40.9619 1296	56.3499 1507	0.0244 1292	48
49	1.3848 3721	0.7221 0654	41.6840 1949	57.7255 8117	0.0239 9001	49
50	1.3940 6946	0.7173 2437	42.4013 4387	59.1104 1837	0.0235 8416	50

Table VII (continued). ⅔ %

Number of periods n	Amount of 1 at compound interest $s^n = (1+i)^n$	Present value of 1 $v^n = \dfrac{1}{(1+i)^n}$	Present value of an annuity of 1 $a_{\overline{n}|} = \dfrac{1-v^n}{i}$	Amount of an annuity of 1 $s_{\overline{n}|} = \dfrac{(1+i)^n-1}{i}$	Annuity whose present value is 1. (CRF) $\dfrac{1}{a_{\overline{n}|}} = \dfrac{1}{s_{\overline{n}|}} + i$	Number of periods n
51	1.4033 6325	0.7125 7388	43.1139 1775	60.5044 8783	0.0231 9437	51
52	1.4127 1901	0.7078 5485	43.8217 7260	61.9078 5108	0.0228 1971	52
53	1.4221 3713	0.7031 6707	44.5249 3967	63.3205 7009	0.0224 5932	53
54	1.4316 1805	0.6985 1033	45.2234 5000	64.7427 0722	0.0221 1242	54
55	1.4411 6217	0.6938 8444	45.9173 3444	66.1743 2527	0.0217 7827	55
56	1.4507 6992	0.6892 8918	46.6066 2362	67.6154 8744	0.0214 5618	56
57	1.4604 4172	0.6847 2435	47.2913 4796	69.0662 5736	0.0211 4552	57
58	1.4701 7799	0.6801 8975	47.9715 3771	70.5266 9907	0.0208 4569	58
59	1.4799 7918	0.6756 8518	48.6472 2289	71.9968 7706	0.0205 5616	59
60	1.4898 4571	0.6712 1044	49.3184 3334	73.4768 5625	0.0202 7639	60
61	1.4997 7801	0.6667 6534	49.9851 9868	74.9667 0195	0.0200 0592	61
62	1.5097 7653	0.6623 4968	50.6475 4835	76.4664 7997	0.0197 4429	62
63	1.5198 4171	0.6579 6326	51.3055 1161	77.9762 5650	0.0194 9108	63
64	1.5299 7399	0.6536 0588	51.9591 1749	79.4960 9821	0.0192 4590	64
65	1.5401 7381	0.6492 7737	52.6083 9486	81.0260 7220	0.0190 0837	65
66	1.5504 4164	0.6449 7752	53.2533 7238	82.5662 4601	0.0187 7815	66
67	1.5607 7792	0.6407 0614	53.8940 7852	84.1166 8765	0.0185 5491	67
68	1.5711 8310	0.6364 6306	54.5305 4158	85.6774 6557	0.0183 3835	68
69	1.5816 5766	0.6322 4807	55.1627 8965	87.2486 4867	0.0181 2816	69
70	1.5922 0204	0.6280 6100	55.7908 5064	88.8303 0633	0.0179 2409	70
71	1.6028 1672	0.6239 0165	56.4147 5229	90.4225 0837	0.0177 2586	71
72	1.6135 0217	0.6197 6985	57.0345 2215	92.0253 2510	0.0175 3324	72
73	1.6242 5885	0.6156 6541	57.6501 8756	93.6388 2726	0.0173 4600	73
74	1.6350 8724	0.6115 8816	58.2617 7572	95.2630 8611	0.0171 6391	74
75	1.6459 8782	0.6075 3791	58.8693 1363	96.8981 7335	0.0169 8678	75
76	1.6569 6107	0.6035 1448	59.4728 2811	98.5441 6118	0.0168 1440	76
77	1.6680 0748	0.5995 1769	60.0723 4581	100.2011 2225	0.0166 4659	77
78	1.6791 2753	0.5955 4738	60.6678 9319	101.8691 2973	0.0164 8318	78
79	1.6903 2172	0.5916 0336	61.2594 9654	103.5482 5726	0.0163 2400	79
80	1.7015 9053	0.5876 8545	61.8471 8200	105.2385 7898	0.0161 6889	80
81	1.7129 3446	0.5837 9350	62.4309 7549	106.9401 6950	0.0160 1769	81
82	1.7243 5403	0.5799 2732	63.0109 0281	108.6531 0397	0.0158 7027	82
83	1.7358 4972	0.5760 8674	63.5869 8954	110.3774 5799	0.0157 2649	83
84	1.7474 2205	0.5722 7159	64.1592 6114	112.1133 0771	0.0155 8621	84
85	1.7590 7153	0.5684 8171	64.7277 4285	113.8607 2977	0.0154 4933	85
86	1.7707 9868	0.5647 1693	65.2924 5979	115.6198 0130	0.0153 1570	86
87	1.7826 0400	0.5609 7709	65.8534 3687	117.3905 9997	0.0151 8524	87
88	1.7944 8803	0.5572 6201	66.4106 9888	119.1732 0397	0.0150 5781	88
89	1.8064 5128	0.5535 7153	66.9642 7041	120.9676 9200	0.0149 3334	89
90	1.8184 9429	0.5499 0549	67.5141 7590	122.7741 4328	0.0148 1170	90
91	1.8306 1758	0.5462 6374	68.0604 3964	124.5926 3757	0.0146 9282	91
92	1.8428 2170	0.5426 4610	68.6030 8574	126.4232 5515	0.0145 7660	92
93	1.8551 0718	0.5390 5241	69.1421 3815	128.2660 7685	0.0144 6296	93
94	1.8674 7456	0.5354 8253	69.6776 2068	130.1211 8403	0.0143 5181	94
95	1.8799 2439	0.5319 3629	70.2095 5696	131.9886 5859	0.0142 4308	95
96	1.8924 5722	0.5284 1353	70.7379 7049	133.8685 8298	0.0141 3668	96
97	1.9050 7360	0.5249 1410	71.2628 8460	135.7610 4020	0.0140 3255	97
98	1.9177 7409	0.5214 3785	71.7843 2245	137.6661 1380	0.0139 3062	98
99	1.9305 5925	0.5179 8462	72.3023 0707	139.5838 8790	0.0138 3082	99
100	1.9434 2965	0.5145 5426	72.8168 6132	141.5144 4715	0.0137 3308	100

539

Table VIII. ¾ %

Number of periods	Amount of 1 at compound interest	Present value of 1	Present value of an annuity of 1	Amount of an annuity of 1	Annuity whose present value is 1. (CRF)	Number of periods
n	$s^n = (1+i)^n$	$v^n = \dfrac{1}{(1+i)^n}$	$a_{\overline{n}\rceil} = \dfrac{1-v^n}{i}$	$s_{\overline{n}\rceil} = \dfrac{(1+i)^n-1}{i}$	$\dfrac{1}{a_{\overline{n}\rceil}} = \dfrac{1}{s_{\overline{n}\rceil}} + i$	n
1	1.0075 0000	0.9925 5583	0.9925 5583	1.0000 0000	1.0075 0000	1
2	1.0150 5625	0.9851 6708	1.9777 2291	2.0075 0000	0.5056 3200	2
3	1.0226 6917	0.9778 3333	2.9555 5624	3.0225 5625	0.3383 4579	3
4	1.0303 3919	0.9705 5417	3.9261 1041	4.0452 2542	0.2547 0501	4
5	1.0380 6673	0.9633 2920	4.8894 3961	5.0755 6461	0.2045 2242	5
6	1.0458 5224	0.9561 5802	5.8455 9763	6.1136 3135	0.1710 6891	6
7	1.0536 9613	0.9490 4022	6.7946 3785	7.1594 8358	0.1471 7488	7
8	1.0615 9885	0.9419 7540	7.7366 1325	8.2131 7971	0.1292 5552	8
9	1.0695 6084	0.9349 6318	8.6715 7642	9.2747 7856	0.1153 1929	9
10	1.0775 8255	0.9280 0315	9.5995 7958	10.3443 3940	0.1041 7123	10
11	1.0856 6441	0.9210 9494	10.5206 7452	11.4219 2194	0.0950 5094	11
12	1.0938 0690	0.9142 3815	11.4349 1267	12.5075 8636	0.0874 5148	12
13	1.1020 1045	0.9074 3241	12.3423 4508	13.6013 9325	0.0810 2188	13
14	1.1102 7553	0.9006 7733	13.2430 2242	14.7034 0370	0.0755 1146	14
15	1.1186 0259	0.8939 7254	14.1369 9495	15.8136 7923	0.0707 3639	15
16	1.1269 9211	0.8873 1766	15.0243 1261	16.9322 8183	0.0665 5879	16
17	1.1354 4455	0.8807 1231	15.9050 2492	18.0592 7394	0.0628 7321	17
18	1.1439 6039	0.8741 5614	16.7791 8107	19.1947 1849	0.0595 9766	18
19	1.1525 4009	0.8676 4878	17.6468 2984	20.3386 7888	0.0566 6740	19
20	1.1611 8414	0.8611 8985	18.5080 1969	21.4912 1897	0.0540 3063	20
21	1.1698 9302	0.8547 7901	19.3627 9870	22.6524 0312	0.0516 4543	21
22	1.1786 6722	0.8484 1589	20.2112 1459	23.8222 9614	0.0494 7748	22
23	1.1875 0723	0.8421 0014	21.0533 1473	25.0009 6336	0.0474 9846	23
24	1.1964 1353	0.8358 3140	21.8891 4614	26.1884 7059	0.0456 8474	24
25	1.2053 8663	0.8296 0933	22.7187 5547	27.3848 8412	0.0440 1650	25
26	1.2144 2703	0.8234 3358	23.5421 8905	28.5902 7075	0.0424 7693	26
27	1.2235 3523	0.8173 0380	24.3594 9286	29.8046 9778	0.0410 5176	27
28	1.2327 1175	0.8112 1966	25.1707 1251	31.0282 3301	0.0397 2871	28
29	1.2419 5709	0.8051 8080	25.9758 9331	32.2609 4476	0.0384 9723	29
30	1.2512 7176	0.7991 8690	26.7750 8021	33.5029 0184	0.0373 4816	30
31	1.2606 5630	0.7932 3762	27.5683 1783	34.7541 7361	0.0362 7352	31
32	1.2701 1122	0.7873 3262	28.3556 5045	36.0148 2991	0.0352 6634	32
33	1.2796 3706	0.7814 7158	29.1371 2203	37.2849 4113	0.0343 2048	33
34	1.2892 3434	0.7756 5418	29.9127 7621	38.5645 7819	0.0334 3053	34
35	1.2989 0359	0.7698 8008	30.6826 5629	39.8538 1253	0.0325 9170	35
36	1.3086 4537	0.7641 4896	31.4468 0525	41.1527 1612	0.0317 9973	36
37	1.3184 6021	0.7584 6051	32.2052 6576	42.4613 6149	0.0310 5082	37
38	1.3283 4866	0.7528 1440	32.9580 8016	43.7798 2170	0.0303 4157	38
39	1.3383 1128	0.7472 1032	33.7052 9048	45.1081 7037	0.0296 6893	39
40	1.3483 4861	0.7416 4796	34.4469 3844	46.4464 8164	0.0290 3016	40
41	1.3584 6123	0.7361 2701	35.1830 6545	47.7948 3026	0.0284 2276	41
42	1.3686 4969	0.7306 4716	35.9137 1260	49.1532 9148	0.0278 4452	42
43	1.3789 1456	0.7252 0809	36.6389 2070	50.5219 4117	0.0272 9338	43
44	1.3892 5642	0.7198 0952	37.3587 3022	51.9008 5573	0.0267 6751	44
45	1.3996 7584	0.7144 5114	38.0731 8136	53.2901 1215	0.0262 6521	45
46	1.4101 7341	0.7091 3264	38.7823 1401	54.6897 8799	0.0257 8495	46
47	1.4207 4971	0.7038 5374	39.4861 6774	56.0999 6140	0.0253 2532	47
48	1.4314 0533	0.6986 1414	40.1847 8189	57.5207 1111	0.0248 8504	48
49	1.4421 4087	0.6934 1353	40.8781 9542	58.9521 1644	0.0244 6292	49
50	1.4529 5693	0.6882 5165	41.5664 4707	60.3942 5732	0.0240 5787	50

Table VIII (*continued*). $\frac{3}{4}\%$

Number of periods n	Amount of 1 at compound interest $s^n = (1+i)^n$	Present value of 1 $v^n = \dfrac{1}{(1+i)^n}$	Present value of an annuity of 1 $a_{\overline{n}|} = \dfrac{1-v^n}{i}$	Amount of an annuity of 1 $s_{\overline{n}|} = \dfrac{(1+i)^n-1}{i}$	Annuity whose present value is 1. (CRF) $\dfrac{1}{a_{\overline{n}|}} = \dfrac{1}{s_{\overline{n}|}} + i$	Number of periods n
51	1.4638 5411	0.6831 2819	42.2495 7525	61.8472 1424	0.0236 6888	51
52	1.4748 3301	0.6780 4286	42.9276 1812	63.3110 6835	0.0232 9503	52
53	1.4858 9426	0.6729 9540	43.6006 1351	64.7859 0136	0.0229 3546	53
54	1.4970 3847	0.6679 8551	44.2685 9902	66.2717 9562	0.0225 8938	54
55	1.5082 6626	0.6630 1291	44.9316 1193	67.7688 3409	0.0222 5605	55
56	1.5195 7825	0.6580 7733	45.5896 8926	69.2771 0035	0.0219 3478	56
57	1.5309 7509	0.6531 7849	46.2428 6776	70.7966 7860	0.0216 2496	57
58	1.5424 5740	0.6483 1612	46.8911 8388	72.3276 5369	0.0213 2597	58
59	1.5540 2583	0.6434 8995	47.5346 7382	73.8701 1109	0.0210 3727	59
60	1.5656 8103	0.6386 9970	48.1733 7352	75.4241 3693	0.0207 5836	60
61	1.5774 2363	0.6339 4511	48.8073 1863	76.9898 1795	0.0204 8873	61
62	1.5892 5431	0.6292 2592	49.4365 4455	78.5672 4159	0.0202 2795	62
63	1.6011 7372	0.6245 4185	50.0610 8640	80.1564 9590	0.0199 7560	63
64	1.6131 8252	0.6198 9266	50.6809 7906	81.7576 6962	0.0197 3127	64
65	1.6252 8139	0.6152 7807	51.2962 5713	83.3708 5214	0.0194 9460	65
66	1.6374 7100	0.6106 9784	51.9069 5497	84.9961 3353	0.0192 6524	66
67	1.6497 5203	0.6061 5170	52.5131 0667	86.6336 0453	0.0190 4286	67
68	1.6621 2517	0.6016 3940	53.1147 4607	88.2833 5657	0.0188 2716	68
69	1.6745 9111	0.5971 6070	53.7119 0677	89.9454 8174	0.0186 1785	69
70	1.6871 5055	0.5927 1533	54.3046 2210	91.6200 7285	0.0184 1464	70
71	1.6998 0418	0.5883 0306	54.8929 2516	93.3072 2340	0.0182 1728	71
72	1.7125 5271	0.5839 2363	55.4768 4880	95.0070 2758	0.0180 2554	72
73	1.7253 9685	0.5795 7681	56.0564 2561	96.7195 8028	0.0178 3917	73
74	1.7383 3733	0.5752 6234	56.6316 8795	98.4449 7714	0.0176 5796	74
75	1.7513 7486	0.5709 7999	57.2026 6794	100.1833 1446	0.0174 8170	75
76	1.7645 1017	0.5667 2952	57.7693 9746	101.9346 8932	0.0173 1020	76
77	1.7777 4400	0.5625 1069	58.3319 0815	103.6991 9949	0.0171 4328	77
78	1.7910 7708	0.5583 2326	58.8902 3141	105.4769 4349	0.0169 8074	78
79	1.8045 1015	0.5541 6701	59.4443 9842	107.2680 2056	0.0168 2244	79
80	1.8180 4398	0.5500 4170	59.9944 4012	109.0725 3072	0.0166 6821	80
81	1.8316 7931	0.5459 4710	60.5403 8722	110.8905 7470	0.0165 1790	81
82	1.8454 1691	0.5418 8297	61.0822 7019	112.7222 5401	0.0163 7136	82
83	1.8592 5753	0.5378 4911	61.6201 1930	114.5676 7091	0.0162 2847	83
84	1.8732 0196	0.5338 4527	62.1539 6456	116.4269 2845	0.0160 8908	84
85	1.8872 5098	0.5298 7123	62.6838 3579	118.3001 3041	0.0159 5308	85
86	1.9014 0536	0.5259 2678	63.2097 6257	120.1873 8139	0.0158 2034	86
87	1.9156 6590	0.5220 1169	63.7317 7427	122.0887 8675	0.0156 9076	87
88	1.9300 3339	0.5181 2575	64.2499 0002	124.0044 5265	0.0155 6423	88
89	1.9445 0865	0.5142 6873	64.7641 6875	125.9344 8604	0.0154 4064	89
90	1.9590 9246	0.5104 4043	65.2746 0918	127.8789 9469	v.0153 1989	90
91	1.9737 8565	0.5066 4063	65.7812 4981	129.8380 8715	0.0152 0190	91
92	1.9885 8905	0.5028 6911	66.2841 1892	131.8118 7280	0.0150 8657	92
93	2.0035 0346	0.4991 2567	66.7832 4458	133.8004 6185	0.0149 7382	93
94	2.0185 2974	0.4954 1009	67.2786 5467	135.8039 6531	0.0148 6356	94
95	2.0336 6871	0.4917 2217	67.7703 7685	137.8224 9505	0.0147 5571	95
96	2.0489 2123	0.4880 6171	68.2584 3856	139.8561 6377	0.0146 5020	96
97	2.0642 8814	0.4844 2850	68.7428 6705	141.9050 8499	0.0145 4696	97
98	2.0797 7030	0.4808 2233	69.2236 8938	143.9693 7313	0.0144 4592	98
99	2.0953 6858	0.4772 4301	69.7009 3239	146.0491 4343	0.0143 4701	99
100	2.1110 8384	0.4736 9033	70.1746 2272	148.1445 1201	0.0142 5017	100

Table IX. 1%

Number of periods n	Amount of 1 at compound interest $s^n = (1+i)^n$	*pwf'* Present value of 1 $v^n = \dfrac{1}{(1+i)^n}$	Present value of an annuity of 1 $a_{\overline{n}|} = \dfrac{1-v^n}{i}$	Amount of an annuity of 1 $s_{\overline{n}|} = \dfrac{(1+i)^n - 1}{i}$	Annuity whose present value is 1. (CRF) $\dfrac{1}{a_{\overline{n}|}} = \dfrac{1}{s_{\overline{n}|}} + i$	Number of periods n
1	1.0100 0000	0.9900 9901	0.9900 9901	1.0000 0000	1.0100 0000	1
2	1.0201 0000	0.9802 9605	1.9703 9506	2.0100 0000	0.5075 1244	2
3	1.0303 0100	0.9705 9015	2.9409 8521	3.0301 0000	0.3400 2211	3
4	1.0406 0401	0.9609 8034	3.9019 6555	4.0604 0100	0.2562 8109	4
5	1.0510 1005	0.9514 6569	4.8534 3124	5.1010 0501	0.2060 3980	5
6	1.0615 2015	0.9420 4524	5.7954 7647	6.1520 1506	0.1725 4837	6
7	1.0721 3535	0.9327 1805	6.7281 9453	7.2135 3521	0.1486 2828	7
8	1.0828 5671	0.9234 8322	7.6516 7775	8.2856 7056	0.1306 9029	8
9	1.0936 8527	0.9143 3982	8.5660 1758	9.3685 2727	0.1167 4037	9
10	1.1046 2213	0.9052 8695	9.4713 0453	10.4622 1254	0.1055 8208	10
11	1.1156 6835	0.8963 2372	10.3676 2825	11.5668 3467	0.0964 5408	11
12	1.1268 2503	0.8874 4923	11.2550 7747	12.6825 0301	0.0888 4879	12
13	1.1380 9328	0.8786 6260	12.1337 4007	13.8093 2804	0.0824 1482	13
14	1.1494 7421	0.8699 6297	13.0037 0304	14.9474 2132	0.0769 0117	14
15	1.1609 6896	0.8613 4947	13.8650 5252	16.0968 9554	0.0721 2378	15
16	1.1725 7864	0.8528 2126	14.7178 7378	17.2578 6449	0.0679 4460	16
17	1.1843 0443	0.8443 7749	15.5622 5127	18.4304 4314	0.0642 5806	17
18	1.1961 4748	0.8360 1731	16.3982 6858	19.6147 4757	0.0609 8205	18
19	1.2081 0895	0.8277 3992	17.2260 0850	20.8108 9504	0.0580 5175	19
20	1.2201 9004	0.8195 4447	18.0455 5297	22.0190 0399	0.0554 1532	20
21	1.2323 9194	0.8114 3017	18.8569 8313	23.2391 9403	0.0530 3075	21
22	1.2447 1586	0.8033 9621	19.6603 7934	24.4715 8598	0.0508 6371	22
23	1.2571 6302	0.7954 4179	20.4558 2113	25.7163 0183	0.0488 8584	23
24	1.2697 3465	0.7875 6613	21.2433 8726	26.9734 6485	0.0470 7347	24
25	1.2824 3200	0.7797 6844	22.0231 5570	28.2431 9950	0.0454 0675	25
26	1.2952 5631	0.7720 4796	22.7952 0366	29.5256 3150	0.0438 6888	26
27	1.3082 0888	0.7644 0392	23.5596 0759	30.8208 8781	0.0424 4553	27
28	1.3212 9097	0.7568 3557	24.3164 4316	32.1290 9669	0.0411 2444	28
29	1.3345 0388	0.7493 4215	25.0657 8530	33.4503 8766	0.0398 9502	29
30	1.3478 4892	0.7419 2292	25.8077 0822	34.7848 9153	0.0387 4811	30
31	1.3613 2740	0.7345 7715	26.5422 8537	36.1327 4045	0.0376 7573	31
32	1.3749 4068	0.7273 0411	27.2695 8947	37.4940 6785	0.0366 7089	32
33	1.3886 9009	0.7201 0307	27.9896 9255	38.8690 0853	0.0357 2744	33
34	1.4025 7699	0.7129 7334	28.7026 6589	40.2576 9862	0.0348 3997	34
35	1.4166 0276	0.7059 1420	29.4085 8009	41.6602 7560	0.0340 0368	35
36	1.4307 6878	0.6989 2495	30.1075 0504	43.0768 7836	0.0332 1431	36
37	1.4450 7647	0.6920 0490	30.7995 0994	44.5076 4714	0.0324 6805	37
38	1.4595 2724	0.6851 5337	31.4846 6330	45.9527 2361	0.0317 6150	38
39	1.4741 2251	0.6783 6967	32.1630 3298	47.4122 5085	0.0310 9160	39
40	1.4888 6373	0.6716 5314	32.8346 8611	48.8863 7336	0.0304 5560	40
41	1.5037 5237	0.6650 0311	33.4996 8922	50.3752 3709	0.0298 5102	41
42	1.5187 8989	0.6584 1892	34.1581 0814	51.8789 8946	0.0292 7563	42
43	1.5339 7779	0.6518 9992	34.8100 0806	53.3977 7936	0.0287 2737	43
44	1.5493 1757	0.6454 4546	35.4554 5352	54.9317 5715	0.0282 0441	44
45	1.5648 1075	0.6390 5492	36.0945 0844	56.4810 7472	0.0277 0505	45
46	1.5804 5885	0.6327 2764	36.7272 3608	58.0458 8547	0.0272 2775	46
47	1.5962 6344	0.6264 6301	37.3536 9909	59.6263 4432	0.0267 7111	47
48	1.6122 2608	0.6202 6041	37.9739 5949	61.2226 0777	0.0263 3384	48
49	1.6283 4834	0.6141 1921	38.5880 7871	62.8348 3385	0.0259 1474	49
50	1.6446 3182	0.6080 3882	39.1961 1753	64.4631 8218	0.0255 1273	50

Table IX (*continued*). 1%

Number of periods n	Amount of 1 at compound interest $s^n = (1+i)^n$	Present value of 1 $v^n = \dfrac{1}{(1+i)^n}$	Present value of an annuity of 1 $a_{\overline{n}|} = \dfrac{1-v^n}{i}$	Amount of an annuity of 1 $s_{\overline{n}|} = \dfrac{(1+i)^n-1}{i}$	Annuity whose present value is 1. (CRF) $\dfrac{1}{a_{\overline{n}|}} = \dfrac{1}{s_{\overline{n}|}} + i$	Number of periods n
51	1.6610 7814	0.6020 1864	39.7981 3617	66.1078 1401	0.0251 2680	51
52	1.6776 8892	0.5960 5806	40.3941 9423	67.7688 9215	0.0247 5603	52
53	1.6944 6581	0.5901 5649	40.9843 5072	69.4465 8107	0.0243 9956	53
54	1.7114 1047	0.5843 1336	41.5686 6408	71.1410 4688	0.0240 5658	54
55	1.7285 2457	0.5785 2808	42.1471 9216	72.8524 5735	0.0237 2637	55
56	1.7458 0982	0.5728 0008	42.7199 9224	74.5809 8192	0.0234 0823	56
57	1.7632 6792	0.5671 2879	43.2871 2102	76.3267 9174	0.0231 0156	57
58	1.7809 0060	0.5615 1365	43.8486 3468	78.0900 5966	0.0228 0573	58
59	1.7987 0960	0.5559 5411	44.4045 8879	79.8709 6025	0.0225 2020	59
60	1.8166 9670	0.5504 4962	44.9550 3841	81.6696 6986	0.0222 4445	60
61	1.8348 6367	0.5449 9962	45.5000 3803	83.4863 6655	0.0219 7800	61
62	1.8532 1230	0.5396 0358	46.0396 4161	85.3212 3022	0.0217 2041	62
63	1.8717 4443	0.5342 6097	46.5739 0258	87.1744 4252	0.0214 7125	63
64	1.8904 6187	0.5289 7126	47.1028 7385	89.0461 8695	0.0212 3013	64
65	1.9093 6649	0.5237 3392	47.6266 0777	90.9366 4882	0.0209 9667	65
66	1.9284 6015	0.5185 4844	48.1451 5621	92.8460 1531	0.0207 7052	66
67	1.9477 4475	0.5134 1429	48.6585 7050	94.7744 7546	0.0205 5136	67
68	1.9672 2220	0.5083 3099	49.1669 0149	96.7222 2021	0.0203 3888	68
69	1.9868 9442	0.5032 9801	49.6701 9949	98.6894 4242	0.0201 3280	69
70	2.0067 6337	0.4983 1486	50.1685 1435	100.6763 3684	0.0199 3282	70
71	2.0268 3100	0.4933 8105	50.6618 9539	102.6831 0021	0.0197 3870	71
72	2.0470 9931	0.4884 9609	51.1503 9148	104.7099 3121	0.0195 5019	72
73	2.0675 7031	0.4836 5949	51.6340 5097	106.7570 3052	0.0193 6706	73
74	2.0882 4601	0.4788 7078	52.1129 2175	108.8246 0083	0.0191 8910	74
75	2.1091 2847	0.4741 2949	52.5870 5124	110.9128 4684	0.0190 1609	75
76	2.1302 1975	0.4694 3514	53.0564 8637	113.0219 7530	0.0188 4784	76
77	2.1515 2195	0.4647 8726	53.5212 7364	115.1521 9506	0.0186 8416	77
78	2.1730 3717	0.4601 8541	53.9814 5905	117.3037 1701	0.0185 2488	78
79	2.1947 6754	0.4556 2912	54.4370 8817	119.4767 5418	0.0183 6984	79
80	2.2167 1522	0.4511 1794	54.8882 0611	121.6715 2172	0.0182 1885	80
81	2.2388 8237	0.4466 5142	55.3348 5753	123.8882 3694	0.0180 7180	81
82	2.2612 7119	0.4422 2913	55.7770 8666	126.1271 1931	0.0179 2851	82
83	2.2838 8390	0.4378 5063	56.2149 3729	128.3883 9050	0.0177 8886	83
84	2.3067 2274	0.4335 1547	56.6484 5276	130.6722 7440	0.0176 5273	84
85	2.3297 8997	0.4292 2324	57.0776 7600	132.9789 9715	0.0175 1998	85
86	2.3530 8787	0.4249 7350	57.5026 4951	135.3087 8712	0.0173 9050	86
87	2.3766 1875	0.4207 6585	57.9234 1535	137.6618 7499	0.0172 6417	87
88	2.4003 8494	0.4165 9985	58.3400 1520	140.0384 9374	0.0171 4089	88
89	2.4243 8879	0.4124 7510	58.7524 9030	142.4388 7868	0.0170 2056	89
90	2.4486 3267	0.4083 9119	59.1608 8148	144.8632 6746	0.0169 0306	90
91	2.4731 1900	0.4043 4771	59.5652 2919	147.3119 0014	0.0167 8832	91
92	2.4978 5019	0.4003 4427	59.9655 7346	149.7850 1914	0.0166 7624	92
93	2.5228 2869	0.3963 8046	60.3619 5392	152.2828 6933	0.0165 6673	93
94	2.5480 5698	0.3924 5590	60.7544 0982	154.8056 9803	0.0164 5971	94
95	2.5735 3755	0.3885 7020	61.1429 8002	157.3537 5501	0.0163 5511	95
96	2.5992 7293	0.3847 2297	61.5277 0299	159.9272 9256	0.0162 5284	96
97	2.6252 6565	0.3809 1383	61.9086 1682	162.5265 6548	0.0161 5284	97
98	2.6515 1831	0.3771 4241	62.2857 5923	165.1518 3114	0.0160 5503	98
99	2.6780 3349	0.3734 0832	62.6591 6755	167.8033 4945	0.0159 5936	99
100	2.7048 1383	0.3697 1121	63.0288 7877	170.4813 8294	0.0158 6574	100

Table X. $1\frac{1}{4}$ %

Number of periods n	Amount of 1 at compound interest $s^n = (1+i)^n$	Present value of 1 $v^n = \dfrac{1}{(1+i)^n}$	Present value of an annuity of 1 $a_{\overline{n}\rceil} = \dfrac{1-v^n}{i}$	Amount of an annuity of 1 $s_{\overline{n}\rceil} = \dfrac{(1+i)^n-1}{i}$	Annuity whose present value is 1. (CRF) $\dfrac{1}{a_{\overline{n}\rceil}} = \dfrac{1}{s_{\overline{n}\rceil}} + i$	Number of periods n
1	1.0125 0000	0.9876 5432	0.9876 5432	1.0000 0000	1.0125 0000	1
2	1.0251 5625	0.9754 6106	1.9631 1538	2.0125 0000	0.5093 9441	2
3	1.0379 7070	0.9634 1833	2.9265 3371	3.0376 5625	0.3417 0117	3
4	1.0509 4534	0.9515 2428	3.8780 5798	4.0756 2695	0.2578 6102	4
5	1.0640 8215	0.9397 7706	4.8178 3504	5.1265 7229	0.2075 6211	5
6	1.0773 8318	0.9281 7488	5.7460 0992	6.1906 5444	0.1740 3381	6
7	1.0908 5047	0.9167 1593	6.6627 2585	7.2680 3762	0.1500 8872	7
8	1.1044 8610	0.9053 9845	7.5681 2429	8.3588 8809	0.1321 3314	8
9	1.1182 9218	0.8942 2069	8.4623 4498	9.4633 7420	0.1181 7055	9
10	1.1322 7083	0.8831 8093	9.3455 2591	10.5816 6637	0.1070 0307	10
11	1.1464 2422	0.8722 7746	10.2178 0337	11.7139 3720	0.0978 6839	11
12	1.1607 5452	0.8615 0860	11.0793 1197	12.8603 6142	0.0902 5831	12
13	1.1752 6395	0.8508 7269	11.9301 8466	14.0211 1594	0.0838 2100	13
14	1.1899 5475	0.8403 6809	12.7705 5275	15.1963 7988	0.0783 0515	14
15	1.2048 2918	0.8299 9318	13.6005 4592	16.3863 3463	0.0735 2646	15
16	1.2198 8955	0.8197 4635	14.4202 9227	17.5911 6382	0.0693 4672	16
17	1.2351 3817	0.8096 2602	15.2299 1829	18.8110 5336	0.0656 6023	17
18	1.2505 7739	0.7996 3064	16.0295 4893	20.0461 9153	0.0623 8479	18
19	1.2662 0961	0.7897 5866	16.8193 0759	21.2967 6893	0.0594 5548	19
20	1.2820 3723	0.7800 0855	17.5993 1613	22.5629 7854	0.0568 2039	20
21	1.2980 6270	0.7703 7881	18.3696 9495	23.8450 1577	0.0544 3748	21
22	1.3142 8848	0.7608 6796	19.1305 6291	25.1430 7847	0.0522 7238	22
23	1.3307 1709	0.7514 7453	19.8820 3744	26.4573 6695	0.0502 9666	23
24	1.3473 5105	0.7421 9707	20.6242 3451	27.7880 8403	0.0484 8665	24
25	1.3641 9294	0.7330 3414	21.3572 6865	29.1354 3508	0.0468 2247	25
26	1.3812 4535	0.7239 8434	22.0812 5299	30.4996 2802	0.0452 8729	26
27	1.3985 1092	0.7150 4626	22.7962 9925	31.8808 7337	0.0438 6677	27
28	1.4159 9230	0.7062 1853	23.5025 1778	33.2793 8429	0.0425 4863	28
29	1.4336 9221	0.6974 9978	24.2000 1756	34.6953 7659	0.0413 2228	29
30	1.4516 1336	0.6888 8867	24.8889 0623	36.1290 6880	0.0401 7854	30
31	1.4697 5853	0.6803 8387	25.5692 9010	37.5806 8216	0.0391 0942	31
32	1.4881 3051	0.6719 8407	26.2412 7418	39.0504 4069	0.0381 0791	32
33	1.5067 3214	0.6636 8797	26.9049 6215	40.5385 7120	0.0371 6786	33
34	1.5255 6629	0.6554 9429	27.5604 5644	42.0453 0334	0.0362 8387	34
35	1.5446 3587	0.6474 0177	28.2078 5822	43.5708 6963	0.0354 5111	35
36	1.5639 4382	0.6394 0916	28.8472 6737	45.1155 0550	0.0346 6533	36
37	1.5834 9312	0.6315 1522	29.4787 8259	46.6794 4932	0.0339 2270	37
38	1.6032 8678	0.6237 1873	30.1025 0133	48.2926 4243	0.0332 1983	38
39	1.6233 2787	0.6160 1850	30.7185 1983	49.8862 2921	0.0325 5365	39
40	1.6436 1946	0.6084 1334	31.3269 3316	51.4895 5708	0.0319 2141	40
41	1.6641 6471	0.6009 0206	31.9278 3522	53.1331 7654	0.0313 2063	41
42	1.6849 6677	0.5934 8352	32.5213 1874	54.7973 4125	0.0307 4906	42
43	1.7060 2885	0.5861 5656	33.1074 7530	56.4823 0801	0.0302 0466	43
44	1.7273 5421	0.5789 2006	33.6863 9536	58.1883 3687	0.0296 8557	44
45	1.7489 4614	0.5717 7290	34.2581 6825	59.9156 9108	0.0291 9012	45
46	1.7708 0797	0.5647 1397	34.8228 8222	61.6646 3721	0.0287 1675	46
47	1.7929 4306	0.5577 4219	35.3806 2442	63.4354 4518	0.0282 6406	47
48	1.8153 5485	0.5508 5649	35.9314 8091	65.2283 8824	0.0278 3075	48
49	1.8380 4679	0.5440 5579	36.4755 3670	67.0437 4310	0.0274 1563	49
50	1.8610 2237	0.5373 3905	37.0128 7574	68.8817 8989	0.0270 1763	50

Table X (*continued*). 1¼ %

Number of periods n	Amount of 1 at compound interest $s^n = (1+i)^n$	Present value of 1 $v^n = \dfrac{1}{(1+i)^n}$	Present value of an annuity of 1 $a_{\overline{n}|} = \dfrac{1-v^n}{i}$	Amount of an annuity of 1 $s_{\overline{n}|} = \dfrac{(1+i)^n-1}{i}$	Annuity whose present value is 1. (CRF) $\dfrac{1}{a_{\overline{n}|}} = \dfrac{1}{s_{\overline{n}|}} + i$	Number of periods n
51	1.8842 8515	0.5307 0524	37.5435 8099	70.7428 1226	0.0266 3571	51
52	1.9078 3872	0.5241 5332	38.0677 3431	72.6270 9741	0.0262 6897	52
53	1.9316 8670	0.5176 8229	38.5854 1660	74.5349 3613	0.0259 1653	53
54	1.9558 3279	0.5112 9115	39.0967 0776	76.4666 2283	0.0255 7760	54
55	1.9802 8070	0.5049 7892	39.6016 8667	78.4224 5562	0.0252 5145	55
56	2.0050 3420	0.4987 4461	40.1004 3128	80.4027 3631	0.0249 3739	56
57	2.0300 9713	0.4925 8727	40.5930 1855	82.4077 7052	0.0246 3478	57
58	2.0554 7335	0.4865 0594	41.0795 2449	84.4378 6765	0.0243 4303	58
59	2.0811 6676	0.4804 9970	41.5600 2419	86.4933 4099	0.0240 6158	59
60	2.1071 8135	0.4745 6760	42.0345 9179	88.5745 0776	0.0237 8993	60
61	2.1335 2111	0.4687 0874	42.5033 0054	90.6816 8910	0.0235 2758	61
62	2.1601 9013	0.4629 2222	42.9662 2275	92.8152 1022	0.0232 7410	62
63	2.1871 9250	0.4572 0713	43.4234 2988	94.9754 0034	0.0230 2904	63
64	2.2145 3241	0.4515 6259	43.8749 9247	97.1625 9285	0.0227 9203	64
65	2.2422 1407	0.4459 8775	44.3209 8022	99.3771 2526	0.0225 6268	65
66	2.2702 4174	0.4404 8173	44.7614 6195	101.6193 3933	0.0223 4065	66
67	2.2986 1976	0.4350 4368	45.1965 0563	103.8895 8107	0.0221 2560	67
68	2.3273 5251	0.4296 7277	45.6261 7840	106.1882 0083	0.0219 1724	68
69	2.3564 4442	0.4243 6817	46.0505 4656	108.5155 5334	0.0217 1527	69
70	2.3858 9997	0.4191 2905	46.4696 7562	110.8719 9776	0.0215 1941	70
71	2.4157 2372	0.4139 5462	46.8836 3024	113.2578 9773	0.0213 2941	71
72	2.4459 2027	0.4088 4407	47.2924 7431	115.6736 2145	0.0211 4501	72
73	2.4764 9427	0.4037 9661	47.6962 7093	118.1195 4172	0.0209 6600	73
74	2.5074 5045	0.3988 1147	48.0950 8240	120.5960 3599	0.0207 9215	74
75	2.5387 9358	0.3938 8787	48.4889 7027	123.1034 8644	0.0206 2325	75
76	2.5705 2850	0.3890 2506	48.8779 9533	125.6422 8002	0.0204 5910	76
77	2.6026 6011	0.3842 2228	49.2622 1761	128.2128 0852	0.0202 9953	77
78	2.6351 9336	0.3794 7879	49.6416 9640	130.8154 6863	0.0201 4435	78
79	2.6681 3327	0.3747 9387	50.0164 9027	133.4506 6199	0.0199 9341	79
80	2.7014 8494	0.3701 6679	50.3866 5706	136.1187 9526	0.0198 4652	80
81	2.7352 5350	0.3655 9683	50.7522 5389	138.8202 8020	0.0197 0356	81
82	2.7694 4417	0.3610 8329	51.1133 3717	141.5555 3370	0.0195 6437	82
83	2.8040 6222	0.3566 2547	51.4699 6264	144.3249 7787	0.0194 2881	83
84	2.8391 1300	0.3522 2268	51.8221 8532	147.1290 4010	0.0192 9675	84
85	2.8746 0191	0.3478 7426	52.1700 5958	149.9681 5310	0.0191 6808	85
86	2.9105 3444	0.3435 7951	52.5136 3909	152.8427 5501	0.0190 4267	86
87	2.9469 1612	0.3393 3779	52.8529 7688	155.7532 8945	0.0189 2041	87
88	2.9837 5257	0.3351 4843	53.1881 2531	158.7002 0557	0.0188 0119	88
89	3.0210 4948	0.3310 1080	53.5191 3611	161.6839 5814	0.0186 8490	89
90	3.0588 1260	0.3269 2425	53.8460 6035	164.7050 0762	0.0185 7146	90
91	3.0970 4775	0.3228 8814	54.1689 4850	167.7638 2021	0.0184 6076	91
92	3.1357 6085	0.3189 0187	54.4878 5037	170.8608 6796	0.0183 5271	92
93	3.1749 5786	0.3149 6481	54.8028 1518	173.9966 2881	0.0182 4724	93
94	3.2146 4483	0.3110 7636	55.1138 9154	177.1715 8667	0.0181 4425	94
95	3.2548 2789	0.3072 3591	55.4211 2744	180.3862 3151	0.0180 4366	95
96	3.2955 1324	0.3034 4287	55.7245 7031	183.6410 5940	0.0179 4540	96
97	3.3367 0716	0.2996 9666	56.0242 6698	186.9365 7264	0.0178 4941	97
98	3.3784 1600	0.2959 9670	56.3202 6368	190.2732 7980	0.0177 5560	98
99	3.4206 4620	0.2923 4242	56.6126 0610	193.6516 9580	0.0176 6391	99
100	3.4634 0427	0.2887 3326	56.9013 3936	197.0723 4200	0.0175 7428	100

Table XI. 1½%

Number of periods n	Amount of 1 at compound interest $s^n = (1 + i)^n$	Present value of 1 $v^n = \dfrac{1}{(1 + i)^n}$	Present value of an annuity of 1 $a_{\overline{n}\rceil} = \dfrac{1 - v^n}{i}$	Amount of an annuity of 1 $s_{\overline{n}\rceil} = \dfrac{(1+i)^n - 1}{i}$	Annuity whose present value is 1. (CRF) $\dfrac{1}{a_{\overline{n}\rceil}} = \dfrac{1}{s_{\overline{n}\rceil}} + i$	Number of periods n
1	1.0150 0000	0.9852 2167	0.9852 2167	1.0000 0000	1.0150 0000	1
2	1.0302 2500	0.9706 6175	1.9558 8342	2.0150 0000	0.5112 7792	2
3	1.0456 7838	0.9563 1699	2.9122 0042	3.0452 2500	0.3433 8296	3
4	1.0613 6355	0.9421 8423	3.8543 8465	4.0909 0338	0.2594 4478	4
5	1.0772 8400	0.9282 6033	4.7826 4497	5.1522 6693	0.2090 8932	5
6	1.0934 4326	0.9145 4219	5.6971 8717	6.2295 5093	0.1755 2521	6
7	1.1098 4491	0.9010 2679	6.5982 1396	7.3229 9419	0.1515 5616	7
8	1.1264 9259	0.8877 1112	7.4859 2508	8.4328 3911	0.1335 8402	8
9	1.1433 8998	0.8745 9224	8.3605 1732	9.5593 3169	0.1196 0982	9
10	1.1605 4083	0.8616 6723	9.2221 8455	10.7027 2167	0.1084 3418	10
11	1.1779 4894	0.8489 3323	10.0711 1779	11.8632 6249	0.0992 9384	11
12	1.1956 1817	0.8363 8742	10.9075 0521	13.0412 1143	0.0916 7999	12
13	1.2135 5244	0.8240 2702	11.7315 3222	14.2368 2960	0.0852 4036	13
14	1.2317 5573	0.8118 4928	12.5433 8150	15.4503 8205	0.0797 2332	14
15	1.2502 3207	0.7998 5150	13.3432 3301	16.6821 3778	0.0749 4436	15
16	1.2689 8555	0.7880 3104	14.1312 6405	17.9323 6984	0.0707 6508	16
17	1.2880 2033	0.7763 8526	14.9076 4931	19.2013 5539	0.0670 7966	17
18	1.3073 4064	0.7649 1159	15.6725 6089	20.4893 7572	0.0638 0578	18
19	1.3269 5075	0.7536 0747	16.4261 6837	21.7967 1636	0.0608 7847	19
20	1.3468 5501	0.7424 7042	17.1686 3879	23.1236 6710	0.0582 4574	20
21	1.3670 5783	0.7314 9795	17.9001 3673	24.4705 2211	0.0558 6550	21
22	1.3875 6370	0.7206 8763	18.6208 2437	25.8375 7994	0.0537 0331	22
23	1.4083 7715	0.7100 3708	19.3308 6145	27.2251 4364	0.0517 3075	23
24	1.4295 0281	0.6995 4392	20.0304 0537	28.6335 2080	0.0499 2410	24
25	1.4509 4535	0.6892 0583	20.7196 1120	30.0630 2361	0.0482 6345	25
26	1.4727 0953	0.6790 2052	21.3986 3172	31.5139 6896	0.0467 3196	26
27	1.4948 0018	0.6689 8574	22.0676 1746	32.9866 7850	0.0453 1527	27
28	1.5172 2218	0.6590 9925	22.7267 1671	34.4814 7867	0.0440 0108	28
29	1.5399 8051	0.6493 5887	23.3760 7558	35.9987 0085	0.0427 7878	29
30	1.5630 8022	0.6397 6243	24.0158 3801	37.5386 8137	0.0416 3919	30
31	1.5865 2642	0.6303 0781	24.6461 4582	39.1017 6159	0.0405 7430	31
32	1.6103 2432	0.6209 9292	25.2671 3874	40.6882 8801	0.0395 7710	32
33	1.6344 7918	0.6118 1568	25.8789 5442	42.2986 1233	0.0386 4144	33
34	1.6589 9637	0.6027 7407	26.4817 2849	43.9330 9152	0.0377 6189	34
35	1.6838 8132	0.5938 6608	27.0755 9458	45.5920 8789	0.0369 3363	35
36	1.7091 3954	0.5850 8974	27.6606 8431	47.2759 6921	0.0361 5240	36
37	1.7347 7663	0.5764 4309	28.2371 2740	48.9851 0874	0.0354 1437	37
38	1.7607 9828	0.5679 2423	28.8050 5163	50.7198 8538	0.0347 1613	38
39	1.7872 1025	0.5595 3126	29.3645 8288	52.4806 8366	0.0340 5463	39
40	1.8140 1841	0.5512 6232	29.9158 4520	54.2678 9391	0.0334 2710	40
41	1.8412 2868	0.5431 1559	30.4589 6079	56.0819 1232	0.0328 3106	41
42	1.8688 4712	0.5350 8925	30.9940 5004	57.9231 4100	0.0322 6426	42
43	1.8968 7982	0.5271 8153	31.5212 3157	59.7919 8812	0.0317 2465	43
44	1.9253 3302	0.5193 9067	32.0406 2223	61.6888 6794	0.0312 1038	44
45	1.9542 1301	0.5117 1494	32.5523 3718	63.6142 0096	0.0307 1976	45
46	1.9835 2621	0.5041 5265	33.0564 8983	65.5684 1398	0.0302 5125	46
47	2.0132 7910	0.4967 0212	33.5531 9195	67.5519 4018	0.0298 0342	47
48	2.0434 7829	0.4893 6170	34.0425 5365	69.5652 1929	0.0293 7500	48
49	2.0741 3046	0.4821 2975	34.5246 8339	71.6086 9758	0.0289 6478	49
50	2.1052 4242	0.4750 0468	34.9996 8807	73.6828 2804	0.0285 7168	50

Table XI (continued). 1½ %

Number of periods n	Amount of 1 at compound interest $s^n = (1+i)^n$	Present value of 1 $v^n = \dfrac{1}{(1+i)^n}$	Present value of an annuity of 1 $a_{\overline{n}|} = \dfrac{1-v^n}{i}$	Amount of an annuity of 1 $s_{\overline{n}|} = \dfrac{(1+i)^n-1}{i}$	Annuity whose present value is 1. (CRF) $\dfrac{1}{a_{\overline{n}|}} = \dfrac{1}{s_{\overline{n}|}}+i$	Number of periods n
51	2.1368 2106	0.4679 8491	35.4676 7298	75.7880 7046	0.0281 9469	51
52	2.1688 7337	0.4610 6887	35.9287 4185	77.9248 9152	0.0278 3287	52
53	2.2014 0647	0.4542 5505	36.3829 9690	80.0937 6489	0.0274 8537	53
54	2.2344 2757	0.4475 4192	36.8305 3882	82.2951 7136	0.0271 5138	54
55	2.2679 4398	0.4409 2800	37.2714 6681	84.5295 9893	0.0268 3018	55
56	2.3019 6314	0.4344 1182	37.7058 7863	86.7975 4292	0.0265 2106	56
57	2.3364 9259	0.4279 9194	38.1338 7058	89.0995 0606	0.0262 2341	57
58	2.3715 3998	0.4216 6694	38.5555 3751	91.4359 9865	0.0259 3661	58
59	2.4071 1308	0.4154 3541	38.9709 7292	93.8075 3863	0.0256 6012	59
60	2.4432 1978	0.4092 9597	39.3802 6889	96.2146 5171	0.0253 9343	60
61	2.4798 6807	0.4032 4726	39.7835 1614	98.6578 7149	0.0251 3604	61
62	2.5170 6609	0.3972 8794	40.1808 0408	101.1377 3956	0.0248 8751	62
63	2.5548 2208	0.3914 1669	40.5722 2077	103.6548 0565	0.0246 4741	63
64	2.5931 4442	0.3856 3221	40.9578 5298	106.2096 2774	0.0244 1534	64
65	2.6320 4158	0.3799 3321	41.3377 8618	108.8027 7215	0.0241 9094	65
66	2.6715 2221	0.3743 1843	41.7121 0461	111.4348 1374	0.0239 7386	66
67	2.7115 9504	0.3687 8663	42.0808 9125	114.1063 3594	0.0237 6376	67
68	2.7522 6896	0.3633 3658	42.4442 2783	116.8179 3098	0.0235 6033	68
69	2.7935 5300	0.3579 6708	42.8021 9490	119.5701 9995	0.0233 6329	69
70	2.8354 5629	0.3526 7692	43.1548 7183	122.3637 5295	0.0231 7235	70
71	2.8779 8814	0.3474 6495	43.5023 3678	125.1992 0924	0.0229 8727	71
72	2.9211 5796	0.3423 3000	43.8446 6677	128.0771 9738	0.0228 0779	72
73	2.9649 7533	0.3372 7093	44.1819 3771	130.9983 5534	0.0226 3368	73
74	3.0094 4996	0.3322 8663	44.5142 2434	133.9633 3067	0.0224 6473	74
75	3.0545 9171	0.3273 7599	44.8416 0034	136.9727 8063	0.0223 0072	75
76	3.1004 1059	0.3225 3793	45.1641 3826	140.0273 7234	0.0221 4146	76
77	3.1469 1674	0.3177 7136	45.4819 0962	143.1277 8292	0.0219 8676	77
78	3.1941 2050	0.3130 7523	45.7949 8485	146.2746 9967	0.0218 3645	78
79	3.2420 3230	0.3084 4850	46.1034 3335	149.4688 2016	0.0216 9036	79
80	3.2906 6279	0.3038 9015	46.4073 2349	152.7108 5247	0.0215 4832	80
81	3.3400 2273	0.2993 9916	46.7067 2265	156.0015 1525	0.0214 1019	81
82	3.3901 2307	0.2949 7454	47.0016 9720	159.3415 3798	0.0212 7583	82
83	3.4409 7492	0.2906 1531	47.2923 1251	162.7316 6105	0.0211 4509	83
84	3.4925 8954	0.2863 2050	47.5786 3301	166.1726 3597	0.0210 1784	84
85	3.5449 7838	0.2820 8917	47.8607 2218	169.6652 2551	0.0208 9396	85
86	3.5981 5306	0.2779 2036	48.1386 4254	173.2102 0389	0.0207 7333	86
87	3.6521 2535	0.2738 1316	48.4124 5571	176.8083 5695	0.0206 5584	87
88	3.7069 0723	0.2697 6666	48.6822 2237	180.4604 8230	0.0205 4138	88
89	3.7625 1084	0.2657 7997	48.9480 0234	184.1673 8954	0.0204 2984	89
90	3.8189 4851	0.2618 5218	49.2098 5452	187.9299 0038	0.0203 2113	90
91	3.8762 3273	0.2579 8245	49.4678 3696	191.7488 4889	0.0202 1516	91
92	3.9343 7622	0.2541 6990	49.7220 0686	195.6250 8162	0.0201 1182	92
93	3.9933 9187	0.2504 1369	49.9724 2055	199.5594 5784	0.0200 1104	93
94	4.0532 9275	0.2467 1300	50.2191 3355	203.5528 4971	0.0199 1273	94
95	4.1140 9214	0.2430 6699	50.4622 0054	207.6061 4246	0.0198 1681	95
96	4.1758 0352	0.2394 7487	50.7016 7541	211.7202 3459	0.0197 2321	96
97	4.2384 4057	0.2359 3583	50.9376 1124	215.8960 3811	0.0196 3186	97
98	4.3020 1718	0.2324 4909	51.1700 6034	220.1344 7868	0.0195 4268	98
99	4.3665 4744	0.2290 1389	51.3990 7422	224.4364 9586	0.0194 5560	99
100	4.4320 4565	0.2256 2944	51.6247 0367	228.8030 4330	0.0193 7057	100

Table XII. 1¾ %

Number of periods n	Amount of 1 at compound interest $s^n = (1 + i)^n$	Present value of 1 $v^n = \dfrac{1}{(1+i)^n}$	Present value of an annuity of 1 $a_{\overline{n}|} = \dfrac{1 - v^n}{i}$	Amount of an annuity of 1 $s_{\overline{n}|} = \dfrac{(1+i)^n - 1}{i}$	Annuity whose present value is 1. (CRF) $\dfrac{1}{a_{\overline{n}|}} = \dfrac{1}{s_{\overline{n}|}} + i$	Number of periods n
1	1.0175 0000	0.9828 0098	0.9828 0098	1.0000 0000	1.0175 0000	1
2	1.0353 0625	0.9658 9777	1.9486 9875	2.0175 0000	0.5131 6295	2
3	1.0534 2411	0.9492 8528	2.8979 8403	3.0528 0625	0.3450 6746	3
4	1.0718 5903	0.9329 5851	3.8309 4254	4.1062 3036	0.2610 3237	4
5	1.0906 1656	0.9169 1254	4.7478 5508	5.1780 8938	0.2106 2142	5
6	1.1097 0235	0.9011 4254	5.6489 9762	6.2687 0596	0.1770 2256	6
7	1.1291 2215	0.8856 4378	6.5346 4139	7.3784 0831	0.1530 3059	7
8	1.1488 8178	0.8704 1157	7.4050 5297	8.5075 3045	0.1350 4292	8
9	1.1689 8721	0.8554 4135	8.2604 9432	9.6564 1224	0.1210 5813	9
10	1.1894 4449	0.8407 2860	9.1012 2291	10.8253 9945	0.1098 7534	10
11	1.2102 5977	0.8262 6889	9.9274 9181	12.0148 4394	0.1007 3038	11
12	1.2314 3931	0.8120 5788	10.7395 4969	13.2251 0371	0.0931 1377	12
13	1.2529 8950	0.7980 9128	11.5376 4097	14.4565 4303	0.0866 7283	13
14	1.2749 1682	0.7843 6490	12.3220 0587	15.7095 3253	0.0811 5562	14
15	1.2972 2786	0.7708 7459	13.0928 8046	16.9844 4935	0.0763 7739	15
16	1.3199 2935	0.7576 1631	13.8504 9677	18.2816 7721	0.0721 9958	16
17	1.3430 2811	0.7445 8605	14.5950 8282	19.6016 0656	0.0685 1623	17
18	1.3665 3111	0.7317 7990	15.3268 6272	20.9446 3468	0.0652 4492	18
19	1.3904 4540	0.7191 9401	16.0460 5673	22.3111 6578	0.0623 2061	19
20	1.4147 7820	0.7068 2458	16.7528 8130	23.7016 1119	0.0596 9122	20
21	1.4395 3681	0.6946 6789	17.4475 4919	25.1163 8938	0.0573 1464	21
22	1.4647 2871	0.6827 2028	18.1302 6948	26.5559 2620	0.0551 5638	22
23	1.4903 6146	0.6709 7817	18.8012 4764	28.0206 5490	0.0531 8796	23
24	1.5164 4279	0.6594 3800	19.4606 8565	29.5110 1637	0.0513 8565	24
25	1.5429 8054	0.6480 9632	20.1087 8196	31.0274 5915	0.0497 2952	25
26	1.5699 8269	0.6369 4970	20.7457 3166	32.5704 3969	0.0482 0269	26
27	1.5974 5739	0.6259 9479	21.3717 2644	34.1404 2238	0.0467 9079	27
28	1.6254 1290	0.6152 2829	21.9869 5474	35.7378 7977	0.0454 8151	28
29	1.6538 5762	0.6046 4697	22.5916 0171	37.3632 9267	0.0442 6424	29
30	1.6828 0013	0.5942 4764	23.1858 4934	39.0171 5029	0.0431 2975	30
31	1.7122 4913	0.5840 2716	23.7698 7650	40.6999 5042	0.0420 7005	31
32	1.7422 1349	0.5739 8247	24.3438 5897	42.4121 9955	0.0410 7812	32
33	1.7727 0223	0.5641 1053	24.9079 6951	44.1544 1305	0.0401 4779	33
34	1.8037 2452	0.5544 0839	25.4623 7789	45.9271 1527	0.0392 7363	34
35	1.8352 8970	0.5448 7311	26.0072 5100	47.7308 3979	0.0384 5082	35
36	1.8674 0727	0.5355 0183	26.5427 5283	49.5661 2949	0.0376 7507	36
37	1.9000 8689	0.5262 9172	27.0690 4455	51.4335 3675	0.0369 4257	37
38	1.9333 3841	0.5172 4002	27.5862 8457	53.3336 2365	0.0362 4990	38
39	1.9671 7184	0.5083 4400	28.0946 2857	55.2669 6206	0.0355 9399	39
40	2.0015 9734	0.4996 0098	28.5942 2955	57.2341 3390	0.0349 7209	40
41	2.0366 2530	0.4910 0834	29.0852 3789	59.2357 3124	0.0343 8170	41
42	2.0722 6624	0.4825 6348	29.5678 0135	61.2723 5654	0.0338 2057	42
43	2.1085 3090	0.4742 6386	30.0420 6522	63.3446 2278	0.0332 8666	43
44	2.1454 3019	0.4661 0699	30.5081 7221	65.4531 5367	0.0327 7810	44
45	2.1829 7522	0.4580 9040	30.9662 6261	67.5985 8386	0.0322 9321	45
46	2.2211 7728	0.4502 1170	31.4164 7431	69.7815 5908	0.0318 3043	46
47	2.2600 4789	0.4424 6850	31.8589 4281	72.0027 3637	0.0313 8836	47
48	2.2995 9872	0.4348 5848	32.2938 0129	74.2627 8425	0.0309 6569	48
49	2.3398 4170	0.4273 7934	32.7211 8063	76.5623 8298	0.0305 6124	49
50	2.3807 8893	0.4200 2883	33.1412 0946	78.9022 2468	0.0301 7391	50

Table XII (*continued*).   1¾ %

Number of periods n	Amount of 1 at compound interest $s^n = (1+i)^n$	Present value of 1 $v^n = \dfrac{1}{(1+i)^n}$	Present value of an annuity of 1 $a_{\overline{n}} = \dfrac{1-v^n}{i}$	Amount of an annuity of 1 $s_{\overline{n}} = \dfrac{(1+i)^n-1}{i}$	Annuity whose present value is 1. (CRF) $\dfrac{1}{a_{\overline{n}}} = \dfrac{1}{s_{\overline{n}}} + i$	Number of periods n
51	2.4224 5274	0.4128 0475	33.5540 1421	81.2830 1361	0.0298 0269	51
52	2.4648 4566	0.4057 0492	33.9597 1913	83.7054 6635	0.0294 4665	52
53	2.5070 8046	0.3987 2719	34.3584 4633	86.1703 1201	0.0291 0492	53
54	2.5518 7012	0.3918 6947	34.7503 1579	88.6782 9247	0.0287 7672	54
55	2.5965 2785	0.3851 2970	35.1354 4550	91.2301 6259	0.0284 6129	55
56	2.6419 6708	0.3785 0585	35.5139 5135	93.8266 9043	0.0281 5795	56
57	2.6882 0151	0.3719 9592	35.8859 4727	96.4686 5752	0.0278 6606	57
58	2.7352 4503	0.3655 9796	36.2515 4523	99.1568 5902	0.0275 8503	58
59	2.7831 1182	0.3593 1003	36.6108 5526	101.8921 0405	0.0273 1430	59
60	2.8318 1628	0.3531 3025	36.9639 8552	104.6752 1588	0.0270 5336	60
61	2.8813 7306	0.3470 5676	37.3110 4228	107.5070 3215	0.0268 0172	61
62	2.9317 9709	0.3410 8772	37.6521 3000	110.3884 0522	0.0265 5892	62
63	2.9831 0354	0.3352 2135	37.9873 5135	113.3202 0231	0.0263 2455	63
64	3.0343 0785	0.3294 5587	38.3168 0723	116.3033 0585	0.0260 9821	64
65	3.0884 2574	0.3237 8956	38.6405 9678	119.3386 1370	0.0258 7952	65
66	3.1424 7319	0.3182 2069	38.9588 1748	122.4270 3944	0.0256 6813	66
67	3.1974 6647	0.3127 4761	39.2715 6509	125.5695 1263	0.0254 6372	67
68	3.2534 2213	0.3073 6866	39.5789 3375	128.7669 7910	0.0252 6596	68
69	3.3103 5702	0.3020 8222	39.8810 1597	132.0204 0124	0.0250 7459	69
70	3.3682 8827	0.2968 8670	40.1779 0267	135.3307 5826	0.0248 8930	70
71	3.4272 3331	0.2917 8054	40.4696 8321	138.6990 4653	0.0247 0985	71
72	3.4872 0990	0.2867 6221	40.7564 4542	142.1262 7984	0.0245 3600	72
73	3.5482 3607	0.2818 3018	41.0382 7560	145.6134 8974	0.0243 6750	73
74	3.6103 3020	0.2769 8298	41.3152 5857	149.1617 2581	0.0242 0413	74
75	3.6735 1098	0.2722 1914	41.5874 7771	152.7720 5601	0.0240 4570	75
76	3.7377 9742	0.2675 3724	41.8550 1495	156.4455 6699	0.0238 9200	76
77	3.8032 0888	0.2629 3586	42.1179 5081	160.1833 6441	0.0237 4284	77
78	3.8697 6503	0.2584 1362	42.3763 6443	163.9865 7329	0.0235 9806	78
79	3.9374 8592	0.2539 6916	42.6303 3359	167.8563 3832	0.0234 5748	79
80	4.0063 9192	0.2496 0114	42.8799 3474	171.7938 2424	0.0233 2093	80
81	4.0765 0378	0.2453 0825	43.1252 4298	175.8002 1617	0.0231 8828	81
82	4.1478 4260	0.2410 8919	43.3663 3217	179.8767 1995	0.0230 5936	82
83	4.2204 2984	0.2369 4269	43.6032 7486	184.0245 6255	0.0229 3406	83
84	4.2942 8737	0.2328 6751	43.8361 4237	188.2449 9239	0.0228 1223	84
85	4.3694 3740	0.2288 6242	44.0650 0479	192.5392 7976	0.0226 9375	85
86	4.4459 0255	0.2249 2621	44.2899 3099	196.9087 1716	0.0225 7850	86
87	4.5237 0584	0.2210 5770	44.5109 8869	201.3546 1971	0.0224 6636	87
88	4.6028 7070	0.2172 5572	44.7282 4441	205.8783 2555	0.0223 5724	88
89	4.6834 2093	0.2135 1914	44.9417 6355	210.4811 9625	0.0222 5102	89
90	4.7653 8080	0.2098 4682	45.1516 1037	215.1646 1718	0.0221 4760	90
91	4.8487 7496	0.2062 3766	45.3578 4803	219.9299 9798	0.0220 4690	91
92	4.9336 2853	0.2026 9057	45.5605 3860	224.7787 7295	0.0219 4882	92
93	5.0199 6703	0.1992 0450	45.7597 4310	229.7124 0148	0.0218 5327	93
94	5.1078 1645	0.1957 7837	45.9555 2147	234.7323 6850	0.0217 6017	94
95	5.1972 0324	0.1924 1118	46.1479 3265	239.8401 8495	0.0216 6944	95
96	5.2881 5429	0.1891 0190	46.3370 3455	245.0373 8819	0.0215 8101	96
97	5.3806 9699	0.1858 4953	46.5228 8408	250.3255 4248	0.0214 9480	97
98	5.4748 5919	0.1826 5310	46.7055 3718	255.7062 3947	0.0214 1074	98
99	5.5706 6923	0.1795 1165	46.8850 4882	261.1810 9866	0.0213 2876	99
100	5.6681 5594	0.1764 2422	47.0614 7304	266.7517 6789	0.0212 4880	100

Table XIII. 2 %

Number of periods n	Amount of 1 at compound interest $s^n = (1+i)^n$	Present value of 1 $v^n = \dfrac{1}{(1+i)^n}$	Present value of an annuity of 1 $a_{\overline{n}|} = \dfrac{1-v^n}{i}$	Amount of an annuity of 1 $s_{\overline{n}|} = \dfrac{(1+i)^n-1}{i}$	Annuity whose present value is 1. (CRF) $\dfrac{1}{a_{\overline{n}|}} = \dfrac{1}{s_{\overline{n}|}} + i$	Number of periods n
1	1.0200 0000	0.9803 9216	0.9803 9216	1.0000 0000	1.0200 0000	1
2	1.0404 0000	0.9611 6878	1.9415 6094	2.0200 0000	0.5150 4950	2
3	1.0612 0800	0.9423 2233	2.8838 8327	3.0604 0000	0.3467 5467	3
4	1.0824 3216	0.9238 4543	3.8077 2870	4.1216 0800	0.2626 2375	4
5	1.1040 8080	0.9057 3081	4.7134 5951	5.2040 4016	0.2121 5839	5
6	1.1261 6242	0.8879 7138	5.6014 3089	6.3081 2096	0.1785 2581	6
7	1.1486 8567	0.8705 6018	6.4719 9107	7.4342 8338	0.1545 1196	7
8	1.1716 5938	0.8534 9037	7.3254 8144	8.5829 6905	0.1365 0980	8
9	1.1950 9257	0.8367 5527	8.1622 3671	9.7546 2843	0.1225 1544	9
10	1.2189 9442	0.8203 4830	8.9825 8501	10.9497 2100	0.1113 2653	10
11	1.2433 7431	0.8042 6304	9.7868 4805	12.1687 1542	0.1021 7794	11
12	1.2682 4179	0.7884 9318	10.5753 4122	13.4120 8973	0.0945 5960	12
13	1.2936 0663	0.7730 3253	11.3483 7375	14.6803 3152	0.0881 1835	13
14	1.3194 7876	0.7578 7502	12.1062 4877	15.9739 3815	0.0826 0197	14
15	1.3458 6834	0.7430 1473	12.8492 6350	17.2934 1692	0.0778 2547	15
16	1.3727 8571	0.7284 4581	13.5777 0931	18.6392 8525	0.0736 5013	16
17	1.4002 4142	0.7141 6256	14.2918 7188	20.0120 7096	0.0699 6984	17
18	1.4282 4625	0.7001 5937	14.9920 3125	21.4123 1238	0.0667 0210	18
19	1.4568 1117	0.6864 3076	15.6784 6201	22.8405 5863	0.0637 8177	19
20	1.4859 4740	0.6729 7133	16.3514 3334	24.2973 6980	0.0611 5672	20
21	1.5156 6634	0.6597 7582	17.0112 0916	25.7833 1719	0.0587 8477	21
22	1.5459 7967	0.6468 3904	17.6580 4820	27.2989 8354	0.0566 3140	22
23	1.5768 9926	0.6341 5592	18.2922 0412	28.8449 6321	0.0546 6810	23
24	1.6084 3725	0.6217 2149	18.9139 2560	30.4218 6247	0.0528 7110	24
25	1.6406 0599	0.6095 3087	19.5234 5647	32.0302 9972	0.0512 2044	25
26	1.6734 1811	0.5975 7928	20.1210 3576	33.6709 0572	0.0496 9923	26
27	1.7068 8648	0.5858 6204	20.7068 9780	35.3443 2383	0.0482 9309	27
28	1.7410 2421	0.5743 7455	21.2812 7236	37.0512 1031	0.0469 8967	28
29	1.7758 4469	0.5631 1231	21.8443 8466	38.7922 3451	0.0457 7836	29
30	1.8113 6158	0.5520 7089	22.3964 5555	40.5680 7921	0.0446 4992	30
31	1.8475 8882	0.5412 4597	22.9377 0152	42.3794 4079	0.0435 9635	31
32	1.8845 4059	0.5306 3330	23.4683 3482	44.2270 2961	0.0426 1061	32
33	1.9222 3140	0.5202 2873	23.9885 6355	46.1115 7020	0.0416 8653	33
34	1.9606 7603	0.5100 2817	24.4985 9172	48.0338 0160	0.0408 1867	34
35	1.9998 8955	0.5000 2761	24.9986 1933	49.9944 7763	0.0400 0221	35
36	2.0398 8734	0.4902 2315	25.4888 4248	51.9943 6719	0.0392 3285	36
37	2.0806 8509	0.4806 1093	25.9694 5341	54.0342 5453	0.0385 0678	37
38	2.1222 9879	0.4711 8719	26.4406 4060	56.1149 3962	0.0378 2057	38
39	2.1647 4477	0.4619 4822	26.9025 8883	58.2372 3841	0.0371 7114	39
40	2.2080 3966	0.4528 9042	27.3554 7924	60.4019 8318	0.0365 5575	40
41	2.2522 0046	0.4440 1021	27.7994 8945	62.6100 2284	0.0359 7188	41
42	2.2972 4447	0.4353 0413	28.2347 9358	64.8622 2330	0.0354 1729	42
43	2.3431 8936	0.4267 6875	28.6615 6233	67.1594 6777	0.0348 8993	43
44	2.3900 5314	0.4184 0074	29.0799 6307	69.5026 5712	0.0343 8794	44
45	2.4378 5421	0.4101 9680	29.4901 5987	71.8927 1027	0.0339 0962	45
46	2.4866 1129	0.4021 5373	29.8923 1360	74.3305 6447	0.0334 5342	46
47	2.5363 4351	0.3942 6836	30.2865 8196	76.8171 7576	0.0330 1792	47
48	2.5870 7039	0.3865 3761	30.6731 1957	79.3535 1927	0.0326 0184	48
49	2.6388 1179	0.3789 5844	31.0520 7801	81.9405 8966	0.0322 0396	49
50	2.6915 8803	0.3715 2788	31.4236 0589	84.5794 0145	0.0318 2321	50

Table XIII (*continued*). 2 %

Number of periods n	Amount of 1 at compound interest $s^n = (1+i)^n$	Present value of 1 $v^n = \dfrac{1}{(1+i)^n}$	Present value of an annuity of 1 $a_{\overline{n}|} = \dfrac{1-v^n}{i}$	Amount of an annuity of 1 $s_{\overline{n}|} = \dfrac{(1+i)^n-1}{i}$	Annuity whose present value is 1. (CRF) $\dfrac{1}{a_{\overline{n}|}} = \dfrac{1}{s_{\overline{n}|}} + i$	Number of periods n
51	2.7454 1979	0.3642 4302	31.7878 4892	87.2709 8948	0.0314 5356	51
52	2.8003 2819	0.3571 0100	32.1449 4992	90.0164 0927	0.0311 0909	52
53	2.8563 3475	0.3500 9902	32.4950 4894	92.8167 3746	0.0307 7392	53
54	2.9134 6144	0.3432 3433	32.8382 8327	95.6730 7221	0.0304 5226	54
55	2.9717 3067	0.3365 0425	33.1747 8752	98.5865 3365	0.0301 4337	55
56	3.0311 6529	0.3299 0613	33.5046 9365	101.5582 6432	0.0298 4656	56
57	3.0917 8859	0.3234 3738	33.8281 3103	104.5894 2961	0.0295 6120	57
58	3.1536 2436	0.3170 9547	34.1452 2650	107.6812 1820	0.0292 8667	58
59	3.2166 9685	0.3108 7791	34.4561 0441	110.8348 4257	0.0290 2243	59
60	3.2810 3079	0.3047 8227	34.7608 8668	114.0515 3942	0.0287 6797	60
61	3.3466 5140	0.2988 0614	35.0596 9282	117.3325 7021	0.0285 2278	61
62	3.4135 8443	0.2929 4720	35.3526 4002	120.6792 2161	0.0282 8643	62
63	3.4818 5612	0.2872 0314	35.6398 4316	124.0928 0604	0.0280 5848	63
64	3.5514 9324	0.2815 7170	35.9214 1486	127.5746 6216	0.0278 3855	64
65	3.6225 2311	0.2760 5069	36.1974 6555	131.1261 5541	0.0276 2624	65
66	3.6949 7357	0.2706 3793	36.4681 0348	134.7486 7852	0.0274 2122	66
67	3.7688 7304	0.2653 3130	36.7334 3478	138.4436 5209	0.0272 2316	67
68	3.8442 5050	0.2601 2873	36.9935 6351	142.2125 2513	0.0270 3173	68
69	3.9211 3551	0.2550 2817	37.2485 9168	146.0567 7563	0.0268 4665	69
70	3.9995 5822	0.2500 2761	37.4986 1929	149.9779 1114	0.0266 6765	70
71	4.0795 4939	0.2451 2511	37.7437 4441	153.9774 6937	0.0264 9446	71
72	4.1611 4038	0.2403 1874	37.9840 6314	158.0570 1875	0.0263 2683	72
73	4.2443 6318	0.2356 0661	38.2196 6975	162.2181 5913	0.0261 6454	73
74	4.3292 5045	0.2309 8687	38.4506 5662	166.4625 2231	0.0260 0736	74
75	4.4158 3546	0.2264 5771	38.6771 1433	170.7917 7276	0.0258 5508	75
76	4.5041 5216	0.2220 1737	38.8991 3170	175.2076 0821	0.0257 0751	76
77	4.5942 3521	0.2176 6408	39.1167 9578	179.7117 6038	0.0255 6447	77
78	4.6861 1991	0.2133 9616	39.3301 9194	184.3059 9558	0.0254 2576	78
79	4.7798 4231	0.2092 1192	39.5394 0386	188.9921 1549	0.0252 9123	79
80	4.8754 3916	0.2051 0973	39.7445 1359	193.7719 5780	0.0251 6071	80
81	4.9729 4794	0.2010 8797	39.9456 0156	198.6473 9696	0.0250 3405	81
82	5.0724 0690	0.1971 4507	40.1427 4663	203.6203 4490	0.0249 1110	82
83	5.1738 5504	0.1932 7948	40.3360 2611	208.6927 5180	0.0247 9173	83
84	5.2773 3214	0.1894 8968	40.5255 1579	213.8666 0683	0.0246 7581	84
85	5.3828 7878	0.1857 7420	40.7112 8999	219.1439 3897	0.0245 6321	85
86	5.4905 3636	0.1821 3157	40.8934 2156	224.5268 1775	0.0244 5381	86
87	5.6003 4708	0.1785 6036	41.0719 8192	230.0173 5411	0.0243 4750	87
88	5.7123 5402	0.1750 5918	41.2470 4110	235.6177 0119	0.0242 4416	88
89	5.8266 0110	0.1716 2665	41.4186 6774	241.3300 5521	0.0241 4370	89
90	5.9431 3313	0.1682 6142	41.5869 2916	247.1566 5632	0.0240 4602	90
91	6.0619 9579	0.1649 6217	41.7518 9133	253.0997 8944	0.0239 5101	91
92	6.1832 3570	0.1617 2762	41.9136 1895	259.1617 8523	0.0238 5859	92
93	6.3069 0042	0.1585 5649	42.0721 7545	265.3450 2094	0.0237 6868	93
94	6.4330 3843	0.1554 4754	42.2276 2299	271.6519 2135	0.0236 8118	94
95	6.5616 9920	0.1523 9955	42.3800 2254	278.0849 5978	0.0235 9602	95
96	6.6929 3318	0.1494 1132	42.5294 3386	284.6466 5898	0.0235 1313	96
97	6.8267 9184	0.1464 8169	42.6759 1555	291.3395 9216	0.0234 3242	97
98	6.9633 2768	0.1436 0950	42.8195 2505	298.1663 8400	0.0233 5383	98
99	7.1025 9423	0.1407 9363	42.9603 1867	305.1297 1168	0.0232 7729	99
100	7.2446 4612	0.1380 3297	43.0983 5164	312.2323 0591	0.0232 0274	100

Table XIV. 2½ %

Number of periods n	Amount of 1 at compound interest $s^n = (1+i)^n$	Present value of 1 $v^n = \dfrac{1}{(1+i)^n}$	Present value of an annuity of 1 $a_{\overline{n}\rceil} = \dfrac{1-v^n}{i}$	Amount of an annuity of 1 $s_{\overline{n}\rceil} = \dfrac{(1+i)^n-1}{i}$	Annuity whose present value is 1. (CRF) $\dfrac{1}{a_{\overline{n}\rceil}} = \dfrac{1}{s_{\overline{n}\rceil}} + i$	Number of periods n
1	1.0250 0000	0.9756 0976	0.9756 0976	1.0000 0000	1.0250 0000	1
2	1.0506 2500	0.9518 1440	1.9274 2415	2.0250 0000	0.5188 2716	2
3	1.0768 9063	0.9285 9941	2.8560 2356	3.0756 2500	0.3501 3717	3
4	1.1038 1289	0.9059 5064	3.7619 7421	4.1525 1563	0.2658 1788	4
5	1.1314 0821	0.8838 5429	4.6458 2850	5.2563 2852	0.2152 4686	5
6	1.1596 9342	0.8622 9687	5.5081 2536	6.3877 3673	0.1815 4997	6
7	1.1886 8575	0.8412 6524	6.3493 9060	7.5474 3015	0.1574 9543	7
8	1.2184 0290	0.8207 4657	7.1701 3717	8.7361 1590	0.1394 6735	8
9	1.2488 6297	0.8007 2836	7.9708 6553	9.9545 1880	0.1254 5689	9
10	1.2800 8454	0.7811 9840	8.7520 6393	11.2033 8177	0.1142 5876	10
11	1.3120 8666	0.7621 4478	9.5142 0871	12.4834 6631	0.1051 0596	11
12	1.3448 8882	0.7435 5589	10.2577 6460	13.7955 5297	0.0974 8713	12
13	1.3785 1104	0.7254 2038	10.9831 8497	15.1404 4179	0.0910 4827	13
14	1.4129 7382	0.7077 2720	11.6909 1217	16.5189 5284	0.0855 3653	14
15	1.4482 9817	0.6904 6556	12.3813 7773	17.9319 2666	0.0807 6646	15
16	1.4845 0562	0.6736 2493	13.0550 0266	19.3802 2483	0.0765 9899	16
17	1.5216 1826	0.6571 9506	13.7121 9772	20.8647 3045	0.0729 2777	17
18	1.5596 5872	0.6411 6591	14.3533 6363	22.3863 4871	0.0696 7008	18
19	1.5986 5019	0.6255 2772	14.9788 9134	23.9460 0743	0.0667 6062	19
20	1.6386 1644	0.6102 7094	15.5891 6229	25.5446 5761	0.0641 4713	20
21	1.6795 8185	0.5953 8629	16.1845 4857	27.1832 7405	0.0617 8733	21
22	1.7215 7140	0.5808 6467	16.7654 1324	28.8628 5590	0.0596 4661	22
23	1.7646 1068	0.5666 9724	17.3321 1048	30.5844 2730	0.0576 9638	23
24	1.8087 2595	0.5528 7535	17.8849 8583	32.3490 3798	0.0559 1282	24
25	1.8539 4410	0.5393 9059	18.4243 7642	34.1577 6393	0.0542 7592	25
26	1.9002 9270	0.5262 3472	18.9506 1114	36.0117 0803	0.0527 6875	26
27	1.9478 0002	0.5133 9973	19.4640 1087	37.9120 0073	0.0513 7687	27
28	1.9964 9502	0.5008 7778	19.9648 8866	39.8598 0075	0.0500 8793	28
29	2.0464 0739	0.4886 6125	20.4535 4991	41.8562 9577	0.0488 9127	29
30	2.0975 6758	0.4767 4269	20.9302 9259	43.9027 0316	0.0477 7764	30
31	2.1500 0677	0.4651 1481	21.3954 0741	46.0002 7074	0.0467 3900	31
32	2.2037 5694	0.4537 7055	21.8491 7796	48.1502 7751	0.0457 6831	32
33	2.2588 5086	0.4427 0298	22.2918 8094	50.3540 3445	0.0448 5938	33
34	2.3153 2213	0.4319 0534	22.7237 8628	52.6128 8531	0.0440 0675	34
35	2.3732 0519	0.4213 7107	23.1451 5734	54.9282 0744	0.0432 0558	35
36	2.4325 3532	0.4110 9372	23.5562 5107	57.3014 1263	0.0424 5158	36
37	2.4933 4870	0.4010 6705	23.9573 1812	59.7339 4794	0.0417 4090	37
38	2.5556 8242	0.3912 8492	24.3486 0304	62.2272 9664	0.0410 7012	38
39	2.6195 7448	0.3817 4139	24.7303 4443	64.7829 7906	0.0404 3615	39
40	2.6850 6384	0.3724 3062	25.1027 7505	67.4025 5354	0.0398 3623	40
41	2.7521 9043	0.3633 4695	25.4661 2200	70.0876 1737	0.0392 6786	41
42	2.8209 9520	0.3544 8483	25.8206 0683	72.8398 0781	0.0387 2876	42
43	2.8915 2008	0.3458 3886	26.1664 4569	75.6608 0300	0.0382 1688	43
44	2.9638 0808	0.3374 0376	26.5038 4945	78.5523 2308	0.0377 3037	44
45	3.0379 0328	0.3291 7440	26.8330 2386	81.5161 3116	0.0372 6752	45
46	3.1138 5086	0.3211 4576	27.1541 6962	84.5540 3443	0.0368 2676	46
47	3.1916 9713	0.3133 1294	27.4674 8255	87.6678 8530	0.0364 0669	47
48	3.2714 8956	0.3056 7116	27.7731 5371	90.8595 8243	0.0360 0599	48
49	3.3532 7680	0.2982 1576	28.0713 6947	94.1310 7199	0.0356 2348	49
50	3.4371 0872	0.2909 4221	28.3623 1168	97.4843 4879	0.0352 5806	50

Table XIV (continued). 2½ %

Number of periods n	Amount of 1 at compound interest $s^n = (1+i)^n$	Present value of 1 $v^n = \dfrac{1}{(1+i)^n}$	Present value of an annuity of 1 $a_{\overline{n}|} = \dfrac{1-v^n}{i}$	Amount of an annuity of 1 $s_{\overline{n}|} = \dfrac{(1+i)^n-1}{i}$	Annuity whose present value is 1. (CRF) $\dfrac{1}{a_{\overline{n}|}} = \dfrac{1}{s_{\overline{n}|}} + i$	Number of periods n
51	3.5230 3644	0.2838 4606	28.6461 5774	100.9214 5751	0.0349 0870	51
52	3.6111 1235	0.2769 2298	28.9230 8072	104.4444 9395	0.0345 7446	52
53	3.7013 9016	0.2701 6876	29.1932 4948	108.0556 0629	0.0342 5449	53
54	3.7939 2491	0.2635 7928	29.4568 2876	111.7569 9645	0.0339 4799	54
55	3.8887 7303	0.2571 5052	29.7139 7928	115.5509 2136	0.0336 5419	55
56	3.9859 9236	0.2508 7855	29.9648 5784	119.4396 9440	0.0333 7243	56
57	4.0856 4217	0.2447 5956	30.2096 1740	123.4256 8676	0.0331 0204	57
58	4.1877 8322	0.2387 8982	30.4484 0722	127.5113 2893	0.0328 4244	58
59	4.2924 7780	0.2329 6568	30.6813 7290	131.6991 1215	0.0325 9307	59
60	4.3997 8975	0.2272 8359	30.9086 5649	135.9915 8995	0.0323 5340	60
61	4.5097 8449	0.2217 4009	31.1303 9657	140.3913 7970	0.0321 2294	61
62	4.6225 2910	0.2163 3179	31.3467 2836	144.9011 6419	0.0319 0126	62
63	4.7380 9233	0.2110 5541	31.5577 8377	149.5236 9330	0.0316 8790	63
64	4.8565 4464	0.2059 0771	31.7636 9148	154.2617 8563	0.0314 8249	64
65	4.9779 5826	0.2008 8557	31.9645 7705	159.1183 3027	0.0312 8463	65
66	5.1024 0721	0.1959 8593	32.1605 6298	164.0962 8853	0.0310 9398	66
67	5.2299 6739	0.1912 0578	32.3517 6876	169.1986 9574	0.0309 1021	67
68	5.3607 1658	0.1865 4223	32.5383 1099	174.4286 6314	0.0307 3300	68
69	5.4947 3449	0.1819 9241	32.7203 0340	179.7893 7971	0.0305 6206	69
70	5.6321 0286	0.1775 5358	32.8978 5698	185.2841 1421	0.0303 9712	70
71	5.7729 0543	0.1732 2300	33.0710 7998	190.9162 1706	0.0302 3790	71
72	5.9172 2806	0.1689 9805	33.2400 7803	196.6891 2249	0.0300 8417	72
73	6.0651 5876	0.1648 7615	33.4049 5417	202.6063 5055	0.0299 3568	73
74	6.2167 8773	0.1608 5478	33.5658 0895	208.6715 0931	0.0297 9222	74
75	6.3722 0743	0.1569 3149	33.7227 4044	214.8882 9705	0.0296 5358	75
76	6.5315 1261	0.1531 0389	33.8758 4433	221.2605 0447	0.0295 1956	76
77	6.6948 0043	0.1493 6965	34.0252 1398	227.7920 1709	0.0293 8997	77
78	6.8621 7044	0.1457 2649	34.1709 4047	234.4868 1751	0.0292 6463	78
79	7.0337 2470	0.1421 7218	34.3131 1265	241.3489 8795	0.0291 4338	79
80	7.2095 6782	0.1387 0457	34.4518 1722	248.3827 1265	0.0290 2605	80
81	7.3898 0701	0.1353 2153	34.5871 3875	255.5922 8047	0.0289 1248	81
82	7.5745 5219	0.1320 2101	34.7191 5976	262.9820 8748	0.0288 0254	82
83	7.7639 1599	0.1288 0098	34.8479 6074	270.5566 3966	0.0286 9608	83
84	7.9580 1389	0.1256 5949	34.9736 2023	278.3205 5566	0.0285 9298	84
85	8.1569 6424	0.1225 9463	35.0962 1486	286.2785 6955	0.0284 9310	85
86	8.3608 8834	0.1196 0452	35.2158 1938	294.4355 3379	0.0283 9633	86
87	8.5699 1055	0.1166 8733	35.3325 0671	302.7964 2213	0.0283 0255	87
88	8.7841 5832	0.1138 4130	35.4463 4801	311.3663 3268	0.0282 1165	88
89	9.0037 6228	0.1110 6468	35.5574 1269	320.1504 9100	0.0281 2353	89
90	9.2288 5633	0.1083 5579	35.6657 6848	329.1542 5328	0.0280 3809	90
91	9.4595 7774	0.1057 1296	35.7714 8144	338.3831 0961	0.0279 5523	91
92	9.6960 6718	0.1031 3460	35.8746 1604	347.8426 8735	0.0278 7486	92
93	9.9384 6886	0.1006 1912	35.9752 3516	357.5387 5453	0.0277 9690	93
94	10.1869 3058	0.0981 6500	36.0734 0016	367.4772 2339	0.0277 2126	94
95	10.4416 0385	0.0957 7073	36.1691 7089	377.6641 5398	0.0276 4786	95
96	10.7026 4395	0.0934 3486	36.2626 0574	388.1057 5783	0.0275 7662	96
97	10.9702 1004	0.0911 5596	36.3537 6170	398.8084 0177	0.0275 0747	97
98	11.2444 6530	0.0889 3264	36.4426 9434	409.7786 1182	0.0274 4034	98
99	11.5255 7693	0.0867 6355	36.5294 5790	421.0230 7711	0.0273 7517	99
100	11.8137 1635	0.0846 4737	36.6141 0526	432.5486 5404	0.0273 1188	100

Table XV. 3%

Number of periods n	Amount of 1 at compound interest $s^n = (1+i)^n$	Present value of 1 $v^n = \dfrac{1}{(1+i)^n}$	Present value of an annuity of 1 $a_{\overline{n}|} = \dfrac{1-v^n}{i}$	Amount of an annuity of 1 $s_{\overline{n}|} = \dfrac{(1+i)^n-1}{i}$	Annuity whose present value is 1. (CRF) $\dfrac{1}{a_{\overline{n}|}} = \dfrac{1}{s_{\overline{n}|}} + i$	Number of periods n
1	1.0300 0000	0.9708 7379	0.9708 7379	1.0000 0000	1.0300 0000	1
2	1.0609 0000	0.9425 9591	1.9134 6970	2.0300 0000	0.5226 1084	2
3	1.0927 2700	0.9151 4166	2.8286 1135	3.0909 0000	0.3535 3036	3
4	1.1255 0881	0.8884 8705	3.7170 9840	4.1836 2700	0.2690 2705	4
5	1.1592 7407	0.8626 0878	4.5797 0719	5.3091 3581	0.2183 5457	5
6	1.1940 5230	0.8374 8426	5.4171 9144	6.4684 0988	0.1845 9750	6
7	1.2298 7387	0.8130 9151	6.2302 8296	7.6624 6218	0.1605 0635	7
8	1.2667 7008	0.7894 0923	7.0196 9219	8.8923 3605	0.1424 5639	8
9	1.3047 7318	0.7664 1673	7.7861 0892	10.1591 0613	0.1284 3386	9
10	1.3439 1638	0.7440 9391	8.5302 0284	11.4638 7931	0.1172 3051	10
11	1.3842 3387	0.7224 2128	9.2526 2411	12.8077 9569	0.1080 7745	11
12	1.4257 6089	0.7013 7988	9.9540 0399	14.1920 2956	0.1004 6209	12
13	1.4685 3371	0.6809 5134	10.6349 5533	15.6177 9045	0.0940 2954	13
14	1.5125 8972	0.6611 1781	11.2960 7314	17.0863 2416	0.0885 2634	14
15	1.5579 6742	0.6418 6195	11.9379 3509	18.5989 1389	0.0837 6658	15
16	1.6047 0644	0.6231 6694	12.5611 0203	20.1568 8130	0.0796 1085	16
17	1.6528 4763	0.6050 1645	13.1661 1847	21.7615 8774	0.0759 5253	17
18	1.7024 3306	0.5873 9461	13.7535 1308	23.4144 3537	0.0727 0870	18
19	1.7535 0605	0.5702 8603	14.3237 9911	25.1168 6844	0.0698 1388	19
20	1.8061 1123	0.5536 7575	14.8774 7486	26.8703 7449	0.0672 1571	20
21	1.8602 9457	0.5375 4928	15.4150 2414	28.6764 8572	0.0648 7178	21
22	1.9161 0341	0.5218 9250	15.9369 1664	30.5367 8030	0.0627 4739	22
23	1.9735 8651	0.5066 9175	16.4436 0839	32.4528 8370	0.0608 1390	23
24	2.0327 9411	0.4919 3374	16.9355 4212	34.4264 7022	0.0590 4742	24
25	2.0937 7793	0.4776 0557	17.4131 4769	36.4592 6432	0.0574 2787	25
26	2.1565 9127	0.4636 9473	17.8768 4242	38.5530 4225	0.0559 3829	26
27	2.2212 8901	0.4501 8906	18.3270 3147	40.7096 3352	0.0545 6421	27
28	2.2879 2768	0.4370 7675	18.7641 0823	42.9309 2252	0.0532 9323	28
29	2.3565 6551	0.4243 4636	19.1884 5459	45.2188 5020	0.0521 1467	29
30	2.4272 6247	0.4119 8676	19.6004 4135	47.5754 1571	0.0510 1926	30
31	2.5000 8035	0.3999 8715	20.0004 2849	50.0026 7818	0.0499 9893	31
32	2.5750 8276	0.3883 3703	20.3887 6553	52.5027 5852	0.0490 4662	32
33	2.6523 3524	0.3770 2625	20.7657 9178	55.0778 4128	0.0481 5612	33
34	2.7319 0530	0.3660 4490	21.1318 3668	57.7301 7652	0.0473 2196	34
35	2.8138 6245	0.3553 8340	21.4872 2007	60.4620 8181	0.0465 3929	35
36	2.8982 7833	0.3450 3243	21.8322 5250	63.2759 4427	0.0458 0379	36
37	2.9852 2668	0.3349 8294	22.1672 3544	66.1742 2259	0.0451 1162	37
38	3.0747 8348	0.3252 2615	22.4924 6159	69.1594 4927	0.0444 5934	38
39	3.1670 2698	0.3157 5355	22.8082 1513	72.2342 3275	0.0438 4385	39
40	3.2620 3779	0.3065 5684	23.1147 7197	75.4012 5973	0.0432 6238	40
41	3.3598 9893	0.2976 2800	23.4123 9997	78.6632 9753	0.0427 1241	41
42	3.4606 9589	0.2889 5922	23.7013 5920	82.0231 9645	0.0421 9167	42
43	3.5645 1677	0.2805 4294	23.9819 0213	85.4838 9234	0.0416 9811	43
44	3.6714 5227	0.2723 7178	24.2542 7392	89.0484 0911	0.0412 2985	44
45	3.7815 9584	0.2644 3862	24.5187 1254	92.7198 6139	0.0407 8518	45
46	3.8950 4372	0.2567 3653	24.7754 4907	96.5014 5723	0.0403 6254	46
47	4.0118 9503	0.2492 5876	25.0247 0783	100.3965 0095	0.0399 6051	47
48	4.1322 5188	0.2419 9880	25.2667 0664	104.4083 9598	0.0395 7777	48
49	4.2562 1944	0.2349 5029	25.5016 5693	108.5406 4785	0.0392 1314	49
50	4.3839 0602	0.2281 0708	25.7297 6401	112.7968 6729	0.0388 6550	50

Table XV (*continued*). 3 %

Number of periods n	Amount of 1 at compound interest $s^n = (1+i)^n$	Present value of 1 $v^n = \dfrac{1}{(1+i)^n}$	Present value of an annuity of 1 $a_{\overline{n}|} = \dfrac{1-v^n}{i}$	Amount of an annuity of 1 $s_{\overline{n}|} = \dfrac{(1+i)^n-1}{i}$	Annuity whose present value is 1. (CRF) $\dfrac{1}{a_{\overline{n}|}} = \dfrac{1}{s_{\overline{n}|}} + i$	Number of periods n
51	4.5154 2320	0.2214 6318	25.9512 2719	117.1807 7331	0.0385 3382	51
52	4.6508 8590	0.2150 1280	26.1662 3999	121.6961 9651	0.0382 1718	52
53	4.7904 1247	0.2087 5029	26.3749 9028	126.3470 8240	0.0379 1471	53
54	4.9341 2485	0.2026 7019	26.5776 6047	131.1374 9488	0.0376 2558	54
55	5.0821 4859	0.1967 6717	26.7744 2764	136.0716 1972	0.0373 4907	55
56	5.2346 1305	0.1910 3609	26.9654 6373	141.1537 6831	0.0370 8447	56
57	5.3916 5144	0.1854 7193	27.1509 3566	146.3883 8136	0.0368 3114	57
58	5.5534 0098	0.1800 6984	27.3310 0549	151.7800 3280	0.0365 8848	58
59	5.7200 0301	0.1748 2508	27.5058 3058	157.3334 3379	0.0363 5593	59
60	5.8916 0310	0.1697 3309	27.6755 6367	163.0534 3680	0.0361 3296	60
61	6.0683 5120	0.1647 8941	27.8403 5307	168.9450 3991	0.0359 1908	61
62	6.2504 0173	0.1599 8972	28.0003 4279	175.0133 9110	0.0357 1385	62
63	6.4379 1379	0.1553 2982	28.1556 7261	181.2637 9284	0.0355 1682	63
64	6.6310 5120	0.1508 0565	28.3064 7826	187.7017 0662	0.0353 2760	64
65	6.8299 8273	0.1464 1325	28.4528 9152	194.3327 5782	0.0351 4581	65
66	7.0348 8222	0.1421 4879	28.5950 4031	201.1627 4055	0.0349 7110	66
67	7.2459 2868	0.1380 0853	28.7330 4884	208.1976 2277	0.0348 0313	67
68	7.4633 0654	0.1339 8887	28.8670 3771	215.4435 5145	0.0346 4159	68
69	7.6872 0574	0.1300 8628	28.9971 2399	222.9068 5800	0.0344 8618	69
70	7.9178 2191	0.1262 9736	29.1234 2135	230.5940 6374	0.0343 3663	70
71	8.1553 5657	0.1226 1880	29.2460 4015	238.5118 8565	0.0341 9266	71
72	8.4000 1727	0.1190 4737	29.3650 8752	246.6672 4222	0.0340 5404	72
73	8.6520 1778	0.1155 7998	29.4806 6750	255.0672 5949	0.0339 2053	73
74	8.9115 7832	0.1122 1357	29.5928 8106	263.7192 7727	0.0337 9191	74
75	9.1789 2567	0.1089 4521	29.7018 2628	272.6308 5559	0.0336 6796	75
76	9.4542 9344	0.1057 7205	29.8075 9833	281.8097 8126	0.0335 4849	76
77	9.7379 2224	0.1026 9131	29.9102 8964	291.2640 7469	0.0334 3331	77
78	10.0300 5991	0.0997 0030	30.0099 8994	301.0019 9693	0.0333 2224	78
79	10.3309 6171	0.0967 9641	30.1067 8635	311.0320 5684	0.0332 1510	79
80	10.6408 9056	0.0939 7710	30.2007 6345	321.3630 1855	0.0331 1175	80
81	10.9601 1727	0.0912 3990	30.2920 0335	332.0039 0910	0.0330 1201	81
82	11.2889 2079	0.0885 8243	30.3805 8577	342.9640 2638	0.0329 1576	82
83	11.6275 8842	0.0860 0236	30.4665 8813	354.2529 4717	0.0328 2284	83
84	11.9764 1607	0.0834 9743	30.5500 8556	365.8805 3558	0.0327 3313	84
85	12.3357 0855	0.0810 6547	30.6311 5103	377.8569 5165	0.0326 4650	85
86	12.7057 7981	0.0787 0434	30.7098 5537	390.1926 6020	0.0325 6284	86
87	13.0869 5320	0.0764 1198	30.7862 6735	402.8984 4001	0.0324 8202	87
88	13.4795 6180	0.0741 8639	30.8604 5374	415.9853 9321	0.0324 0393	88
89	13.8839 4865	0.0720 2562	30.9324 7936	429.4649 5500	0.0323 2848	89
90	14.3004 6711	0.0699 2779	31.0024 0714	443.3489 0365	0.0322 5556	90
91	14.7294 8112	0.0678 9105	31.0702 9820	457.6493 7076	0.0321 8508	91
92	15.1713 6556	0.0659 1364	31.1362 1184	472.3788 5189	0.0321 1694	92
93	15.6265 0652	0.0639 9383	31.2002 0567	487.5502 1744	0.0320 5107	93
94	16.0953 0172	0.0621 2993	31.2623 3560	503.1767 2397	0.0319 8737	94
95	16.5781 6077	0.0603 2032	31.3226 5592	519.2720 2569	0.0319 2577	95
96	17.0755 0559	0.0585 6342	31.3812 1934	535.8501 8645	0.0318 6619	96
97	17.5877 7076	0.0568 5769	31.4380 7703	552.9256 9205	0.0318 0856	97
98	18.1154 0388	0.0552 0164	31.4932 7867	570.5134 6281	0.0317 5281	98
99	18.6588 6600	0.0535 9383	31.5468 7250	588.6288 6669	0.0316 9886	99
100	19.2186 3198	0.0520 3284	31.5989 0534	607.2877 3270	0.0316 4667	100

Table XVI. 3½ %

Number of periods n	Amount of 1 at compound interest $s^n = (1+i)^n$	Present value of 1 $v^n = \dfrac{1}{(1+i)^n}$	Present value of an annuity of 1 $a_{\overline{n}|} = \dfrac{1-v^n}{i}$	Amount of an annuity of 1 $s_{\overline{n}|} = \dfrac{(1+i)^n-1}{i}$	Annuity whose present value is 1. (CRF) $\dfrac{1}{a_{\overline{n}|}} = \dfrac{1}{s_{\overline{n}|}} + i$	Number of periods n
1	1.0350 0000	0.9661 8357	0.9661 8357	1.0000 0000	1.0350 0000	1
2	1.0712 2500	0.9335 1070	1.8996 9428	2.0350 0000	0.5264 0049	2
3	1.1087 1788	0.9019 4271	2.8016 3698	3.1062 2500	0.3569 3418	3
4	1.1475 2300	0.8714 4223	3.6730 7921	4.2149 4288	0.2722 5114	4
5	1.1876 8631	0.8419 7317	4.5150 5238	5.3624 6588	0.2214 8137	5
6	1.2292 5533	0.8135 0064	5.3285 5302	6.5501 5218	0.1876 6821	6
7	1.2722 7926	0.7859 9096	6.1145 4398	7.7794 0751	0.1635 4449	7
8	1.3168 0904	0.7594 1156	6.8739 5554	9.0516 8677	0.1454 7665	8
9	1.3628 9735	0.7337 3097	7.6076 8651	10.3684 9581	0.1314 4601	9
10	1.4105 9876	0.7089 1881	8.3166 0532	11.7313 9316	0.1202 4137	10
11	1.4599 6972	0.6849 4571	9.0015 5104	13.1419 9192	0.1110 9197	11
12	1.5110 6866	0.6617 8330	9.6633 3433	14.6019 6164	0.1034 8395	12
13	1.5639 5606	0.6394 0415	10.3027 3849	16.1130 3030	0.0970 6157	13
14	1.6186 9452	0.6177 8179	10.9205 2028	17.6769 8636	0.0915 7073	14
15	1.6753 4883	0.5968 9062	11.5174 1090	19.2956 8088	0.0868 2507	15
16	1.7339 8604	0.5767 0591	12.0941 1681	20.9710 2971	0.0826 8483	16
17	1.7946 7555	0.5572 0378	12.6513 2059	22.7050 1575	0.0790 4313	17
18	1.8574 8920	0.5383 6114	13.1896 8173	24.4996 9130	0.0758 1684	18
19	1.9225 0132	0.5201 5569	13.7098 3742	26.3571 8050	0.0729 4033	19
20	1.9897 8886	0.5025 6588	14.2124 0330	28.2796 8181	0.0703 6108	20
21	2.0594 3147	0.4855 7090	14.6979 7420	30.2694 7068	0.0680 3659	21
22	2.1315 1158	0.4691 5063	15.1671 2484	32.3289 0215	0.0659 3207	22
23	2.2061 1448	0.4532 8563	15.6204 1047	34.4604 1373	0.0640 1880	23
24	2.2833 2849	0.4379 5713	16.0583 6760	36.6665 2821	0.0622 7283	24
25	2.3632 4498	0.4231 4699	16.4815 1459	38.9498 5669	0.0606 7404	25
26	2.4459 5856	0.4088 3767	16.8903 5226	41.3131 0168	0.0592 0540	26
27	2.5315 6711	0.3950 1224	17.2853 6451	43.7590 6024	0.0578 5241	27
28	2.6201 7196	0.3816 5434	17.6670 1885	46.2906 2734	0.0566 0265	28
29	2.7118 7798	0.3687 4815	18.0357 6700	48.9107 9930	0.0554 4538	29
30	2.8067 9370	0.3562 7841	18.3920 4541	51.6226 7728	0.0543 7133	30
31	2.9050 3148	0.3442 3035	18.7362 7576	54.4294 7098	0.0533 7240	31
32	3.0067 0759	0.3325 8971	19.0688 6547	57.3345 0247	0.0524 4150	32
33	3.1119 4235	0.3213 4271	19.3902 0818	60.3412 1005	0.0515 7242	33
34	3.2208 6033	0.3104 7605	19.7006 8423	63.4531 5240	0.0507 5966	34
35	3.3335 9045	0.2999 7686	20.0006 6110	66.6740 1274	0.0499 9835	35
36	3.4502 6611	0.2898 3272	20.2904 9381	70.0076 0318	0.0492 8416	36
37	3.5710 2543	0.2800 3161	20.5705 2542	73.4578 6930	0.0486 1325	37
38	3.6960 1132	0.2705 6194	20.8410 8736	77.0288 9472	0.0479 8214	38
39	3.8253 7171	0.2614 1250	21.1024 9987	80.7249 0604	0.0473 8775	39
40	3.9592 5972	0.2525 7247	21.3550 7234	84.5502 7775	0.0468 2728	40
41	4.0978 3381	0.2440 3137	21.5991 0371	88.5095 3747	0.0462 9822	41
42	4.2412 5799	0.2357 7910	21.8348 8281	92.6073 7128	0.0457 9828	42
43	4.3897 0202	0.2278 0590	22.0626 8870	96.8486 2928	0.0453 2539	43
44	4.5433 4160	0.2201 0231	22.2827 9102	101.2383 3130	0.0448 7768	44
45	4.7023 5855	0.2126 5924	22.4954 5026	105.7816 7290	0.0444 5343	45
46	4.8669 4110	0.2054 6787	22.7009 1813	110.4840 3145	0.0440 5108	46
47	5.0372 8404	0.1985 1968	22.8994 3780	115.3509 7255	0.0436 6919	47
48	5.2135 8898	0.1918 0645	23.0912 4425	120.3882 5659	0.0433 0646	48
49	5.3960 6459	0.1853 2024	23.2765 6450	125.6018 4557	0.0429 6167	49
50	5.5849 2686	0.1790 5337	23.4556 1787	130.9979 1016	0.0426 3371	50

Table **XVI** (*continued*). 3½ %

Number of periods n	Amount of 1 at compound interest $s^n = (1+i)^n$	Present value of 1 $v^n = \dfrac{1}{(1+i)^n}$	Present value of an annuity of 1 $a_{\overline{n}|} = \dfrac{1-v^n}{i}$	Amount of an annuity of 1 $s_{\overline{n}|} = \dfrac{(1+i)^n-1}{i}$	Annuity whose present value is 1. (CRF) $\dfrac{1}{a_{\overline{n}|}} = \dfrac{1}{s_{\overline{n}|}} + i$	Number of periods n
51	5.7803 9930	0.1729 9843	23.6286 1630	136.5828 3702	0.0423 2156	51
52	5.9827 1327	0.1671 4824	23.7957 6454	142.3632 3631	0.0420 2429	52
53	6.1921 0824	0.1614 9589	23.9572 6043	148.3459 4958	0.0417 4100	53
54	6.4088 3202	0.1560 3467	24.1132 9510	154.5380 5782	0.0414 7090	54
55	6.6331 4114	0.1507 5814	24.2640 5323	160.9468 8984	0.0412 1323	55
56	6.8653 0108	0.1456 6004	24.4097 1327	167.5800 3099	0.0409 6730	56
57	7.1055 8662	0.1407 3433	24.5504 4760	174.4453 3207	0.0407 3245	57
58	7.3542 8215	0.1359 7520	24.6864 2281	181.5509 1869	0.0405 0810	58
59	7.6116 8203	0.1313 7701	24.8177 9981	188.9052 0085	0.0402 9366	59
60	7.8780 9090	0.1269 3431	24.9447 3412	196.5168 8288	0.0400 8862	60
61	8.1538 2408	0.1226 4184	25.0673 7596	204.3949 7378	0.0398 9249	61
62	8.4392 0793	0.1184 9453	25.1858 7049	212.5487 9786	0.0397 0480	62
63	8.7345 8020	0.1144 8747	25.3003 5796	220.9880 0579	0.0395 2513	63
64	9.0402 9051	0.1106 1591	25.4109 7388	229.7225 8599	0.0393 5308	64
65	9.3567 0068	0.1068 7528	25.5178 4916	238.7628 7650	0.0391 8826	65
66	9.6841 8520	0.1032 6114	25.6211 1030	248.1195 7718	0.0390 3031	66
67	10.0231 3168	0.0997 6922	25.7208 7951	257.8037 6238	0.0388 7892	67
68	10.3739 4129	0.0963 9538	25.8172 7489	267.8268 9406	0.0387 3375	68
69	10.7370 2924	0.0931 3563	25.9104 1052	278.2008 3535	0.0385 9453	69
70	11.1128 2526	0.0899 8612	26.0003 9664	288.9378 6459	0.0384 6095	70
71	11.5017 7414	0.0869 4311	26.0873 3975	300.0506 8985	0.0383 3277	71
72	11.9043 3624	0.0840 0300	26.1713 4275	311.5524 6400	0.0382 0973	72
73	12.3209 8801	0.0811 6232	26.2525 0508	323.4568 0024	0.0380 9160	73
74	12.7522 2259	0.0784 1770	26.3309 2278	335.7777 8824	0.0379 7816	74
75	13.1985 5038	0.0757 6590	26.4066 8868	348.5300 1083	0.0378 6919	75
76	13.6604 9964	0.0732 0376	26.4798 9244	361.7285 6121	0.0377 6450	76
77	14.1386 1713	0.0707 2827	26.5506 2072	375.3890 6085	0.0376 6390	77
78	14.6334 6873	0.0683 3650	26.6189 5721	389.5276 7798	0.0375 6721	78
79	15.1456 4013	0.0660 2560	26.6849 8281	404.1611 4671	0.0374 7426	79
80	15.6757 3754	0.0637 9285	26.7487 7567	419.3067 8685	0.0373 8489	80
81	16.2243 8835	0.0616 3561	26.8104 1127	434.9825 2439	0.0372 9894	81
82	16.7922 4195	0.0595 5131	26.8699 6258	451.2069 1274	0.0372 1628	82
83	17.3799 7041	0.0575 3750	26.9275 0008	467.9991 5469	0.0371 3676	83
84	17.9882 6938	0.0555 9178	26.9830 9186	485.3791 2510	0.0370 6025	84
85	18.6178 5881	0.0537 1187	27.0368 0373	503.3673 9448	0.0369 8662	85
86	19.2694 8387	0.0518 9553	27.0886 9926	521.9852 5329	0.0369 1576	86
87	19.9439 1580	0.0501 4060	27.1388 3986	541.2547 3715	0.0368 4756	87
88	20.6419 5285	0.0484 4503	27.1872 8489	561.1986 5295	0.0367 8190	88
89	21.3644 2120	0.0468 0679	27.2340 9168	581.8406 0581	0.0367 1868	89
90	22.1121 7595	0.0452 2395	27.2793 1564	603.2050 2701	0.0366 5781	90
91	22.8861 0210	0.0436 9464	27.3230 1028	625.3172 0295	0.0365 9919	91
92	23.6871 1568	0.0422 1704	27.3652 2732	648.2033 0506	0.0365 4273	92
93	24.5161 6473	0.0407 8941	27.4060 1673	671.8904 2073	0.0364 8834	93
94	25.3742 3049	0.0394 1006	27.4454 2680	696.4065 8546	0.0364 3594	94
95	26.2623 2856	0.0380 7735	27.4835 0415	721.7808 1595	0.0363 8546	95
96	27.1815 1006	0.0367 8971	27.5202 9387	748.0431 4451	0.0363 3682	96
97	28.1328 6291	0.0355 4562	27.5558 3948	775.2246 5457	0.0362 8995	97
98	29.1175 1311	0.0343 4359	27.5901 8308	803.3575 1748	0.0362 4478	98
99	30.1366 2607	0.0331 8221	27.6233 6529	832.4750 3059	0.0362 0124	99
100	31.1914 0798	0.0320 6011	27.6554 2540	862.6116 5666	0.0361 5927	100

Table XVII. 4 %

Number of periods n	Amount of 1 at compound interest $s^n = (1+i)^n$	Present value of 1 $v^n = \dfrac{1}{(1+i)^n}$	Present value of an annuity of 1 $a_{\overline{n}|} = \dfrac{1-v^n}{i}$	Amount of an annuity of 1 $s_{\overline{n}|} = \dfrac{(1+i)^n-1}{i}$	Annuity whose present value is 1. (CRF) $\dfrac{1}{a_{\overline{n}|}} = \dfrac{1}{s_{\overline{n}|}}+i$	Number of periods n
1	1.0400 0000	0.9615 3846	0.9615 3846	1.0000 0000	1.0400 0000	1
2	1.0816 0000	0.9245 5621	1.8860 9467	2.0400 0000	0.5301 9608	2
3	1.1248 6400	0.8889 9636	2.7750 9103	3.1216 0000	0.3603 4854	3
4	1.1698 5856	0.8548 0419	3.6298 9522	4.2464 6400	0.2754 9005	4
5	1.2166 5290	0.8219 2711	4.4518 2233	5.4163 2256	0.2246 2711	5
6	1.2653 1902	0.7903 1453	5.2421 3686	6.6329 7546	0.1907 6190	6
7	1.3159 3178	0.7599 1781	6.0020 5467	7.8982 9448	0.1666 0961	7
8	1.3685 6905	0.7306 9021	6.7327 4487	9.2142 2626	0.1485 2783	8
9	1.4233 1181	0.7025 8674	7.4353 3161	10.5827 9531	0.1344 9299	9
10	1.4802 4428	0.6755 6417	8.1108 9578	12.0061 0712	0.1232 9094	10
11	1.5394 5406	0.6495 8093	8.7604 7671	13.4863 5141	0.1141 4904	11
12	1.6010 3222	0.6245 9705	9.3850 7376	15.0258 0546	0.1065 5217	12
13	1.6650 7351	0.6005 7409	9.9856 4785	16.6268 3768	0.1001 4373	13
14	1.7316 7645	0.5774 7508	10.5631 2293	18.2919 1119	0.0946 6897	14
15	1.8009 4351	0.5552 6450	11.1183 8743	20.0235 8764	0.0899 4110	15
16	1.8729 8125	0.5339 0818	11.6522 9561	21.8245 3114	0.0858 2000	16
17	1.9479 0050	0.5133 7325	12.1656 6885	23.6975 1239	0.0821 9852	17
18	2.0258 1652	0.4936 2812	12.6592 9697	25.6454 1288	0.0789 9333	18
19	2.1068 4918	0.4746 4242	13.1339 3940	27.6712 2940	0.0761 3862	19
20	2.1911 2314	0.4563 8695	13.5903 2634	29.7780 7858	0.0735 8175	20
21	2.2787 6807	0.4388 3360	14.0291 5995	31.9692 0172	0.0712 8011	21
22	2.3699 1879	0.4219 5539	14.4511 1533	34.2479 6979	0.0691 9881	22
23	2.4647 1554	0.4057 2633	14.8568 4167	36.6178 8858	0.0673 0906	23
24	2.5633 0416	0.3901 2147	15.2469 6314	39.0826 0412	0.0655 8683	24
25	2.6658 3633	0.3751 1680	15.6220 7994	41.6459 0829	0.0640 1196	25
26	2.7724 6978	0.3606 8923	15.9827 6918	44.3117 4462	0.0625 6738	26
27	2.8833 6858	0.3468 1657	16.3295 8575	47.0842 1440	0.0612 3854	27
28	2.9987 0332	0.3334 7747	16.6630 6322	49.9675 8298	0.0600 1298	28
29	3.1186 5145	0.3206 5141	16.9837 1463	52.9662 8630	0.0588 7993	29
30	3.2433 9751	0.3083 1867	17.2920 3330	56.0849 3775	0.0578 3010	30
31	3.3731 3341	0.2964 6026	17.5884 9356	59.3283 3526	0.0568 5535	31
32	3.5080 5875	0.2850 5794	17.8735 5150	62.7014 6867	0.0559 4859	32
33	3.6483 8110	0.2740 9417	18.1476 4567	66.2095 2742	0.0551 0357	33
34	3.7943 1634	0.2635 5209	18.4111 9776	69.8579 0851	0.0543 1477	34
35	3.9460 8899	0.2534 1547	18.6646 1323	73.6522 2486	0.0535 7732	35
36	4.1039 3255	0.2436 6872	18.9082 8195	77.5983 1385	0.0528 8688	36
37	4.2680 8986	0.2342 9685	19.1425 7880	81.7022 4640	0.0522 3957	37
38	4.4388 1345	0.2252 8543	19.3678 6423	85.9703 3626	0.0516 3192	38
39	4.6163 6599	0.2166 2061	19.5844 8484	90.4091 4971	0.0510 6083	39
40	4.8010 2063	0.2082 8904	19.7927 7388	95.0255 1570	0.0505 2349	40
41	4.9930 6145	0.2002 7793	19.9930 5181	99.8265 3633	0.0500 1738	41
42	5.1927 8391	0.1925 7493	20.1856 2674	104.8195 9778	0.0495 4020	42
43	5.4004 9527	0.1851 6820	20.3707 9494	110.0123 8169	0.0490 8989	43
44	5.6165 1508	0.1780 4635	20.5488 4129	115.4128 7696	0.0486 6454	44
45	5.8411 7568	0.1711 9841	20.7200 3970	121.0293 9204	0.0482 6246	45
46	6.0748 2271	0.1646 1386	20.8846 5356	126.8705 6772	0.0478 8205	46
47	6.3178 1562	0.1582 8256	21.0429 3612	132.9453 9043	0.0475 2189	47
48	6.5705 2824	0.1521 9476	21.1951 3088	139.2632 0604	0.0471 8065	48
49	6.8333 4937	0.1463 4112	21.3414 7200	145.8337 3429	0.0468 5712	49
50	7.1066 8335	0.1407 1262	21.4821 8462	152.6670 8366	0.0465 5020	50

Table XVII (continued). 4%

Number of periods n	Amount of 1 at compound interest $s^n = (1+i)^n$	Present value of 1 $v^n = \dfrac{1}{(1+i)^n}$	Present value of an annuity of 1 $a_{\overline{n}|} = \dfrac{1-v^n}{i}$	Amount of an annuity of 1 $s_{\overline{n}|} = \dfrac{(1+i)^n-1}{i}$	Annuity whose present value is 1. (CRF) $\dfrac{1}{a_{\overline{n}|}} = \dfrac{1}{s_{\overline{n}|}}+i$	Number of periods n
51	7.3909 5068	0.1353 0059	21.6174 8521	159.7737 6700	0.0462 5885	51
52	7.6865 8871	0.1300 9672	21.7475 8193	167.1647 1768	0.0459 8212	52
53	7.9940 5226	0.1250 9300	21.8726 7493	174.8513 0639	0.0457 1915	53
54	8.3138 1435	0.1202 8173	21.9929 5667	182.8453 5865	0.0454 6910	54
55	8.6463 6692	0.1156 5551	22.1086 1218	191.1591 7299	0.0452 3124	55
56	8.9922 2160	0.1112 0722	22.2189 1940	199.8055 3991	0.0450 0487	56
57	9.3519 1046	0.1069 3002	22.3267 4943	208.7977 6151	0.0447 8932	57
58	9.7259 8688	0.1028 1733	22.4295 6676	218.1496 7197	0.0445 8401	58
59	10.1150 2635	0.0988 6282	22.5284 2957	227.8756 5885	0.0443 8836	59
60	10.5196 2741	0.0950 6040	22.6234 8997	237.9906 8520	0.0442 0185	60
61	10.9404 1250	0.0914 0423	22.7148 9421	248.5103 1261	0.0440 2398	61
62	11.3780 2900	0.0878 8868	22.8027 8289	259.4507 2511	0.0438 5430	62
63	11.8331 5016	0.0845 0835	22.8872 9124	270.8287 5412	0.0436 9237	63
64	12.3064 7617	0.0812 5803	22.9685 4927	282.6619 0428	0.0435 3780	64
65	12.7987 3522	0.0781 3272	23.0466 8199	294.9683 8045	0.0433 9019	65
66	13.3106 8463	0.0751 2762	23.1218 0961	307.7671 1567	0.0432 4921	66
67	13.8431 1201	0.0722 3809	23.1940 4770	321.0778 0030	0.0431 1451	67
68	14.3968 3649	0.0694 5970	23.2635 0740	334.9209 1231	0.0429 8578	68
69	14.9727 0995	0.0667 8818	23.3302 9558	349.3177 4880	0.0428 6272	69
70	15.5716 1835	0.0642 1940	23.3945 1498	364.2904 5876	0.0427 4506	70
71	16.1944 8308	0.0617 4942	23.4562 6440	379.8620 7711	0.0426 3253	71
72	16.8422 6241	0.0593 7445	23.5156 3885	396.0565 6019	0.0425 2489	72
73	17.5159 5290	0.0570 9081	23.5727 2966	412.8988 2260	0.0424 2190	73
74	18.2165 9102	0.0548 9501	23.6276 2468	430.4147 7550	0.0423 2334	74
75	18.9452 5466	0.0527 8367	23.6804 0834	448.6313 6652	0.0422 2900	75
76	19.7030 6485	0.0507 5353	23.7311 6187	467.5766 2118	0.0421 3869	76
77	20.4911 8744	0.0488 0147	23.7799 6333	487.2796 8603	0.0420 5221	77
78	21.3108 3494	0.0469 2449	23.8268 8782	507.7708 7347	0.0419 6939	78
79	22.1632 6834	0.0451 1970	23.8720 0752	529.0817 0841	0.0418 9007	79
80	23.0497 9907	0.0433 8433	23.9153 9185	551.2449 7675	0.0418 1408	80
81	23.9717 9103	0.0417 1570	23.9571 0754	574.2947 7582	0.0417 4127	81
82	24.9306 6267	0.0401 1125	23.9972 1879	598.2665 6685	0.0416 7150	82
83	25.9278 8918	0.0385 6851	24.0357 8730	623.1972 2952	0.0416 0463	83
84	26.9650 0475	0.0370 8510	24.0728 7240	649.1251 1870	0.0415 4054	84
85	28.0436 0494	0.0356 5875	24.1085 3116	676.0901 2345	0.0414 7909	85
86	29.1653 4914	0.0342 8726	24.1428 1842	704.1337 2839	0.0414 2018	86
87	30.3319 6310	0.0329 6852	24.1757 8694	733.2990 7753	0.0413 6370	87
88	31.5452 4163	0.0317 0050	24.2074 8745	763.6310 4063	0.0413 0953	88
89	32.8070 5129	0.0304 8125	24.2379 6870	795.1762 8225	0.0412 5758	89
90	34.1193 3334	0.0293 0890	24.2672 7759	827.9833 3354	0.0412 0775	90
91	35.4841 0668	0.0281 8163	24.2954 5923	862.1026 6688	0.0411 5995	91
92	36.9034 7094	0.0270 9772	24.3225 5695	897.5867 7356	0.0411 1410	92
93	38.3796 0978	0.0260 5550	24.3486 1245	934.4902 4450	0.0410 7010	93
94	39.9147 9417	0.0250 5337	24.3736 6582	972.8698 5428	0.0410 2789	94
95	41.5113 8594	0.0240 8978	24.3977 5559	1012.7846 4845	0.0409 8738	95
96	43.1718 4138	0.0231 6325	24.4209 1884	1054.2960 3439	0.0409 4850	96
97	44.8987 1503	0.0222 7235	24.4431 9119	1097.4678 7577	0.0409 1119	97
98	46.6946 6363	0.0214 1572	24.4646 0692	1142.3665 9080	0.0408 7538	98
99	48.5624 5018	0.0205 9204	24.4851 9896	1189.0612 5443	0.0408 4100	99
100	50.5049 4818	0.0198 0004	24.5049 9900	1237.6237 0461	0.0408 0800	100

Table XVIII.   5%

Number of periods n	Amount of 1 at compound interest $s^n = (1 + i)^n$	Present value of 1 $v^n = \dfrac{1}{(1 + i)^n}$	Present value of an annuity of 1 $a_{\overline{n}|} = \dfrac{1 - v^n}{i}$	Amount of an annuity of 1 $s_{\overline{n}|} = \dfrac{(1+i)^n - 1}{i}$	Annuity whose present value is 1. (CRF) $\dfrac{1}{a_{\overline{n}|}} = \dfrac{1}{s_{\overline{n}|}} + i$	Number of periods n
1	1.0500 0000	0.9523 8095	0.9523 8095	1.0000 0000	1.0500 0000	1
2	1.1025 0000	0.9070 2948	1.8594 1043	2.0500 0000	0.5378 0488	2
3	1.1576 2500	0.8638 3760	2.7232 4803	3.1525 0000	0.3672 0856	3
4	1.2155 0625	0.8227 0247	3.5459 5050	4.3101 2500	0.2820 1183	4
5	1.2762 8156	0.7835 2617	4.3294 7667	5.5256 3125	0.2309 7480	5
6	1.3400 9564	0.7462 1540	5.0756 9206	6.8019 1281	0.1970 1747	6
7	1.4071 0042	0.7106 8133	5.7863 7340	8.1420 0845	0.1728 1982	7
8	1.4774 5544	0.6768 3936	6.4632 1276	9.5491 0888	0.1547 2181	8
9	1.5513 2822	0.6446 0892	7.1078 2168	11.0265 6432	0.1406 9008	9
10	1.6288 9463	0.6139 1325	7.7217 3493	12.5778 9254	0.1295 0458	10
11	1.7103 3936	0.5846 7929	8.3064 1422	14.2067 8716	0.1203 8889	11
12	1.7958 5633	0.5568 3742	8.8632 5164	15.9171 2652	0.1128 2541	12
13	1.8856 4914	0.5303 2135	9.3935 7299	17.7129 8285	0.1064 5577	13
14	1.9799 3160	0.5050 6795	9.8986 4094	19.5986 3199	0.1010 2397	14
15	2.0789 2818	0.4810 1710	10.3796 5804	21.5785 6359	0.0963 4229	15
16	2.1828 7459	0.4581 1152	10.8377 6956	23.6574 9177	0.0922 6991	16
17	2.2920 1832	0.4362 9669	11.2740 6625	25.8403 6636	0.0886 9914	17
18	2.4066 1923	0.4155 2065	11.6895 8690	28.1323 8467	0.0855 4622	18
19	2.5269 5020	0.3957 3396	12.0853 2086	30.5390 0391	0.0827 4501	19
20	2.6532 9771	0.3768 8948	12.4622 1034	33.0659 5410	0.0802 4259	20
21	2.7859 6259	0.3589 4236	12.8211 5271	35.7192 5181	0.0779 9611	21
22	2.9252 6072	0.3418 4987	13.1630 0258	38.5052 1440	0.0759 7051	22
23	3.0715 2376	0.3255 7131	13.4885 7388	41.4304 7512	0.0741 3682	23
24	3.2250 9994	0.3100 6791	13.7986 4179	44.5019 9887	0.0724 7090	24
25	3.3863 5494	0.2953 0277	14.0939 4457	47.7270 9882	0.0709 5246	25
26	3.5556 7269	0.2812 4073	14.3751 8530	51.1134 5376	0.0695 6432	26
27	3.7334 5632	0.2678 4832	14.6430 3362	54.6691 2645	0.0682 9186	27
28	3.9201 2914	0.2550 9364	14.8981 2726	58.4025 8277	0.0671 2253	28
29	4.1161 3560	0.2429 4632	15.1410 7358	62.3227 1191	0.0660 4551	29
30	4.3219 4238	0.2313 7745	15.3724 5103	66.4388 4750	0.0650 5144	30
31	4.5380 3949	0.2203 5947	15.5928 1050	70.7607 8988	0.0641 3212	31
32	4.7649 4147	0.2098 6617	15.8026 7667	75.2988 2937	0.0632 8042	32
33	5.0031 8854	0.1998 7254	16.0025 4921	80.0637 7084	0.0624 9004	33
34	5.2533 4797	0.1903 5480	16.1929 0401	85.0669 5938	0.0617 5545	34
35	5.5160 1537	0.1812 9029	16.3741 9429	90.3203 0735	0.0610 7171	35
36	5.7918 1614	0.1726 5741	16.5468 5171	95.8363 2272	0.0604 3446	36
37	6.0814 0694	0.1644 3563	16.7112 8734	101.6281 3886	0.0598 3979	37
38	6.3854 7729	0.1566 0536	16.8678 9271	107.7095 4580	0.0592 8423	38
39	6.7047 5115	0.1491 4797	17.0170 4067	114.0950 2309	0.0587 6462	39
40	7.0399 8871	0.1420 4568	17.1590 8635	120.7997 7424	0.0582 7816	40
41	7.3919 8815	0.1352 8160	17.2943 6796	127.8397 6295	0.0578 2229	41
42	7.7615 8756	0.1288 3962	17.4232 0758	135.2317 5110	0.0573 9471	42
43	8.1496 6693	0.1227 0440	17.5459 1198	142.9933 3866	0.0569 9333	43
44	8.5571 5028	0.1168 6133	17.6627 7331	151.1430 0559	0.0566 1625	44
45	8.9850 0779	0.1112 9651	17.7740 6982	159.7001 5587	0.0562 6173	45
46	9.4342 5818	0.1059 9668	17.8800 6650	168.6851 6366	0.0559 2820	46
47	9.9059 7109	0.1009 4921	17.9810 1571	178.1194 2185	0.0556 1421	47
48	10.4012 6965	0.0961 4211	18.0771 5782	188.0253 9294	0.0553 1843	48
49	10.9213 3313	0.0915 6391	18.1687 2173	198.4266 6259	0.0550 3965	49
50	11.4673 9979	0.0872 0373	18.2559 2546	209.3479 9572	0.0547 7674	50

Table XVIII (*continued*). 5 %

Number of periods n	Amount of 1 at compound interest $s^n = (1+i)^n$	Present value of 1 $v^n = \dfrac{1}{(1+i)^n}$	Present value of an annuity of 1 $a_{\overline{n}|} = \dfrac{1-v^n}{i}$	Amount of an annuity of 1 $s_{\overline{n}|} = \dfrac{(1+i)^n-1}{i}$	Annuity whose present value is 1. (CRF) $\dfrac{1}{a_{\overline{n}|}} = \dfrac{1}{s_{\overline{n}|}} + i$	Number of periods n
51	12.0407 6978	0.0830 5117	18.3389 7663	220.8153 9550	0.0545 2867	51
52	12.6428 0826	0.0790 9635	18.4180 7298	232.8561 6528	0.0542 9450	52
53	13.2749 4868	0.0753 2986	18.4934 0284	245.4989 7354	0.0540 7334	53
54	13.9386 9611	0.0717 4272	18.5651 4556	258.7739 2222	0.0538 6438	54
55	14.6356 3092	0.0683 2640	18.6334 7196	272.7126 1833	0.0536 6686	55
56	15.3674 1246	0.0650 7276	18.6985 4473	287.3482 4924	0.0534 8010	56
57	16.1357 8309	0.0619 7406	18.7605 1879	302.7156 6171	0.0533 0343	57
58	16.9425 7224	0.0590 2291	18.8195 4170	318.8514 4479	0.0531 3626	58
59	17.7897 0085	0.0562 1230	18.8757 5400	335.7940 1703	0.0529 7802	59
60	18.6791 8589	0.0535 3552	18.9292 8952	353.5837 1788	0.0528 2818	60
61	19.6131 4519	0.0509 8621	18.9802 7574	372.2629 0378	0.0526 8627	61
62	20.5938 0245	0.0485 5830	19.0288 3404	391.8760 4897	0.0525 5183	62
63	21.6234 9257	0.0462 4600	19.0750 8003	412.4698 5141	0.0524 2442	63
64	22.7046 6720	0.0440 4381	19.1191 2384	434.0933 4398	0.0523 0365	64
65	23.8399 0056	0.0419 4648	19.1610 7033	456.7980 1118	0.0521 8915	65
66	25.0318 9559	0.0399 4903	19.2010 1936	480.6379 1174	0.0520 8057	66
67	26.2834 9037	0.0380 4670	19.2390 6606	505.6698 0733	0.0519 7757	67
68	27.5976 6488	0.0362 3495	19.2753 0101	531.9532 9770	0.0518 7986	68
69	28.9775 4813	0.0345 0948	19.3098 1048	559.5509 6258	0.0517 8715	69
70	30.4264 2554	0.0328 6617	19.3426 7665	588.5285 1071	0.0516 9915	70
71	31.9477 4681	0.0313 0111	19.3739 7776	618.9549 3625	0.0516 1563	71
72	33.5451 3415	0.0298 1058	19.4037 8834	650.9026 8306	0.0515 3633	72
73	35.2223 9086	0.0283 9103	19.4321 7937	684.4478 1721	0.0514 6103	73
74	36.9835 1040	0.0270 3908	19.4592 1845	719.6702 0807	0.0513 8953	74
75	38.8326 8592	0.0257 5150	19.4849 6995	756.6537 1848	0.0513 2161	75
76	40.7743 2022	0.0245 2524	19.5094 9519	795.4864 0440	0.0512 5709	76
77	42.8130 3623	0.0233 5737	19.5328 5257	836.2607 2462	0.0511 9580	77
78	44.9536 8804	0.0222 4512	19.5550 9768	879.0737 6085	0.0511 3756	78
79	47.2013 7244	0.0211 8582	19.5762 8351	924.0274 4889	0.0510 8222	79
80	49.5614 4107	0.0201 7698	19.5964 6048	971.2288 2134	0.0510 2962	80
81	52.0395 1312	0.0192 1617	19.6156 7665	1020.7902 6240	0.0509 7963	81
82	54.6414 8878	0.0183 0111	19.6339 7776	1072.8297 7552	0.0509 3211	82
83	57.3735 6322	0.0174 2963	19.6514 0739	1127.4712 6430	0.0508 8694	83
84	60.2422 4138	0.0165 9965	19.6680 0704	1184.8448 2752	0.0508 4399	84
85	63.2543 5344	0.0158 0919	19.6838 1623	1245.0870 6889	0.0508 0316	85
86	66.4170 7112	0.0150 5637	19.6988 7260	1308.3414 2234	0.0507 6433	86
87	69.7379 2467	0.0143 3940	19.7132 1200	1374.7584 9345	0.0507 2740	87
88	73.2248 2091	0.0136 5657	19.7268 6857	1444.4964 1812	0.0506 9228	88
89	76.8860 6195	0.0130 0626	19.7398 7483	1517.7212 3903	0.0506 5888	89
90	80.7303 6505	0.0123 8691	19.7522 6174	1594.6073 0098	0.0506 2711	90
91	84.7668 8330	0.0117 9706	19.7640 5880	1675.3376 6603	0.0505 9689	91
92	89.0052 2747	0.0112 3530	19.7752 9410	1760.1045 4933	0.0505 6815	92
93	93.4554 8884	0.0107 0028	19.7859 9438	1849.1097 7680	0.0505 4080	93
94	98.1282 6328	0.0101 9074	19.7961 8512	1942.5652 6564	0.0505 1478	94
95	103.0346 7645	0.0097 0547	19.8058 9059	2040.6935 2892	0.0504 9003	95
96	108.1864 1027	0.0092 4331	19.8151 3390	2143.7282 0537	0.0504 6648	96
97	113.5957 3078	0.0088 0315	19.8239 3705	2251.9146 1564	0.0504 4407	97
98	119.2755 1732	0.0083 8395	19.8323 2100	2365.5103 4642	0.0504 2274	98
99	125.2392 9319	0.0079 8471	19.8403 0571	2484.7858 6374	0.0504 0245	99
100	131.5012 5785	0.0076 0449	19.8479 1020	2610.0251 5693	0.0503 8314	100

Table XIX. 6%

Number of periods	Amount of 1 at compound interest	Present value of 1	Present value of an annuity of 1	Amount of an annuity of 1	Annuity whose present value is 1. (CRF)	Number of periods
n	$s^n = (1+i)^n$	$v^n = \dfrac{1}{(1+i)^n}$	$a_{\overline{n}|} = \dfrac{1-v^n}{i}$	$s_{\overline{n}|} = \dfrac{(1+i)^n-1}{i}$	$\dfrac{1}{a_{\overline{n}|}} = \dfrac{1}{s_{\overline{n}|}} + i$	n
1	1.0600 0000	0.9433 9623	0.9433 9623	1.0000 0000	1.0600 0000	1
2	1.1236 0000	0.8899 9644	1.8333 9267	2.0600 0000	0.5454 3689	2
3	1.1910 1600	0.8396 1928	2.6730 1195	3.1836 0000	0.3741 0981	3
4	1.2624 7696	0.7920 9366	3.4651 0561	4.3746 1600	0.2885 9149	4
5	1.3382 2558	0.7472 5817	4.2123 6379	5.6370 9296	0.2373 9640	5
6	1.4185 1911	0.7049 6054	4.9173 2433	6.9753 1854	0.2033 6263	6
7	1.5036 3026	0.6650 5711	5.5823 8144	8.3938 3765	0.1791 3502	7
8	1.5938 4807	0.6274 1237	6.2097 9381	9.8974 6791	0.1610 3594	8
9	1.6894 7896	0.5918 9846	6.8016 9227	11.4913 1598	0.1470 2224	9
10	1.7908 4770	0.5583 9478	7.3600 8705	13.1807 9494	0.1358 6796	10
11	1.8982 9856	0.5267 8753	7.8868 7458	14.9716 4264	0.1267 9294	11
12	2.0121 9647	0.4969 6936	8.3838 4394	16.8699 4120	0.1192 7703	12
13	2.1329 2826	0.4688 3902	8.8526 8296	18.8821 3767	0.1129 6011	13
14	2.2609 0396	0.4423 0096	9.2949 8393	21.0150 6593	0.1075 8491	14
15	2.3965 5819	0.4172 6506	9.7122 4899	23.2759 6988	0.1029 6276	15
16	2.5403 5168	0.3936 4628	10.1058 9527	25.6725 2808	0.0989 5214	16
17	2.6927 7279	0.3713 6442	10.4772 5969	28.2128 7976	0.0954 4480	17
18	2.8543 3915	0.3503 4379	10.8276 0348	30.9056 5255	0.0923 5654	18
19	3.0255 9950	0.3305 1301	11.1581 1649	33.7599 9170	0.0896 2086	19
20	3.2071 3547	0.3118 0473	11.4699 2122	36.7855 9120	0.0871 8456	20
21	3.3995 6360	0.2941 5540	11.7640 7662	39.9927 2668	0.0850 0455	21
22	3.6035 3742	0.2775 0510	12.0415 8172	43.3922 9028	0.0830 4557	22
23	3.8197 4966	0.2617 9726	12.3033 7898	46.9958 2769	0.0812 7848	23
24	4.0489 3464	0.2469 7855	12.5503 5753	50.8155 7735	0.0796 7900	24
25	4.2918 7072	0.2329 9863	12.7833 5616	54.8645 1200	0.0782 2672	25
26	4.5493 8296	0.2198 1003	13.0031 6619	59.1563 8272	0.0769 0435	26
27	4.8223 4594	0.2073 6795	13.2105 3414	63.7057 6568	0.0756 9717	27
28	5.1116 8670	0.1956 3014	13.4061 6428	68.5281 1162	0.0745 9255	28
29	5.4183 8790	0.1845 5674	13.5907 2102	73.6397 9832	0.0735 7961	29
30	5.7434 9117	0.1741 1013	13.7648 3115	79.0581 8622	0.0726 4891	30
31	6.0881 0064	0.1642 5484	13.9290 8599	84.8016 7739	0.0717 9222	31
32	6.4533 8668	0.1549 5740	14.0840 4339	90.8897 7803	0.0710 0234	32
33	6.8405 8988	0.1461 8622	14.2302 2961	97.3431 6471	0.0702 7293	33
34	7.2510 2528	0.1379 1153	14.3681 4114	104.1837 5460	0.0695 9843	34
35	7.6860 8679	0.1301 0522	14.4982 4636	111.4347 7987	0.0689 7386	35
36	8.1472 5200	0.1227 4077	14.6209 8713	119.1208 6666	0.0683 9483	36
37	8.6360 8712	0.1157 9318	14.7367 8031	127.2681 1866	0.0678 5743	37
38	9.1542 5235	0.1092 3885	14.8460 1916	135.9042 0578	0.0673 5812	38
39	9.7035 0749	0.1030 5552	14.9490 7468	145.0584 5813	0.0668 9377	39
40	10.2857 1794	0.0972 2219	15.0462 9687	154.7619 6562	0.0664 6154	40
41	10.9028 6101	0.0917 1905	15.1380 1592	165.0476 8356	0.0660 5886	41
42	11.5570 3267	0.0865 2740	15.2245 4332	175.9505 4457	0.0656 8342	42
43	12.2504 5463	0.0816 2962	15.3061 7294	187.5075 7724	0.0653 3312	43
44	12.9854 8191	0.0770 0908	15.3831 8202	199.7580 3188	0.0650 0606	44
45	13.7646 1083	0.0726 5007	15.4558 3209	212.7435 1379	0.0647 0050	45
46	14.5904 8748	0.0685 3781	15.5243 6990	226.5081 2462	0.0644 1485	46
47	15.4659 1673	0.0646 5831	15.5890 2821	241.0986 1210	0.0641 4768	47
48	16.3938 7173	0.0609 9840	15.6500 2661	256.5645 2882	0.0638 9766	48
49	17.3775 0403	0.0575 4566	15.7075 7227	272.9584 0055	0.0636 6356	49
50	18.4201 5427	0.0542 8836	15.7618 6064	290.3359 0458	0.0634 4429	50

Table XIX (*continued*). 6%

Number of periods n	Amount of 1 at compound interest $s^n = (1+i)^n$	Present value of 1 $v^n = \dfrac{1}{(1+i)^n}$	Present value of an annuity of 1 $a_{\overline{n}\rvert} = \dfrac{1-v^n}{i}$	Amount of an annuity of 1 $s_{\overline{n}\rvert} = \dfrac{(1+i)^n - 1}{i}$	Annuity whose present value is 1. (CRF) $\dfrac{1}{a_{\overline{n}\rvert}} = \dfrac{1}{s_{\overline{n}\rvert}} + i$	Number of periods n
51	19.5253 6353	0.0512 1544	15.8130 7607	308.7560 5886	0.0632 3880	51
52	20.6968 8534	0.0483 1645	15.8613 9252	328.2814 2239	0.0630 4617	52
53	21.9386 9846	0.0455 8156	15.9069 7408	348.9783 0773	0.0628 6551	53
54	23.2550 2037	0.0430 0147	15.9499 7554	370.9170 0620	0.0626 9602	54
55	24.6503 2159	0.0405 6742	15.9905 4297	394.1720 2657	0.0625 3696	55
56	26.1293 4089	0.0382 7115	16.0288 1412	418.8223 4816	0.0623 8765	56
57	27.6971 0134	0.0361 0486	16.0649 1898	444.9516 8905	0.0622 4744	57
58	29.3589 2742	0.0340 6119	16.0989 8017	472.6487 9040	0.0621 1574	58
59	31.1204 6307	0.0321 3320	16.1311 1337	502.0077 1782	0.0619 9200	59
60	32.9876 9085	0.0303 1434	16.1614 2771	533.1281 8089	0.0618 7572	60
61	34.9669 5230	0.0285 9843	16.1900 2614	566.1158 7174	0.0617 6642	61
62	37.0649 6944	0.0269 7965	16.2170 0579	601.0828 2405	0.0616 6366	62
63	39.2888 6761	0.0254 5250	16.2424 5829	638.1477 9349	0.0615 6704	63
64	41.6461 9967	0.0240 1179	16.2664 7009	677.4366 6110	0.0614 7615	64
65	44.1449 7165	0.0226 5264	16.2891 2272	719.0828 6076	0.0613 9066	65
66	46.7936 6994	0.0213 7041	16.3104 9314	763.2278 3241	0.0613 1022	66
67	49.6012 9014	0.0201 6077	16.3306 5390	810.0215 0236	0.0612 3454	67
68	52.5773 6755	0.0190 1959	16.3496 7349	859.6227 9250	0.0611 6330	68
69	55.7320 0960	0.0179 4301	16.3676 1650	912.2001 6005	0.0610 9625	69
70	59.0759 3018	0.0169 2737	16.3845 4387	967.9321 6965	0.0610 3313	70
71	62.6204 8599	0.0159 6921	16.4005 1308	1027.0080 9983	0.0609 7370	71
72	66.3777 1515	0.0150 6530	16.4155 7838	1089.6285 8582	0.0609 1774	72
73	70.3603 7806	0.0142 1254	16.4297 9093	1156.0063 0097	0.0608 6505	73
74	74.5820 0074	0.0134 0806	16.4431 9899	1226.3666 7903	0.0608 1542	74
75	79.0569 2079	0.0126 4911	16.4558 4810	1300.9486 7977	0.0607 6867	75
76	83.8003 3603	0.0119 3313	16.4677 8123	1380.0056 0055	0.0607 2463	76
77	88.8283 5620	0.0112 5767	16.4790 3889	1463.8059 3659	0.0606 8315	77
78	94.1580 5757	0.0106 2044	16.4896 5933	1552.6342 9278	0.0606 4407	78
79	99.8075 4102	0.0100 1928	16.4996 7862	1646.7923 5035	0.0606 0724	79
80	105.7959 9348	0.0094 5215	16.5091 3077	1746.5998 9137	0.0605 7254	80
81	112.1437 5309	0.0089 1713	16.5180 4790	1852.3958 8485	0.0605 3984	81
82	118.8723 7828	0.0084 1238	16.5264 6028	1964.5396 3794	0.0605 0903	82
83	126.0047 2097	0.0079 3621	16.5343 9649	2083.4120 1622	0.0604 7998	83
84	133.5650 0423	0.0074 8699	16.5418 8348	2209.4167 3719	0.0604 5261	84
85	141.5789 0449	0.0070 6320	16.5489 4668	2342.9817 4142	0.0604 2681	85
86	150.0736 3875	0.0066 6340	16.5556 1008	2484.5606 4591	0.0604 0249	86
87	159.0780 5708	0.0062 8622	16.5618 9630	2634.6342 8466	0.0603 7956	87
88	168.6227 4050	0.0059 3040	16.5678 2670	2793.7123 4174	0.0603 5795	88
89	178.7401 0493	0.0055 9472	16.5734 2141	2962.3350 8225	0.0603 3757	89
90	189.4645 1123	0.0052 7803	16.5786 9944	3141.0751 8718	0.0603 1836	90
91	200.8323 8190	0.0049 7928	16.5836 7872	3330.5396 9841	0.0603 0025	91
92	212.8823 2482	0.0046 9743	16.5883 7615	3531.3720 8032	0.0602 8318	92
93	225.6552 6431	0.0044 3154	16.5928 0769	3744.2544 0514	0.0602 6708	93
94	239.1945 8017	0.0041 8070	16.5969 8839	3969.9096 6944	0.0602 5190	94
95	253.5462 5498	0.0039 4405	16.6009 3244	4209.1042 4961	0.0602 3758	95
96	268.7590 3028	0.0037 2081	16.6046 5325	4462.6505 0459	0.0602 2408	96
97	284.8845 7209	0.0035 1019	16.6081 6344	4731.4095 3486	0.0602 1135	97
98	301.9776 4642	0.0033 1150	16.6114 7494	5016.2941 0696	0.0601 9935	98
99	320.0963 0520	0.0031 2406	16.6145 9900	5318.2717 5337	0.0601 8803	99
100	339.3020 8351	0.0029 4723	16.6175 4623	5638.3680 5857	0.0601 7736	100

Table XX.   7 %

Number of periods n	Amount of 1 at compound interest $s^n = (1+i)^n$	Present value of 1 $v^n = \dfrac{1}{(1+i)^n}$	Present value of an annuity of 1 $a_{\overline{n}\rceil} = \dfrac{1-v^n}{i}$	Amount of an annuity of 1 $s_{\overline{n}\rceil} = \dfrac{(1+i)^n-1}{i}$	Annuity whose present value is 1. (CRF) $\dfrac{1}{a_{\overline{n}\rceil}} = \dfrac{1}{s_{\overline{n}\rceil}} + i$	Number of periods n
1	1.0700 0000	0.9345 7944	0.9345 7944	1.0000 0000	1.0700 0000	1
2	1.1449 0000	0.8734 3873	1.8080 1817	2.0700 0000	0.5530 9179	2
3	1.2250 4300	0.8162 9788	2.6243 1604	3.2149 0000	0.3810 5166	3
4	1.3107 9601	0.7628 9521	3.3872 1126	4.4399 4300	0.2952 2812	4
5	1.4025 5173	0.7129 8618	4.1001 9744	5.7507 3901	0.2438 9069	5
6	1.5007 3035	0.6663 4222	4.7665 3966	7.1532 9074	0.2097 9580	6
7	1.6057 8148	0.6227 4974	5.3892 8940	8.6540 2109	0.1855 5322	7
8	1.7181 8618	0.5820 0910	5.9712 9851	10.2598 0257	0.1674 6776	8
9	1.8384 5921	0.5439 3374	6.5152 3225	11.9779 8875	0.1534 8647	9
10	1.9671 5136	0.5083 4929	7.0235 8154	13.8164 4796	0.1423 7750	10
11	2.1048 5195	0.4750 9280	7.4986 7434	15.7835 9932	0.1333 5690	11
12	2.2521 9159	0.4440 1196	7.9426 8630	17.8884 5127	0.1259 0199	12
13	2.4098 4500	0.4149 6445	8.3576 5074	20.1406 4286	0.1196 5085	13
14	2.5785 3415	0.3878 1724	8.7454 6799	22.5504 8786	0.1143 4494	14
15	2.7590 3154	0.3624 4602	9.1079 1401	25.1290 2201	0.1097 9462	15
16	2.9521 6375	0.3387 3460	9.4466 4860	27.8880 5355	0.1058 5765	16
17	3 1588 1521	0.3165 7439	9.7632 2299	30.8402 1730	0.1024 2519	17
18	3.3799 3228	0.2958 6392	10.0590 8691	33.9990 3251	0.0994 1260	18
19	3.6165 2754	0.2765 0832	10.3355 9524	37.3789 6479	0.0967 5301	19
20	3.8696 8446	0.2584 1900	10.5940 1425	40.9954 9232	0.0943 9293	20
21	4.1405 6237	0.2415 1309	10.8355 2733	44.8651 7678	0.0922 8900	21
22	4.4304 0174	0.2257 1317	11.0612 4050	49.0057 3916	0.0904 0577	22
23	4.7405 2986	0.2109 4688	11.2721 8738	53.4361 4090	0.0887 1393	23
24	5.0723 6695	0.1971 4662	11.4693 3400	58.1766 7076	0.0871 8902	24
25	5.4274 3264	0.1842 4918	11.6535 8318	63.2490 3772	0.0858 1052	25
26	5.8073 5292	0.1721 9549	11.8257 7867	68.6764 7036	0.0845 6103	26
27	6.2138 6763	0.1609 3037	11.9867 0904	74.4838 2328	0.0834 2573	27
28	6.6488 3836	0.1504 0221	12.1371 1125	80.6976 9091	0.0823 9193	28
29	7.1142 5705	0.1405 6282	12.2776 7407	87.3465 2927	0.0814 4865	29
30	7.6122 5504	0.1313 6712	12.4090 4118	94.4607 8632	0.0805 8640	30
31	8.1451 1290	0.1227 7301	12.5318 1419	102.0730 4137	0.0797 9691	31
32	8.7152 7080	0.1147 4113	12.6465 5532	110.2181 5426	0.0790 7292	32
33	9.3253 3975	0.1072 3470	12.7537 9002	118.9334 2506	0.0784 0807	33
34	9.9781 1354	0.1002 1934	12.8540 0936	128.2587 6481	0.0777 9674	34
35	10.6765 8148	0.0936 6294	12.9476 7230	138.2368 7835	0.0772 3396	35
36	11.4239 4219	0.0875 3546	13.0352 0776	148.9134 5984	0.0767 1531	36
37	12.2236 1814	0.0818 0884	13.1170 1660	160.3374 0202	0.0762 3685	37
38	13.0792 7141	0.0764 5686	13.1934 7345	172.5610 2017	0.0757 9505	38
39	13.9948 2041	0.0714 5501	13.2649 2846	185.6402 9158	0.0753 8676	39
40	14.9744 5784	0.0667 8038	13.3317 0884	199.6351 1199	0.0750 0914	40
41	16.0226 6989	0.0624 1157	13.3941 2041	214.6095 6983	0.0746 5962	41
42	17.1442 5678	0.0583 2857	13.4524 4898	230.6322 3972	0.0743 3591	42
43	18.3443 5475	0.0545 1268	13.5069 6167	247.7764 9650	0.0740 3590	43
44	19.6284 5959	0.0509 4643	13.5579 0810	266.1208 5125	0.0737 5769	44
45	21.0024 5176	0.0476 1349	13.6055 2159	285.7493 1084	0.0734 9957	45
46	22.4726 2338	0.0444 9859	13.6500 2018	306.7517 6260	0.0732 5996	46
47	24.0457 0702	0.0415 8747	13.6916 0764	329.2243 8598	0.0730 3744	47
48	25.7289 0651	0.0388 6679	13.7304 7443	353.2700 9300	0.0728 3070	48
49	27.5299 2997	0.0363 2410	13.7667 9853	378.9989 9951	0.0726 3853	49
50	29.4570 2506	0.0339 4776	13.8007 4629	406.5289 2947	0.0724 5985	50

Table **XX** (*continued*). 7 %

Number of periods n	Amount of 1 at compound interest $s^n = (1 + i)^n$	Present value of 1 $v^n = \dfrac{1}{(1 + i)^n}$	Present value of an annuity of 1 $a_{\overline{n}|} = \dfrac{1 - v^n}{i}$	Amount of an annuity of 1 $s_{\overline{n}|} = \dfrac{(1+i)^n-1}{i}$	Annuity whose present value is 1. (CRF) $\dfrac{1}{a_{\overline{n}|}} = \dfrac{1}{s_{\overline{n}|}} + i$	Number of periods n
51	31.5190 1682	0.0317 2688	13.8324 7317	435.9859 5454	0.0722 9365	51
52	33.7253 4799	0.0296 5129	13.8621 2446	467.5049 7135	0.0721 3901	52
53	36.0861 2235	0.0277 1148	13.8898 3594	501.2303 1935	0.0719 9509	53
54	38.6121 5092	0.0258 9858	13.9157 3453	537.3164 4170	0.0718 6110	54
55	41.3150 0148	0.0242 0428	13.9399 3881	575.9285 9262	0.0717 3633	55
56	44.2070 5159	0.0226 2083	13.9625 5964	617.2435 9410	0.0716 2011	56
57	47.3015 4520	0.0211 4096	13.9837 0059	661.4506 4569	0.0715 1183	57
58	50.6126 5336	0.0197 5791	14.0034 5850	708.7521 9089	0.0714 1093	58
59	54.1555 3910	0.0184 6533	14.0219 2383	759.3648 4425	0.0713 1689	59
60	57.9464 2683	0.0172 5732	14.0391 8115	813.5203 8335	0.0712 2923	60
61	62.0026 7671	0.0161 2834	14.0553 0949	871.4668 1019	0.0711 4749	61
62	66.3428 6408	0.0150 7321	14.0703 8270	933.4694 8690	0.0710 7127	62
63	70.9868 6457	0.0140 8711	14.0844 6981	999.8123 5098	0.0710 0019	63
64	75.9559 4509	0.0131 6553	14.0976 3534	1070.7992 1555	0.0709 3388	64
65	81.2728 6124	0.0123 0423	14.1099 3957	1146.7551 6064	0.0708 7203	65
66	86.9619 6153	0.0114 9928	14.1214 3885	1228.0280 2188	0.0708 1431	66
67	93.0492 9884	0.0107 4699	14.1321 8584	1314.9899 8341	0.0707 6046	67
68	99.5627 4976	0.0100 4392	14.1422 2976	1408.0392 8225	0.0707 1021	68
69	106.5321 4224	0.0093 8684	14.1516 1660	1507.6020 3201	0.0706 6331	69
70	113.9893 9220	0.0087 7275	14.1603 8934	1614.1341 7425	0.0706 1953	70
71	121.9686 4965	0.0081 9883	14.1685 8817	1728.1235 6645	0.0705 7866	71
72	130.5064 5513	0.0076 6246	14.1762 5063	1850.0922 1610	0.0705 4051	72
73	139.6419 0699	0.0071 6117	14.1834 1180	1980.5986 7123	0.0705 0490	73
74	149.4168 4047	0.0066 9269	14.1901 0449	2120.2405 7821	0.0704 7164	74
75	159.8760 1931	0.0062 5485	14.1963 5933	2269.6574 1869	0.0704 4060	75
76	171.0673 4066	0.0058 4565	14.2022 0498	2429.5334 3800	0.0704 1160	76
77	183.0420 5451	0.0054 6323	14.2076 6821	2600.6007 7866	0.0703 8453	77
78	195.8549 9832	0.0051 0582	14.2127 7403	2783.6428 3316	0.0703 5924	78
79	209.5648 4820	0.0047 7179	14.2175 4582	2979.4978 3148	0.0703 3563	79
80	224.2343 8758	0.0044 5962	14.2220 0544	3189.0626 7969	0.0703 1357	80
81	239.9307 9471	0.0041 6787	14.2261 7331	3413.2970 6727	0.0702 9297	81
82	256.7259 5034	0.0038 9520	14.2300 6851	3653.2278 6198	0.0702 7373	82
83	274.6967 6686	0.0036 4038	14.2337 0889	3909.9538 1231	0.0702 5576	83
84	293.9255 4054	0.0034 0222	14.2371 1111	4184.6505 7918	0.0702 3897	84
85	314.5003 2838	0.0031 7965	14.2402 9076	4478.5761 1972	0.0702 2329	85
86	336.5153 5137	0.0029 7163	14.2432 6239	4793.0764 4810	0.0702 0863	86
87	360.0714 2596	0.0027 7723	14.2460 3962	5129.5917 9946	0.0701 9495	87
88	385.2764 2578	0.0025 9554	14.2486 3516	5489.6632 2543	0.0701 8216	88
89	412.2457 7558	0.0024 2574	14.2510 6089	5874.9396 5121	0.0701 7021	89
90	441.1029 7988	0.0022 6704	14.2533 2794	6287.1854 2679	0.0701 5905	90
91	471.9801 8847	0.0021 1873	14.2554 4667	6728.2884 0667	0.0701 4863	91
92	505.0188 0166	0.0019 8012	14.2574 2680	7200.2685 9513	0.0701 3888	92
93	540.3701 1778	0.0018 5058	14.2592 7738	7705.2873 9679	0.0701 2978	93
94	578.1960 2602	0.0017 2952	14.2610 0690	8245.6575 1457	0.0701 2128	94
95	618.6697 4784	0.0016 1637	14.2626 2327	8823.8535 4059	0.0701 1333	95
96	661.9766 3019	0.0015 1063	14.2641 3390	9442.5232 8843	0.0701 0590	96
97	708.3149 9430	0.0014 1180	14.2655 4570	10104.4999 1862	0.0700 9897	97
98	757.8970 4390	0.0013 1944	14.2668 6514	10812.8149 1292	0.0700 9248	98
99	810.9498 3698	0.0012 3312	14.2680 9826	11570.7119 5683	0.0700 8643	99
100	867.7163 2557	0.0011 5245	14.2692 5071	12381.6617 9381	0.0700 8076	100

Table XXI. 8 %

Number of periods n	Amount of 1 at compound interest $s^n = (1 + i)^n$	Present value of 1 $v^n = \dfrac{1}{(1+i)^n}$	Present value of an annuity of 1 $a_{\overline{n}|} = \dfrac{1 - v^n}{i}$	Amount of an annuity of 1 $s_{\overline{n}|} = \dfrac{(1+i)^n - 1}{i}$	Annuity whose present value is 1. (CRF) $\dfrac{1}{a_{\overline{n}|}} = \dfrac{1}{s_{\overline{n}|}} + i$	Number of periods n
1	1.0800 0000	0.9259 2593	0.9259 2593	1.0000 0000	1.0800 0000	1
2	1.1664 0000	0.8573 3882	1.7832 6475	2.0800 0000	0.5607 6923	2
3	1.2597 1200	0.7938 3224	2.5770 9699	3.2464 0000	0.3880 3351	3
4	1.3604 8896	0.7350 2985	3.3121 2684	4.5061 1200	0.3019 2080	4
5	1.4693 2808	0.6805 8320	3.9927 1004	5.8666 0096	0.2504 5645	5
6	1.5868 7432	0.6301 6963	4.6228 7966	7.3359 2904	0.2163 1539	6
7	1.7138 2427	0.5834 9040	5.2063 7006	8.9228 0336	0.1920 7240	7
8	1.8509 3021	0.5402 6888	5.7466 3894	10.6366 2763	0.1740 1476	8
9	1.9990 0463	0.5002 4897	6.2468 8791	12.4875 5784	0.1600 7971	9
10	2.1589 2500	0.4631 9349	6.7100 8140	14.4865 6247	0.1490 2949	10
11	2.3316 3900	0.4288 8286	7.1389 6426	16.6454 8746	0.1400 7634	11
12	2.5181 7012	0.3971 1376	7.5360 7802	18.9771 2646	0.1326 9502	12
13	2.7196 2373	0.3676 9792	7.9037 7594	21.4952 9658	0.1265 2181	13
14	2.9371 9362	0.3404 6104	8.2442 3698	24.2149 2030	0.1212 9685	14
15	3.1721 6911	0.3152 4170	8.5594 7869	27.1521 1393	0.1168 2954	15
16	3.4259 4264	0.2918 9047	8.8513 6916	30.3242 8304	0.1129 7687	16
17	3.7000 1805	0.2702 6895	9.1216 3811	33.7502 2569	0.1096 2943	17
18	3.9960 1950	0.2502 4903	9.3718 8714	37.4502 4374	0.1067 0210	18
19	4.3157 0106	0.2317 1206	9.6035 9920	41.4462 6324	0.1041 2763	19
20	4.6609 5714	0.2145 4821	9.8181 4741	45.7619 6430	0.1018 5221	20
21	5.0338 3372	0.1986 5575	10.0168 0316	50.4229 2144	0.0998 3225	21
22	5.4365 4041	0.1839 4051	10.2007 4366	55.4567 5516	0.0980 3207	22
23	5.8714 6365	0.1703 1528	10.3710 5895	60.8932 9557	0.0964 2217	23
24	6.3411 8074	0.1576 9934	10.5287 5828	66.7647 5922	0.0949 7796	24
25	6.8484 7520	0.1460 1790	10.6747 7619	73.1059 3995	0.0936 7878	25
26	7.3963 5321	0.1352 0176	10.8099 7795	79.9544 1515	0.0925 0713	26
27	7.9880 6147	0.1251 8682	10.9351 6477	87.3507 6836	0.0914 4809	27
28	8.6271 0639	0.1159 1372	11.0510 7849	95.3388 2983	0.0904 8891	28
29	9.3172 7490	0.1073 2752	11.1584 0601	103.9659 3622	0.0896 1854	29
30	10.0626 5689	0.0993 7733	11.2577 8334	113.2832 1111	0.0888 2743	30
31	10.8676 6944	0.0920 1605	11.3497 9939	123.3458 6800	0.0881 0728	31
32	11.7370 8300	0.0852 0005	11.4349 9944	134.2135 3744	0.0874 5081	32
33	12.6760 4964	0.0788 8893	11.5138 8837	145.9506 2044	0.0868 5163	33
34	13.6901 3361	0.0730 4531	11.5869 3367	158.6266 7007	0.0863 0411	34
35	14.7853 4429	0.0676 3454	11.6545 6822	172.3168 0368	0.0858 0326	35
36	15.9681 7184	0.0626 2458	11.7171 9279	187.1021 4797	0.0853 4467	36
37	17.2456 2558	0.0579 8572	11.7751 7851	203.0703 1981	0.0849 2440	37
38	18.6252 7563	0.0536 9048	11.8288 6899	220.3159 4540	0.0845 3894	38
39	20.1152 9768	0.0497 1341	11.8785 8240	238.9412 2103	0.0841 8513	39
40	21.7245 2150	0.0460 3093	11.9246 1333	259.0565 1871	0.0838 6016	40
41	23.4624 8322	0.0426 2123	11.9672 3457	280.7810 4021	0.0835 6149	41
42	25.3394 8187	0.0394 6411	12.0066 9867	304.2435 2342	0.0832 8684	42
43	27.3666 4042	0.0365 4084	12.0432 3951	329.5830 0530	0.0830 3414	43
44	29.5559 7166	0.0338 3411	12.0770 7362	356.9496 4572	0.0828 0152	44
45	31.9204 4939	0.0313 2788	12.1084 0150	386.5056 1738	0.0825 8728	45
46	34.4740 8534	0.0290 0730	12.1374 0880	418.4260 6677	0.0823 8991	46
47	37.2320 1217	0.0268 5861	12.1642 6741	452.9001 5211	0.0822 0799	47
48	40.2105 7314	0.0248 6908	12.1891 3649	490.1321 6428	0.0820 4027	48
49	43.4274 1899	0.0230 2693	12.2121 6341	530.3427 3742	0.0818 8557	59
50	46.9016 1251	0.0213 2123	12.2334 8464	573.7701 5642	0.0817 4286	50

Table **XXI** (*continued*). 8 %

Number of periods n	Amount of 1 at compound interest $s^n = (1+i)^n$	Present value of 1 $v^n = \dfrac{1}{(1+i)^n}$	Present value of an annuity of 1 $a_{\overline{n}|} = \dfrac{1-v^n}{i}$	Amount of an annuity of 1 $s_{\overline{n}|} = \dfrac{(1+i)^n-1}{i}$	Annuity whose present value is 1. (CRF) $\dfrac{1}{a_{\overline{n}|}} = \dfrac{1}{s_{\overline{n}|}} + i$	Number of periods n
51	50.6537 4151	0.0197 4188	12.2532 2652	620.6717 6893	0.0816 1116	51
52	54.7060 4084	0.0182 7952	12.2715 0604	671.3255 1044	0.0814 8959	52
53	59.0825 2410	0.0169 2548	12.2884 3152	726.0315 5128	0.0813 7735	53
54	63.8091 2603	0.0156 7174	12.3041 0326	785.1140 7538	0.0812 7370	54
55	68.9138 5611	0.0145 1087	12.3186 1413	848.9232 0141	0.0811 7796	55
56	74.4269 6460	0.0134 3599	12.3320 5012	917.8370 5752	0.0810 8952	56
57	80.3811 2177	0.0124 4073	12.3444 9085	992.2640 2213	0.0810 0780	57
58	86.8116 1151	0.0115 1920	12.3560 1005	1072.6451 4390	0.0809 3227	58
59	93.7565 4043	0.0106 6592	12.3666 7597	1159.4567 5541	0.0808 6247	59
60	101.2570 6367	0.0098 7585	12.3765 5182	1253.2132 9584	0.0807 9795	60
61	109.3576 2876	0.0091 4431	12.3856 9613	1354.4703 5951	0.0807 3830	61
62	118.1062 3906	0.0084 6695	12.3941 6309	1463.8279 8827	0.0806 8314	62
63	127.5547 3819	0.0078 3977	12.4020 0286	1581.9342 2733	0.0806 3214	63
64	137.7591 1724	0.0072 5905	12.4092 6190	1709.4889 6552	0.0805 8497	64
65	148.7798 4662	0.0067 2134	12.4159 8324	1847.2480 8276	0.0805 4135	65
66	160.6822 3435	0.0062 2346	12.4222 0671	1996.0279 2938	0.0805 0100	66
67	173.5368 1310	0.0057 6247	12.4279 6917	2156.7101 6373	0.0804 6367	67
68	187.4197 5815	0.0053 3562	12.4333 0479	2330.2469 7683	0.0804 2914	68
69	202.4133 3880	0.0049 4039	12.4382 4518	2517.6667 3497	0.0803 9719	69
70	218.6064 0590	0.0045 7443	12.4428 1961	2720.0800 7377	0.0803 6764	70
71	236.0949 1837	0.0042 3558	12.4470 5519	2938.6864 7967	0.0803 4029	71
72	254.9825 1184	0.0039 2184	12.4509 7703	3174.7813 9805	0.0803 1498	72
73	275.3811 1279	0.0036 3133	12.4546 0836	3429.7639 0989	0.0802 9157	73
74	297.4116 0181	0.0033 6234	12.4579 7071	3705.1450 2268	0.0802 6989	74
75	321.2045 2996	0.0031 1328	12.4610 8399	4002.5566 2449	0.0802 4984	75
76	346.9008 9236	0.0028 8267	12.4639 6665	4323.7611 5445	0.0802 3128	76
77	374.6529 6374	0.0026 6914	12.4666 3579	4670.6620 4681	0.0802 1410	77
78	404.6252 0084	0.0024 7142	12.4691 0721	5045.3150 1056	0.0801 9820	78
79	436.9952 1691	0.0022 8835	12.4713 9557	5449.9402 1140	0.0801 8349	79
80	471.9548 3426	0.0021 1885	12.4735 1441	5886.9354 2831	0.0801 6987	80
81	509.7112 2101	0.0019 6190	12.4754 7631	6358.8902 6258	0.0801 5726	81
82	550.4881 1869	0.0018 1657	12.4772 9288	6868.6014 8358	0.0801 4559	82
83	594.5271 6818	0.0016 8201	12.4789 7489	7419.0896 0227	0.0801 3479	83
84	642.0893 4164	0.0015 5742	12.4805 3230	8013.6167 7045	0.0801 2479	84
85	693.4564 8897	0.0014 4205	12.4819 7436	8655.7061 1209	0.0801 1553	85
86	748.9330 0808	0.0013 3523	12.4833 0959	9349.1626 0105	0.0801 0696	86
87	808.8476 4873	0.0012 3633	12.4845 4592	10098.0956 0914	0.0800 9903	87
88	873.5554 6063	0.0011 4475	12.4856 9066	10906.9432 5787	0.0800 9168	88
89	943.4398 9748	0.0010 5995	12.4867 5061	11780.4987 1850	0.0800 8489	89
90	1018.9150 8928	0.0009 8144	12.4877 3205	12723.9386 1598	0.0800 7859	90
91	1100.4282 9642	0.0009 0874	12.4886 4079	13742.8537 0526	0.0800 7277	91
92	1188.4625 6013	0.0008 4142	12.4894 8221	14843.2820 0168	0.0800 6737	92
93	1283.5395 6494	0.0007 7910	12.4902 6131	16031.7445 6181	0.0800 6238	93
94	1386.2227 3014	0.0007 2138	12.4909 8269	17315.2841 2676	0.0800 5775	94
95	1497.1205 4855	0.0006 6795	12.4916 5064	18701.5068 5690	0.0800 5347	95
96	1616.8901 9244	0.0006 1847	12.4922 6911	20198.6274 0545	0.0800 4951	96
97	1746.2414 0783	0.0005 7266	12.4928 4177	21815.5175 9788	0.0800 4584	97
98	1885.9407 2046	0.0005 3024	12.4933 7201	23561.7590 0572	0.0800 4244	98
99	2036.8159 7809	0.0004 9096	12.4938 6297	25447.6997 2617	0.0800 3930	99
100	2199.7612 5634	0.0004 5459	12.4943 1757	27484.5157 0427	0.0800 3638	100

Table XXII. 10%

Number of periods n	Amount of 1 at compound interest $s^n = (1+i)^n$	Present value of 1 $v^n = \dfrac{1}{(1+i)^n}$	Present value of an annuity of 1 $a_{\overline{n}|} = \dfrac{1-v^n}{i}$	Amount of an annuity of 1 $s_{\overline{n}|} = \dfrac{(1+i)^n - 1}{i}$	Annuity whose present value is 1. (CRF) $\dfrac{1}{a_{\overline{n}|}} = \dfrac{1}{s_{\overline{n}|}} + i$	Number of periods n
1	1.1000 0000	0.9090 9091	0.9090 9091	1.0000 0000	1.1000 0000	1
2	1.2100 0000	0.8264 4628	1.7355 3719	2.1000 0000	0.5761 9047	2
3	1.3310 0000	0.7513 1480	2.4868 5199	3.3100 0000	0.4021 1480	3
4	1.4641 0000	0.6830 1346	3.1698 6545	4.6410 0000	0.3154 7080	4
5	1.6105 1000	0.6209 2132	3.7907 8677	6.1051 0000	0.2637 9748	5
6	1.7715 6100	0.5644 7393	4.3552 6070	7.7156 1000	0.2296 0738	6
7	1.9487 1710	0.5131 5812	4.8684 1882	9.4871 7100	0.2054 0550	7
8	2.1435 8881	0.4665 0738	5.3349 2620	11.4358 8810	0.1874 4402	8
9	2.3579 4769	0.4240 9762	5.7590 2382	13.5794 7691	0.1736 4054	9
10	2.5937 4246	0.3855 4329	6.1445 6711	15.9374 2460	0.1627 4539	10
11	2.8531 1671	0.3504 9390	6.4950 6101	18.5311 6706	0.1539 6314	11
12	3.1384 2838	0.3186 3082	6.8136 9182	21.3842 8377	0.1467 6332	12
13	3.4522 7121	0.2896 6438	7.1033 5620	24.5227 1214	0.1407 7852	13
14	3.7974 9834	0.2633 3125	7.3666 8746	27.9749 8336	0.1357 4622	14
15	4.1772 4817	0.2393 9205	7.6060 7951	31.7724 8169	0.1314 7378	15
16	4.5949 7299	0.2176 2914	7.8237 0864	35.9497 2986	0.1278 1662	16
17	5.0544 7029	0.1978 4467	8.0215 5331	40.5447 0285	0.1246 6413	17
18	5.5599 1731	0.1798 5879	8.2014 1210	45.5991 7313	0.1219 3022	18
19	6.1159 0904	0.1635 0799	8.3649 2009	51.1590 9045	0.1195 4687	19
20	6.7274 9995	0.1486 4363	8.5135 6372	57.2749 9949	0.1174 5962	20
21	7.4002 4994	0.1351 3057	8.6486 9429	64.0024 9944	0.1156 2439	21
22	8.1402 7494	0.1228 4597	8.7715 4026	71.4027 4939	0.1140 0506	22
23	8.9543 0243	0.1116 7816	8.8832 1842	79.5430 2433	0.1125 7181	23
24	9.8497 3268	0.1015 2560	8.9847 4402	88.4973 2676	0.1112 9978	24
25	10.8347 0594	0.0922 9600	9.0770 4002	98.3470 5943	0.1101 6807	25
26	11.9181 7654	0.0839 0545	9.1609 4547	109.1817 6538	0.1091 5904	26
27	13.1099 9419	0.0762 7768	9.2372 2316	121.0999 4192	0.1082 5764	27
28	14.4209 9361	0.0693 4335	9.3065 6651	134.2099 3611	0.1074 5101	28
29	15.8630 9297	0.0630 3941	9.3696 0591	148.6309 2972	0.1067 2807	29
30	17.4494 0227	0.0573 0855	9.4269 1447	164.4940 2269	0.1060 7925	30
31	19.1943 4250	0.0520 9868	9.4790 1315	181.9434 2496	0.1054 9621	31
32	21.1137 7675	0.0473 6244	9.5263 7559	201.1377 6745	0.1049 7172	32
33	23.2251 5442	0.0430 5676	9.5694 3236	222.2515 4420	0.1044 9941	33
34	25.5476 6986	0.0391 4251	9.6085 7487	245.4766 9862	0.1040 7371	34
35	28.1024 3685	0.0355 8410	9.6441 5897	271.0243 6848	0.1036 8971	35
36	30.9126 8053	0.0323 4918	9.6765 0816	299.1268 0533	0.1033 4306	36
37	34.0039 4859	0.0294 0835	9.7059 1651	330.0394 8586	0.1030 2994	37
38	37.4043 4344	0.0267 3486	9.7326 5137	364.0434 3445	0.1027 4693	38
39	41.1447 7779	0.0243 0442	9.7569 5579	401.4477 7789	0.1024 9098	39
40	45.2592 5557	0.0220 9493	9.7790 5072	442.5925 5568	0.1022 5941	40
41	49.7851 8113	0.0200 8630	9.7991 3702	487.8518 1125	0.1020 4980	41
42	54.7636 9924	0.0182 6027	9.8173 9729	537.6369 9237	0.1018 5999	42
43	60.2400 6916	0.0166 0025	9.8339 9753	592.4006 9161	0.1016 8805	43
44	66.2640 7608	0.0150 9113	9.8490 8867	652.6407 6077	0.1015 3224	44
45	72.8904 8369	0.0137 1921	9.8628 0788	718.9048 3685	0.1013 9100	45
46	80.1795 3205	0.0124 7201	9.8752 7989	791.7953 2053	0.1012 6295	46
47	88.1974 8526	0.0113 3819	9.8866 1808	871.9748 5259	0.1011 4682	47
48	97.0172 3378	0.0103 0745	9.8969 2553	960.1723 3785	0.1010 4148	48
49	106.7189 5716	0.0093 7041	9.9062 9584	1057.1895 7163	0.1009 4590	49
50	117.3908 5288	0.0085 1855	9.9148 1449	1163.9085 2880	0.1008 5917	50

Table XXII. 10% (continued)

Number of periods	Amount of 1 at compound interest	Present value of 1	Present value of an annuity of 1	Amount of an annuity of 1	Annuity whose present value is 1. (CRF)	Number of periods
n	$s^n = (1+i)^n$	$v^n = \dfrac{1}{(1+i)^n}$	$a_{\overline{n}\rvert} = \dfrac{1-v^n}{i}$	$s_{\overline{n}\rvert} = \dfrac{(1+i)^n - 1}{i}$	$\dfrac{1}{a_{\overline{n}\rvert}} = \dfrac{1}{s_{\overline{n}\rvert}} + i$	n
51	129.1299 3817	0.0077 4414	9.9225 5862	1281.2993 8168	0.1007 8046	51
52	142.0429 3198	0.0070 4013	9.9295 9875	1410.4293 1984	0.1007 0900	52
53	156.2472 2518	0.0064 0011	9.9359 9886	1552.4722 5183	0.1006 4413	53
54	171.8719 4770	0.0058 1829	9.9418 1715	1708.7194 7701	0.1005 8523	54
55	189.0591 4247	0.0052 8935	9.9471 0650	1880.5914 2471	0.1005 3175	55
56	207.9650 5672	0.0048 0850	9.9519 1500	2069.6505 6718	0.1004 8317	56
57	228.7615 6239	0.0043 7136	9.9562 8636	2277.6156 2390	0.1004 3906	57
58	251.6377 1863	0.0039 7397	9.9602 6033	2506.3771 8629	0.1003 9898	58
59	276.8014 9049	0.0036 1270	9.9638 7303	2758.0149 0492	0.1003 6258	59
60	304.4816 3954	0.0032 8427	9.9671 5730	3034.8163 9541	0.1003 2951	60
61	334.9298 0350	0.0029 8570	9.9701 4300	3339.2980 3496	0.1002 9946	61
62	368.4227 8385	0.0027 1427	9.9728 5727	3674.2278 3845	0.1002 7217	62
63	405.2650 6223	0.0024 6752	9.9753 2479	4042.6506 2230	0.1002 4736	63
64	445.7915 6845	0.0022 4320	9.9775 6799	4447.9156 8453	0.1002 2482	64
65	490.3707 2530	0.0020 3927	9.9796 0727	4893.7072 5298	0.1002 0434	65
66	539.4077 9783	0.0018 5389	9.9814 6115	5384.0779 7828	0.1001 8573	66
67	593.3485 7761	0.0016 8535	9.9831 4650	5923.4857 7610	0.1001 6882	67
68	652.6834 3537	0.0015 3214	9.9846 7864	6516.8343 5371	0.1001 5345	68
69	717.9517 7891	0.0013 9285	9.9860 7149	7169.5177 8909	0.1001 3948	69
70	789.7469 5680	0.0012 6623	9.9873 3772	7887.4695 6799	0.1001 2678	70
71	868.7216 5248	0.0011 5112	9.9884 8883	8677.2165 2479	0.1001 1524	71
72	955.5938 1773	0.0010 4647	9.9895 3530	9545.9381 7727	0.1001 0476	72
73	1051.1531 9950	0.0009 5134	9.9904 8664	10501.5319 9500	0.1000 9522	73
74	1156.2685 1945	0.0008 6485	9.9913 5149	11552.6851 9450	0.1000 8656	74
75	1271.8953 7140	0.0007 8623	9.9921 3772	12708.9537 1395	0.1000 7868	75
76	1399.0849 0853	0.0007 1475	9.9928 5247	13980.8490 8535	0.1000 7153	76
77	1538.9933 9939	0.0006 4978	9.9935 0225	15379.9339 9388	0.1000 6502	77
78	1692.8927 3933	0.0005 9070	9.9940 9295	16918.9273 9327	0.1000 5911	78
79	1862.1820 1326	0.0005 3700	9.9946 2996	18611.8201 3260	0.1000 5373	79
80	2048.4002 1459	0.0004 8819	9.9951 1814	20474.0021 4585	0.1000 4884	80
81	2253.2402 3604	0.0004 4381	9.9955 6195	22522.4023 6044	0.1000 4440	81
82	2478.5642 5965	0.0004 0346	9.9959 6540	24775.6425 9648	0.1000 4036	82
83	2726.4206 8561	0.0003 6678	9.9963 3219	27254.2068 5613	0.1000 3669	83
84	2999.0627 5417	0.0003 3344	9.9966 6563	29980.6275 4175	0.1000 3335	84
85	3298.9690 2959	0.0003 0313	9.9969 6875	32979.6902 9592	0.1000 3032	85
86	3628.8659 3255	0.0002 7557	9.9972 4432	36278.6593 2551	0.1000 2756	86
87	3991.7525 2581	0.0002 5052	9.9974 9483	39907.5252 5806	0.1000 2506	87
88	4390.9277 7839	0.0002 2774	9.9977 2258	43899.2777 8387	0.1000 2278	88
89	4830.0205 5623	0.0002 0704	9.9979 2962	48290.2055 6226	0.1000 2071	89
90	5313.0226 1185	0.0001 8822	9.9981 1783	53120.2261 1848	0.1000 1883	90
91	5844.3248 7303	0.0001 7111	9.9982 8894	58433.2487 3033	0.1000 1711	91
92	6428.7573 6034	0.0001 5555	9.9984 4449	64277.5736 0336	0.1000 1556	92
93	7071.6330 9637	0.0001 4141	9.9985 8590	70706.3309 6370	0.1000 1414	93
94	7778.7964 0601	0.0001 2855	9.9987 1445	77777.9640 6007	0.1000 1286	94
95	8556.6760 4661	0.0001 1687	9.9988 3132	85556.7604 6608	0.1000 1169	95
96	9412.3436 5127	0.0001 0624	9.9989 3757	94113.4365 1269	0.1000 1063	96
97	10353.5780 1640	0.0000 9659	9.9990 3415	103525.7801 6395	0.1000 0966	97
98	11388.9358 1803	0.0000 8780	9.9991 2195	113879.3581 8035	0.1000 0878	98
99	12527.8293 9984	0.0000 7982	9.9992 0178	125268.2939 9838	0.1000 0798	99
100	13780.6123 3982	0.0000 7257	9.9992 7434	137796.1233 9822	0.1000 0726	100

TABLE XXIII   Present-Worth Factors for Interest Rates from 6% to 25%

$$v^n = 1/(1 + i)^n$$

n	6%	8%	10%	12%	15%	20%	25%	n
1	0.9434	0.9259	0.9091	0.8929	0.8696	0.8333	0.8000	1
2	0.8900	0.8473	0.8264	0.7972	0.7561	0.6944	0.6400	2
3	0.8396	0.7938	0.7513	0.7118	0.6575	0.5787	0.5120	3
4	0.7921	0.7350	0.6830	0.6355	0.5718	0.4823	0.4096	4
5	0.7473	0.6806	0.6209	0.5674	0.4972	0.4019	0.3277	5
6	0.7050	0.6302	0.5645	0.5066	0.4323	0.3349	0.2621	6
7	0.6651	0.5835	0.5132	0.4523	0.3759	0.2791	0.2097	7
8	0.6274	0.5403	0.4665	0.4039	0.3269	0.2326	0.1678	8
9	0.5919	0.5002	0.4241	0.3606	0.2843	0.1938	0.1342	9
10	0.5584	0.4632	0.3855	0.3220	0.2472	0.1615	0.1074	10
11	0.5268	0.4289	0.3505	0.2875	0.2149	0.1346	0.0859	11
12	0.4970	0.3971	0.3186	0.2567	0.1869	0.1122	0.0687	12
13	0.4688	0.3677	0.2897	0.2292	0.1625	0.0935	0.0550	13
14	0.4423	0.3405	0.2633	0.2046	0.1413	0.0779	0.0440	14
15	0.4173	0.3152	0.2394	0.1827	0.1229	0.0649	0.0352	15
16	0.3936	0.2919	0.2176	0.1631	0.1069	0.0541	0.0281	16
17	0.3714	0.2703	0.1978	0.1456	0.0929	0.0451	0.0225	17
18	0.3503	0.2502	0.1799	0.1300	0.0808	0.0376	0.0180	18
19	0.3305	0.2317	0.1635	0.1161	0.0703	0.0313	0.0144	19
20	0.3118	0.2145	0.1486	0.1037	0.0611	0.0261	0.0115	20
25	0.2330	0.1460	0.0923	0.0588	0.0304	0.0105	0.0038	25
30	0.1741	0.0994	0.0573	0.0334	0.0151	0.0042	0.0012	30
40	0.0972	0.0460	0.0221	0.0107	0.0037	0.0007	0.0001	40
50	0.0543	0.0213	0.0085	0.0035	0.0009	0.0001	a	50
100	0.0029	0.005	0.0001	a	a	a	a	100

a Value is less than 0.0001.

TABLE XXIV Sinking-Fund Factors, $1/s_{\overline{n}|}$, for Interest Rates from 6% to 25%

i / n	6%	8%	10%	12%	15%	20%	25%	i / n
1	1.0000	1.0000	1.0000	1.0000	1.0000	1.0000	1.0000	1
2	0.4854	0.4808	0.4762	0.4717	0.4651	0.4546	0.4444	2
3	0.3141	0.3080	0.3021	0.2964	0.2880	0.2747	0.2623	3
4	0.2286	0.2219	0.2155	0.2092	0.2003	0.1863	0.1734	4
5	0.1774	0.1705	0.1638	0.1574	0.1483	0.1344	0.1218	5
6	0.1434	0.1363	0.1296	0.1232	0.1142	0.1007	0.0888	6
7	0.1191	0.1121	0.1054	0.0991	0.0904	0.0774	0.0663	7
8	0.1010	0.0940	0.0874	0.0813	0.0729	0.0606	0.0504	8
9	0.0870	0.0801	0.0736	0.0677	0.0596	0.0481	0.0388	9
10	0.0759	0.0690	0.0628	0.0570	0.0493	0.0385	0.0301	10
11	0.0668	0.0601	0.0540	0.0484	0.0411	0.0311	0.0235	11
12	0.0593	0.0527	0.0468	0.0414	0.0345	0.0253	0.0185	12
13	0.0530	0.0465	0.0408	0.0357	0.0291	0.0206	0.0145	13
14	0.0476	0.0413	0.0358	0.0309	0.0247	0.0169	0.0115	14
15	0.0430	0.0368	0.0315	0.0268	0.0210	0.0139	0.0091	15
16	0.0390	0.0330	0.0278	0.0234	0.0180	0.0114	0.0072	16
17	0.0354	0.0296	0.0247	0.0205	0.0154	0.0094	0.0058	17
18	0.0324	0.0267	0.0219	0.0179	0.0132	0.0078	0.0046	18
19	0.0296	0.0241	0.0196	0.0158	0.0113	0.0065	0.0037	19
20	0.0272	0.0219	0.0175	0.0139	0.0098	0.0054	0.0029	20
25	0.0182	0.0137	0.0102	0.0075	0.0047	0.0021	0.0010	25
30	0.0127	0.0088	0.0061	0.0041	0.0023	0.0009	0.0003	30
40	0.0065	0.0039	0.0023	0.0013	0.0006	0.0001	0.0000	40
50	0.0034	0.0017	0.0009	0.0004	0.0001	a	a	50
100	0.0002	a	a	a	a	a	a	100

a Value is less than 0.0001.

TABLE XXV Capital Recovery Factors, $1/a_{\overline{n}|}$, for Interest Rates from 6% to 25%

n	6%	8%	10%	12%	15%	20%	25%	n
1	1.0600	1.0800	1.1000	1.1200	1.1500	1.2000	1.2500	1
2	0.5454	0.5608	0.5762	0.5917	0.6151	0.6546	0.6944	2
3	0.3741	0.3880	0.4021	0.4164	0.4380	0.4747	0.5123	3
4	0.2886	0.3019	0.3155	0.3292	0.3503	0.3863	0.4234	4
5	0.2374	0.2505	0.2638	0.2774	0.2983	0.3344	0.3718	5
6	0.2034	0.2163	0.2296	0.2432	0.2642	0.3007	0.3388	6
7	0.1791	0.1921	0.2054	0.2191	0.2404	0.2774	0.3163	7
8	0.1610	0.1740	0.1874	0.2013	0.2229	0.2606	0.3004	8
9	0.1470	0.1601	0.1736	0.1877	0.2096	0.2481	0.2888	9
10	0.1359	0.1490	0.1628	0.1770	0.1993	0.2385	0.2801	10
11	0.1268	0.1401	0.1540	0.1684	0.1911	0.2311	0.2735	11
12	0.1193	0.1327	0.1468	0.1614	0.1845	0.2253	0.2685	12
13	0.1130	0.1265	0.1408	0.1557	0.1791	0.2206	0.2645	13
14	0.1076	0.1213	0.1358	0.1509	0.1747	0.2169	0.2615	14
15	0.1030	0.1168	0.1315	0.1468	0.1710	0.2139	0.2591	15
16	0.0990	0.1130	0.1278	0.1434	0.1680	0.2114	0.2572	16
17	0.0954	0.1096	0.1247	0.1405	0.1654	0.2094	0.2558	17
18	0.0924	0.1067	0.1219	0.1379	0.1632	0.2078	0.2546	18
19	0.0896	0.1041	0.1196	0.1358	0.1613	0.2065	0.2537	19
20	0.0872	0.1019	0.1175	0.1339	0.1598	0.2054	0.2529	20
25	0.0782	0.0937	0.1102	0.1275	0.1547	0.2021	0.2510	25
30	0.0727	0.0888	0.1061	0.1241	0.1523	0.2009	0.2503	30
40	0.0665	0.0839	0.1023	0.1213	0.1506	0.2001	0.2500	40
50	0.0634	0.0817	0.1009	0.1204	0.1501	0.2000	0.2500	50
100	0.0602	0.0800	0.1000	0.1200	0.1500	0.2000	0.2500	100

TABLE XXVI Amount at the End of One Year of p Deposits Each of $1/p$ Deposited at End of Each pth Part of a Year; $s_{\overline{1}|}^{(p)} = i/j_{(p)}$

p	3%	4%	5%	6%	7%	8%	10%	p
2	1.0074	1.0099	1.0123	1.0148	1.0172	1.0196	1.0244	2
3	1.0099	1.0132	1.0165	1.0197	1.0230	1.0262	1.0327	3
4	1.0112	1.0149	1.0186	1.0222	1.0259	1.0295	1.0368	4
6	1.0124	1.0165	1.0206	1.0247	1.0288	1.0328	1.0409	6
12	1.0137	1.0182	1.0227	1.0272	1.0317	1.0362	1.0450	12

Index

573